SECOND CUSTOM EDITION FOR CONCORDIA UNIVERSITY

CALCULUS

FOR BUSINESS, ECONOMICS, LIFE SCIENCES, AND SOCIAL SCIENCES

Raymond A. Barnett
Michael R. Ziegler
Karl E. Byleen

Taken from:
Calculus for Business, Economics, Life Sciences, and Social Sciences, Twelfth Edition
by Raymond A. Barnett, Michael R. Ziegler, and Karl E. Byleen

Note to students: The material in this book has been specifically selected by your instructors to include only what is necessary for your coursework. They have chosen to eliminate some material which is not critical to your course, and in so doing have created a significant savings to you.

Learning Solutions

New York Boston San Francisco
London Toronto Sydney Tokyo Singapore Madrid
Mexico City Munich Paris Cape Town Hong Kong Montreal

Cover Art: Courtesy of PhotoDisc/Getty Images.

Taken from:

Calculus for Business, Economics, Life Sciences, and Social Sciences, Twelfth Edition
by Raymond A. Barnett, Michael R. Ziegler, and Karl E. Byleen
Copyright © 2011, 2008, 2005 by Pearson Education, Inc.
Published by Prentice Hall
Toronto, Ontario
Cananda

This special edition published in cooperation with Pearson Learning Solutions.

Pearson Learning Solutions, 501 Boylston Street, Suite 900, Boston, MA 02116
A Pearson Education Company
www.pearsoned.com

Printed in Canada

2 3 4 5 6 7 8 9 10 XXXX 15 14 13 12 11 10

000200010270568834

BK

ISBN 10: 0-558-69501-9
ISBN 13: 978-0-558-69501-9

CONTENTS

CHAPTER DEPENDENCIES

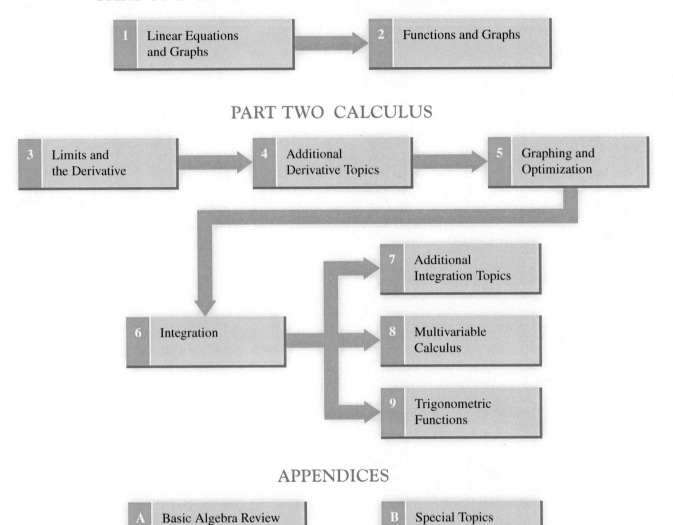

PART ONE A LIBRARY OF ELEMENTARY FUNCTIONS*

1 Linear Equations and Graphs → **2** Functions and Graphs

PART TWO CALCULUS

3 Limits and the Derivative → **4** Additional Derivative Topics → **5** Graphing and Optimization

6 Integration

7 Additional Integration Topics

8 Multivariable Calculus

9 Trigonometric Functions

APPENDICES

A Basic Algebra Review

B Special Topics

*Selected topics from Part One may be referred to as needed in Part Two or reviewed systematically before starting Part Two.

- **Chapter 8** deals with multivariable calculus. The first five sections can be covered any time after Section 5-6 has been completed. Sections 8-6 and 8-7 require the integration concepts discussed in Chapter 6.
- **Chapter 9** provides brief coverage of trigonometric functions that can be incorporated into the course, if desired. Section 9-1 provides a review of basic trigonometric concepts. Section 9-2 can be covered any time after Section 5-3 has been completed. Section 9-3 requires the material in Chapter 6.
- **Appendix A** contains a concise review of basic algebra that may be covered as part of the course or referenced as needed. As mentioned previously, **Appendix B** contains additional topics that can be covered in conjunction with certain sections in the text, if desired.

Accuracy Check

Because of the careful checking and proofing by a number of mathematics instructors (acting independently), the authors and publisher believe this book to be substantially error free. If an error should be found, the authors would be grateful if notification were sent to Karl E. Byleen, 9322 W. Garden Court, Hales Corners, WI 53130; or by e-mail, to kbyleen@wi.rr.com.

STUDENT SUPPLEMENTS

Student's Solutions Manual

By Garret J. Etgen, University of Houston

This manual contains detailed, carefully worked-out solutions to all odd-numbered section exercises and all Chapter Review exercises. Each section begins with Things to Remember, a list of key material for review.

ISBN 13: 978-0-321-65498-4; ISBN 10: 0-321-65498-6

Additional Calculus Topics to Accompany Calculus, 12e and College Mathematics, 12e

This separate book contains three unique chapters: Differential Equations, Taylor Polynomials and Infinite Series, and Probability and Calculus.

ISBN 13: 978-0-321-65509-7; ISBN 10: 0-321-65509-5

Worksheets for Classroom or Lab Practice

These Worksheets provide students with a structured place to take notes, define key concepts and terms, and work through unique examples to reinforce what is taught in the lecture.

ISBN 13: 978-0-321-65398-7; ISBN 10: 0-321-65398-X

Videos on DVD-ROM with Optional Captioning

The video lectures with optional captioning for this text make it easy and convenient for students to watch videos from a computer at home or on campus. The complete digitized set, affordable and portable for students, is ideal for distance learning or supplemental instruction. There is a video for every text example.

ISBN 13: 0-978-0-321-70869-4; ISBN 10: 0-321-70869-5

INSTRUCTOR SUPPLEMENTS

Instructor's Edition

This book contains answers to all exercises in the text.

ISBN 13: 978-0-321-64543-2; ISBN 10: 0-321-64543-X

Online Instructor's Solutions Manual (downloadable)

By Jason Aubrey, University of Missouri—Columbia

This manual contains detailed solutions to all even-numbered section problems.

Available in MyMathLab or through http://www.pearson highered.com.

Mini Lectures (downloadable)

Mini Lectures are provided for the teaching assistant, adjunct, part-time, or even full-time instructor for lecture preparation by providing learning objectives, examples (and answers) not found in the text, and teaching notes.

Available in MyMathLab or through http://www.pearson highered.com.

TestGen®

TestGen® (www.pearsoned.com/testgen) enables instructors to build, edit, print, and administer tests using a computerized bank of questions developed to cover all the objectives of the text. TestGen is algorithmically based, allowing instructors to create multiple but equivalent versions of the same question or test with the click of a button. Instructors can also modify test bank questions or add new questions. The software and testbank are available for download from Pearson Education's online catalog.

PowerPoint® Lecture Slides

These slides present key concepts and definitions from the text. They are available in MyMathLab or at http://www.pearsonhighered.com/educator.

MyMathLab® Online Course (access code required)

MyMathLab is a text-specific, easily customizable online course that integrates interactive multimedia instruction with textbook content. MyMathLab gives you the tools you need to deliver all or a portion of your course online, whether your students are in a lab setting or working from home.

- **Interactive homework exercises**, correlated to your textbook at the objective level, are algorithmically generated for unlimited practice and mastery. Most exercises are free-response and provide guided solutions, sample problems, and tutorial learning aids for extra help.

- **Personalized Study Plan**, generated when students complete a test or quiz, indicates which topics have been mastered and links to tutorial exercises for topics students have not mastered. You can customize the Study Plan so that the topics available match your course contents or so that students' homework results also determine mastery.

- **Multimedia learning aids, such as videos for every example in the text**, provide help for students when they need it. Other student-help features include Help Me Solve This and Additional Examples. You can assign these multimedia learning aids as homework to help your students grasp the concepts.

- **Homework and Test Manager** lets you assign homework, quizzes, and tests that are automatically graded. Select just the right mix of questions from the MyMathLab exercise bank, instructor-created custom exercises, and/or TestGen® test items.

- **Gradebook,** designed specifically for mathematics and statistics, automatically tracks students' results, lets you stay on top of student performance, and gives you control over how to calculate final grades. You can also add offline (paper-and-pencil) grades to the gradebook.

- **MathXL Exercise Builder** allows you to create static and algorithmic exercises for your online assignments. You can use the library of sample exercises as an easy starting point, or you can edit any course-related exercise.

- **Pearson Tutor Center** (www.pearsontutorservices.com) access is automatically included with MyMathLab. The Tutor Center is staffed by qualified math instructors who provide textbook-specific tutoring for students via toll-free phone, fax, email, and interactive Web sessions.

Students do the assignments in the new Flash®-based MathXL Player, which is compatible with almost any browser (Firefox®, Safari™, or Internet Explorer®) on almost any platform (Macintosh® or Windows®). MyMathLab is powered by CourseCompass™, Pearson Education's online teaching and learning environment, and by MathXL®, our online homework, tutorial, and assessment system. MyMathLab is available to qualified adopters. For more information, visit www.mymathlab.com or contact your Pearson representative.

MathXL® Online Course (access code required)

MathXL® is an online homework, tutorial, and assessment system that accompanies Pearson's textbooks in mathematics or statistics.

- **Interactive homework exercises**, correlated to your textbook at the objective level, are algorithmically generated for unlimited practice and mastery. Most exercises are free-response and provide guided solutions, sample problems, and learning aids for extra help.

- **Personalized Study Plan,** generated when students complete a test or quiz, indicates which topics have been mastered and links to tutorial exercises for topics students have not mastered. Instructors can customize the available topics in the study plan to match their course concepts.

- **Multimedia learning aids, such as videos for every example in the text**, provide help for students when they need it. Other student-help features include Help Me Solve This and Additional Examples. These are assignable as homework, to further encourage their use.

- **Gradebook,** designed specifically for mathematics and statistics, automatically tracks students' results, lets you stay on top of student performance, and gives you control over how to calculate final grades.

- **MathXL Exercise Builder** allows you to create static and algorithmic exercises for your online assignments. You can use the library of sample exercises as an easy starting point or use the Exercise Builder to edit any of the course-related exercises.

- **Homework and Test Manager** lets you create online homework, quizzes, and tests that are automatically graded. Select just the right mix of questions from the MathXL exercise bank, instructor-created custom exercises, and/or TestGen test items.

The new Flash®-based MathXL Player is compatible with almost any browser (Firefox®, Safari™, or Internet

Explorer®) on almost any platform (Macintosh® or Windows®). MathXL is available to qualified adopters. For more information, visit our website at www.mathxl.com, or contact your Pearson sales representative.

InterAct Math Tutorial Website:
www.interactmath.com

Get practice and tutorial help online! This interactive tutorial website provides algorithmically generated practice exercises that correlate directly to the exercises in the textbook. Students can retry an exercise as many times as they like with new values each time for unlimited practice and mastery. Every exercise is accompanied by an interactive guided solution that provides helpful feedback for incorrect answers, and students can also view a worked-out sample problem that steps them through an exercise similar to the one they're working on.

Acknowledgments

In addition to the authors many others are involved in the successful publication of a book. We wish to thank the following reviewers of the 11th and 12th editions:

Christine Cosgrove, *Fitchburg State College*
Darryl Egley, *North Harris College*
Lauren Fern, *University of Montana*
Gregory Goeckel, *Presbyterian College*
Garland Guyton, *Montgomery College*
Virginia Hanning, *San Jacinto College*
Bruce Hedman, *University of Connecticut*
Yvette Hester, *Texas A&M University*
Fritz Keinert, *Iowa State University*
Steven Klassen, *Missouri Western State University*
Wesley W. Maiers, *Valparaiso University*
James Martin, *Christopher Newport University*
Gary R. Penner, *Richland College*
Jon Prewett, *University of Wyoming*
Cynthia Schultz, *Illinois Valley Community College*
Maria Terrell, *Cornell University*
Fred M. Wright, *Iowa State University*
Amy Ann Yielding, *Washington State University*

We also wish to thank our colleagues who have provided input on previous editions:

Chris Boldt, Bob Bradshaw, Bruce Chaffee, Robert Chaney, Dianne Clark, Charles E. Cleaver, Barbara Cohen, Richard L. Conlon, Catherine Cron, Lou D'Alotto, Madhu Deshpande, Kenneth A. Dodaro, Michael W. Ecker, Jerry R. Ehman, Lucina Gallagher, Martha M. Harvey, Sue Henderson, Lloyd R. Hicks, Louis F. Hoelzle, Paul Hutchins, K. Wayne James, Jeffrey Lynn Johnson, Robert H. Johnston, Robert Krystock, Inessa Levi, James T. Loats, Frank Lopez, Roy H. Luke, Wayne Miller, Mel Mitchell, Linda M. Neal, Ronald Persky, Kenneth A. Peters, Jr., Dix Petty, Tom Plavchak, Bob Prielipp, Thomas Riedel, Stephen Rodi, Arthur Rosenthal, Sheldon Rothman, Elaine Russell, John Ryan, Daniel E. Scanlon, George R. Schriro, Arnold L. Schroeder, Hari Shanker, Joan Smith, J. Sriskandarajah, Steven Terry, Beverly Vredevelt, Delores A. Williams, Caroline Woods, Charles W. Zimmerman, Pat Zrolka, and Cathleen A. Zucco-Tevelot.

We also express our thanks to:

Caroline Woods, Anthony Gagliardi, Damon Demas, John Samons, Theresa Schille, Blaise DeSesa, and Debra McGivney for providing a careful and thorough accuracy check of the text, problems and answers.

Garret Etgen, Jason Aubrey, Dale R. Buske, and Karla Neal for developing the supplemental materials so important to the success of a text.

All the people at Pearson Education who contributed their efforts to the production of this book.

Diagnostic Algebra Test

Work through all the problems in this self-test and check your answers in the back of the book. Answers are keyed to relevant sections in Appendix A. Based on your results, review the appropriate sections in Appendix A to refresh your algebra skills and better prepare yourself for this course.

1. Replace each question mark with an appropriate expression that will illustrate the use of the indicated real number property:
   (A) Commutative $(\cdot)$: $x(y + z) = ?$
   (B) Associative $(+)$: $2 + (x + y) = ?$
   (C) Distributive: $(2 + 3)x = ?$

Problems 2–6 refer to the following polynomials:
   (A) $3x - 4$ (B) $x + 2$
   (C) $2 - 3x^2$ (D) $x^3 + 8$

2. Add all four.

3. Subtract the sum of (A) and (C) from the sum of (B) and (D).

4. Multiply (C) and (D).

5. What is the degree of each polynomial?

6. What is the leading coefficient of each polynomial?

In Problems 7–12, perform the indicated operations and simplify.

7. $5x^2 - 3x[4 - 3(x - 2)]$

8. $(2x + y)(3x - 4y)$

9. $(2a - 3b)^2$

10. $(2x - y)(2x + y) - (2x - y)^2$

11. $(3x^3 - 2y)^2$ 12. $(x - 2y)^3$

13. Write in scientific notation:
    (A) 4,065,000,000,000   (B) 0.0073

14. Write in standard decimal form:
    (A) 2.55×10^8 (B) 4.06×10^{-4}

15. Indicate true (T) or false (F):
    (A) A natural number is a rational number.
    (B) A number with a repeating decimal expansion is an irrational number.

16. Give an example of an integer that is not a natural number.

Simplify Problems 17–25 and write answers using positive exponents only. All variables represent positive real numbers.

17. $6(xy^3)^5$ 18. $\dfrac{9u^8v^6}{3u^4v^8}$

19. $(2 \times 10^5)(3 \times 10^{-3})$ 20. $(x^{-3}y^2)^{-2}$

21. $u^{5/3}u^{2/3}$ 22. $(9a^4b^{-2})^{1/2}$

23. $\dfrac{5^0}{3^2} + \dfrac{3^{-2}}{2^{-2}}$ 24. $(x^{1/2} + y^{1/2})^2$

25. $(3x^{1/2} - y^{1/2})(2x^{1/2} + 3y^{1/2})$

Write Problems 26–31 in completely factored form relative to the integers. If a polynomial cannot be factored further relative to the integers, say so.

26. $12x^2 + 5x - 3$ 27. $8x^2 - 18xy + 9y^2$

28. $t^2 - 4t - 6$ 29. $6n^3 - 9n^2 - 15n$

30. $(4x - y)^2 - 9x^2$ 31. $6x(2x + 1)^2 - 15x^2(2x + 1)$

In Problems 32–37, perform the indicated operations and reduce to lowest terms. Represent all compound fractions as simple fractions reduced to lowest terms.

32. $\dfrac{2}{5b} - \dfrac{4}{3a^3} - \dfrac{1}{6a^2b^2}$ 33. $\dfrac{3x}{3x^2 - 12x} + \dfrac{1}{6x}$

34. $\dfrac{x}{x^2 - 16} - \dfrac{x + 4}{x^2 - 4x}$ 35. $\dfrac{(x + y)^2 - x^2}{y}$

36. $\dfrac{\dfrac{1}{7 + h} - \dfrac{1}{7}}{h}$ 37. $\dfrac{x^{-1} + y^{-1}}{x^{-2} - y^{-2}}$

38. Each statement illustrates the use of one of the following real number properties or definitions. Indicate which one.

Commutative $(+, \cdot)$	Associative $(+, \cdot)$	Distributive
Identity $(+, \cdot)$	Inverse $(+, \cdot)$	Subtraction
Division	Negatives	Zero

   (A) $(-7) - (-5) = (-7) + [-(-5)]$
   (B) $5u + (3v + 2) = (3v + 2) + 5u$
   (C) $(5m - 2)(2m + 3) =$
       $(5m - 2)2m + (5m - 2)3$
   (D) $9 \cdot (4y) = (9 \cdot 4)y$
   (E) $\dfrac{u}{-(v - w)} = -\dfrac{u}{v - w}$
   (F) $(x - y) + 0 = (x - y)$

39. Change to rational exponent form:
$$6\sqrt[5]{x^2} - 7\sqrt[4]{(x - 1)^3}$$

40. Change to radical form: $2x^{1/2} - 3x^{2/3}$

41. Write in the form $ax^p + bx^q$, where a and b are real numbers and p and q are rational numbers:
$$\dfrac{4\sqrt{x} - 3}{2\sqrt{x}}$$

In Problems 42 and 43, rationalize the denominator.

42. $\dfrac{3x}{\sqrt{3x}}$ 43. $\dfrac{x - 5}{\sqrt{x} - \sqrt{5}}$

In Problems 44 and 45, rationalize the numerator.

44. $\dfrac{\sqrt{x} - 5}{x - 5}$ 45. $\dfrac{\sqrt{u + h} - \sqrt{u}}{h}$

Solve Problems 46–49 for x.

46. $x^2 = 5x$ 47. $3x^2 - 21 = 0$

48. $x^2 - x - 20 = 0$ 49. $-6x^2 + 7x - 1 = 0$

PART 2

CALCULUS

Limits and the Derivative

Introduction

How do algebra and calculus differ? The two words *static* and *dynamic* probably come as close as any to expressing the difference between the two disciplines. In algebra, we solve equations for a particular value of a variable—a static notion. In calculus, we are interested in how a change in one variable affects another variable—a dynamic notion.

Isaac Newton (1642–1727) of England and Gottfried Wilhelm von Leibniz (1646–1716) of Germany developed calculus independently to solve problems concerning motion. Today calculus is used not just in the physical sciences, but also in business, economics, life sciences, and social sciences—any discipline that seeks to understand dynamic phenomena.

In Chapter 3 we introduce the *derivative*, one of the two key concepts of calculus. The second, the *integral*, is the subject of Chapter 6. Both key concepts depend on the notion of *limit*, which is explained in Sections 3–1 and 3–2. We consider many applications of limits and derivatives. See, for example, Problems 69 and 70 in Section 3–3 on the concentration of a drug in the bloodstream.

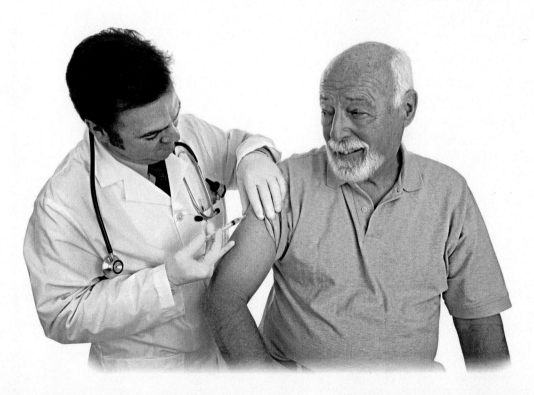

3-1 Introduction to Limits

Basic to the study of calculus is the concept of a *limit*. This concept helps us to describe, in a precise way, the behavior of $f(x)$ when x is close, but not equal, to a particular value c. In this section, we develop an intuitive and informal approach to evaluating limits.

Functions and Graphs: Brief Review

The graph of the function $y = f(x) = x + 2$ is the graph of the set of all ordered pairs $(x, f(x))$. For example, if $x = 2$, then $f(2) = 4$ and $(2, f(2)) = (2, 4)$ is a point on the graph of f. Figure 1 shows $(-1, f(-1))$, $(1, f(1))$, and $(2, f(2))$ plotted on the graph of f. Notice that the domain values -1, 1, and 2 are associated with the x axis and the range values $f(-1) = 1$, $f(1) = 3$, and $f(2) = 4$ are associated with the y axis.

Given x, it is sometimes useful to read $f(x)$ directly from the graph of f. Example 1 reviews this process.

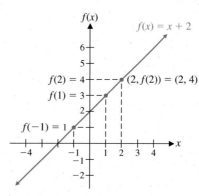

Figure 1

EXAMPLE 1 **Finding Values of a Function from Its Graph** Complete the following table, using the given graph of the function g.

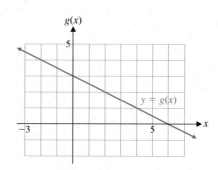

x	$g(x)$
-2	
1	
3	
4	

SOLUTION To determine $g(x)$, proceed vertically from the x value on the x axis to the graph of g and then horizontally to the corresponding y value $g(x)$ on the y axis (as indicated by the dashed lines).

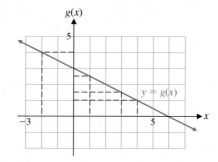

x	$g(x)$
-2	4.0
1	2.5
3	1.5
4	1.0

Matched Problem 1   Complete the following table, using the given graph of the function h.

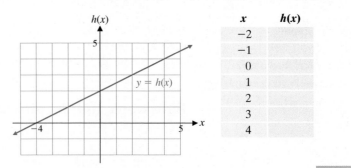

x	$h(x)$
-2	
-1	
0	
1	
2	
3	
4	

Limits: A Graphical Approach

We introduce the important concept of a *limit* through an example, which leads to an intuitive definition of the concept.

EXAMPLE 2   **Analyzing a Limit** Let $f(x) = x + 2$. Discuss the behavior of the values of $f(x)$ when x is close to 2.

SOLUTION   We begin by drawing a graph of f that includes the domain value $x = 2$ (Fig. 2).

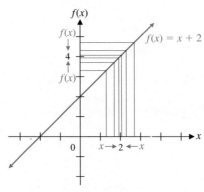

Figure 2

In Figure 2, we are using a static drawing to describe a dynamic process. This requires careful interpretation. The thin vertical lines in Figure 2 represent values of x that are close to 2. The corresponding horizontal lines identify the value of $f(x)$ associated with each value of x. [Example 1 dealt with the relationship between x and $f(x)$ on a graph.] The graph in Figure 2 indicates that as the values of x get closer and closer to 2 on either side of 2, the corresponding values of $f(x)$ get closer and closer to 4. Symbolically, we write

$$\lim_{x \to 2} f(x) = 4$$

This equation is read as "The limit of $f(x)$ as x approaches 2 is 4." Note that $f(2) = 4$. That is, the value of the function at 2 and the limit of the function as x approaches 2 are the same. This relationship can be expressed as

$$\lim_{x \to 2} f(x) = f(2) = 4$$

Graphically, this means that there is no hole or break in the graph of f at $x = 2$.

Matched Problem 2   Let $f(x) = x + 1$. Discuss the behavior of the values of $f(x)$ when x is close to 1.

We now present an informal definition of the important concept of a limit. A precise definition is not needed for our discussion, but one is given in a footnote.*

DEFINITION Limit

We write

$$\lim_{x \to c} f(x) = L \qquad \text{or} \qquad f(x) \to L \quad \text{as} \quad x \to c$$

if the functional value $f(x)$ is close to the single real number L whenever x is close, but not equal, to c (on either side of c).

Note: The existence of a limit at c has nothing to do with the value of the function at c. In fact, c may not even be in the domain of f. However, the function must be defined on both sides of c.

The next example involves the **absolute value function**:

$$f(x) = |x| = \begin{cases} -x & \text{if } x < 0 \\ x & \text{if } x \ge 0 \end{cases}$$

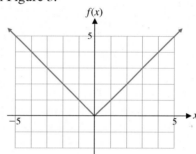

$$f(-2) = |-2| = -(-2) = 2$$
$$f(3) = |3| = 3$$

The graph of f is shown in Figure 3.

$$f(x)$$

Figure 3 $f(x) = |x|$

EXAMPLE 3   **Analyzing a Limit** Let $h(x) = |x|/x$. Explore the behavior of $h(x)$ for x near, but not equal, to 0. Find $\lim_{x \to 0} h(x)$ if it exists.

SOLUTION   The function h is defined for all real numbers except 0. For example,

$$h(-2) = \frac{|-2|}{-2} = \frac{2}{-2} = -1$$

$$h(0) = \frac{|0|}{0} = \frac{0}{0} \qquad \text{Not defined}$$

$$h(2) = \frac{|2|}{2} = \frac{2}{2} = 1$$

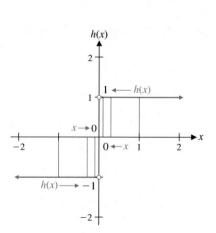

Figure 4

In general, $h(x)$ is -1 for all negative x and 1 for all positive x. Figure 4 illustrates the behavior of $h(x)$ for x near 0. Note that the absence of a solid dot on the vertical axis indicates that h is not defined when $x = 0$.

When x is near 0 (on either side of 0), is $h(x)$ near one specific number? The answer is "No," because $h(x)$ is -1 for $x < 0$ and 1 for $x > 0$. Consequently, we say that

$$\lim_{x \to 0} \frac{|x|}{x} \quad \text{does not exist}$$

Neither $h(x)$ nor the limit of $h(x)$ exists at $x = 0$. However, the limit from the left and the limit from the right both exist at 0, but they are not equal.

---

*To make the informal definition of *limit* precise, we must make the word *close* more precise. This is done as follows: We write $\lim_{x \to c} f(x) = L$ if, for each $e > 0$, there exists a $d > 0$ such that $|f(x) - L| < e$ whenever $0 < |x - c| < d$. This definition is used to establish particular limits and to prove many useful properties of limits that will be helpful in finding particular limits.

Matched Problem 3

Graph

$$h(x) = \frac{x - 2}{|x - 2|}$$

and find $\lim_{x \to 2} h(x)$ if it exists.

In Example 3, we see that the values of the function $h(x)$ approach two different numbers, depending on the direction of approach, and it is natural to refer to these values as "the limit from the left" and "the limit from the right." These experiences suggest that the notion of **one-sided limits** will be very useful in discussing basic limit concepts.

DEFINITION   One-Sided Limits

We write

$$\lim_{x \to c^-} f(x) = K \qquad$$ $x \to c^-$ is read "x approaches c from the left" and means $x \to c$ and $x < c$.

and call K the **limit from the left** or the **left-hand limit** if $f(x)$ is close to K whenever x is close to, but to the left of, c on the real number line. We write

$$\lim_{x \to c^+} f(x) = L \qquad$$ $x \to c^+$ is read "x approaches c from the right" and means $x \to c$ and $x > c$.

and call L the **limit from the right** or the **right-hand limit** if $f(x)$ is close to L whenever x is close to, but to the right of, c on the real number line.

If no direction is specified in a limit statement, we will always assume that the limit is **two-sided** or **unrestricted**. Theorem 1 states an important relationship between one-sided limits and unrestricted limits.

THEOREM 1   On the Existence of a Limit

For a (two-sided) limit to exist, the limit from the left and the limit from the right must exist and be equal. That is,

$$\lim_{x \to c} f(x) = L \text{ if and only if } \lim_{x \to c^-} f(x) = \lim_{x \to c^+} f(x) = L$$

In Example 3,

$$\lim_{x \to 0^-} \frac{|x|}{x} = -1 \qquad \text{and} \qquad \lim_{x \to 0^+} \frac{|x|}{x} = 1$$

Since the left- and right-hand limits are *not* the same,

$$\lim_{x \to 0} \frac{|x|}{x} \text{ does not exist}$$

EXAMPLE 4

Analyzing Limits Graphically Given the graph of the function f in Figure 5, discuss the behavior of $f(x)$ for x near (A) -1, (B) 1, and (C) 2.

SOLUTION

(A) Since we have only a graph to work with, we use vertical and horizontal lines to relate the values of x and the corresponding values of $f(x)$. For any x near -1 on either side of -1, we see that the corresponding value of $f(x)$, determined by a horizontal line, is close to 1.

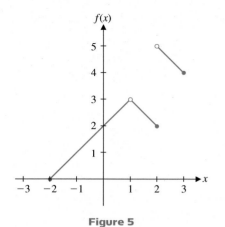

Figure 5

$$\lim_{x \to -1^-} f(x) = 1$$

$$\lim_{x \to -1^+} f(x) = 1$$

$$\lim_{x \to -1} f(x) = 1$$

$$f(-1) = 1$$

(B)   Again, for any x near, but not equal to, 1, the vertical and horizontal lines indicate that the corresponding value of $f(x)$ is close to 3. The open dot at
$(1, 3)$, together with the absence of a solid dot anywhere on the vertical line
through $x = 1$, indicates that $f(1)$ is not defined.

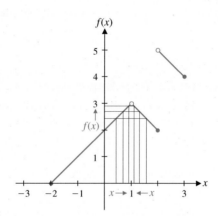

$$\lim_{x \to 1^-} f(x) = 3$$

$$\lim_{x \to 1^+} f(x) = 3$$

$$\lim_{x \to 1} f(x) = 3$$

$$f(1) \text{ not defined}$$

(C)   The abrupt break in the graph at $x = 2$ indicates that the behavior of the
graph near $x = 2$ is more complicated than in the two preceding cases. If x is
close to 2 on the left side of 2, the corresponding horizontal line intersects
the y axis at a point close to 2. If x is close to 2 on the right side of 2, the corresponding horizontal line intersects the y axis at a point close to 5. This is a
case where the one-sided limits are different.

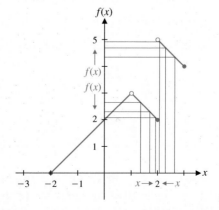

$$\lim_{x \to 2^-} f(x) = 2$$

$$\lim_{x \to 2^+} f(x) = 5$$

$$\lim_{x \to 2} f(x) \text{ does not exist}$$

$$f(2) = 2$$

Matched Problem 4 Given the graph of the function f shown in Figure 6, discuss the following, as we did in Example 4:

(A) Behavior of $f(x)$ for x near 0

(B) Behavior of $f(x)$ for x near 1

(C) Behavior of $f(x)$ for x near 3

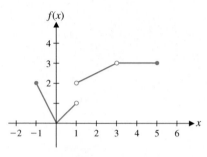

Figure 6

CONCEPTUAL INSIGHT

In Example 4B, note that $\lim_{x \to 1} f(x)$ exists even though f is not defined at $x = 1$ and the graph has a hole at $x = 1$. In general, the value of a function at $x = c$ has no effect on the limit of the function as x approaches c.

Limits: An Algebraic Approach

Graphs are very useful tools for investigating limits, especially if something unusual happens at the point in question. However, many of the limits encountered in calculus are routine and can be evaluated quickly with a little algebraic simplification, some intuition, and basic properties of limits. The following list of properties of limits forms the basis for this approach:

THEOREM 2 Properties of Limits

Let f and g be two functions, and assume that

$$\lim_{x \to c} f(x) = L \qquad \lim_{x \to c} g(x) = M$$

where L and M are real numbers (both limits exist). Then

1. $\lim_{x \to c} k = k$ for any constant k

2. $\lim_{x \to c} x = c$

3. $\lim_{x \to c} [f(x) + g(x)] = \lim_{x \to c} f(x) + \lim_{x \to c} g(x) = L + M$

4. $\lim_{x \to c} [f(x) - g(x)] = \lim_{x \to c} f(x) - \lim_{x \to c} g(x) = L - M$

5. $\lim_{x \to c} kf(x) = k \lim_{x \to c} f(x) = kL$ for any constant k

6. $\lim_{x \to c} [f(x) \cdot g(x)] = [\lim_{x \to c} f(x)][\lim_{x \to c} g(x)] = LM$

7. $\lim_{x \to c} \dfrac{f(x)}{g(x)} = \dfrac{\lim_{x \to c} f(x)}{\lim_{x \to c} g(x)} = \dfrac{L}{M}$ if $M \neq 0$

8. $\lim_{x \to c} \sqrt[n]{f(x)} = \sqrt[n]{\lim_{x \to c} f(x)} = \sqrt[n]{L}$ $L > 0$ for n even

---

Each property in Theorem 2 is also valid if $x \to c$ is replaced everywhere by $x \to c^-$ or replaced everywhere by $x \to c^+$.

The properties listed in Theorem 2 can be paraphrased in brief verbal statements. For example, property 3 simply states that *the limit of a sum is equal to the sum of the limits*. Write brief verbal statements for the remaining properties in Theorem 2.

EXAMPLE 5   **Using Limit Properties** Find $\lim_{x \to 3}(x^2 - 4x)$.

SOLUTION

$$\lim_{x \to 3}(x^2 - 4x) = \lim_{x \to 3} x^2 - \lim_{x \to 3} 4x \qquad \text{Property 4}$$

$$= \left(\lim_{x \to 3} x \right) \cdot \left(\lim_{x \to 3} x \right) - 4 \lim_{x \to 3} x \qquad \text{Properties 5 and 6}$$

$$= 3 \cdot 3 - 4 \cdot 3 = -3 \qquad \text{Property 2}$$

With a little practice, you will soon be able to omit the steps in the dashed boxes and simply write

$$\lim_{x \to 3}(x^2 - 4x) = 3 \cdot 3 - 4 \cdot 3 = -3$$

Matched Problem 5   Find $\lim_{x \to -2}(x^2 + 5x)$.

What happens if we try to evaluate a limit like the one in Example 5, but with x approaching an unspecified number, such as c? Proceeding as we did in Example 5, we have

$$\lim_{x \to c}(x^2 - 4x) = c \cdot c - 4 \cdot c = c^2 - 4c$$

If we let $f(x) = x^2 - 4x$, we have

$$\lim_{x \to c} f(x) = \lim_{x \to c}(x^2 - 4x) = c^2 - 4c = f(c)$$

That is, this limit can be evaluated simply by evaluating the function f at c. It would certainly simplify the process of evaluating limits if we could identify the functions for which

$$\lim_{x \to c} f(x) = f(c) \tag{1}$$

since we could use this fact to evaluate the limit. It turns out that there are many functions that satisfy equation (1). We postpone a detailed discussion of these functions until the next section. For now, we note that if

$$f(x) = a_n x^n + a_{n-1} x^{n-1} + \cdots + a_0$$

is a polynomial function, then, by the properties in Theorem 1,

$$\lim_{x \to c} f(x) = \lim_{x \to c}(a_n x^n + a_{n-1} x^{n-1} + \cdots + a_0)$$

$$= a_n c^n + a_{n-1} c^{n-1} + \cdots + a_0 = f(c)$$

and if

$$r(x) = \frac{n(x)}{d(x)}$$

is a rational function, where $n(x)$ and $d(x)$ are polynomials with $d(c) \neq 0$, then by property 7 and the fact that polynomials $n(x)$ and $d(x)$ satisfy equation (1),

$$\lim_{x \to c} r(x) = \lim_{x \to c} \frac{n(x)}{d(x)} = \frac{\lim_{x \to c} n(x)}{\lim_{x \to c} d(x)} = \frac{n(c)}{d(c)} = r(c)$$

These results are summarized in Theorem 3.

> **THEOREM 3   Limits of Polynomial and Rational Functions**
>
> 1. $\lim\limits_{x \to c} f(x) = f(c)$ for f any polynomial function.
>
> 2. $\lim\limits_{x \to c} r(x) = r(c)$ for r any rational function with a nonzero denominator at $x = c$.

EXAMPLE 6   **Evaluating Limits** Find each limit.

(A) $\lim\limits_{x \to 2} (x^3 - 5x - 1)$ (B) $\lim\limits_{x \to -1} \sqrt{2x^2 + 3}$ (C) $\lim\limits_{x \to 4} \dfrac{2x}{3x + 1}$

SOLUTION   (A) $\lim\limits_{x \to 2} (x^3 - 5x - 1) = 2^3 - 5 \cdot 2 - 1 = -3$ Theorem 3

(B) $\lim\limits_{x \to -1} \sqrt{2x^2 + 3} = \sqrt{\lim\limits_{x \to -1} (2x^2 + 3)}$ Property 8

$\qquad\qquad\qquad\quad = \sqrt{2(-1)^2 + 3}$ Theorem 3

$\qquad\qquad\qquad\quad = \sqrt{5}$

(C) $\lim\limits_{x \to 4} \dfrac{2x}{3x + 1} = \dfrac{2 \cdot 4}{3 \cdot 4 + 1}$ Theorem 3

$\qquad\qquad\qquad\ = \dfrac{8}{13}$

Matched Problem 6   Find each limit.

(A) $\lim\limits_{x \to -1} (x^4 - 2x + 3)$ (B) $\lim\limits_{x \to 2} \sqrt{3x^2 - 6}$ (C) $\lim\limits_{x \to -2} \dfrac{x^2}{x^2 + 1}$

EXAMPLE 7   **Evaluating Limits** Let

$$f(x) = \begin{cases} x^2 + 1 & \text{if } x < 2 \\ x - 1 & \text{if } x > 2 \end{cases}$$

Find each limit.

(A) $\lim\limits_{x \to 2^-} f(x)$ (B) $\lim\limits_{x \to 2^+} f(x)$ (C) $\lim\limits_{x \to 2} f(x)$ (D) $f(2)$

SOLUTION   (A) $\lim\limits_{x \to 2^-} f(x) = \lim\limits_{x \to 2^-} (x^2 + 1)$ If $x < 2$, $f(x) = x^2 + 1$.

$\qquad\qquad\qquad\quad\ = 2^2 + 1 = 5$

(B) $\lim\limits_{x \to 2^+} f(x) = \lim\limits_{x \to 2^+} (x - 1)$ If $x > 2$, $f(x) = x - 1$.

$\qquad\qquad\qquad\quad\ = 2 - 1 = 1$

(C) Since the one-sided limits are not equal, $\lim\limits_{x \to 2} f(x)$ does not exist.

(D) Because the definition of f does not assign a value to f for $x = 2$, only for $x < 2$ and $x > 2$, $f(2)$ does not exist.

Matched Problem 7   Let

$$f(x) = \begin{cases} 2x + 3 & \text{if } x < 5 \\ -x + 12 & \text{if } x > 5 \end{cases}$$

Find each limit.

(A) $\lim\limits_{x \to 5^-} f(x)$ (B) $\lim\limits_{x \to 5^+} f(x)$ (C) $\lim\limits_{x \to 5} f(x)$ (D) $f(5)$

It is important to note that there are restrictions on some of the limit properties. In particular, if

$$\lim_{x\to c} f(x) = 0 \text{ and } \lim_{x\to c} g(x) = 0, \text{ then finding } \lim_{x\to c} \frac{f(x)}{g(x)}$$

may present some difficulties, since limit property 7 (the limit of a quotient) does not apply when $\lim_{x\to c} g(x) = 0$. The next example illustrates some techniques that can be useful in this situation.

EXAMPLE 8 **Evaluating Limits** Find each limit.

(A) $\lim_{x\to 2} \dfrac{x^2 - 4}{x - 2}$ (B) $\lim_{x\to -1} \dfrac{x|x + 1|}{x + 1}$

SOLUTION (A) Algebraic simplification is often useful when the numerator and denominator are both approaching 0.

$$\lim_{x\to 2} \frac{x^2 - 4}{x - 2} = \lim_{x\to 2} \frac{(x - 2)(x + 2)}{x - 2} = \lim_{x\to 2}(x + 2) = 4$$

(B) One-sided limits are helpful for limits involving the absolute value function.

$$\lim_{x\to -1^+} \frac{x|x + 1|}{x + 1} = \lim_{x\to -1^+}(x) = -1 \quad \text{If } x > -1, \text{ then } \frac{|x + 1|}{x + 1} = 1.$$

$$\lim_{x\to -1^-} \frac{x|x + 1|}{x + 1} = \lim_{x\to -1^-}(-x) = 1 \quad \text{If } x < -1, \text{ then } \frac{|x + 1|}{x + 1} = -1.$$

Since the limit from the left and the limit from the right are not the same, we conclude that

$$\lim_{x\to -1} \frac{x|x + 1|}{x + 1} \quad \text{does not exist}$$

Matched Problem 8 Find each limit.

(A) $\lim_{x\to -3} \dfrac{x^2 + 4x + 3}{x + 3}$ (B) $\lim_{x\to 4} \dfrac{x^2 - 16}{|x - 4|}$

CONCEPTUAL INSIGHT

In the solution to Example 8A we used the following algebraic identity:

$$\frac{x^2 - 4}{x - 2} = \frac{(x - 2)(x + 2)}{x - 2} = x + 2, \quad x \neq 2$$

The restriction $x \neq 2$ is necessary here because the first two expressions are not defined at $x = 2$. Why didn't we include this restriction in the solution? When x approaches 2 in a limit problem, it is assumed that x is close, but not equal, to 2. It is important that you understand that both of the following statements are valid:

$$\lim_{x\to 2} \frac{x^2 - 4}{x - 2} = \lim_{x\to 2}(x + 2) \quad \text{and} \quad \frac{x^2 - 4}{x - 2} = x + 2, \ x \neq 2$$

Limits like those in Example 8 occur so frequently in calculus that they are given a special name.

DEFINITION Indeterminate Form

If $\lim_{x \to c} f(x) = 0$ and $\lim_{x \to c} g(x) = 0$, then $\lim_{x \to c} \dfrac{f(x)}{g(x)}$ is said to be **indeterminate**, or, more specifically, a **0/0 indeterminate form**.

The term *indeterminate* is used because the limit of an indeterminate form may or may not exist (see Example 8A and 8B).

⚠ **CAUTION** The expression 0/0 does not represent a real number and should never be used as the value of a limit. If a limit is a 0/0 indeterminate form, further investigation is always required to determine whether the limit exists and to find its value if it does exist.

If the denominator of a quotient approaches 0 and the numerator approaches a nonzero number, then the limit of the quotient is not an indeterminate form. In fact, a limit of this form never exists.

THEOREM 4   Limit of a Quotient
If $\lim_{x \to c} f(x) = L, L \neq 0$, and $\lim_{x \to c} g(x) = 0$,

then

$$\lim_{x \to c} \frac{f(x)}{g(x)} \qquad \text{does not exist}$$

EXPLORE & DISCUSS 2

Use algebraic and/or graphical techniques to analyze each of the following indeterminate forms.

(A) $\lim_{x \to 1} \dfrac{x-1}{x^2-1}$ (B) $\lim_{x \to 1} \dfrac{(x-1)^2}{x^2-1}$ (C) $\lim_{x \to 1} \dfrac{x^2-1}{(x-1)^2}$

Limits of Difference Quotients

Let the function f be defined in an open interval containing the number a. One of the most important limits in calculus is the limit of the **difference quotient**,

$$\lim_{h \to 0} \frac{f(a+h)-f(a)}{h} \tag{2}$$

If

$$\lim_{h \to 0} [f(a+h)-f(a)] = 0$$

as it often does, then limit (2) is an indeterminate form.

EXAMPLE 9   **Limit of a Difference Quotient** Find the following limit for $f(x) = 4x - 5$:

$$\lim_{h \to 0} \frac{f(3+h)-f(3)}{h}$$

SOLUTION
$$\lim_{h \to 0} \frac{f(3+h)-f(3)}{h} = \lim_{h \to 0} \frac{[4(3+h)-5]-[4(3)-5]}{h}$$
$$= \lim_{h \to 0} \frac{12+4h-5-12+5}{h}$$
$$= \lim_{h \to 0} \frac{4h}{h} = \lim_{h \to 0} 4 = 4$$

Since this is a 0/0 indeterminate form and property 7 in Theorem 2 does not apply, we proceed with algebraic simplification.

Matched Problem 9 Find the following limit for $f(x) = 7 - 2x$: $\lim\limits_{h \to 0} \dfrac{f(4+h) - f(4)}{h}$.

EXAMPLE 10 **Limit of a Difference Quotient** Find the following limit for $f(x) = |x + 5|$:

$$\lim\limits_{h \to 0} \dfrac{f(-5+h) - f(-5)}{h}$$

SOLUTION

$$\lim\limits_{h \to 0} \dfrac{f(-5+h) - f(-5)}{h} = \lim\limits_{h \to 0} \dfrac{|(-5+h)+5| - |-5+5|}{h}$$

$$= \lim\limits_{h \to 0} \dfrac{|h|}{h} \text{ does not exist}$$

Since this is a 0/0 indeterminate form and property 7 in Theorem 2 does not apply, we proceed with algebraic simplification.

Matched Problem 10 Find the following limit for $f(x) = |x - 1|$: $\lim\limits_{h \to 0} \dfrac{f(1+h) - f(1)}{h}$.

EXAMPLE 11 **Limit of a Difference Quotient** Find the following limit for $f(x) = \sqrt{x}$:

$$\lim\limits_{h \to 0} \dfrac{f(2+h) - f(2)}{h}$$

SOLUTION

$$\lim\limits_{h \to 0} \dfrac{f(2+h) - f(2)}{h} = \lim\limits_{h \to 0} \dfrac{\sqrt{2+h} - \sqrt{2}}{h}$$

$$= \lim\limits_{h \to 0} \dfrac{\sqrt{2+h} - \sqrt{2}}{h} \cdot \dfrac{\sqrt{2+h} + \sqrt{2}}{\sqrt{2+h} + \sqrt{2}}$$

$$= \lim\limits_{h \to 0} \dfrac{2+h-2}{h(\sqrt{2+h} + \sqrt{2})}$$

$$= \lim\limits_{h \to 0} \dfrac{1}{\sqrt{2+h} + \sqrt{2}}$$

$$= \dfrac{1}{\sqrt{2} + \sqrt{2}} = \dfrac{1}{2\sqrt{2}}$$

This is a 0/0 indeterminate form, so property 7 in Theorem 2 does not apply. Rationalizing the numerator will help.

$(A - B)(A + B) = A^2 - B^2$

Matched Problem 11 Find the following limit for $f(x) = \sqrt{x}$: $\lim\limits_{h \to 0} \dfrac{f(3+h) - f(3)}{h}$.

Exercises 3-1

In Problems 1–8, use the graph of the function f shown to estimate the indicated limits and function values.

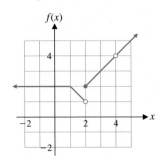

Figure for 1–8

1. $f(-0.5)$ **2.** $f(-1.5)$

3. $f(1.75)$ **4.** $f(1.25)$

5. (A) $\lim\limits_{x \to 0^-} f(x)$ (B) $\lim\limits_{x \to 0^+} f(x)$
   (C) $\lim\limits_{x \to 0} f(x)$ (D) $f(0)$

6. (A) $\lim\limits_{x \to 1^-} f(x)$ (B) $\lim\limits_{x \to 1^+} f(x)$
   (C) $\lim\limits_{x \to 1} f(x)$ (D) $f(1)$

7. (A) $\lim\limits_{x \to 2^-} f(x)$ (B) $\lim\limits_{x \to 2^+} f(x)$
   (C) $\lim\limits_{x \to 2} f(x)$ (D) $f(2)$
   (E) Is it possible to redefine $f(2)$ so that $\lim\limits_{x \to 2} f(x) = f(2)$? Explain.

8. (A) $\lim\limits_{x \to 4^-} f(x)$ (B) $\lim\limits_{x \to 4^+} f(x)$
   (C) $\lim\limits_{x \to 4} f(x)$ (D) $f(4)$
   (E) Is it possible to define $f(4)$ so that $\lim\limits_{x \to 4} f(x) = f(4)$? Explain.

In Problems 9–16, use the graph of the function g shown to estimate the indicated limits and function values.

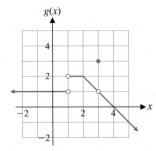

Figure for 9–16

9. $g(1.9)$ **10.** $g(0.1)$

11. $g(3.5)$ **12.** $g(2.5)$

13. (A) $\lim\limits_{x \to 1^-} g(x)$ (B) $\lim\limits_{x \to 1^+} g(x)$
   (C) $\lim\limits_{x \to 1} g(x)$ (D) $g(1)$
   (E) Is it possible to define $g(1)$ so that $\lim\limits_{x \to 1} g(x) = g(1)$? Explain.

14. (A) $\lim\limits_{x \to 2^-} g(x)$ (B) $\lim\limits_{x \to 2^+} g(x)$
   (C) $\lim\limits_{x \to 2} g(x)$ (D) $g(2)$

15. (A) $\lim\limits_{x \to 3^-} g(x)$ (B) $\lim\limits_{x \to 3^+} g(x)$
   (C) $\lim\limits_{x \to 3} g(x)$ (D) $g(3)$
   (E) Is it possible to redefine $g(3)$ so that $\lim\limits_{x \to 3} g(x) = g(3)$? Explain.

16. (A) $\lim\limits_{x \to 4^-} g(x)$ (B) $\lim\limits_{x \to 4^+} g(x)$
   (C) $\lim\limits_{x \to 4} g(x)$ (D) $g(4)$

In Problems 17–20, use the graph of the function f shown to estimate the indicated limits and function values.

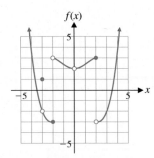

Figure for 17–20

17. (A) $\lim\limits_{x \to -3^+} f(x)$ (B) $\lim\limits_{x \to -3^-} f(x)$
   (C) $\lim\limits_{x \to -3} f(x)$ (D) $f(-3)$
   (E) Is it possible to redefine $f(-3)$ so that $\lim\limits_{x \to -3} f(x) = f(-3)$? Explain.

18. (A) $\lim\limits_{x \to -2^+} f(x)$ (B) $\lim\limits_{x \to -2^-} f(x)$
   (C) $\lim\limits_{x \to -2} f(x)$ (D) $f(-2)$
   (E) Is it possible to define $f(-2)$ so that $\lim\limits_{x \to -2} f(x) = f(-2)$? Explain.

19. (A) $\lim\limits_{x \to 0^+} f(x)$ (B) $\lim\limits_{x \to 0^-} f(x)$
   (C) $\lim\limits_{x \to 0} f(x)$ (D) $f(0)$
   (E) Is it possible to redefine $f(0)$ so that $\lim\limits_{x \to 0} f(x) = f(0)$? Explain.

20. (A) $\lim\limits_{x \to 2^+} f(x)$ (B) $\lim\limits_{x \to 2^-} f(x)$
   (C) $\lim\limits_{x \to 2} f(x)$ (D) $f(2)$
   (E) Is it possible to redefine $f(2)$ so that $\lim\limits_{x \to 2} f(x) = f(2)$? Explain.

In Problems 21–30, find each limit if it exists.

21. $\lim\limits_{x \to 3} 4x$ **22.** $\lim\limits_{x \to -2} 3x$

23. $\lim\limits_{x \to -4} (x + 5)$ **24.** $\lim\limits_{x \to 5} (x - 3)$

25. $\lim\limits_{x \to 2} x(x - 4)$ **26.** $\lim\limits_{x \to -1} x(x + 3)$

27. $\lim\limits_{x \to -3} \dfrac{x}{x + 5}$ **28.** $\lim\limits_{x \to 4} \dfrac{x - 2}{x}$

29. $\lim\limits_{x \to 1} \sqrt{5x + 4}$ **30.** $\lim\limits_{x \to 0} \sqrt{16 - 7x}$

Given that $\lim_{x \to 1} f(x) = -5$ *and* $\lim_{x \to 1} g(x) = 4$, *find the indicated limits in Problems 31–38.*

31. $\lim_{x \to 1} (-3) f(x)$

32. $\lim_{x \to 1} 2g(x)$

33. $\lim_{x \to 1} [2f(x) + g(x)]$

34. $\lim_{x \to 1} [g(x) - 3f(x)]$

35. $\lim_{x \to 1} \dfrac{2 - f(x)}{x + g(x)}$

36. $\lim_{x \to 1} \dfrac{3 - f(x)}{1 - 4g(x)}$

37. $\lim_{x \to 1} \sqrt{g(x) - f(x)}$

38. $\lim_{x \to 1} \sqrt[3]{2x + 2f(x)}$

In Problems 39–42, sketch a possible graph of a function that satisfies the given conditions.

39. $f(0) = 1$; $\lim_{x \to 0^-} f(x) = 3$; $\lim_{x \to 0^+} f(x) = 1$

40. $f(1) = -2$; $\lim_{x \to 1^-} f(x) = 2$; $\lim_{x \to 1^+} f(x) = -2$

41. $f(-2) = 2$; $\lim_{x \to -2^-} f(x) = 1$; $\lim_{x \to -2^+} f(x) = 1$

42. $f(0) = -1$; $\lim_{x \to 0^-} f(x) = 2$; $\lim_{x \to 0^+} f(x) = 2$

B

In Problems 43–58, find each indicated quantity if it exists.

43. Let $f(x) = \begin{cases} 1 - x^2 & \text{if } x \le 0 \\ 1 + x^2 & \text{if } x > 0 \end{cases}$. Find

(A) $\lim_{x \to 0^+} f(x)$ (B) $\lim_{x \to 0^-} f(x)$

(C) $\lim_{x \to 0} f(x)$ (D) $f(0)$

44. Let $f(x) = \begin{cases} 2 + x & \text{if } x \le 0 \\ 2 - x & \text{if } x > 0 \end{cases}$. Find

(A) $\lim_{x \to 0^+} f(x)$ (B) $\lim_{x \to 0^-} f(x)$

(C) $\lim_{x \to 0} f(x)$ (D) $f(0)$

45. Let $f(x) = \begin{cases} x^2 & \text{if } x < 1 \\ 2x & \text{if } x > 1 \end{cases}$. Find

(A) $\lim_{x \to 1^+} f(x)$ (B) $\lim_{x \to 1^-} f(x)$

(C) $\lim_{x \to 1} f(x)$ (D) $f(1)$

46. Let $f(x) = \begin{cases} x + 3 & \text{if } x < -2 \\ \sqrt{x + 2} & \text{if } x > -2 \end{cases}$. Find

(A) $\lim_{x \to -2^+} f(x)$ (B) $\lim_{x \to -2^-} f(x)$

(C) $\lim_{x \to -2} f(x)$ (D) $f(-2)$

47. Let $f(x) = \begin{cases} \dfrac{x^2 - 9}{x + 3} & \text{if } x < 0 \\ \dfrac{x^2 - 9}{x - 3} & \text{if } x > 0 \end{cases}$. Find

(A) $\lim_{x \to -3} f(x)$ (B) $\lim_{x \to 0} f(x)$

(C) $\lim_{x \to 3} f(x)$

48. Let $f(x) = \begin{cases} \dfrac{x}{x + 3} & \text{if } x < 0 \\ \dfrac{x}{x - 3} & \text{if } x > 0 \end{cases}$. Find

(A) $\lim_{x \to -3} f(x)$ (B) $\lim_{x \to 0} f(x)$

(C) $\lim_{x \to 3} f(x)$

49. Let $f(x) = \dfrac{|x - 1|}{x - 1}$. Find

(A) $\lim_{x \to 1^+} f(x)$ (B) $\lim_{x \to 1^-} f(x)$

(C) $\lim_{x \to 1} f(x)$ (D) $f(1)$

50. Let $f(x) = \dfrac{x - 3}{|x - 3|}$. Find

(A) $\lim_{x \to 3^+} f(x)$ (B) $\lim_{x \to 3^-} f(x)$

(C) $\lim_{x \to 3} f(x)$ (D) $f(3)$

51. Let $f(x) = \dfrac{x - 2}{x^2 - 2x}$. Find

(A) $\lim_{x \to 0} f(x)$ (B) $\lim_{x \to 2} f(x)$

(C) $\lim_{x \to 4} f(x)$

52. Let $f(x) = \dfrac{x + 3}{x^2 + 3x}$. Find

(A) $\lim_{x \to -3} f(x)$ (B) $\lim_{x \to 0} f(x)$

(C) $\lim_{x \to 3} f(x)$

53. Let $f(x) = \dfrac{x^2 - x - 6}{x + 2}$. Find

(A) $\lim_{x \to -2} f(x)$ (B) $\lim_{x \to 0} f(x)$

(C) $\lim_{x \to 3} f(x)$

54. Let $f(x) = \dfrac{x^2 + x - 6}{x + 3}$. Find

(A) $\lim_{x \to -3} f(x)$ (B) $\lim_{x \to 0} f(x)$

(C) $\lim_{x \to 2} f(x)$

55. Let $f(x) = \dfrac{(x + 2)^2}{x^2 - 4}$. Find

(A) $\lim_{x \to -2} f(x)$ (B) $\lim_{x \to 0} f(x)$

(C) $\lim_{x \to 2} f(x)$

56. Let $f(x) = \dfrac{x^2 - 1}{(x + 1)^2}$. Find

(A) $\lim_{x \to -1} f(x)$ (B) $\lim_{x \to 0} f(x)$

(C) $\lim_{x \to 1} f(x)$

57. Let $f(x) = \dfrac{2x^2 - 3x - 2}{x^2 + x - 6}$. Find

(A) $\lim_{x \to 2} f(x)$ (B) $\lim_{x \to 0} f(x)$

(C) $\lim_{x \to 1} f(x)$

58. Let $f(x) = \dfrac{3x^2 + 2x - 1}{x^2 + 3x + 2}$. Find

(A) $\lim_{x \to -3} f(x)$ (B) $\lim_{x \to -1} f(x)$

(C) $\lim_{x \to 2} f(x)$

In Problems 59–64, discuss the validity of each statement. If the statement is always true, explain why. If not, give a counterexample.

59. If $\lim_{x \to 1} f(x) = 0$ and $\lim_{x \to 1} g(x) = 0$, then $\lim_{x \to 1} \dfrac{f(x)}{g(x)} = 0$.

60. If $\lim_{x \to 1} f(x) = 1$ and $\lim_{x \to 1} g(x) = 1$, then $\lim_{x \to 1} \dfrac{f(x)}{g(x)} = 1$.

61. If f is a polynomial, then, as x approaches 0, the right-hand limit exists and is equal to the left-hand limit.

62. If f is a rational function, then, as x approaches 0, the right-hand limit exists and is equal to the left-hand limit.

63. If f is a function such that $\lim_{x \to 0} f(x)$ exists, then $f(0)$ exists.

64. If f is a function such that $f(0)$ exists, then $\lim_{x \to 0} f(x)$ exists.

Compute the following limit for each function in Problems 65–68.

$$\lim_{h \to 0} \frac{f(2 + h) - f(2)}{h}$$

65. $f(x) = 3x + 1$ **66.** $f(x) = 5x - 1$

67. $f(x) = x^2 + 1$ **68.** $f(x) = x^2 - 2$

C

69. Let f be defined by

$$f(x) = \begin{cases} 1 + mx & \text{if } x \le 1 \\ 4 - mx & \text{if } x > 1 \end{cases}$$

where m is a constant.

(A) Graph f for $m = 1$, and find

$$\lim_{x \to 1^-} f(x) \quad \text{and} \quad \lim_{x \to 1^+} f(x)$$

(B) Graph f for $m = 2$, and find

$$\lim_{x \to 1^-} f(x) \quad \text{and} \quad \lim_{x \to 1^+} f(x)$$

(C) Find m so that

$$\lim_{x \to 1^-} f(x) = \lim_{x \to 1^+} f(x)$$

and graph f for this value of m.

✎ (D) Write a brief verbal description of each graph. How does the graph in part (C) differ from the graphs in parts (A) and (B)?

70. Let f be defined by

$$f(x) = \begin{cases} -3m + 0.5x & \text{if } x \le 2 \\ 3m - x & \text{if } x > 2 \end{cases}$$

where m is a constant.

(A) Graph f for $m = 0$, and find

$$\lim_{x \to 2^-} f(x) \quad \text{and} \quad \lim_{x \to 2^+} f(x)$$

(B) Graph f for $m = 1$, and find

$$\lim_{x \to 2^-} f(x) \quad \text{and} \quad \lim_{x \to 2^+} f(x)$$

(C) Find m so that

$$\lim_{x \to 2^-} f(x) = \lim_{x \to 2^+} f(x)$$

and graph f for this value of m.

✎ (D) Write a brief verbal description of each graph. How does the graph in part (C) differ from the graphs in parts (A) and (B)?

Find each limit in Problems 71–74, where a is a real constant.

71. $\displaystyle\lim_{h \to 0} \frac{(a + h)^2 - a^2}{h}$

72. $\displaystyle\lim_{h \to 0} \frac{[3(a + h) - 2] - (3a - 2)}{h}$

73. $\displaystyle\lim_{h \to 0} \frac{\sqrt{a + h} - \sqrt{a}}{h}, \quad a > 0$

74. $\displaystyle\lim_{h \to 0} \frac{\dfrac{1}{a + h} - \dfrac{1}{a}}{h}, \quad a \ne 0$

Applications

75. Telephone rates. A long-distance telephone service charges $0.99 for the first 20 minutes or less of a call and $0.07 per minute for each additional minute or fraction thereof.

(A) Write a piecewise definition of the charge $F(x)$ for a long-distance call lasting x minutes.

(B) Graph $F(x)$ for $0 < x \le 40$.

(C) Find $\lim_{x \to 20^-} F(x)$, $\lim_{x \to 20^+} F(x)$, and $\lim_{x \to 20} F(x)$, whichever exist.

76. Telephone rates. A second long-distance telephone service charges $0.09 per minute or fraction thereof for calls lasting 10 minutes or more and $0.18 per minute or fraction thereof for calls lasting less than 10 minutes.

(A) Write a piecewise definition of the charge $G(x)$ for a long-distance call lasting x minutes.

(B) Graph $G(x)$ for $0 < x \le 40$.

(C) Find $\lim_{x \to 10^-} G(x)$, $\lim_{x \to 10^+} G(x)$, and $\lim_{x \to 10} G(x)$, whichever exist.

✎ **77. Telephone rates.** Refer to Problems 75 and 76. Write a brief verbal comparison of the two services described for calls lasting 20 minutes or less.

✎ **78. Telephone rates.** Refer to Problems 75 and 76. Write a brief verbal comparison of the two services described for calls lasting more than 20 minutes.

A company sells custom embroidered apparel and promotional products. Table 1 shows the volume discounts offered by the company, where x is the volume of a purchase in dollars. Problems 79 and 80 deal with two different interpretations of this discount method.

Table 1	
Volume Discount (Excluding Tax)	
Volume (x)	**Discount Amount**
$300 \le x < 1{,}000$	3%
$1{,}000 \le x < 3{,}000$	5%
$3{,}000 \le x < 5{,}000$	7%
$5{,}000 \le x$	10%

79. Volume discount. Assume that the volume discounts in Table 1 apply to the entire purchase. That is, if the volume x satisfies $300 \le x < 1{,}000$, then the entire purchase is discounted 3%. If the volume x satisfies $1{,}000 \le x < 3{,}000$, the entire purchase is discounted 5%, and so on.

(A) If x is the volume of a purchase before the discount is applied, then write a piecewise definition for the discounted price $D(x)$ of this purchase.

(B) Use one-sided limits to investigate the limit of $D(x)$ as x approaches $1,000$. As x approaches $3,000$.

80. Volume discount. Assume that the volume discounts in Table 1 apply only to that portion of the volume in each interval. That is, the discounted price for a $4,000 purchase would be computed as follows:

$$300 + 0.97(700) + 0.95(2{,}000) + 0.93(1{,}000) = 3{,}809$$

(A) If x is the volume of a purchase before the discount is applied, then write a piecewise definition for the discounted price $P(x)$ of this purchase.

(B) Use one-sided limits to investigate the limit of $P(x)$ as x approaches \$1,000. As x approaches \$3,000.

(C) Compare this discount method with the one in Problem 79. Does one always produce a lower price than the other? Discuss.

81. Pollution. A state charges polluters an annual fee of \$20 per ton for each ton of pollutant emitted into the atmosphere, up to a maximum of 4,000 tons. No fees are charged for emissions beyond the 4,000-ton limit. Write a piecewise definition of the fees $F(x)$ charged for the emission of x tons of pollutant in a year. What is the limit of $F(x)$ as x approaches 4,000 tons? As x approaches 8,000 tons?

82. Pollution. Refer to Problem 81. The fee per ton of pollution is given by $A(x) = F(x)/x$. Write a piecewise definition of $A(x)$. What is the limit of $A(x)$ as x approaches 4,000 tons? As x approaches 8,000 tons?

83. Voter turnout. Statisticians often use piecewise-defined functions to predict outcomes of elections. For the following functions f and g, find the limit of each function as x approaches 5 and as x approaches 10.

$$f(x) = \begin{cases} 0 & \text{if } x \le 5 \\ 0.8 - 0.08x & \text{if } 5 < x < 10 \\ 0 & \text{if } 10 \le x \end{cases}$$

$$g(x) = \begin{cases} 0 & \text{if } x \le 5 \\ 0.8x - 0.04x^2 - 3 & \text{if } 5 < x < 10 \\ 1 & \text{if } 10 \le x \end{cases}$$

Answers to Matched Problems

1.

x	-2	-1	0	1	2	3	4
$h(x)$	1.0	1.5	2.0	2.5	3.0	3.5	4.0

2. $\lim\limits_{x \to 1^-} f(x) = 2$

3.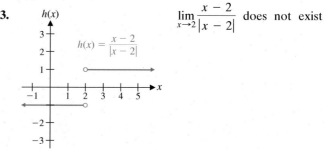

$\lim\limits_{x \to 2} \dfrac{x-2}{|x-2|}$ does not exist

4. (A) $\lim\limits_{x \to 0^-} f(x) = 0$
      $\lim\limits_{x \to 0^+} f(x) = 0$
      $\lim\limits_{x \to 0} f(x) = 0$
      $f(0) = 0$

   (B) $\lim\limits_{x \to 1^-} f(x) = 1$
      $\lim\limits_{x \to 1^+} f(x) = 2$
      $\lim\limits_{x \to 1} f(x)$ does not exist
      $f(1)$ not defined

   (C) $\lim\limits_{x \to 3^-} f(x) = 3$
      $\lim\limits_{x \to 3^+} f(x) = 3$
      $\lim\limits_{x \to 3} f(x) = 3$
      $f(3)$ not defined

5. -6

6. (A) 6
   (B) $\sqrt{6}$
   (C) $\frac{4}{5}$

7. (A) 13
   (B) 7
   (C) Does not exist
   (D) Not defined

8. (A) -2
   (B) Does not exist

9. -2
   10. Does not exist
   11. $1/(2\sqrt{3})$

3-2 Infinite Limits and Limits at Infinity

- Infinite Limits
- Locating Vertical Asymptotes
- Limits at Infinity
- Finding Horizontal Asymptotes

In this section, we consider two new types of limits: infinite limits and limits at infinity. Infinite limits and vertical asymptotes are used to describe the behavior of functions that are unbounded near $x = a$. Limits at infinity and horizontal asymptotes are used to describe the behavior of functions as x assumes arbitrarily large positive values or arbitrarily large negative values. Although we will include graphs to illustrate basic concepts, we postpone a discussion of graphing techniques until Chapter 5.

Infinite Limits

The graph of $f(x) = \dfrac{1}{x-1}$ (Fig. 1) indicates that

$$\lim_{x \to 1^+} \frac{1}{x-1}$$

does not exist. There does not exist a real number L that the values of $f(x)$ approach as x approaches 1 from the right. Instead, as x approaches 1 from the right, the values of $f(x)$ are positive and become larger and larger; that is, $f(x)$ increases without bound (Table 1). We express this behavior symbolically as

$$\lim_{x \to 1^+} \frac{1}{x-1} = \infty \quad \text{or} \quad f(x) = \frac{1}{x-1} \to \infty \quad \text{as} \quad x \to 1^+ \qquad (1)$$

Since ∞ is a not a real number, *the limit in (1) does not exist.* We are using the symbol ∞ to describe the manner in which the limit fails to exist, and we call this situation an **infinite limit**. If x approaches 1 from the left, the values of $f(x)$ are negative and become larger and larger in absolute value; that is, $f(x)$ decreases through negative values without bound (Table 2). We express this behavior symbolically as

$$\lim_{x \to 1^-} \frac{1}{x-1} = -\infty \quad \text{or} \quad f(x) = \frac{1}{x-1} \to -\infty \quad \text{as} \quad x \to 1^- \tag{2}$$

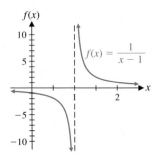

Figure 1

Table 1	
x	$f(x) = \dfrac{1}{x-1}$
1.1	10
1.01	100
1.001	1,000
1.0001	10,000
1.00001	100,000
1.000001	1,000,000

Table 2	
x	$f(x) = \dfrac{1}{x-1}$
0.9	−10
0.99	−100
0.999	−1,000
0.9999	−10,000
0.99999	−100,000
0.999999	−1,000,000

The one-sided limits in (1) and (2) describe the behavior of the graph as $x \to 1$ (Fig. 1). Does the two-sided limit of $f(x)$ as $x = 1$ exist? No, because neither of the one-sided limits exists. Also, there is no reasonable way to use the symbol ∞ to describe the behavior of $f(x)$ as $x \to 1$ on both sides of 1. We say that

$$\lim_{x \to 1} \frac{1}{x-1} \text{ does not exist}$$

Let $g(x) = \dfrac{1}{(x-1)^2}$

Construct tables for $g(x)$ as $x \to 1^+$ and as $x \to 1^-$. Use these tables and infinite limits to discuss the behavior of $g(x)$ near $x = 1$.

We used the dashed vertical line $x = 1$ in Figure 1 to illustrate the infinite limits as x approaches 1 from the right and from the left. We call this line a *vertical asymptote.*

DEFINITION   Infinite Limits and Vertical Asymptotes

The vertical line $x = a$ is a **vertical asymptote** for the graph of $y = f(x)$ if

$$f(x) \to \infty \quad \text{or} \quad f(x) \to -\infty \quad \text{as} \quad x \to a^+ \quad \text{or} \quad x \to a^-$$

[That is, if $f(x)$ either increases or decreases without bound as x approaches a from the right or from the left].

Locating Vertical Asymptotes

How do we locate vertical asymptotes? If f is a polynomial function, then $\lim\limits_{x \to a} f(x)$ is equal to the real number $f(a)$ [Theorem 3, Section 3-1]. So *a polynomial function has no vertical asymptotes.* Similarly (again by Theorem 3, Section 3-1), *a vertical asymptote of a rational function can occur only at a zero of its denominator.* Theorem 1 provides a simple procedure for locating the vertical asymptotes of a rational function.

THEOREM 1   Locating Vertical Asymptotes of Rational Functions

If $f(x) = n(x)/d(x)$ is a rational function, $d(c) = 0$ and $n(c) \neq 0$, then the line $x = c$ is a vertical asymptote of the graph of f.

If $f(x) = n(x)/d(x)$ and both $n(c) = 0$ and $d(c) = 0$, then the limit of $f(x)$ as x approaches c involves an indeterminate form and Theorem 1 does not apply:

$$\lim_{x \to c} f(x) = \lim_{x \to c} \frac{n(x)}{d(x)} \quad \frac{0}{0} \text{ indeterminate form}$$

Algebraic simplification is often useful in this situation.

EXAMPLE 1 **Locating Vertical Asymptotes** Let $f(x) = \dfrac{x^2 + x - 2}{x^2 - 1}$.

Describe the behavior of f at each zero of the denominator. Use ∞ and $-\infty$ when appropriate. Identify all vertical asymptotes.

SOLUTION Let $n(x) = x^2 + x - 2$ and $d(x) = x^2 - 1$. Factoring the denominator, we see that

$$d(x) = x^2 - 1 = (x - 1)(x + 1)$$

has two zeros: $x = -1$ and $x = 1$.

First, we consider $x = -1$. Since $d(-1) = 0$ and $n(-1) = -2 \neq 0$, Theorem 1 tells us that the line $x = -1$ is a vertical asymptote. So at least one of the one-sided limits at $x = -1$ must be either ∞ or $-\infty$. Examining tables of values of f for x near -1 or a graph on a graphing calculator will show which is the case. From Tables 3 and 4, we see that

$$\lim_{x \to -1^-} \frac{x^2 + x - 2}{x^2 - 1} = -\infty \quad \text{and} \quad \lim_{x \to -1^+} \frac{x^2 + x - 2}{x^2 - 1} = \infty$$

Table 3

x	$f(x) = \dfrac{x^2 + x - 2}{x^2 - 1}$
-1.1	-9
-1.01	-99
-1.001	-999
-1.0001	$-9,999$
-1.00001	$-99,999$

Table 4

x	$f(x) = \dfrac{x^2 + x - 2}{x^2 - 1}$
-0.9	11
-0.99	101
-0.999	$1,001$
-0.9999	$10,001$
-0.99999	$100,001$

Now we consider the other zero of $d(x)$, $x = 1$. This time $n(1) = 0$ and Theorem 1 does not apply. We use algebraic simplification to investigate the behavior of the function at $x = 1$:

$$\lim_{x \to 1} f(x) = \lim_{x \to 1} \frac{x^2 + x - 2}{x^2 - 1} \quad \frac{0}{0} \text{ indeterminate form}$$

$$= \lim_{x \to 1} \frac{(x - 1)(x + 2)}{(x - 1)(x + 1)}$$

$$= \lim_{x \to 1} \frac{x + 2}{x + 1} \quad \text{Reduced to lowest terms (see Appendix A-4)}$$

$$= \frac{3}{2}$$

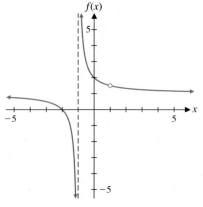

Figure 2 $f(x) = \dfrac{x^2 + x - 2}{x^2 - 1}$

Since the limit exists as x approaches 1, f does not have a vertical asymptote at $x = 1$. The graph of f (Fig. 2) shows the behavior at the vertical asymptote $x = -1$ and also at $x = 1$.

Matched Problem 1 Let $f(x) = \dfrac{x - 3}{x^2 - 4x + 3}$.

Describe the behavior of f at each zero of the denominator. Use ∞ and $-\infty$ when appropriate. Identify all vertical asymptotes.

EXAMPLE 2   **Locating Vertical Asymptotes**   Let $f(x) = \dfrac{x^2 + 20}{5(x - 2)^2}$

Describe the behavior of f at each zero of the denominator. Use ∞ and $-\infty$ when appropriate. Identify all vertical asymptotes.

SOLUTION   Let $n(x) = x^2 + 20$ and $d(x) = 5(x - 2)^2$. The only zero of $d(x)$ is $x = 2$. Since $n(2) = 24 \neq 0$, f has a vertical asymptote at $x = 2$ (Theorem 1). Tables 5 and 6 show that $f(x) \to \infty$ as $x \to 2$ from either side, and we have

$$\lim_{x \to 2^+} \frac{x^2 + 20}{5(x - 2)^2} = \infty \quad \text{and} \quad \lim_{x \to 2^-} \frac{x^2 + 20}{5(x - 2)^2} = \infty$$

Table 5

x	$f(x) = \dfrac{x^2 + 20}{5(x - 2)^2}$
2.1	488.2
2.01	48,080.02
2.001	4,800,800.2

Table 6

x	$f(x) = \dfrac{x^2 + 20}{5(x - 2)^2}$
1.9	472.2
1.99	47,920.02
1.999	4,799,200.2

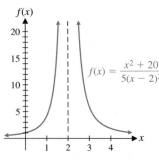

$f(x) = \dfrac{x^2 + 20}{5(x - 2)^2}$

Figure 3

The denominator d has no other zeros, so f does not have any other vertical asymptotes. The graph of f (Fig. 3) shows the behavior at the vertical asymptote $x = 2$. Because the left- and right-hand limits are both infinite, we write

$$\lim_{x \to 2} \frac{x^2 + 20}{5(x - 2)^2} = \infty$$

Matched Problem 2   Let $f(x) = \dfrac{x - 1}{(x + 3)^2}$.

Describe the behavior of f at each zero of the denominator. Use ∞ and $-\infty$ when appropriate. Identify all vertical asymptotes.

CONCEPTUAL INSIGHT

When is it correct to say that a limit does not exist, and when is it correct to use $\pm\infty$? It depends on the situation. Table 7 lists the infinite limits that we discussed in Examples 1 and 2.

Table 7

Right-Hand Limit	Left-Hand Limit	Two-Sided Limit
$\lim\limits_{x \to -1^+} \dfrac{x^2 + x - 2}{x^2 - 1} = \infty$	$\lim\limits_{x \to -1^-} \dfrac{x^2 + x - 2}{x^2 - 1} = -\infty$	$\lim\limits_{x \to -1} \dfrac{x^2 + x - 2}{x^2 - 1}$ does not exist
$\lim\limits_{x \to 2^+} \dfrac{x^2 + 20}{5(x - 2)^2} = \infty$	$\lim\limits_{x \to 2^-} \dfrac{x^2 + 20}{5(x - 2)^2} = \infty$	$\lim\limits_{x \to 2} \dfrac{x^2 + 20}{5(x - 2)^2} = \infty$

The instructions in Examples 1 and 2 said that we should use infinite limits to describe the behavior at vertical asymptotes. If we had been asked to *evaluate* the limits, with no mention of ∞ or asymptotes, then the correct answer would be that **all of these limits do not exist**. Remember, ∞ is a symbol used to describe the behavior of functions at vertical asymptotes.

Limits at Infinity

The symbol ∞ can also be used to indicate that an independent variable is increasing or decreasing without bound. We write $x \rightarrow \infty$ to indicate that x is increasing without bound through positive values and $x \rightarrow -\infty$ to indicate that x is decreasing without bound through negative values. We begin by considering power functions of the form x^p and $1/x^p$ where p is a positive real number.

If p is a positive real number, then x^p increases as x increases. There is no upper bound on the values of x^p. We indicate this behavior by writing

$$\lim_{x \to \infty} x^p = \infty \quad \text{or} \quad x^p \to \infty \quad \text{as} \quad x \to \infty$$

Since the reciprocals of very large numbers are very small numbers, it follows that $1/x^p$ approaches 0 as x increases without bound. We indicate this behavior by writing

$$\lim_{x \to \infty} \frac{1}{x^p} = 0 \quad \text{or} \quad \frac{1}{x^p} \to 0 \quad \text{as} \quad x \to \infty$$

Figure 4 illustrates the preceding behavior for $f(x) = x^2$ and $g(x) = 1/x^2$, and we write

$$\lim_{x \to \infty} f(x) = \infty \quad \text{and} \quad \lim_{x \to \infty} g(x) = 0$$

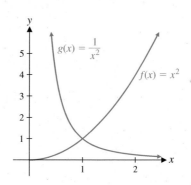

Figure 4

Limits of power forms as x decreases without bound behave in a similar manner, with two important differences. First, if x is negative, then x^p is not defined for all values of p. For example, $x^{1/2} = \sqrt{x}$ is not defined for negative values of x. Second, if x^p is defined, then it may approach ∞ or $-\infty$, depending on the value of p. For example,

$$\lim_{x \to -\infty} x^2 = \infty \quad \text{but} \quad \lim_{x \to -\infty} x^3 = -\infty$$

For the function g in Figure 4, the line $y = 0$ (the x axis) is called a *horizontal asymptote*. In general, a line $y = b$ is a **horizontal asymptote** of the graph of $y = f(x)$ if $f(x)$ approaches b as either x increases without bound or x decreases without bound. Symbolically, $y = b$ is a horizontal asymptote if either

$$\lim_{x \to -\infty} f(x) = b \quad \text{or} \quad \lim_{x \to \infty} f(x) = b$$

In the first case, the graph of f will be close to the horizontal line $y = b$ for large (in absolute value) negative x. In the second case, the graph will be close to the horizontal line $y = b$ for large positive x. Figure 5 shows the graph of a function with two horizontal asymptotes: $y = 1$ and $y = -1$.

Theorem 2 summarizes the various possibilities for limits of power functions as x increases or decreases without bound.

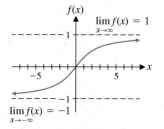

Figure 5

THEOREM 2   Limits of Power Functions at Infinity

If p is a positive real number and k is any real number except 0, then

1. $\displaystyle\lim_{x \to -\infty} \frac{k}{x^p} = 0$ 2. $\displaystyle\lim_{x \to \infty} \frac{k}{x^p} = 0$

3. $\displaystyle\lim_{x \to -\infty} kx^p = \pm\infty$ 4. $\displaystyle\lim_{x \to \infty} kx^p = \pm\infty$

provided that x^p is a real number for negative values of x. The limits in 3 and 4 will be either $-\infty$ or ∞, depending on k and p.

How can we use Theorem 2 to evaluate limits at infinity? It turns out that the limit properties listed in Theorem 2, Section 3-1, are also valid if we replace the statement $x \to c$ with $x \to \infty$ or $x \to -\infty$.

EXAMPLE 3   **Limit of a Polynomial Function at Infinity**   Let $p(x) = 2x^3 - x^2 - 7x + 3$. Find the limit of $p(x)$ as x approaches ∞ and as x approaches $-\infty$.

SOLUTION   Since limits of power functions of the form $1/x^p$ approach 0 as x approaches ∞ or $-\infty$, it is convenient to work with these reciprocal forms whenever possible. If we factor out the term involving the highest power of x, then we can write $p(x)$ as

$$p(x) = 2x^3\left(1 - \frac{1}{2x} - \frac{7}{2x^2} + \frac{3}{2x^3}\right)$$

Using Theorem 2 in Section 3-3 and Theorem 2 in Section 3-1, we write

$$\lim_{x \to \infty}\left(1 - \frac{1}{2x} - \frac{7}{2x^2} + \frac{3}{2x^3}\right) = 1 - 0 - 0 + 0 = 1$$

For large values of x,

$$\left(1 - \frac{1}{2x} - \frac{7}{2x^2} + \frac{3}{2x^3}\right) \approx 1$$

and

$$p(x) = 2x^3\left(1 - \frac{1}{2x} - \frac{7}{2x^2} + \frac{3}{2x^3}\right) \approx 2x^3$$

Since $2x^3 \to \infty$ as $x \to \infty$, it follows that

$$\lim_{x \to \infty} p(x) = \lim_{x \to \infty} 2x^3 = \infty$$

Similarly, $2x^3 \to -\infty$ as $x \to -\infty$ implies that

$$\lim_{x \to -\infty} p(x) = \lim_{x \to -\infty} 2x^3 = -\infty$$

So the behavior of $p(x)$ for large values is the same as the behavior of the highest-degree term, $2x^3$.

Matched Problem 3   Let $p(x) = -4x^4 + 2x^3 + 3x$. Find the limit of $p(x)$ as x approaches ∞ and as x approaches $-\infty$.

The term with highest degree in a polynomial is called the **leading term**. In the solution to Example 3, the limits at infinity of $p(x) = 2x^3 - x^2 - 7x + 3$ were the same as the limits of the leading term $2x^3$. Theorem 3 states that this is true for any polynomial of degree greater than or equal to 1.

THEOREM 3   Limits of Polynomial Functions at Infinity

If

$$p(x) = a_n x^n + a_{n-1} x^{n-1} + \cdots + a_1 x + a_0, \ a_n \neq 0, n \geq 1$$

then

$$\lim_{x \to \infty} p(x) = \lim_{x \to \infty} a_n x^n = \pm\infty$$

and

$$\lim_{x \to -\infty} p(x) = \lim_{x \to -\infty} a_n x^n = \pm\infty$$

Each limit will be either $-\infty$ or ∞, depending on a_n and n.

A polynomial of degree 0 is a constant function $p(x) = a_0$, and its limit as x approaches ∞ or $-\infty$ is the number a_0. For any polynomial of degree 1 or greater, Theorem 3 states that the limit as x approaches ∞ or $-\infty$ cannot be equal to a number. This means that **polynomials of degree 1 or greater never have horizontal asymptotes**.

A description of the behavior of the limits of any function f at infinity is called the **end behavior** of f. $\lim_{x \to \infty} f(x)$ determines the right end behavior, and $\lim_{x \to -\infty} f(x)$ determines the left end behavior. According to Theorem 3, the right and left end behavior of a nonconstant polynomial $p(x)$ is always an infinite limit.

EXAMPLE 4   **End Behavior of a Polynomial** Describe the end behavior of each polynomial.

(A) $p(x) = 3x^3 - 500x^2$ (B) $p(x) = 3x^3 - 500x^4$

SOLUTION   (A) According to Theorem 3, as x increases without bound to the right, the right end behavior is

$$\lim_{x \to \infty} (3x^3 - 500x^2) = \lim_{x \to \infty} 3x^3 = \infty$$

and as x increases without bound to the left, the end behavior is

$$\lim_{x \to -\infty} (3x^3 - 500x^2) = \lim_{x \to -\infty} 3x^3 = -\infty$$

(B) As x increases without bound to the right, the end behavior is

$$\lim_{x \to \infty} (3x^3 - 500x^4) = \lim_{x \to \infty} (-500x^4) = -\infty$$

and as x increases without bound to the left, the end behavior is

$$\lim_{x \to -\infty} (3x^3 - 500x^4) = \lim_{x \to -\infty} (-500x^4) = -\infty$$

Matched Problem 4   Describe the end behavior of each polynomial.

(A) $p(x) = 300x^2 - 4x^5$ (B) $p(x) = 300x^6 - 4x^5$

Finding Horizontal Asymptotes

Since a rational function is the ratio of two polynomials, it is not surprising that reciprocals of powers of x can be used to analyze limits of rational functions at infinity. For example, consider the rational function

$$f(x) = \frac{3x^2 - 5x + 9}{2x^2 + 7}$$

Factoring the highest-degree term out of the numerator and the denominator, we write

$$f(x) = \frac{3x^2}{2x^2} \cdot \frac{1 - \dfrac{5}{3x} + \dfrac{3}{x^2}}{1 + \dfrac{7}{2x^2}}$$

$$\lim_{x \to \infty} f(x) = \lim_{x \to \infty} \frac{3x^2}{2x^2} \cdot \lim_{x \to \infty} \frac{1 - \dfrac{5}{3x} + \dfrac{3}{x^2}}{1 + \dfrac{7}{2x^2}} = \frac{3}{2} \cdot \frac{1 - 0 + 0}{1 + 0} = \frac{3}{2}$$

The behavior of this rational function as x approaches infinity is determined by the ratio of the highest-degree term in the numerator $(3x^2)$ to the highest-degree term in the denominator $(2x^2)$. Theorem 4 generalizes this result to any rational function and lists the three possible outcomes.

THEOREM 4   Limits of Rational Functions at Infinity and Horizontal Asymptotes of Rational Functions

(A) If $f(x) = \dfrac{a_m x^m + a_{m-1} x^{m-1} + \cdots + a_1 x + a_0}{b_n x^n + b_{n-1} x^{n-1} + \cdots + b_1 x + b_0}$, $a_m \neq 0$, $b_n \neq 0$

then $\displaystyle\lim_{x \to \infty} f(x) = \lim_{x \to \infty} \frac{a_m x^m}{b_n x^n}$ and $\displaystyle\lim_{x \to -\infty} f(x) = \lim_{x \to -\infty} \frac{a_m x^m}{b_n x^n}$

(B) There are three possible cases for these limits:

1. If $m < n$, then $\displaystyle\lim_{x \to \infty} f(x) = \lim_{x \to -\infty} f(x) = 0$, and the line $y = 0$ (the x axis) is a horizontal asymptote of $f(x)$.

2. If $m = n$, then $\displaystyle\lim_{x \to \infty} f(x) = \lim_{x \to -\infty} f(x) = \frac{a_m}{b_n}$, and the line $y = \dfrac{a_m}{b_n}$ is a horizontal asymptote of $f(x)$.

3. If $m > n$, then each limit will be ∞ or $-\infty$, depending on m, n, a_m, and b_n, and $f(x)$ does not have a horizontal asymptote.

Notice that in cases 1 and 2 of Theorem 4, the limit is the same if x approaches ∞ or $-\infty$. So, **a rational function can have at most one horizontal asymptote** (see Fig. 6).

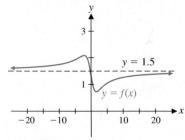

Figure 6 $f(x) = \dfrac{3x^2 - 5x + 9}{2x^2 + 7}$

CONCEPTUAL INSIGHT

The graph of f in Figure 6 dispels the misconception that the graph of a function cannot cross a horizontal asymptote. Horizontal asymptotes give us information about the graph of a function only as $x \to \infty$ and $x \to -\infty$, not at any specific value of x.

EXAMPLE 5   **Finding Horizontal Asymptotes** Find all horizontal asymptotes, if any, of each function.

(A) $f(x) = \dfrac{5x^3 - 2x^2 + 1}{4x^3 + 2x - 7}$ (B) $f(x) = \dfrac{3x^4 - x^2 + 1}{8x^6 - 10}$

(C) $f(x) = \dfrac{2x^5 - x^3 - 1}{6x^3 + 2x^2 - 7}$

SOLUTION   We will make use of part A of Theorem 4.

(A) $\lim\limits_{x \to \infty} f(x) = \lim\limits_{x \to \infty} \dfrac{5x^3 - 2x^2 + 1}{4x^3 + 2x - 7} = \lim\limits_{x \to \infty} \dfrac{5x^3}{4x^3} = \dfrac{5}{4}$

The line $y = 5/4$ is a horizontal asymptote of $f(x)$.

(B) $\lim\limits_{x \to \infty} f(x) = \lim\limits_{x \to \infty} \dfrac{3x^4 - x^2 + 1}{8x^6 - 10} = \lim\limits_{x \to \infty} \dfrac{3x^4}{8x^6} = \lim\limits_{x \to \infty} \dfrac{3}{8x^2} = 0$

The line $y = 0$ (the x axis) is a horizontal asymptote of $f(x)$.

(C) $\lim\limits_{x \to \infty} f(x) = \lim\limits_{x \to \infty} \dfrac{2x^5 - x^3 - 1}{6x^3 + 2x^2 - 7} = \lim\limits_{x \to \infty} \dfrac{2x^5}{6x^3} = \lim\limits_{x \to \infty} \dfrac{x^2}{3} = \infty$

The function $f(x)$ has no horizontal asymptotes.

Matched Problem 5   Find all horizontal asymptotes, if any, of each function.

(A) $f(x) = \dfrac{4x^3 - 5x + 8}{2x^4 - 7}$ (B) $f(x) = \dfrac{5x^6 + 3x}{2x^5 - x - 5}$

(C) $f(x) = \dfrac{2x^3 - x + 7}{4x^3 + 3x^2 - 100}$

An accurate sketch of the graph of a rational function requires knowledge of both vertical and horizontal asymptotes. As we mentioned earlier, we are postponing a detailed discussion of graphing techniques until Section 5-4.

EXAMPLE 6   **Finding the Asymptotes of a Rational Function** Find all the asymptotes of the function

$$f(x) = \dfrac{2x^2 - 5}{x^2 + 4x + 4}$$

SOLUTION   Let $n(x) = 2x^2 - 5$ and $d(x) = x^2 + 4x + 4 = (x + 2)^2$. Since $d(x) = 0$ only at $x = -2$ and $n(-2) = 3$, the only vertical asymptote of f is the line $x = -2$ (Theorem 1). Since

$$\lim\limits_{x \to \infty} f(x) = \lim\limits_{x \to \infty} \dfrac{2x^2 - 5}{x^2 + 4x + 4} = \lim\limits_{x \to \infty} \dfrac{2x^2}{x^2} = 2$$

the horizontal asymptote is the line $y = 2$ (Theorem 3).

Matched Problem 6   Find all the asymptotes of the function $f(x) = \dfrac{x^2 - 9}{x^2 - 4}$.

Exercises 3-2

A

Problems 1–8 refer to the following graph of $y = f(x)$.

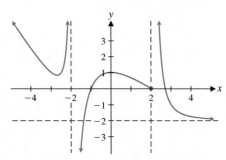

Figure for 1–8

1. $\lim\limits_{x \to \infty} f(x) = ?$

2. $\lim\limits_{x \to -\infty} f(x) = ?$

3. $\lim\limits_{x \to -2^+} f(x) = ?$

4. $\lim\limits_{x \to -2^-} f(x) = ?$

5. $\lim\limits_{x \to -2} f(x) = ?$

6. $\lim\limits_{x \to 2^+} f(x) = ?$

7. $\lim\limits_{x \to 2^-} f(x) = ?$

8. $\lim\limits_{x \to 2} f(x) = ?$

In Problems 9–16, find each limit. Use $-\infty$ and ∞ when appropriate.

9. $f(x) = \dfrac{x}{x - 5}$

    (A) $\lim\limits_{x \to 5^-} f(x)$ (B) $\lim\limits_{x \to 5^+} f(x)$ (C) $\lim\limits_{x \to 5} f(x)$

10. $f(x) = \dfrac{x^2}{x + 3}$

    (A) $\lim\limits_{x \to -3^-} f(x)$ (B) $\lim\limits_{x \to -3^+} f(x)$ (C) $\lim\limits_{x \to -3} f(x)$

11. $f(x) = \dfrac{2x - 4}{(x - 4)^2}$

    (A) $\lim\limits_{x \to 4^-} f(x)$ (B) $\lim\limits_{x \to 4^+} f(x)$ (C) $\lim\limits_{x \to 4} f(x)$

12. $f(x) = \dfrac{2x + 2}{(x + 2)^2}$

    (A) $\lim\limits_{x \to -2^-} f(x)$ (B) $\lim\limits_{x \to -2^+} f(x)$ (C) $\lim\limits_{x \to -2} f(x)$

13. $f(x) = \dfrac{x^2 + x - 2}{x - 1}$

    (A) $\lim\limits_{x \to 1^-} f(x)$ (B) $\lim\limits_{x \to 1^+} f(x)$ (C) $\lim\limits_{x \to 1} f(x)$

14. $f(x) = \dfrac{x^2 + x + 2}{x - 1}$

    (A) $\lim\limits_{x \to 1^-} f(x)$ (B) $\lim\limits_{x \to 1^+} f(x)$ (C) $\lim\limits_{x \to 1} f(x)$

15. $f(x) = \dfrac{x^2 - 3x + 2}{x + 2}$

    (A) $\lim\limits_{x \to -2^-} f(x)$ (B) $\lim\limits_{x \to -2^+} f(x)$ (C) $\lim\limits_{x \to -2} f(x)$

16. $f(x) = \dfrac{x^2 + x - 2}{x + 2}$

    (A) $\lim\limits_{x \to -2^-} f(x)$ (B) $\lim\limits_{x \to -2^+} f(x)$ (C) $\lim\limits_{x \to -2} f(x)$

In Problems 17–20, find the limit of each polynomial $p(x)$ (A) as x approaches ∞ (B) as x approaches $-\infty$

17. $p(x) = 4x^5 - 3x^4 + 1$

18. $p(x) = 4x^3 - 3x^4 + x^2$

19. $p(x) = 2x^5 - 2x^6 - 11$

20. $p(x) = 2x^4 - 2x^3 + 9x$

B

In Problems 21–30, use $-\infty$ or ∞ where appropriate to describe the behavior at each zero of the denominator and identify all vertical asymptotes.

21. $f(x) = \dfrac{1}{x + 3}$

22. $g(x) = \dfrac{x}{4 - x}$

23. $h(x) = \dfrac{x^2 + 4}{x^2 - 4}$

24. $k(x) = \dfrac{x^2 - 9}{x^2 + 9}$

25. $F(x) = \dfrac{x^2 - 4}{x^2 + 4}$

26. $G(x) = \dfrac{x^2 + 9}{9 - x^2}$

27. $H(x) = \dfrac{x^2 - 2x - 3}{x^2 - 4x + 3}$

28. $K(x) = \dfrac{x^2 + 2x - 3}{x^2 - 4x + 3}$

29. $T(x) = \dfrac{8x - 16}{x^4 - 8x^3 + 16x^2}$

30. $S(x) = \dfrac{6x + 9}{x^4 + 6x^3 + 9x^2}$

In Problems 31–38, find each function value and limit. Use $-\infty$ or ∞ where appropriate.

31. $f(x) = \dfrac{4x + 7}{5x - 9}$

    (A) $f(10)$ (B) $f(100)$ (C) $\lim\limits_{x \to \infty} f(x)$

32. $f(x) = \dfrac{2 - 3x^3}{7 + 4x^3}$

    (A) $f(5)$ (B) $f(10)$ (C) $\lim\limits_{x \to \infty} f(x)$

33. $f(x) = \dfrac{5x^2 + 11}{7x - 2}$

    (A) $f(20)$ (B) $f(50)$ (C) $\lim\limits_{x \to \infty} f(x)$

34. $f(x) = \dfrac{5x + 11}{7x^3 - 2}$

    (A) $f(8)$ (B) $f(16)$ (C) $\lim\limits_{x \to -\infty} f(x)$

35. $f(x) = \dfrac{7x^4 - 14x^2}{6x^5 + 3}$

    (A) $f(-6)$ (B) $f(-12)$ (C) $\lim\limits_{x \to -\infty} f(x)$

36. $f(x) = \dfrac{4x^7 - 8x}{6x^4 + 9x^2}$

    (A) $f(-3)$ (B) $f(-6)$ (C) $\lim\limits_{x \to -\infty} f(x)$

37. $f(x) = \dfrac{10 - 7x^3}{4 + x^3}$

    (A) $f(-10)$ (B) $f(-20)$ (C) $\lim\limits_{x \to -\infty} f(x)$

38. $f(x) = \dfrac{3 + x}{5 + 4x}$

    (A) $f(-50)$ (B) $f(-100)$ (C) $\lim\limits_{x \to -\infty} f(x)$

In Problems 39–52, find all horizontal and vertical asymptotes.

39. $f(x) = \dfrac{2x}{x + 2}$

40. $f(x) = \dfrac{3x + 2}{x - 4}$

41. $f(x) = \dfrac{x^2 + 1}{x^2 - 1}$

42. $f(x) = \dfrac{x^2 - 1}{x^2 + 2}$

43. $f(x) = \dfrac{x^3}{x^2 + 6}$

44. $f(x) = \dfrac{x}{x^2 - 4}$

45. $f(x) = \dfrac{x}{x^2 + 4}$

46. $f(x) = \dfrac{x^2 + 9}{x}$

47. $f(x) = \dfrac{x^2}{x - 3}$

48. $f(x) = \dfrac{x + 5}{x^2}$

49. $f(x) = \dfrac{2x^2 + 3x - 2}{x^2 - x - 2}$

50. $f(x) = \dfrac{2x^2 + 7x + 12}{2x^2 + 5x - 12}$

51. $f(x) = \dfrac{2x^2 - 5x + 2}{x^2 - x - 2}$

52. $f(x) = \dfrac{x^2 - x - 12}{2x^2 + 5x - 12}$

In Problems 53–58, discuss the validity of each statement. If the statement is always true, explain why. If not, give a counterexample.

53. A rational function has at least one vertical asymptote.

54. A rational function has at most one vertical asymptote.

55. A rational function has at least one horizontal asymptote.

56. A rational function has at most one horizontal asymptote.

57. A polynomial function of degree ≥ 1 has neither horizontal nor vertical asymptotes.

58. The graph of a rational function cannot cross a horizontal asymptote.

C

59. Theorem 3 states that

$$\lim_{x \to \infty} (a_n x^n + a_{n-1} x^{n-1} + \cdots + a_0) = \pm\infty.$$

What conditions must n and a_n satisfy for the limit to be ∞? For the limit to be $-\infty$?

60. Theorem 3 also states that

$$\lim_{x \to -\infty} (a_n x^n + a_{n-1} x^{n-1} + \cdots + a_0) = \pm\infty.$$

What conditions must n and a_n satisfy for the limit to be ∞? For the limit to be $-\infty$?

Describe the end behavior of each function in Problems 61–68.

61. $f(x) = 2x^4 - 5x + 11$

62. $f(x) = 3x - 7x^5 - 2$

63. $f(x) = 7x^2 + 9x^3 + 5x$

64. $f(x) = 4x^3 - 5x^2 - 6x^6$

65. $f(x) = \dfrac{x^2 - 5x - 7}{x + 11}$

66. $f(x) = \dfrac{5x^4 + 7x^7 - 10}{x^2 + 6x^4 + 3}$

67. $f(x) = \dfrac{5x^5 + 7x^4 - 10}{-x^3 + 6x^2 + 3}$

68. $f(x) = \dfrac{-3x^6 + 4x^4 + 2}{2x^2 - 2x - 3}$

Applications

69. Average cost. A company manufacturing snowboards has fixed costs of $200 per day and total costs of $3,800 per day for a daily output of 20 boards.

(A) Assuming that the total cost per day $C(x)$ is linearly related to the total output per day x, write an equation for the cost function.

(B) The average cost per board for an output of x boards is given by $\overline{C}(x) = C(x)/x$. Find the average cost function.

(C) Sketch a graph of the average cost function, including any asymptotes, for $1 \leq x \leq 30$.

(D) What does the average cost per board tend to as production increases?

70. Average cost. A company manufacturing surfboards has fixed costs of $300 per day and total costs of $5,100 per day for a daily output of 20 boards.

(A) Assuming that the total cost per day $C(x)$ is linearly related to the total output per day x, write an equation for the cost function.

(B) The average cost per board for an output of x boards is given by $\overline{C}(x) = C(x)/x$. Find the average cost function.

(C) Sketch a graph of the average cost function, including any asymptotes, for $1 \leq x \leq 30$.

(D) What does the average cost per board tend to as production increases?

71. Energy costs. Most appliance manufacturers produce conventional and energy-efficient models. The energy-efficient models are more expensive to make but cheaper to operate. The costs of purchasing and operating a 23-cubic-foot refrigerator of each type are given in Table 8. These costs do not include maintenance charges or changes in electricity prices.

Table 8 23-ft^3 Refrigerators	Energy-Efficient Model	Conventional Model
Initial cost	$950	$900
Total volume	23 ft^3	23 ft^3
Annual cost of electricity	$56	$66

(A) Express the total cost $C_e(x)$ and the average cost $\overline{C}_e(x) = C_e(x)/x$ of purchasing and operating an energy-efficient model for x years.

(B) Express the total cost $C_c(x)$ and the average cost $\overline{C}_c(x) = C_c(x)/x$ of purchasing and operating a conventional model for x years.

(C) Are the total costs for an energy-efficient model and for a conventional model ever the same? If so, when?

(D) Are the average costs for an energy-efficient model and for a conventional model ever the same? If so, when?

(E) Find the limit of each average cost function as $x \to \infty$ and discuss the implications of the results.

72. Energy costs. Most appliance manufacturers produce conventional and energy-efficient models. The energy-efficient models are more expensive to make but cheaper to operate. The costs of purchasing and operating a 36,000-Btu central air conditioner of each type are given in Table 9. These costs do not include maintenance charges or changes in electricity prices.

Table 9 36,000 Btu Central Air Conditioner

	Energy-Efficient Model	Conventional Model
Initial cost	$4,000	$2,700
Total capacity	36,000 Btu	36,000 Btu
Annual cost of electricity	$932	$1,332

(A) Express the total cost $C_e(x)$ and the average cost $\overline{C}_e(x) = C_e(x)/x$ of purchasing and operating an energy-efficient model for x years.

(B) Express the total cost $C_c(x)$ and the average cost $\overline{C}_c(x) = C_c(x)/x$ of purchasing and operating a conventional model for x years.

(C) Are the total costs for an energy-efficient model and for a conventional model ever the same? If so, when?

(D) Are the average costs for an energy-efficient model and for a conventional model ever the same? If so, when?

(E) Find the limit of each average cost function as $x \to \infty$ and discuss the implications of the results.

73. Drug concentration. A drug is administered to a patient through an injection. The drug concentration (in milligrams/milliliter) in the bloodstream t hours after the injection is given by $C(t) = \dfrac{5t^2(t + 50)}{t^3 + 100}$. Find and interpret $\lim\limits_{t \to \infty} C(t)$.

74. Drug concentration. A drug is administered to a patient through an IV drip. The drug concentration (in milligrams/milliliter) in the bloodstream t hours after the drip was started is given by $C(t) = \dfrac{5t(t + 50)}{t^3 + 100}$. Find and interpret $\lim\limits_{t \to \infty} C(t)$.

75. Pollution. In Silicon Valley, a number of computer-related manufacturing firms were contaminating underground water supplies with toxic chemicals stored in leaking underground containers. A water quality control agency ordered the companies to take immediate corrective action and contribute to a monetary pool for the testing and cleanup of the underground contamination. Suppose that the monetary pool (in millions of dollars) for the testing and cleanup is given by

$$P(x) = \frac{2x}{1 - x} \qquad 0 \le x < 1$$

where x is the percentage (expressed as a decimal) of the total contaminant removed.

(A) How much must be in the pool to remove 90% of the contaminant?

(B) How much must be in the pool to remove 95% of the contaminant?

(C) Find $\lim\limits_{x \to 1^-} P(x)$ and discuss the implications of this limit.

76. Employee training. A company producing computer components has established that, on average, a new employee can assemble $N(t)$ components per day after t days of on-the-job training, as given by

$$N(t) = \frac{100t}{t + 9} \qquad t \ge 0$$

(A) How many components per day can a new employee assemble after 6 days of on-the-job training?

(B) How many days of on-the-job training will a new employee need to reach the level of 70 components per day?

(C) Find $\lim\limits_{t \to \infty} N(t)$ and discuss the implications of this limit.

77. Biochemistry. In 1913, biochemists Leonor Michaelis and Maude Menten proposed the rational function model (see figure)

$$v(s) = \frac{V_{max}\, s}{K_M + s}$$

for the velocity of the enzymatic reaction v, where s is the substrate concentration. The constants V_{max} and K_M are determined from experimental data.

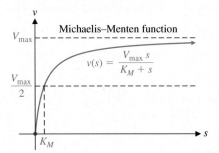

Figure for 77

(A) Show that $\lim\limits_{s \to \infty} v(s) = V_{max}$.

(B) Show that $v(K_M) = \dfrac{V_{max}}{2}$.

(C) Table 10* lists data for an enzyme treated with the substrate saccharose.

Plot the preceding points on graph paper and estimate V_{max} to the nearest integer. To estimate K_M, add the

Table 10

s	v
5.2	0.866
10.4	1.466
20.8	2.114
41.6	2.666
83.3	3.236
167	3.636
333	3.636

*Michaelis and Menten (1913) *Biochem. Z.* 49, 333–369.

horizontal line $v = \dfrac{V_{\max}}{2}$ to your graph, connect successive points on the graph with straight-line segments, and estimate the value of s (to the nearest multiple of 10) that satisfies $v(s) = \dfrac{V_{\max}}{2}$.

(D) Use the constants $V_{\max}$ and K_M from part C to form a Michaelis–Menten function for the data in Table 10.

(E) Use the function from part D to estimate the velocity of the enzyme reaction when the saccharose is 15 and to estimate the saccharose when the velocity is 3.

78. Biochemistry. Table 11* lists data for the enzyme invertase treated with the substrate sucrose. We want to model these data with a Michaelis–Menten function.

Table 11

s	v
2.92	18.2
5.84	26.5
8.76	31.1
11.7	33
14.6	34.9
17.5	37.2
23.4	37.1

(A) Plot the points in Table 11 on graph paper and estimate $V_{\max}$ to the nearest integer. To estimate K_M, add the horizontal line $v = \dfrac{V_{\max}}{2}$ to your graph, connect successive points on the graph with straight-line segments, and estimate the value of s (to the nearest integer) that satisfies $v(s) = \dfrac{V_{\max}}{2}$.

(B) Use the constants $V_{\max}$ and K_M from part (A) to form a Michaelis–Menten function for the data in Table 11.

(C) Use the function from part (B) to estimate the velocity of the enzyme reaction when the sucrose is 9 and to estimate the sucrose when the velocity is 32.

79. Physics. The coefficient of thermal expansion (CTE) is a measure of the expansion of an object subjected to extreme temperatures. To model this coefficient, we use a Michaelis–Menten function of the form

$$C(T) = \frac{C_{\max}\, T}{M + T} \qquad \text{(Problem 77)}$$

where $C = $ CTE, T is temperature in K (degrees Kelvin), and $C_{\max}$ and M are constants. Table 12[†] lists the coeffi-

cients of thermal expansion for nickel and for copper at various temperatures.

Table 12 Coefficients of Thermal Expansion

T (K)	Nickel	Copper
100	6.6	10.3
200	11.3	15.2
293	13.4	16.5
500	15.3	18.3
800	16.8	20.3
1,100	17.8	23.7

(A) Plot the points in columns 1 and 2 of Table 12 on graph paper and estimate $C_{\max}$ to the nearest integer. To estimate M, add the horizontal line CTE $= \dfrac{C_{\max}}{2}$ to your graph, connect successive points on the graph with straight-line segments, and estimate the value of T (to the nearest multiple of fifty) that satisfies $C(T) = \dfrac{C_{\max}}{2}$.

(B) Use the constants $\dfrac{C_{\max}}{2}$ and M from part (A) to form a Michaelis–Menten function for the CTE of nickel.

(C) Use the function from part (B) to estimate the CTE of nickel at 600 K and to estimate the temperature when the CTE of nickel is 12.

80. Physics. Repeat Problem 79 for the CTE of copper (column 3 of Table 12).

Answers to Matched Problems

1. Vertical asymptote: $x = 1$; $\lim\limits_{x \to 1^+} f(x) = \infty$, $\lim\limits_{x \to 1^-} f(x) = -\infty$
$\lim\limits_{x \to 3} f(x) = 1/2$ so f does not have a vertical asymptote at $x = 3$

2. Vertical asymptote: $x = -3$; $\lim\limits_{x \to -3^+} f(x) = \lim\limits_{x \to -3^-} f(x) = -\infty$

3. $\lim\limits_{x \to \infty} p(x) = \lim\limits_{x \to -\infty} p(x) = -\infty$

4. (A) $\lim\limits_{x \to \infty} p(x) = -\infty$, $\lim\limits_{x \to -\infty} p(x) = \infty$
(B) $\lim\limits_{x \to \infty} p(x) = \infty$, $\lim\limits_{x \to -\infty} p(x) = \infty$

5. (A) $y = 0$ (B) No horizontal asymptotes
(C) $y = 1/2$

6. Vertical asymptotes: $x = -2$, $x = 2$;
horizontal asymptote: $y = 1$

---

*Institute of Chemistry, Macedonia.

[†]National Physical Laboratory

3-3   Continuity

Theorem 3 in Section 3-1 states that if f is a polynomial function or a rational function with a nonzero denominator at $x = c$, then

$$\lim_{x \to c} f(x) = f(c) \tag{1}$$

Functions that satisfy equation (1) are said to be *continuous* at $x = c$. A firm understanding of continuous functions is essential for sketching and analyzing graphs. We will also see that continuity properties provide a simple and efficient method for solving inequalities—a tool that we will use extensively in later sections.

Continuity

Compare the graphs shown in Figure 1. Notice that two of the graphs are broken; that is, they cannot be drawn without lifting a pen off the paper. Informally, a function is *continuous over an interval* if its graph over the interval can be drawn without removing a pen from the paper. A function whose graph is broken (disconnected) at $x = c$ is said to be *discontinuous* at $x = c$. Function f (Fig. 1A) is continuous for all x. Function g (Fig. 1B) is discontinuous at $x = 2$ but is continuous over any interval that does not include 2. Function h (Fig. 1C) is discontinuous at $x = 0$ but is continuous over any interval that does not include 0.

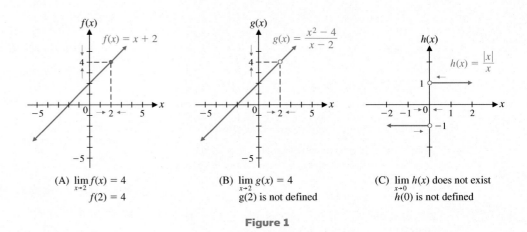

(A) $\lim\limits_{x \to 2} f(x) = 4$ (B) $\lim\limits_{x \to 2} g(x) = 4$ (C) $\lim\limits_{x \to 0} h(x)$ does not exist
$f(2) = 4$ $g(2)$ is not defined $h(0)$ is not defined

Figure 1

Most graphs of natural phenomena are continuous, whereas many graphs in business and economics applications have discontinuities. Figure 2A illustrates temperature variation over a 24-hour period—a continuous phenomenon. Figure 2B illustrates warehouse inventory over a 1-week period—a discontinuous phenomenon.

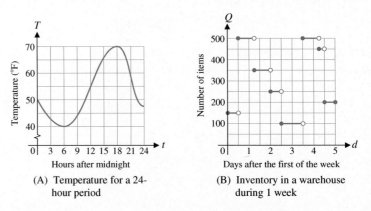

(A) Temperature for a 24-hour period   (B) Inventory in a warehouse during 1 week

Figure 2

EXPLORE & DISCUSS 1

(A) Write a brief verbal description of the temperature variation illustrated in Figure 2A, including estimates of the high and low temperatures during the period shown and the times at which they occurred.

(B) Write a brief verbal description of the changes in inventory illustrated in Figure 2B, including estimates of the changes in inventory and the times at which those changes occurred.

The preceding discussion leads to the following formal definition of continuity:

DEFINITION Continuity

A function f is **continuous at the point** $x = c$ if

1. $\lim\limits_{x \to c} f(x)$ exists   **2.** $f(c)$ exists   **3.** $\lim\limits_{x \to c} f(x) = f(c)$

A function is **continuous on the open interval*** (a, b) if it is continuous at each point on the interval.

---

*See Section 1-1 for a review of interval notation.

If one or more of the three conditions in the definition fails, then the function is **discontinuous** at $x = c$.

EXAMPLE 1   **Continuity of a Function Defined by a Graph** Use the definition of continuity to discuss the continuity of the function whose graph is shown in Figure 3.

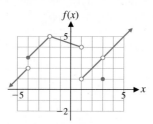

Figure 3

SOLUTION   We begin by identifying the points of discontinuity. Examining the graph, we see breaks or holes at $x = -4, -2, 1$, and 3. Now we must determine which conditions in the definition of continuity are not satisfied at each of these points. In each case, we find the value of the function and the limit of the function at the point in question.

Discontinuity at $x = -4$:

$$\lim_{x \to -4^-} f(x) = 2 \qquad \text{Since the one-sided limits are different,}$$
$$\lim_{x \to -4^+} f(x) = 3 \qquad \text{the limit does not exist (Section 3-1).}$$

$$\lim_{x \to -4} f(x) \text{ does not exist}$$
$$f(-4) = 3$$

So, f is not continuous at $x = -4$ because condition 1 is not satisfied.

Discontinuity at $x = -2$:

$$\lim_{x \to -2^-} f(x) = 5 \qquad \text{The hole at } (-2, 5) \text{ indicates that 5 is not the value of } f$$
$$\lim_{x \to -2^+} f(x) = 5 \qquad \text{at } -2. \text{ Since there is no solid dot elsewhere on the verti-}$$
$$\lim_{x \to -2} f(x) = 5 \qquad \text{cal line } x = -2, f(-2) \text{ is not defined.}$$

$$f(-2) \text{ does not exist}$$

So f is not continuous at $x = -2$ because condition 2 is not satisfied.

Discontinuity at $x = 1$:

$$\lim_{x \to 1^-} f(x) = 4$$
$$\lim_{x \to 1^+} f(x) = 1$$
$$\lim_{x \to 1} f(x) \text{ does not exist}$$
$$f(1) \text{ does not exist}$$

This time, f is not continuous at $x = 1$ because neither of conditions 1 and 2 is satisfied.

Discontinuity at $x = 3$:

$$\lim_{x \to 3^-} f(x) = 3 \qquad \text{\textit{The solid dot at (3, 1) indicates that f(3) = 1.}}$$
$$\lim_{x \to 3^+} f(x) = 3$$
$$\lim_{x \to 3} f(x) = 3$$
$$f(3) = 1$$

Conditions 1 and 2 are satisfied, but f is not continuous at $x = 3$ because condition 3 is not satisfied.

Having identified and discussed all points of discontinuity, we can now conclude that f is continuous except at $x = -4, -2, 1,$ and 3.

CONCEPTUAL INSIGHT

Rather than list the points where a function is discontinuous, sometimes it is useful to state the intervals on which the function is continuous. Using the set operation **union,** denoted by $\cup$, we can express the set of points where the function in Example 1 is continuous as follows:

$$(-\infty, -4) \cup (-4, -2) \cup (-2, 1) \cup (1, 3) \cup (3, \infty)$$

Matched Problem 1   Use the definition of continuity to discuss the continuity of the function whose graph is shown in Figure 4.

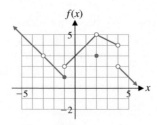

Figure 4

For functions defined by equations, it is important to be able to locate points of discontinuity by examining the equation.

EXAMPLE 2   **Continuity of Functions Defined by Equations** Using the definition of continuity, discuss the continuity of each function at the indicated point(s).

(A) $f(x) = x + 2$ at $x = 2$ (B) $g(x) = \dfrac{x^2 - 4}{x - 2}$ at $x = 2$

(C) $h(x) = \dfrac{|x|}{x}$ at $x = 0$ and   at $x = 1$

SOLUTION   (A) f is continuous at $x = 2$, since

$$\lim_{x \to 2} f(x) = 4 = f(2) \quad \textit{See Figure 1A.}$$

(B) g is not continuous at $x = 2$, since $g(2) = 0/0$ is not defined (see Fig. 1B).

(C) h is not continuous at $x = 0$, since $h(0) = |0|/0$ is not defined; also, $\lim_{x \to 0} h(x)$ does not exist.

h is continuous at $x = 1$, since

$$\lim_{x \to 1} \frac{|x|}{x} = 1 = h(1) \quad \textit{See Figure 1C.}$$

Matched Problem 2   Using the definition of continuity, discuss the continuity of each function at the indicated point(s).

(A) $f(x) = x + 1$ at $x = 1$ (B) $g(x) = \dfrac{x^2 - 1}{x - 1}$ at $x = 1$

(C) $h(x) = \dfrac{x - 2}{|x - 2|}$ at $x = 2$ and at $x = 0$

We can also talk about one-sided continuity, just as we talked about one-sided limits. For example, a function is said to be **continuous on the right** at $x = c$ if $\lim_{x \to c^+} f(x) = f(c)$ and **continuous on the left** at $x = c$ if $\lim_{x \to c^-} f(x) = f(c)$. A function is **continuous on the closed interval [a, b]** if it is continuous on the open interval (a, b) and is continuous both on the right at a and on the left at b.

Figure 5A illustrates a function that is continuous on the closed interval $[-1, 1]$. Figure 5B illustrates a function that is continuous on the half-closed interval $[0, \infty)$.

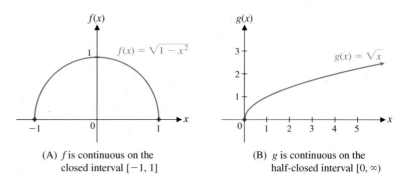

(A) f is continuous on the closed interval $[-1, 1]$

(B) g is continuous on the half-closed interval $[0, \infty)$

Figure 5 Continuity on closed and half-closed intervals

Continuity Properties

Functions have some useful **general continuity properties**:

> **If two functions are continuous on the same interval, then their sum, difference, product, and quotient are continuous on the same interval except for values of x that make a denominator 0.**

These properties, along with Theorem 1, enable us to determine intervals of continuity for some important classes of functions without having to look at their graphs or use the three conditions in the definition.

THEOREM 1 **Continuity Properties of Some Specific Functions**

(A) A constant function $f(x) = k$, where k is a constant, is continuous for all x.

$f(x) = 7$ is continuous for all x.

(B) For n a positive integer, $f(x) = x^n$ is continuous for all x.

$f(x) = x^5$ is continuous for all x.

(C) A polynomial function is continuous for all x.

$2x^3 - 3x^2 + x - 5$ is continuous for all x.

(D) A rational function is continuous for all x except those values that make a denominator 0.

$\dfrac{x^2 + 1}{x - 1}$ is continuous for all x except x = 1, a value that makes the denominator 0.

(E) For n an odd positive integer greater than 1, $\sqrt[n]{f(x)}$ is continuous wherever $f(x)$ is continuous.

$\sqrt[3]{x^2}$ is continuous for all x.

(F) For n an even positive integer, $\sqrt[n]{f(x)}$ is continuous wherever $f(x)$ is continuous and nonnegative.

$\sqrt[4]{x}$ is continuous on the interval $[0, \infty)$.

Parts C and D of Theorem 1 are the same as Theorem 3 in Section 3-1. They are repeated here to emphasize their importance.

EXAMPLE 3 **Using Continuity Properties** Using Theorem 1 and the general properties of continuity, determine where each function is continuous.

(A) $f(x) = x^2 - 2x + 1$ (B) $f(x) = \dfrac{x}{(x + 2)(x - 3)}$

(C) $f(x) = \sqrt[3]{x^2 - 4}$ (D) $f(x) = \sqrt{x - 2}$

SOLUTION (A) Since f is a polynomial function, f is continuous for all x.

(B) Since f is a rational function, f is continuous for all x except -2 and 3 (values that make the denominator 0).

(C) The polynomial function $x^2 - 4$ is continuous for all x. Since $n = 3$ is odd, f is continuous for all x.

(D) The polynomial function $x - 2$ is continuous for all x and nonnegative for $x \geq 2$. Since $n = 2$ is even, f is continuous for $x \geq 2$, or on the interval $[2, \infty)$.

Matched Problem 3 Using Theorem 1 and the general properties of continuity, determine where each function is continuous.

(A) $f(x) = x^4 + 2x^2 + 1$ (B) $f(x) = \dfrac{x^2}{(x + 1)(x - 4)}$

(C) $f(x) = \sqrt{x - 4}$ (D) $f(x) = \sqrt[3]{x^3 + 1}$

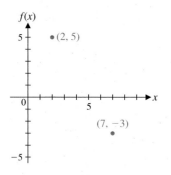

Figure 6

Solving Inequalities Using Continuity Properties

One of the basic tools for analyzing graphs in calculus is a special line graph called a *sign chart.* We will make extensive use of this type of chart in later sections. In the discussion that follows, we use continuity properties to develop a simple and efficient procedure for constructing sign charts.

Suppose that a function f is continuous over the interval $(1, 8)$ and $f(x) \neq 0$ for any x in $(1, 8)$. Suppose also that $f(2) = 5$, a positive number. Is it possible for $f(x)$ to be negative for any x in the interval $(1, 8)$? The answer is "no." If $f(7)$ were -3, for example, as shown in Figure 6, then how would it be possible to join the points $(2, 5)$ and $(7, -3)$ with the graph of a continuous function without crossing the x axis between 1 and 8 at least once? [Crossing the x axis would violate our assumption that $f(x) \neq 0$ for any x in $(1, 8)$.] We conclude that $f(x)$ must be positive for all x in $(1, 8)$. If $f(2)$ were negative, then, using the same type of reasoning, $f(x)$ would have to be negative over the entire interval $(1, 8)$.

In general, **if f is continuous and $f(x) \neq 0$ on the interval (a, b), then $f(x)$ cannot change sign on (a, b).** This is the essence of Theorem 2.

THEOREM 2 Sign Properties on an Interval (a, b)

If f is continuous on (a, b) and $f(x) \neq 0$ for all x in (a, b), then either $f(x) > 0$ for all x in (a, b) or $f(x) < 0$ for all x in (a, b).

Theorem 2 provides the basis for an effective method of solving many types of inequalities. Example 4 illustrates the process.

EXAMPLE 4 Solving an Inequality Solve $\dfrac{x + 1}{x - 2} > 0$.

SOLUTION We start by using the left side of the inequality to form the function f.

$$f(x) = \frac{x + 1}{x - 2}$$

The rational function f is discontinuous at $x = 2$, and $f(x) = 0$ for $x = -1$ (a fraction is 0 when the numerator is 0 and the denominator is not 0). We plot $x = 2$ and $x = -1$, which we call *partition numbers,* on a real-number line (Fig. 7). (Note that the dot at 2 is open because the function is not defined at $x = 2$.) The partition numbers 2 and -1 determine three open intervals: $(-\infty, -1)$, $(-1, 2)$, and $(2, \infty)$. The function f is continuous and nonzero on each of these intervals. From Theorem 2, we know that $f(x)$ does not change sign on any of these intervals. We can find the sign of $f(x)$ on each of the intervals by selecting a **test number** in each interval and evaluating $f(x)$ at that number. Since any number in each subinterval will do, we choose test numbers that are easy to evaluate: -2, 0, and 3. The table in the margin shows the results.

The sign of $f(x)$ at each test number is the same as the sign of $f(x)$ over the interval containing that test number. Using this information, we construct a **sign chart** for $f(x)$ as shown in Figure 8.

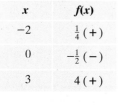

Figure 7

Test Numbers

x	$f(x)$
-2	$\frac{1}{4}$ $(+)$
0	$-\frac{1}{2}$ $(-)$
3	4 $(+)$

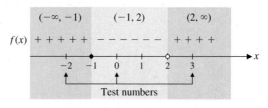

Figure 8

From the sign chart, we can easily write the solution of the given nonlinear inequality:

$$f(x) > 0 \quad \text{for} \quad \begin{array}{l} x < -1 \quad \text{or} \quad x > 2 \quad \text{Inequality notation} \\ (-\infty, -1) \cup (2, \infty) \quad \text{Interval notation} \end{array}$$

Matched Problem 4   Solve $\dfrac{x^2 - 1}{x - 3} < 0$.

Most of the inequalities we encounter will involve strict inequalities ($>$ or $<$). If it is necessary to solve inequalities of the form $\geq$ or $\leq$, we simply include the endpoint x of any interval if f is defined at x and $f(x)$ satisfies the given inequality. For example, from the sign chart in Figure 8, the solution of the inequality

$$\dfrac{x + 1}{x - 2} \geq 0 \quad \text{is} \quad \begin{array}{l} x \leq -1 \quad \text{or} \quad x > 2 \quad \text{Inequality notation} \\ (-\infty, -1] \cup (2, \infty) \quad \text{Interval notation} \end{array}$$

In general, given a function f, a **partition number** is a value of x such that f is discontinuous at x or $f(x) = 0$. **Partition numbers determine open intervals in which $f(x)$ does not change sign.** By using a test number from each interval, we can construct a sign chart for $f(x)$ on the real-number line. It is then easy to solve the inequality $f(x) < 0$ or $f(x) > 0$.

We summarize the procedure for constructing sign charts in the following box:

PROCEDURE Constructing Sign Charts

Given a function f,

Step 1 Find all partition numbers:

(A) Find all numbers such that f is discontinuous. (Rational functions are discontinuous for values of x that make a denominator 0.)

(B) Find all numbers such that $f(x) = 0$. (For a rational function, this occurs where the numerator is 0 and the denominator is not 0.)

Step 2 Plot the numbers found in step 1 on a real-number line, dividing the number line into intervals.

Step 3 Select a test number in each open interval determined in step 2 and evaluate $f(x)$ at each test number to determine whether $f(x)$ is positive (+) or negative (−) in each interval.

Step 4 Construct a sign chart, using the real-number line in step 2. This will show the sign of $f(x)$ on each open interval.

Exercises 3-3

A

In Problems 1–6, sketch a possible graph of a function that satisfies the given conditions at x = 1 and discuss the continuity of f at x = 1.

1. $f(1) = 2$ and $\lim\limits_{x \to 1} f(x) = 2$

2. $f(1) = -2$ and $\lim\limits_{x \to 1} f(x) = 2$

3. $f(1) = 2$ and $\lim\limits_{x \to 1} f(x) = -2$

4. $f(1) = -2$ and $\lim\limits_{x \to 1} f(x) = -2$

5. $f(1) = -2$, $\lim\limits_{x \to 1^-} f(x) = 2$, and $\lim\limits_{x \to 1^+} f(x) = -2$

6. $f(1) = 2$, $\lim\limits_{x \to 1^-} f(x) = 2$, and $\lim\limits_{x \to 1^+} f(x) = -2$

Problems 7–14 refer to the function f shown in the figure. Use the graph to estimate the indicated function values and limits.

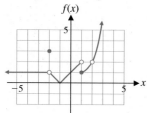

Figure for 7–14

7. $f(0.9)$ **8.** $f(0.1)$

9. $f(-1.9)$ **10.** $f(-0.9)$

11. (A) $\lim\limits_{x \to 1^-} f(x)$ (B) $\lim\limits_{x \to 1^+} f(x)$
(C) $\lim\limits_{x \to 1} f(x)$ (D) $f(1)$
(E) Is f continuous at $x = 1$? Explain.

12. (A) $\lim\limits_{x \to 2^-} f(x)$ (B) $\lim\limits_{x \to 2^+} f(x)$
(C) $\lim\limits_{x \to 2} f(x)$ (D) $f(2)$
(E) Is f continuous at $x = 2$? Explain.

13. (A) $\lim\limits_{x \to -2^-} f(x)$ (B) $\lim\limits_{x \to -2^+} f(x)$
(C) $\lim\limits_{x \to -2} f(x)$ (D) $f(-2)$
(E) Is f continuous at $x = -2$? Explain.

14. (A) $\lim\limits_{x \to -1^-} f(x)$ (B) $\lim\limits_{x \to -1^+} f(x)$
(C) $\lim\limits_{x \to -1} f(x)$ (D) $f(-1)$
(E) Is f continuous at $x = -1$? Explain.

Problems 15–22 refer to the function g shown in the figure. Use the graph to estimate the indicated function values and limits.

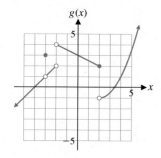

Figure for 15–22

15. $g(-3.1)$ **16.** $g(-2.1)$

17. $g(1.9)$ **18.** $g(-1.9)$

19. (A) $\lim\limits_{x \to -3^-} g(x)$ (B) $\lim\limits_{x \to -3^+} g(x)$
(C) $\lim\limits_{x \to -3} g(x)$ (D) $g(-3)$
(E) Is g continuous at $x = -3$? Explain.

20. (A) $\lim\limits_{x \to -2^-} g(x)$ (B) $\lim\limits_{x \to -2^+} g(x)$
(C) $\lim\limits_{x \to -2} g(x)$ (D) $g(-2)$
(E) Is g continuous at $x = -2$? Explain.

21. (A) $\lim\limits_{x \to 2^-} g(x)$ (B) $\lim\limits_{x \to 2^+} g(x)$
(C) $\lim\limits_{x \to 2} g(x)$ (D) $g(2)$
(E) Is g continuous at $x = 2$? Explain.

22. (A) $\lim\limits_{x \to 4^-} g(x)$ (B) $\lim\limits_{x \to 4^+} g(x)$
(C) $\lim\limits_{x \to 4} g(x)$ (D) $g(4)$
(E) Is g continuous at $x = 4$? Explain.

Use Theorem 1 to determine where each function in Problems 23–32 is continuous.

23. $f(x) = 3x - 4$ **24.** $h(x) = 4 - 2x$

25. $g(x) = \dfrac{3x}{x + 2}$ **26.** $k(x) = \dfrac{2x}{x - 4}$

27. $m(x) = \dfrac{x + 1}{(x - 1)(x + 4)}$ **28.** $n(x) = \dfrac{x - 2}{(x - 3)(x + 1)}$

29. $F(x) = \dfrac{2x}{x^2 + 9}$ **30.** $G(x) = \dfrac{1 - x^2}{x^2 + 1}$

31. $M(x) = \dfrac{x - 1}{4x^2 - 9}$ **32.** $N(x) = \dfrac{x^2 + 4}{4 - 25x^2}$

B

33. Given the function

$$f(x) = \begin{cases} 2 & \text{if } x \text{ is an integer} \\ 1 & \text{if } x \text{ is not an integer} \end{cases}$$

(A) Graph f.

(B) $\lim\limits_{x \to 2} f(x) = ?$

(C) $f(2) = ?$

(D) Is f continuous at $x = 2$?

(E) Where is f discontinuous?

34. Given the function

$$g(x) = \begin{cases} -1 & \text{if } x \text{ is an even integer} \\ 1 & \text{if } x \text{ is not an even integer} \end{cases}$$

(A) Graph g.

(B) $\lim\limits_{x \to 1} g(x) = ?$

(C) $g(1) = ?$

(D) Is g continuous at $x = 1$?

(E) Where is g discontinuous?

In Problems 35–42, use a sign chart to solve each inequality. Express answers in inequality and interval notation.

35. $x^2 - x - 12 < 0$ **36.** $x^2 - 2x - 8 < 0$

37. $x^2 + 21 > 10x$ **38.** $x^2 + 7x > -10$

39. $x^3 < 4x$ **40.** $x^4 - 9x^2 > 0$

41. $\dfrac{x^2 + 5x}{x - 3} > 0$ **42.** $\dfrac{x - 4}{x^2 + 2x} < 0$

43. Use the graph of f to determine where

(A) $f(x) > 0$ (B) $f(x) < 0$

Express answers in interval notation.

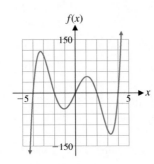

Figure for 43

44. Use the graph of g to determine where

(A) $g(x) > 0$ (B) $g(x) < 0$

Express answers in interval notation.

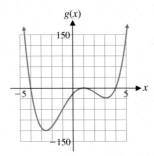

Figure for 44

In Problems 45–48, use a graphing calculator to approximate the partition numbers of each function $f(x)$ to four decimal places. Then solve the following inequalities:

(A) $f(x) > 0$ (B) $f(x) < 0$

Express answers in interval notation.

45. $f(x) = x^4 - 6x^2 + 3x + 5$

46. $f(x) = x^4 - 4x^2 - 2x + 2$

47. $f(x) = \dfrac{3 + 6x - x^3}{x^2 - 1}$ **48.** $f(x) = \dfrac{x^3 - 5x + 1}{x^2 - 1}$

Use Theorem 1 to determine where each function in Problems 49–56 is continuous. Express the answer in interval notation.

49. $\sqrt{x - 6}$ **50.** $\sqrt{7 - x}$

51. $\sqrt[3]{5 - x}$ **52.** $\sqrt[3]{x - 8}$

53. $\sqrt{x^2 - 9}$ **54.** $\sqrt{4 - x^2}$

55. $\sqrt{x^2 + 1}$ **56.** $\sqrt[3]{x^2 + 2}$

In Problems 57–62, graph f, locate all points of discontinuity, and discuss the behavior of f at these points.

57. $f(x) = \begin{cases} 1 + x & \text{if } x < 1 \\ 5 - x & \text{if } x \geq 1 \end{cases}$

58. $f(x) = \begin{cases} x^2 & \text{if } x \leq 1 \\ 2x & \text{if } x > 1 \end{cases}$

59. $f(x) = \begin{cases} 1 + x & \text{if } x \leq 2 \\ 5 - x & \text{if } x > 2 \end{cases}$

60. $f(x) = \begin{cases} x^2 & \text{if } x \leq 2 \\ 2x & \text{if } x > 2 \end{cases}$

61. $f(x) = \begin{cases} -x & \text{if } x < 0 \\ 1 & \text{if } x = 0 \\ x & \text{if } x > 0 \end{cases}$

62. $f(x) = \begin{cases} 1 & \text{if } x < 0 \\ 0 & \text{if } x = 0 \\ 1 + x & \text{if } x > 0 \end{cases}$

C

*Problems 63 and 64 refer to the **greatest integer function**, which is denoted by $[x]$ and is defined as*

$$[x] = greatest\ integer \leq x$$

For example,

$$[-3.6] = greatest\ integer \leq -3.6 = -4$$

$$[2] = greatest\ integer \leq 2 = 2$$

$$[2.5] = greatest\ integer \leq 2.5 = 2$$

The graph of $f(x) = [x]$ is shown. There, we can see that

$$[x] = -2 \quad for \quad -2 \leq x < -1$$

$$[x] = -1 \quad for \quad -1 \leq x < 0$$

$$[x] = 0 \quad for \quad 0 \leq x < 1$$

$$[x] = 1 \quad for \quad 1 \leq x < 2$$

$$[x] = 2 \quad for \quad 2 \leq x < 3$$

and so on.

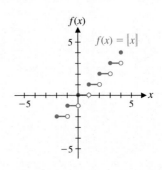

Figure for 63 and 64

63. (A) Is f continuous from the right at $x = 0$?

   (B) Is f continuous from the left at $x = 0$?

   (C) Is f continuous on the open interval $(0, 1)$?

   (D) Is f continuous on the closed interval $[0, 1]$?

   (E) Is f continuous on the half-closed interval $[0, 1)$?

64. (A) Is f continuous from the right at $x = 2$?

   (B) Is f continuous from the left at $x = 2$?

   (C) Is f continuous on the open interval $(1, 2)$?

   (D) Is f continuous on the closed interval $[1, 2]$?

   (E) Is f continuous on the half-closed interval $[1, 2)$?

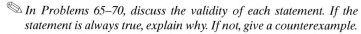 *In Problems 65–70, discuss the validity of each statement. If the statement is always true, explain why. If not, give a counterexample.*

65. A polynomial function is continuous for all real numbers.

66. A rational function is continuous for all but finitely many real numbers.

67. If f is a function that is continuous at $x = 0$ and $x = 2$, then f is continuous at $x = 1$.

68. If f is a function that is continuous on the open interval $(0, 2)$, then f is continuous at $x = 1$.

69. If f is a function that has no partition numbers in the interval (a, b), then f is continuous on (a, b).

70. The greatest integer function (see Problem 61) is a rational function.

In Problems 71–74, sketch a possible graph of a function f that is continuous for all real numbers and satisfies the given conditions. Find the x intercepts of f.

71. $f(x) < 0$ on $(-\infty, -5)$ and $(2, \infty)$; $f(x) > 0$ on $(-5, 2)$

72. $f(x) > 0$ on $(-\infty, -4)$ and $(3, \infty)$; $f(x) < 0$ on $(-4, 3)$

73. $f(x) < 0$ on $(-\infty, -6)$ and $(-1, 4)$; $f(x) > 0$ on $(-6, -1)$ and $(4, \infty)$

74. $f(x) > 0$ on $(-\infty, -3)$ and $(2, 7)$; $f(x) < 0$ on $(-3, 2)$ and $(7, \infty)$

75. The function $f(x) = 2/(1 - x)$ satisfies $f(0) = 2$ and $f(2) = -2$. Is f equal to 0 anywhere on the interval $(-1, 3)$? Does this contradict Theorem 2? Explain.

76. The function $f(x) = 6/(x - 4)$ satisfies $f(2) = -3$ and $f(7) = 2$. Is f equal to 0 anywhere on the interval $(0, 9)$? Does this contradict Theorem 2? Explain.

Applications

77. **Postal rates.** First-class postage in 2009 was $0.44 for the first ounce (or any fraction thereof) and $0.17 for each additional ounce (or fraction thereof) up to a maximum weight of 3.5 ounces.

   (A) Write a piecewise definition of the first-class postage $P(x)$ for a letter weighing x ounces.

   (B) Graph $P(x)$ for $0 < x \le 3.5$.

   (C) Is $P(x)$ continuous at $x = 2.5$? At $x = 3$? Explain.

78. **Telephone rates.** A long-distance telephone service charges $0.07 for the first minute (or any fraction thereof) and $0.05 for each additional minute (or fraction thereof).

   (A) Write a piecewise definition of the charge $R(x)$ for a long-distance call lasting x minutes.

   (B) Graph $R(x)$ for $0 < x \le 6$.

   (C) Is $R(x)$ continuous at $x = 3.5$? At $x = 3$? Explain.

79. **Postal rates.** Discuss the differences between the function $Q(x) = 0.44 + 0.17[\![x]\!]$ and the function $P(x)$ defined in Problem 77.

80. **Telephone rates.** Discuss the differences between the function $S(x) = 0.07 + 0.05[\![x]\!]$ and the function $R(x)$ defined in Problem 78.

81. **Natural-gas rates.** Table 1 shows the rates for natural gas charged by the Middle Tennessee Natural Gas Utility District during summer months. The customer charge is a fixed monthly charge, independent of the amount of gas used per month.

Table 1 Summer (May–September)

Base charge	$5.00
First 50 therms	0.63 per therm
Over 50 therms	0.45 per therm

   (A) Write a piecewise definition of the monthly charge $S(x)$ for a customer who uses x therms* in a summer month.

   (B) Graph $S(x)$.

   (C) Is $S(x)$ continuous at $x = 50$? Explain.

82. **Natural-gas rates.** Table 2 shows the rates for natural gas charged by the Middle Tennessee Natural Gas Utility District during winter months. The customer charge is a fixed monthly charge, independent of the amount of gas used per month.

Table 2 Winter (October– April)

Base charge	$5.00
First 5 therms	0.69 per therm
Next 45 therms	0.65 per therm
Over 50 therms	0.63 per therm

---

*A British thermal unit (Btu) is the amount of heat required to raise the temperature of 1 pound of water 1 degree Fahrenheit, and a therm is 100,000 Btu.

(A) Write a piecewise definition of the monthly charge $S(x)$ for a customer who uses x therms in a winter month.

(B) Graph $S(x)$.

✎ (C) Is $S(x)$ continuous at $x = 5$? At $x = 50$? Explain.

83. Income. A personal-computer salesperson receives a base salary of \$1,000 per month and a commission of 5% of all sales over \$10,000 during the month. If the monthly sales are \$20,000 or more, then the salesperson is given an additional \$500 bonus. Let $E(s)$ represent the person's earnings per month as a function of the monthly sales s.

(A) Graph $E(s)$ for $0 \le s \le 30,000$.

(B) Find $\lim_{s \to 10,000} E(s)$ and $E(10,000)$.

(C) Find $\lim_{s \to 20,000} E(s)$ and $E(20,000)$.

(D) Is E continuous at $s = 10,000$? At $s = 20,000$?

84. Equipment rental. An office equipment rental and leasing company rents copiers for \$10 per day (and any fraction thereof) or for \$50 per 7-day week. Let $C(x)$ be the cost of renting a copier for x days.

(A) Graph $C(x)$ for $0 \le x \le 10$.

(B) Find $\lim_{x \to 4.5} C(x)$ and $C(4.5)$.

(C) Find $\lim_{x \to 8} C(x)$ and $C(8)$.

(D) Is C continuous at $x = 4.5$? At $x = 8$?

85. Animal supply. A medical laboratory raises its own rabbits. The number of rabbits $N(t)$ available at any time t depends on the number of births and deaths. When a birth or death occurs, the function N generally has a discontinuity, as shown in the figure.

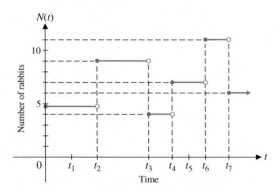

Figure for 85

(A) Where is the function N discontinuous?

(B) $\lim_{t \to t_5} N(t) = ?$; $N(t_5) = ?$

(C) $\lim_{t \to t_3} N(t) = ?$; $N(t_3) = ?$

86. Learning. The graph shown represents the history of a person learning the material on limits and continuity in this book. At time t_2, the student's mind goes blank during a quiz. At time t_4, the instructor explains a concept particularly well, then suddenly a big jump in understanding takes place.

(A) Where is the function p discontinuous?

(B) $\lim_{t \to t_1} p(t) = ?$; $p(t_1) = ?$

(C) $\lim_{t \to t_2} p(t) = ?$; $p(t_2) = ?$

(D) $\lim_{t \to t_4} p(t) = ?$; $p(t_4) = ?$

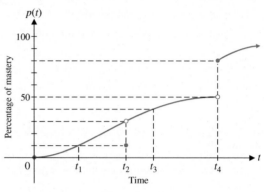

Figure for 86

Answers to Matched Problems

1. f is not continuous at $x = -3, -1, 2,$ and 4.

$x = -3$: $\lim_{x \to -3} f(x) = 3$, but $f(-3)$ does not exist

$x = -1$: $f(-1) = 1$, but $\lim_{x \to -1} f(x)$ does not exist

$x = 2$: $\lim_{x \to 2} f(x) = 5$, but $f(2) = 3$

$x = 4$: $\lim_{x \to 4} f(x)$ does not exist, and $f(4)$ does not exist

2. (A) f is continuous at $x = 1$, since $\lim_{x \to 1} f(x) = 2 = f(1)$.

(B) g is not continuous at $x = 1$, since $g(1)$ is not defined.

(C) h is not continuous at $x = 2$ for two reasons: $h(2)$ does not exist and $\lim_{x \to 2} h(x)$ does not exist.

h is continuous at $x = 0$, since $\lim_{x \to 0} h(x) = -1 = h(0)$.

3. (A) Since f is a polynomial function, f is continuous for all x.

(B) Since f is a rational function, f is continuous for all x except -1 and 4 (values that make the denominator 0).

(C) The polynomial function $x - 4$ is continuous for all x and nonnegative for $x \ge 4$. Since $n = 2$ is even, f is continuous for $x \ge 4$, or on the interval $[4, \infty)$.

(D) The polynomial function $x^3 + 1$ is continuous for all x. Since $n = 3$ is odd, f is continuous for all x.

4. $-\infty < x < -1$ or $1 < x < 3$; $(-\infty, -1) \cup (1, 3)$

3-4   The Derivative

We will now make use of the limit concepts developed in Sections 3-1, 3-2, and 3-3 to solve the two important problems illustrated in Figure 1. The solution of each of these apparently unrelated problems involves a common concept called the *derivative*.

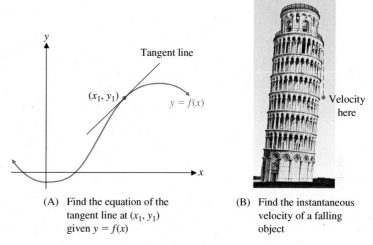

(A) Find the equation of the tangent line at (x_1, y_1) given $y = f(x)$

(B) Find the instantaneous velocity of a falling object

Figure 1 Two basic problems of calculus

Rate of Change

Let us start by considering a simple example.

EXAMPLE 1   **Revenue Analysis** The revenue (in dollars) from the sale of x plastic planter boxes is given by

$$R(x) = 20x - 0.02x^2 \qquad 0 \le x \le 1,000$$

and is graphed in Figure 2.

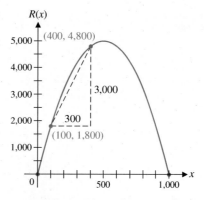

Figure 2 $R(x) = 20x - 0.02x^2$

(A) What is the change in revenue if production is changed from 100 planters to 400 planters?

(B) What is the average change in revenue for this change in production?

SOLUTION   (A) The change in revenue is given by

$$R(400) - R(100) = 20(400) - 0.02(400)^2 - [20(100) - 0.02(100)^2]$$
$$= 4{,}800 - 1{,}800 = \$3{,}000$$

Increasing production from 100 planters to 400 planters will increase revenue by \$3,000.

(B) To find the average change in revenue, we divide the change in revenue by the change in production:

$$\frac{R(400) - R(100)}{400 - 100} = \frac{3{,}000}{300} = \$10$$

The average change in revenue is \$10 per planter when production is increased from 100 to 400 planters.

Matched Problem 1   Refer to the revenue function in Example 1.

(A) What is the change in revenue if production is changed from 600 planters to 800 planters?

(B) What is the average change in revenue for this change in production?

In general, if we are given a function $y = f(x)$ and if x is changed from a to $a + h$, then y will change from $f(a)$ to $f(a + h)$. The *average rate of change is the ratio of the change in y to the change in x.*

DEFINITION   Average Rate of Change

For $y = f(x)$, the **average rate of change from $x = a$ to $x = a + h$** is

$$\frac{f(a + h) - f(a)}{(a + h) - a} = \frac{f(a + h) - f(a)}{h} \qquad h \neq 0 \qquad (1)$$

As we noted in Section 3-1, equation (1) is called the **difference quotient**. The preceding discussion shows that the difference quotient can be interpreted as an average rate of change. The next example illustrates another interpretation of this quotient: the velocity of a moving object.

EXAMPLE 2   **Velocity** A small steel ball dropped from a tower will fall a distance of y feet in x seconds, as given approximately by the formula

$$y = f(x) = 16x^2$$

Figure 3 shows the position of the ball on a coordinate line (positive direction down) at the end of 0, 1, 2, and 3 seconds.

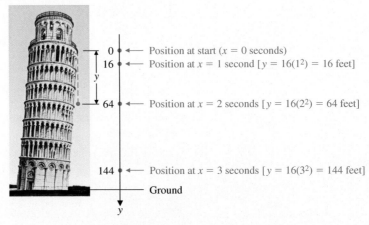

0 ← Position at start ($x = 0$ seconds)
16 ← Position at $x = 1$ second [$y = 16(1^2) = 16$ feet]
64 ← Position at $x = 2$ seconds [$y = 16(2^2) = 64$ feet]
144 ← Position at $x = 3$ seconds [$y = 16(3^2) = 144$ feet]
Ground

Figure 3 Note: Positive y direction is down.

(A) Find the average velocity from $x = 2$ seconds to $x = 3$ seconds.

(B) Find and simplify the average velocity from $x = 2$ seconds to $x = 2 + h$ seconds, $h \neq 0$.

(C) Find the limit of the expression from part B as $h \to 0$ if that limit exists.

(D) Discuss possible interpretations of the limit from part C.

SOLUTION

(A) Recall the formula $d = rt$, which can be written in the form

$$r = \frac{d}{t} = \frac{\text{Distance covered}}{\text{Elapsed time}} = \text{Average velocity}$$

For example, if a person drives from San Francisco to Los Angeles (a distance of about 420 miles) in 7 hours, then the average velocity is

$$r = \frac{d}{t} = \frac{420}{7} = 60 \text{ miles per hour}$$

Sometimes the person will be traveling faster and sometimes slower, but the average velocity is 60 miles per hour. In our present problem, the average velocity of the steel ball from $x = 2$ seconds to $x = 3$ seconds is

$$\text{Average velocity} = \frac{\text{Distance covered}}{\text{Elapsed time}}$$

$$= \frac{f(3) - f(2)}{3 - 2}$$

$$= \frac{16(3)^2 - 16(2)^2}{1} = 80 \text{ feet per second}$$

We see that if $y = f(x)$ is the position of the falling ball, then the average velocity is simply the average rate of change of $f(x)$ with respect to time x, and we have another interpretation of the difference quotient (1).

(B) Proceeding as in part A, we have

$$\text{Average velocity} = \frac{\text{Distance covered}}{\text{Elapsed time}}$$

$$= \frac{f(2 + h) - f(2)}{h} \qquad \text{Difference quotient}$$

$$= \frac{16(2 + h)^2 - 16(2)^2}{h} \qquad \text{Simplify this 0/0 indeterminate form.}$$

$$= \frac{64 + 64h + 16h^2 - 64}{h}$$

$$= \frac{h(64 + 16h)}{h} = 64 + 16h \qquad h \neq 0$$

Notice that if $h = 1$, the average velocity is 80 feet per second, which is the result in part A.

(C) The limit of the average velocity expression from part B as $h \to 0$ is

$$\lim_{h \to 0} \frac{f(2 + h) - f(2)}{h} = \lim_{h \to 0} (64 + 16h)$$

$$= 64 \text{ feet per second}$$

(D) The average velocity over smaller and smaller time intervals approaches 64 feet per second. This limit can be interpreted as the velocity of the ball at the *instant* that the ball has been falling for exactly 2 seconds. Therefore, 64 feet per second is referred to as the **instantaneous velocity** at $x = 2$ seconds, and we have solved one of the basic problems of calculus (see Fig. 1B).

Matched Problem 2 For the falling steel ball in Example 2, find

(A) The average velocity from $x = 1$ second to $x = 2$ seconds

(B) The average velocity (in simplified form) from $x = 1$ second to $x = 1 + h$ seconds, $h \neq 0$

(C) The instantaneous velocity at $x = 1$ second

The ideas introduced in Example 2 are not confined to average velocity, but can be applied to the average rate of change of any function.

DEFINITION   Instantaneous Rate of Change

For $y = f(x)$, the **instantaneous rate of change at $x = a$** is

$$\lim_{h \to 0} \frac{f(a + h) - f(a)}{h} \tag{2}$$

if the limit exists.

The adjective *instantaneous* is often omitted with the understanding that the phrase **rate of change** always refers to the instantaneous rate of change and not the average rate of change. Similarly, **velocity** always refers to the instantaneous rate of change of distance with respect to time.

Slope of the Tangent Line

So far, our interpretations of the difference quotient have been numerical in nature. Now we want to consider a geometric interpretation. A line through two points on the graph of a function is called a **secant line**. If $(a, f(a))$ and $(a + h, f(a + h))$ are two points on the graph of $y = f(x)$, then we can use the slope formula from Section 1-2 to find the slope of the secant line through these points (Fig. 4).

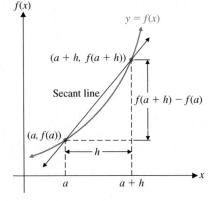

Figure 4 Secant line

$$\textbf{Slope of secant line} = \frac{f(a + h) - f(a)}{(a + h) - a}$$

$$= \frac{f(a + h) - f(a)}{h} \quad \text{Difference quotient}$$

The difference quotient can be interpreted as both the average rate of change and the slope of the secant line.

CONCEPTUAL INSIGHT

If (x_1, y_1) and (x_2, y_2) are two points in the plane with $x_1 \neq x_2$ and L is the line passing through these two points (see Section 1-2), then

Slope of L   Point–slope form for L

$$m = \frac{y_2 - y_1}{x_2 - x_1} \qquad y - y_1 = m(x - x_1)$$

These formulas will be used extensively in the remainder of this chapter.

EXAMPLE 3 **Slope of a Secant Line** Given $f(x) = x^2$,

(A) Find the slope of the secant line for $a = 1$ and $h = 2$ and 1, respectively. Graph $y = f(x)$ and the two secant lines.

(B) Find and simplify the slope of the secant line for $a = 1$ and h any nonzero number.

(C) Find the limit of the expression in part B.

(D) Discuss possible interpretations of the limit in part C.

SOLUTION (A) For $a = 1$ and $h = 2$, the secant line goes through $(1, f(1)) = (1, 1)$ and $(3, f(3)) = (3, 9)$, and its slope is

$$\frac{f(1 + 2) - f(1)}{2} = \frac{3^2 - 1^2}{2} = 4$$

For $a = 1$ and $h = 1$, the secant line goes through $(1, f(1)) = (1, 1)$ and $(2, f(2)) = (2, 4)$, and its slope is

$$\frac{f(1 + 1) - f(1)}{1} = \frac{2^2 - 1^2}{1} = 3$$

The graphs of $y = f(x)$ and the two secant lines are shown in Figure 5.

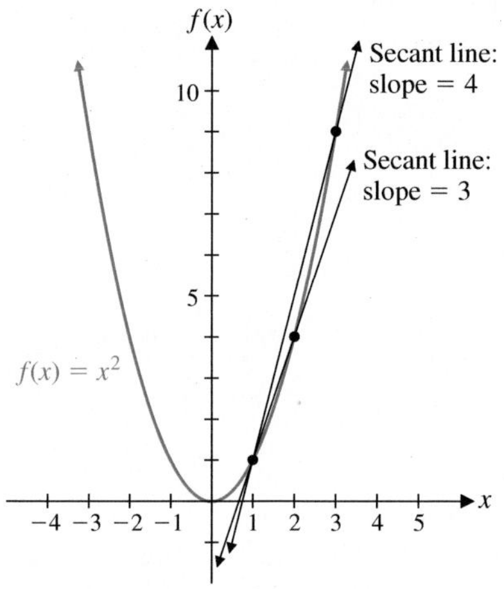

(B) For $a = 1$ and h any nonzero number, the secant line goes through $(1, f(1)) = (1, 1)$ and $(1 + h, f(1 + h)) = (1 + h, (1 + h)^2)$, and its slope is

$$\frac{f(1 + h) - f(1)}{h} = \frac{(1 + h)^2 - 1^2}{h} \qquad \text{Square the binomial.}$$

$$= \frac{1 + 2h + h^2 - 1}{h} \qquad \text{Combine like terms and factor the numerator.}$$

$$= \frac{h(2 + h)}{h} \qquad \text{Cancel.}$$

$$= 2 + h \qquad h \neq 0$$

(C) The limit of the secant line slope from part B is

$$\lim_{h \to 0} \frac{f(1 + h) - f(1)}{h} = \lim_{h \to 0} (2 + h)$$
$$= 2$$

(D) In part C, we saw that the limit of the slopes of the secant lines through the point $(1, f(1))$ is 2. If we graph the line through $(1, f(1))$ with slope 2 (Fig. 6), then this line is the limit of the secant lines. The slope obtained from the limit of slopes of secant lines is called the *slope of the graph* at $x = 1$. The line through the point $(1, f(1))$ with this slope is called the *tangent line*. We have solved another basic problem of calculus (see Fig. 1A on page 165).

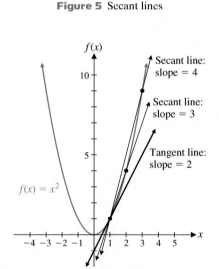

Figure 5 Secant lines

Figure 6 Tangent line

Matched Problem 3 Given $f(x) = x^2$,

(A) Find the slope of the secant line for $a = 2$ and $h = 2$ and 1, respectively.

(B) Find and simplify the slope of the secant line for $a = 2$ and h any nonzero number.

(C) Find the limit of the expression in part B.

(D) Find the slope of the graph and the slope of the tangent line at $a = 2$.

The ideas introduced in the preceding example are summarized next:

DEFINITION   Slope of a Graph

Given $y = f(x)$, the **slope of the graph** at the point $(a, f(a))$ is given by

$$\lim_{h \to 0} \frac{f(a + h) - f(a)}{h} \tag{3}$$

provided that the limit exists. The slope of the graph is also the **slope of the tangent line** at the point $(a, f(a))$.

CONCEPTUAL INSIGHT

If the function f is continuous at a, then

$$\lim_{h \to 0} f(a + h) = f(a)$$

and limit (3) will be a 0/0 indeterminate form. As we saw in Examples 2 and 3, evaluating this type of limit typically involves algebraic simplification.

From plane geometry, we know that a line tangent to a circle is a line that passes through one and only one point of the circle (Fig. 7A). Although this definition cannot be extended to graphs of functions in general, the visual relationship between graphs of functions and their tangent lines (Fig. 7B) is similar to the circle case. Limit (3) provides both a mathematically sound definition of a tangent line and a method for approximating the slope of the tangent line.

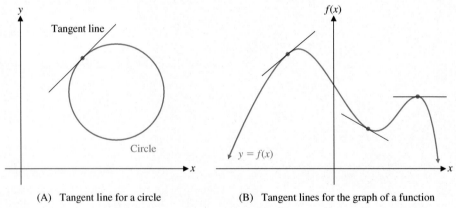

(A) Tangent line for a circle   (B) Tangent lines for the graph of a function

Figure 7

The Derivative

We have seen that the limit of a difference quotient can be interpreted as a rate of change, as a velocity, or as the slope of a tangent line. In addition, this limit provides solutions to two of the three basic problems stated at the beginning of the chapter. We are now ready to introduce some terms that refer to that limit. To follow customary practice, we use x in place of a and think of the difference quotient

$$\frac{f(x + h) - f(x)}{h}$$

as a function of h, with x held fixed as h tends to 0.

DEFINITION   The Derivative

For $y = f(x)$, we define the **derivative of f at x**, denoted by $f'(x)$, to be

$$f'(x) = \lim_{h \to 0} \frac{f(x + h) - f(x)}{h} \text{ if the limit exists}$$

If $f'(x)$ exists for each x in the open interval (a, b), then f is said to be **differentiable** over (a, b).

(Differentiability from the left or from the right is defined by using $h \to 0^-$ or $h \to 0^+$, respectively, in place of $h \to 0$ in the preceding definition.)

The process of finding the derivative of a function is called **differentiation**. The derivative of a function is obtained by **differentiating** the function.

SUMMARY   Interpretations of the Derivative

The derivative of a function f is a new function f'. The domain of f' is a subset of the domain of f. The derivative has various applications and interpretations, including the following:

1. *Slope of the tangent line.* For each x in the domain of f', $f'(x)$ is the slope of the line tangent to the graph of f at the point $(x, f(x))$.
2. *Instantaneous rate of change.* For each x in the domain of f', $f'(x)$ is the instantaneous rate of change of $y = f(x)$ with respect to x.
3. *Velocity.* If $f(x)$ is the position of a moving object at time x, then $v = f'(x)$ is the velocity of the object at that time.

Example 4 illustrates the **four-step process** that we use to find derivatives in this section. In subsequent sections, we develop rules for finding derivatives that do not involve limits. However, it is important that you master the limit process in order to fully comprehend and appreciate the various applications we will consider.

EXAMPLE 4   **Finding a Derivative** Find $f'(x)$, the derivative of f at x, for $f(x) = 4x - x^2$.

SOLUTION   To find $f'(x)$, we use a four-step process.

Step 1   Find $f(x + h)$.

$$f(x + h) = 4(x + h) - (x + h)^2$$
$$= 4x + 4h - x^2 - 2xh - h^2$$

Step 2   Find $f(x + h) - f(x)$.

$$f(x + h) - f(x) = 4x + 4h - x^2 - 2xh - h^2 - (4x - x^2)$$
$$= 4h - 2xh - h^2$$

Step 3   Find $\dfrac{f(x + h) - f(x)}{h}$.

$$\frac{f(x + h) - f(x)}{h} = \frac{4h - 2xh - h^2}{h} = \frac{h(4 - 2x - h)}{h}$$
$$= 4 - 2x - h, \quad h \neq 0$$

Step 4   Find $f'(x) = \lim\limits_{h \to 0} \dfrac{f(x + h) - f(x)}{h}$.

$$f'(x) = \lim_{h \to 0} \frac{f(x + h) - f(x)}{h} = \lim_{h \to 0}(4 - 2x - h) = 4 - 2x$$

So if $f(x) = 4x - x^2$, then $f'(x) = 4 - 2x$. The function f' is a new function derived from the function f.

Matched Problem 4 Find $f'(x)$, the derivative of f at x, for $f(x) = 8x - 2x^2$.

The four-step process used in Example 4 is summarized as follows for easy reference:

PROCEDURE The four-step process for finding the derivative of a function f:

Step 1 Find $f(x + h)$.

Step 2 Find $f(x + h) - f(x)$.

Step 3 Find $\dfrac{f(x + h) - f(x)}{h}$.

Step 4 Find $\lim\limits_{h \to 0} \dfrac{f(x + h) - f(x)}{h}$.

EXAMPLE 5 **Finding Tangent Line Slopes** In Example 4, we started with the function $f(x) = 4x - x^2$ and found the derivative of f at x to be $f'(x) = 4 - 2x$. So the slope of a line tangent to the graph of f at any point $(x, f(x))$ on the graph is

$$m = f'(x) = 4 - 2x$$

(A) Find the slope of the graph of f at $x = 0$, $x = 2$, and $x = 3$.

(B) Graph $y = f(x) = 4x - x^2$ and use the slopes found in part (A) to make a rough sketch of the lines tangent to the graph at $x = 0$, $x = 2$, and $x = 3$.

SOLUTION (A) Using $f'(x) = 4 - 2x$, we have

$$f'(0) = 4 - 2(0) = 4 \quad \textit{Slope at x = 0}$$
$$f'(2) = 4 - 2(2) = 0 \quad \textit{Slope at x = 2}$$
$$f'(3) = 4 - 2(3) = -2 \quad \textit{Slope at x = 3}$$

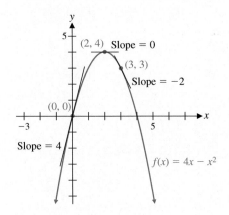

Matched Problem 5 In Matched Problem 4, we started with the function $f(x) = 8x - 2x^2$. Using the derivative found there,

(A) Find the slope of the graph of f at $x = 1$, $x = 2$, and $x = 4$.

(B) Graph $y = f(x) = 8x - 2x^2$, and use the slopes from part (A) to make a rough sketch of the lines tangent to the graph at $x = 1$, $x = 2$, and $x = 4$.

EXPLORE & DISCUSS 1

In Example 4, we found that the derivative of $f(x) = 4x - x^2$ is $f'(x) = 4 - 2x$. In Example 5, we graphed $f(x)$ and several tangent lines.

(A) Graph f and f' on the same set of axes.

(B) The graph of f' is a straight line. Is it a tangent line for the graph of f? Explain.

(C) Find the x intercept for the graph of f'. What is the slope of the line tangent to the graph of f for this value of x? Write a verbal description of the relationship between the slopes of the tangent lines of a function and the x intercepts of the derivative of the function.

EXAMPLE 6   **Finding a Derivative** Find $f'(x)$, the derivative of f at x, for $f(x) = \sqrt{x} + 2$.

SOLUTION   We use the four-step process to find $f'(x)$.

Step 1 Find $f(x + h)$.
$$f(x + h) = \sqrt{x + h} + 2$$

Step 2 Find $f(x + h) - f(x)$.
$$f(x + h) - f(x) = \sqrt{x + h} + 2 - (\sqrt{x} + 2) \quad \text{Combine like terms.}$$
$$= \sqrt{x + h} - \sqrt{x}$$

Step 3 Find $\dfrac{f(x + h) - f(x)}{h}$.

$$\frac{f(x + h) - f(x)}{h} = \frac{\sqrt{x + h} - \sqrt{x}}{h}$$
$$= \frac{\sqrt{x + h} - \sqrt{x}}{h} \cdot \frac{\sqrt{x + h} + \sqrt{x}}{\sqrt{x + h} + \sqrt{x}}$$
$$= \frac{x + h - x}{h(\sqrt{x + h} + \sqrt{x})}$$
$$= \frac{h}{h(\sqrt{x + h} + \sqrt{x})}$$
$$= \frac{1}{\sqrt{x + h} + \sqrt{x}} \quad h \neq 0$$

We rationalize the numerator (Appendix A, Section A-6) to change the form of this fraction. Combine like terms. Cancel.

Step 4 Find $f'(x) = \lim\limits_{h \to 0} \dfrac{f(x + h) - f(x)}{h}$.

$$\lim_{h \to 0} \frac{f(x + h) - f(x)}{h} = \lim_{h \to 0} \frac{1}{\sqrt{x + h} + \sqrt{x}}$$
$$= \frac{1}{\sqrt{x} + \sqrt{x}} = \frac{1}{2\sqrt{x}} \quad x > 0$$

So the derivative of $f(x) = \sqrt{x} + 2$ is $f'(x) = 1/(2\sqrt{x})$, a new function. The domain of f is $[0, \infty)$. Since $f'(0)$ is not defined, the domain of f' is $(0, \infty)$, a subset of the domain of f.

Matched Problem 6   Find $f'(x)$ for $f(x) = \sqrt{x} + 4$.

EXAMPLE 7   **Sales Analysis** A company's total sales (in millions of dollars) t months from now are given by $S(t) = \sqrt{t} + 2$. Find and interpret $S(25)$ and $S'(25)$. Use these results to estimate the total sales after 26 months and after 27 months.

SOLUTION The total sales function S has the same form as the function f in Example 6. Only the letters used to represent the function and the independent variable have been changed. It follows that S' and f' also have the same form:

$$S(t) = \sqrt{t} + 2 \qquad f(x) = \sqrt{x} + 2$$

$$S'(t) = \frac{1}{2\sqrt{t}} \qquad f'(x) = \frac{1}{2\sqrt{x}}$$

Evaluating S and S' at $t = 25$, we have

$$S(25) = \sqrt{25} + 2 = 7 \qquad S'(25) = \frac{1}{2\sqrt{25}} = 0.1$$

So 25 months from now, the total sales will be \$7 million and will be increasing at the rate of \$0.1 million (\$100,000) per month. If this instantaneous rate of change of sales remained constant, the sales would grow to \$7.1 million after 26 months, \$7.2 million after 27 months, and so on. Even though $S'(t)$ is not a constant function in this case, these values provide useful estimates of the total sales.

Matched Problem 7 A company's total sales (in millions of dollars) t months from now are given by $S(t) = \sqrt{t} + 4$. Find and interpret $S(12)$ and $S'(12)$. Use these results to estimate the total sales after 13 months and after 14 months. (Use the derivative found in Matched Problem 6.)

In Example 7, we can compare the estimates of total sales by using the derivative with the corresponding exact values of $S(t)$:

Exact values	Estimated values

$$S(26) = \sqrt{26} + 2 = 7.099\ldots \approx 7.1$$

$$S(27) = \sqrt{27} + 2 = 7.196\ldots \approx 7.2$$

For this function, the estimated values provide very good approximations to the exact values of $S(t)$. For other functions, the approximation might not be as accurate.

Using the instantaneous rate of change of a function at a point to estimate values of the function at nearby points is an important application of the derivative.

Nonexistence of the Derivative

The existence of a derivative at $x = a$ depends on the existence of a limit at $x = a$, that is, on the existence of

$$f'(a) = \lim_{h \to 0} \frac{f(a + h) - f(a)}{h} \tag{4}$$

If the limit does not exist at $x = a$, we say that the function f is **nondifferentiable at $x = a$**, or **$f'(a)$ does not exist.**

EXPLORE & DISCUSS 2

Let $f(x) = |x - 1|$.

(A) Graph f.

(B) Complete the following table:

h	-0.1	-0.01	-0.001	$\to 0 \leftarrow$	0.001	0.01	0.1
$\dfrac{f(1 + h) - f(1)}{h}$	?	?	?	$\to ? \leftarrow$	?	?	?

(C) Find the following limit if it exists:

$$\lim_{h \to 0} \frac{f(1 + h) - f(1)}{h}$$

(D) Use the results of parts (A)–(C) to discuss the existence of $f'(1)$.
(E) Repeat parts (A)–(D) for $\sqrt[3]{x-1}$.

How can we recognize the points on the graph of f where $f'(a)$ does not exist? It is impossible to describe all the ways that the limit of a difference quotient can fail to exist. However, we can illustrate some common situations where $f'(a)$ fails to exist (see Fig. 8):

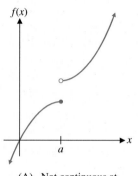
(A) Not continuous at $x = a$

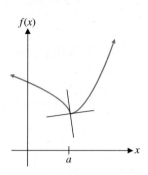
(B) Graph has sharp corner at $x = a$

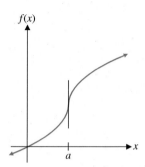
(C) Vertical tangent at $x = a$

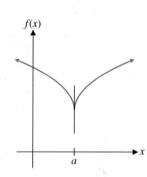
(D) Vertical tangent at $x = a$

Figure 8 The function f is nondifferentiable at $x = a$.

1. If the graph of f has a hole or a break at $x = a$, then $f'(a)$ does not exist (Fig. 8A).

2. If the graph of f has a sharp corner at $x = a$, then $f'(a)$ does not exist, and the graph has no tangent line at $x = a$ (Fig. 8B). (In Fig. 8B, the left- and right-hand derivatives exist but are not equal.)

3. If the graph of f has a vertical tangent line at $x = a$, then $f'(a)$ does not exist (Fig. 8C and D).

Exercises 3-4

A

In Problems 1 and 2, find the indicated quantity for $y = f(x) = 5 - x^2$ and interpret that quantity in terms of the following graph.

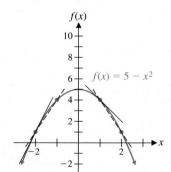

1. (A) $\dfrac{f(2) - f(1)}{2 - 1}$ (B) $\dfrac{f(1 + h) - f(1)}{h}$

   (C) $\lim\limits_{h \to 0} \dfrac{f(1 + h) - f(1)}{h}$

2. (A) $\dfrac{f(-1) - f(-2)}{-1 - (-2)}$

   (B) $\dfrac{f(-2 + h) - f(-2)}{h}$

   (C) $\lim\limits_{h \to 0} \dfrac{f(-2 + h) - f(-2)}{h}$

3. Find the indicated quantities for $f(x) = 3x^2$.

   (A) The average rate of change of $f(x)$ if x changes from 1 to 4.

   (B) The slope of the secant line through the points $(1, f(1))$ and $(4, f(4))$ on the graph of $y = f(x)$.

   (C) The slope of the secant line through the points $(1, f(1))$ and $(1 + h, f(1 + h))$, $h \neq 0$. Simplify your answer.

   (D) The slope of the graph at $(1, f(1))$.

   (E) The instantaneous rate of change of $y = f(x)$ with respect to x at $x = 1$.

   (F) The slope of the tangent line at $(1, f(1))$.

   (G) The equation of the tangent line at $(1, f(1))$.

4. Find the indicated quantities for $f(x) = 3x^2$.

(A) The average rate of change of $f(x)$ if x changes from 2 to 5.

(B) The slope of the secant line through the points $(2, f(2))$ and $(5, f(5))$ on the graph of $y = f(x)$.

(C) The slope of the secant line through the points $(2, f(2))$ and $(2 + h, f(2 + h))$, $h \neq 0$. Simplify your answer.

(D) The slope of the graph at $(2, f(2))$.

(E) The instantaneous rate of change of $y = f(x)$ with respect to x at $x = 2$.

(F) The slope of the tangent line at $(2, f(2))$.

(G) The equation of the tangent line at $(2, f(2))$.

In Problems 5–26, use the four-step process to find $f'(x)$ and then find $f'(1)$, $f'(2)$, and $f'(3)$.

5. $f(x) = -5$

6. $f(x) = 9$

7. $f(x) = 3x - 7$

8. $f(x) = 4 - 6x$

9. $f(x) = 2 - 3x^2$

10. $f(x) = 2x^2 + 8$

11. $f(x) = x^2 + 6x - 10$

12. $f(x) = x^2 + 4x + 7$

13. $f(x) = 2x^2 - 7x + 3$

14. $f(x) = 2x^2 + 5x + 1$

15. $f(x) = -x^2 + 4x - 9$

16. $f(x) = -x^2 + 9x - 2$

17. $f(x) = 2x^3 + 1$

18. $f(x) = -2x^3 + 5$

19. $f(x) = 4 + \dfrac{4}{x}$

20. $f(x) = \dfrac{6}{x} - 2$

21. $f(x) = 5 + 3\sqrt{x}$

22. $f(x) = 3 - 7\sqrt{x}$

23. $f(x) = 10\sqrt{x + 5}$

24. $f(x) = 16\sqrt{x + 9}$

25. $f(x) = \dfrac{3x}{x + 2}$

26. $f(x) = \dfrac{5x}{3 + x}$

B

Problems 27 and 28 refer to the graph of $y = f(x) = x^2 + x$ shown.

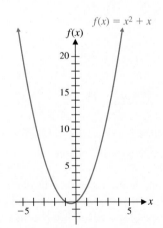

$f(x) = x^2 + x$

27. (A) Find the slope of the secant line joining $(1, f(1))$ and $(3, f(3))$.

(B) Find the slope of the secant line joining $(1, f(1))$ and $(1 + h, f(1 + h))$.

(C) Find the slope of the tangent line at $(1, f(1))$.

(D) Find the equation of the tangent line at $(1, f(1))$.

28. (A) Find the slope of the secant line joining $(2, f(2))$ and $(4, f(4))$.

(B) Find the slope of the secant line joining $(2, f(2))$ and $(2 + h, f(2 + h))$.

(C) Find the slope of the tangent line at $(2, f(2))$.

(D) Find the equation of the tangent line at $(2, f(2))$.

In Problems 29 and 30, suppose an object moves along the y axis so that its location is $y = f(x) = x^2 + x$ at time x (y is in meters and x is in seconds). Find

29. (A) The average velocity (the average rate of change of y with respect to x) for x changing from 1 to 3 seconds

(B) The average velocity for x changing from 1 to $1 + h$ seconds

(C) The instantaneous velocity at $x = 1$ second

30. (A) The average velocity (the average rate of change of y with respect to x) for x changing from 2 to 4 seconds

(B) The average velocity for x changing from 2 to $2 + h$ seconds

(C) The instantaneous velocity at $x = 2$ seconds

Problems 31–38 refer to the function F in the graph shown. Use the graph to determine whether $F'(x)$ exists at each indicated value of x.

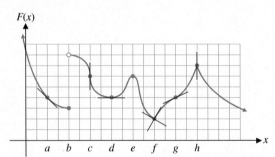

$F(x)$

31. $x = a$

32. $x = b$

33. $x = c$

34. $x = d$

35. $x = e$

36. $x = f$

37. $x = g$

38. $x = h$

39. Given $f(x) = x^2 - 4x$,

(A) Find $f'(x)$.

(B) Find the slopes of the lines tangent to the graph of f at $x = 0, 2$, and 4.

(C) Graph f and sketch in the tangent lines at $x = 0, 2$, and 4.

40. Given $f(x) = x^2 + 2x$,

(A) Find $f'(x)$.

(B) Find the slopes of the lines tangent to the graph of f at $x = -2, -1$, and 1.

(C) Graph f and sketch in the tangent lines at $x = -2, -1$, and 1.

41. If an object moves along a line so that it is at $y = f(x) = 4x^2 - 2x$ at time x (in seconds), find the instantaneous velocity function $v = f'(x)$ and find the velocity at times $x = 1, 3$, and 5 seconds (y is measured in feet).

42. Repeat Problem 41 with $f(x) = 8x^2 - 4x$.

43. Let $f(x) = x^2$, $g(x) = x^2 - 1$, and $h(x) = x^2 + 2$.

(A) How are the graphs of these functions related? How would you expect the derivatives of these functions to be related?

(B) Use the four-step process to find the derivative of $m(x) = x^2 + C$, where C is any real constant.

44. Let $f(x) = -x^2$, $g(x) = -x^2 - 1$, and $h(x) = -x^2 + 2$.

(A) How are the graphs of these functions related? How would you expect the derivatives of these functions to be related?

(B) Use the four-step process to find the derivative of $m(x) = -x^2 + C$, where C is any real constant.

In Problems 45–50, discuss the validity of each statement. If the statement is always true, explain why. If not, give a counterexample.

45. If $f(x) = C$ is a constant function, then $f'(x) = 0$.

46. If $f(x) = mx + b$ is a linear function, then $f'(x) = m$.

47. If a function f is continuous on the interval (a, b), then f is differentiable on (a, b).

48. If a function f is differentiable on the interval (a, b), then f is continuous on (a, b).

49. The average rate of change of a function f from $x = a$ to $x = a + h$ is less than the instantaneous rate of change at $x = a + \dfrac{h}{2}$.

50. If the graph of f has a sharp corner at $x = a$, then f is not continuous at $x = a$.

C

In Problems 51–54, sketch the graph of f and determine where f is nondifferentiable.

51. $f(x) = \begin{cases} 2x & \text{if } x < 1 \\ 2 & \text{if } x \geq 1 \end{cases}$ **52.** $f(x) = \begin{cases} 2x & \text{if } x < 2 \\ 6 - x & \text{if } x \geq 2 \end{cases}$

53. $f(x) = \begin{cases} x^2 + 1 & \text{if } x < 0 \\ 1 & \text{if } x \geq 0 \end{cases}$

54. $f(x) = \begin{cases} 2 - x^2 & \text{if } x \leq 0 \\ 2 & \text{if } x > 0 \end{cases}$

In Problems 55–60, determine whether f is differentiable at $x = 0$ by considering

$$\lim_{h \to 0} \frac{f(0 + h) - f(0)}{h}$$

55. $f(x) = |x|$ **56.** $f(x) = 1 - |x|$

57. $f(x) = x^{1/3}$ **58.** $f(x) = x^{2/3}$

59. $f(x) = \sqrt{1 - x^2}$ **60.** $f(x) = \sqrt{1 + x^2}$

61. A ball dropped from a balloon falls $y = 16x^2$ feet in x seconds. If the balloon is 576 feet above the ground when the ball is dropped, when does the ball hit the ground? What is the velocity of the ball at the instant it hits the ground?

62. Repeat Problem 61 if the balloon is 1,024 feet above the ground when the ball is dropped.

Applications

63. **Revenue.** The revenue (in dollars) from the sale of x infant car seats is given by

$$R(x) = 60x - 0.025x^2 \qquad 0 \leq x \leq 2{,}400$$

(A) Find the average change in revenue if production is changed from 1,000 car seats to 1,050 car seats.

(B) Use the four-step process to find $R'(x)$.

(C) Find the revenue and the instantaneous rate of change of revenue at a production level of 1,000 car seats, and write a brief verbal interpretation of these results.

64. **Profit.** The profit (in dollars) from the sale of x infant car seats is given by

$$P(x) = 45x - 0.025x^2 - 5{,}000 \qquad 0 \leq x \leq 2{,}400$$

(A) Find the average change in profit if production is changed from 800 car seats to 850 car seats.

(B) Use the four-step process to find $P'(x)$.

(C) Find the profit and the instantaneous rate of change of profit at a production level of 800 car seats, and write a brief verbal interpretation of these results.

65. **Sales analysis.** A company's total sales (in millions of dollars) t months from now are given by

$$S(t) = 2\sqrt{t + 10}$$

(A) Use the four-step process to find $S'(t)$.

(B) Find $S(15)$ and $S'(15)$. Write a brief verbal interpretation of these results.

(C) Use the results in part (B) to estimate the total sales after 16 months and after 17 months.

66. **Sales analysis.** A company's total sales (in millions of dollars) t months from now are given by

$$S(t) = 2\sqrt{t + 6}$$

(A) Use the four-step process to find $S'(t)$.

(B) Find $S(10)$ and $S'(10)$. Write a brief verbal interpretation of these results.

(C) Use the results in part (B) to estimate the total sales after 11 months and after 12 months.

67. **Mineral consumption.** The U.S. consumption of tungsten (in metric tons) is given approximately by

$$p(t) = 164t^2 + 161t + 12{,}326$$

where t is time in years and $t = 0$ corresponds to 2005.

(A) Use the four-step process to find $p'(t)$.

(B) Find the annual production in 2015 and the instantaneous rate of change of production in 2015, and write a brief verbal interpretation of these results.

68. **Mineral consumption.** The U.S. consumption of copper (in thousands of metric tons) is given approximately by

$$p(t) = 29t^2 - 258t + 4{,}658$$

where t is time in years and $t = 0$ corresponds to 2005.

(A) Use the four-step process to find $p'(t)$.

(B) Find the annual production in 2017 and the instantaneous rate of change of production in 2017, and write a brief verbal interpretation of these results.

69. Electricity consumption. Table 1 gives the retail sales of electricity (in billions of kilowatt-hours) for the residential and commercial sectors in the United States. (*Source:* Energy Information Administration)

Table 1   Electricity Sales

Year	Residential	Commercial
2000	1,192	1,055
2002	1,265	1,104
2004	1,292	1,230
2006	1,352	1,300
2008	1,379	1,352

(A) Let x represent time (in years) with $x = 0$ corresponding to 2000, and let y represent the corresponding residential sales. Enter the appropriate data set in a graphing calculator and find a quadratic regression equation for the data.

(B) If $y = R(x)$ denotes the regression equation found in part (A), find $R(20)$ and $R'(20)$, and write a brief verbal interpretation of these results. Round answers to the nearest tenth of a billion.

70. Electricity consumption. Refer to the data in Table 1.

(A) Let x represent time (in years) with $x = 0$ corresponding to 2000, and let y represent the corresponding commercial sales. Enter the appropriate data set in a graphing calculator and find a quadratic regression equation for the data.

(B) If $y = C(x)$ denotes the regression equation found in part (A), find $C(20)$ and $C'(20)$, and write a brief verbal interpretation of these results. Round answers to the nearest tenth of a billion.

71. Air pollution. The ozone level (in parts per billion) on a summer day in a metropolitan area is given by

$$P(t) = 80 + 12t - t^2$$

where t is time in hours and $t = 0$ corresponds to 9 A.M.

(A) Use the four-step process to find $P'(t)$.

(B) Find $P(3)$ and $P'(3)$. Write a brief verbal interpretation of these results.

72. Medicine. The body temperature (in degrees Fahrenheit) of a patient t hours after taking a fever-reducing drug is given by

$$F(t) = 98 + \frac{4}{t + 1}$$

(A) Use the four-step process to find $F'(t)$.

(B) Find $F(3)$ and $F'(3)$. Write a brief verbal interpretation of these results.

Answers to Matched Problems

1. (A) $-\$1,600$ (B) $-\$8$ per planter

2. (A) 48 ft/s
   (B) $32 + 16h$
   (C) 32 ft/s

3. (A) $6, 5$ (B) $4 + h$
   (C) 4   (D) Both are 4

4. $f'(x) = 8 - 4x$

5. (A) $f'(1) = 4, f'(2) = 0, f'(4) = -8$
   (B)

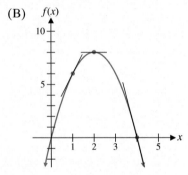

6. $f'(x) = 1/(2\sqrt{x + 4})$

7. $S(12) = 4$, $S'(12) = 0.125$; 12 months from now, the total sales will be $4 million and will be increasing at the rate of $0.125 million ($125,000) per month. The estimated total sales are $4.125 million after 13 months and $4.25 million after 14 months.

3-5   Basic Differentiation Properties

- Constant Function Rule
- Power Rule
- Constant Multiple Property
- Sum and Difference Properties
- Applications

In Section 3-4, we defined the derivative of f at x as

$$f'(x) = \lim_{h \to 0} \frac{f(x + h) - f(x)}{h}$$

if the limit exists, and we used this definition and a four-step process to find the derivatives of several functions. Now we want to develop some rules of differentiation. These rules will enable us to find the derivative of many functions without using the four-step process.

Before exploring these rules, we list some symbols that are often used to represent derivatives.

NOTATION   The Derivative

If $y = f(x)$, then

$$f'(x) \qquad y' \qquad \frac{dy}{dx}$$

all represent the derivative of f at x.

Each of these derivative symbols has its particular advantage in certain situations. All of them will become familiar to you after a little experience.

Constant Function Rule

If $f(x) = C$ is a constant function, then the four-step process can be used to show that $f'(x) = 0$. Therefore,

The derivative of any constant function is 0.

THEOREM 1   Constant Function Rule

If $y = f(x) = C$, then

$$f'(x) = 0$$

Also, $y' = 0$ and $dy/dx = 0$.

Note: When we write $C' = 0$ or $\dfrac{d}{dx}C = 0$, we mean that $y' = \dfrac{dy}{dx} = 0$ when $y = C$.

CONCEPTUAL INSIGHT

The graph of $f(x) = C$ is a horizontal line with slope 0 (Fig. 1), so we would expect that $f'(x) = 0$.

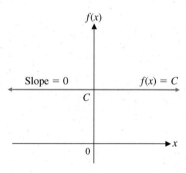

Figure 1

EXAMPLE 1   Differentiating Constant Functions

(A) If $f(x) = 3$, then $f'(x) = 0$.   (B) If $y = -1.4$, then $y' = 0$.

(C) If $y = \pi$, then $\dfrac{dy}{dx} = 0$.   (D) $\dfrac{d}{dx}23 = 0$

Matched Problem 1   Find

(A) $f'(x)$ for $f(x) = -24$ (B) y' for $y = 12$

(C) $\dfrac{dy}{dx}$ for $y = -\sqrt{7}$ (D) $\dfrac{d}{dx}(-\pi)$

Power Rule

A function of the form $f(x) = x^k$, where k is a real number, is called a **power function**. The following elementary functions are examples of power functions:

$$f(x) = x \qquad h(x) = x^2 \qquad m(x) = x^3$$
$$n(x) = \sqrt{x} \qquad p(x) = \sqrt[3]{x} \tag{1}$$

EXPLORE & DISCUSS 1

(A) It is clear that the functions f, h, and m in (1) are power functions. Explain why the functions n and p are also power functions.

(B) The domain of a power function depends on the power. Discuss the domain of each of the following power functions:

$$r(x) = x^4 \qquad s(x) = x^{-4} \qquad t(x) = x^{1/4}$$
$$u(x) = x^{-1/4} \qquad v(x) = x^{1/5} \qquad w(x) = x^{-1/5}$$

The definition of the derivative and the four-step process introduced in Section 3-4 can be used to find the derivatives of many power functions. For example, it can be shown that

$$\text{If} \quad f(x) = x^2, \quad \text{then} \quad f'(x) = 2x.$$
$$\text{If} \quad f(x) = x^3, \quad \text{then} \quad f'(x) = 3x^2.$$
$$\text{If} \quad f(x) = x^4, \quad \text{then} \quad f'(x) = 4x^3.$$
$$\text{If} \quad f(x) = x^5, \quad \text{then} \quad f'(x) = 5x^4.$$

Notice the pattern in these derivatives. In each case, the power in f becomes the coefficient in f' and the power in f' is 1 less than the power in f. In general, for any positive integer n,

$$\text{If} \quad f(x) = x^n, \quad \text{then} \quad f'(x) = nx^{n-1}. \tag{2}$$

In fact, more advanced techniques can be used to show that (2) holds for *any* real number n. We will assume this general result for the remainder of the book.

THEOREM 2   Power Rule

If $y = f(x) = x^n$, where n is a real number, then

$$f'(x) = nx^{n-1}$$

Also, $y' = nx^{n-1}$ and $dy/dx = nx^{n-1}$.

EXAMPLE 2

Differentiating Power Functions

(A) If $f(x) = x^5$, then $f'(x) = 5x^{5-1} = 5x^4$.

(B) If $y = x^{25}$, then $y' = 25x^{25-1} = 25x^{24}$.

(C) If $y = t^{-3}$, then $\dfrac{dy}{dt} = -3t^{-3-1} = -3t^{-4} = -\dfrac{3}{t^4}$.

(D) $\dfrac{d}{dx}x^{5/3} = \dfrac{5}{3}x^{(5/3)-1} = \dfrac{5}{3}x^{2/3}$.

Matched Problem 2

Find

(A) $f'(x)$ for $f(x) = x^6$

(B) y' for $y = x^{30}$

(C) $\dfrac{dy}{dt}$ for $y = t^{-2}$

(D) $\dfrac{d}{dx}x^{3/2}$

In some cases, properties of exponents must be used to rewrite an expression before the power rule is applied.

EXAMPLE 3   **Differentiating Power Functions**

(A) If $f(x) = 1/x^4$, we can write $f(x) = x^{-4}$ and

$$f'(x) = -4x^{-4-1} = -4x^{-5}, \quad \text{or} \quad \frac{-4}{x^5}$$

(B) If $y = \sqrt{u}$, we can write $y = u^{1/2}$ and

$$y' = \frac{1}{2}u^{(1/2)-1} = \frac{1}{2}u^{-1/2}, \quad \text{or} \quad \frac{1}{2\sqrt{u}}$$

(C) $\dfrac{d}{dx}\dfrac{1}{\sqrt[3]{x}} = \dfrac{d}{dx}x^{-1/3} = -\dfrac{1}{3}x^{(-1/3)-1} = -\dfrac{1}{3}x^{-4/3}, \text{or} \dfrac{-1}{3\sqrt[3]{x^4}}$

Matched Problem 3   Find

(A) $f'(x)$ for $f(x) = \dfrac{1}{x}$ (B) y' for $y = \sqrt[3]{u^2}$ (C) $\dfrac{d}{dx}\dfrac{1}{\sqrt{x}}$

Constant Multiple Property

Let $f(x) = ku(x)$, where k is a constant and u is differentiable at x. Using the four-step process, we have the following:

Step 1 $f(x + h) = ku(x + h)$

Step 2 $f(x + h) - f(x) = ku(x + h) - ku(x) = k[u(x + h) - u(x)]$

Step 3 $\dfrac{f(x + h) - f(x)}{h} = \dfrac{k[u(x + h) - u(x)]}{h} = k\left[\dfrac{u(x + h) - u(x)}{h}\right]$

Step 4 $f'(x) = \lim\limits_{h \to 0} \dfrac{f(x + h) - f(x)}{h}$

$\qquad\qquad = \lim\limits_{h \to 0} k\left[\dfrac{u(x + h) - u(x)}{h}\right] \qquad \lim\limits_{x \to c} kg(x) = k \lim\limits_{x \to c} g(x)$

$\qquad\qquad = k \lim\limits_{h \to 0}\left[\dfrac{u(x + h) - u(x)}{h}\right] \qquad \text{Definition of } u'(x)$

$\qquad\qquad = ku'(x)$

Therefore,

The derivative of a constant times a differentiable function is the constant times the derivative of the function.

THEOREM 3   Constant Multiple Property

If $y = f(x) = ku(x)$, then

$$f'(x) = ku'(x)$$

Also,

$$y' = ku' \qquad \frac{dy}{dx} = k\frac{du}{dx}$$

EXAMPLE 4 **Differentiating a Constant Times a Function**

(A) If $f(x) = 3x^2$, then $f'(x) \boxed{= 3 \cdot 2x^{2-1}} = 6x$.

(B) If $y = \dfrac{t^3}{6} = \dfrac{1}{6}t^3$, then $\dfrac{dy}{dt} \boxed{= \dfrac{1}{6} \cdot 3t^{3-1}} = \dfrac{1}{2}t^2$.

(C) If $y = \dfrac{1}{2x^4} = \dfrac{1}{2}x^{-4}$, then $y' \boxed{= \dfrac{1}{2}(-4x^{-4-1})} = -2x^{-5}$, or $\dfrac{-2}{x^5}$.

(D) $\dfrac{d}{dx}\dfrac{0.4}{\sqrt{x^3}} = \dfrac{d}{dx}\dfrac{0.4}{x^{3/2}} = \dfrac{d}{dx}0.4x^{-3/2} \boxed{= 0.4\left[-\dfrac{3}{2}x^{(-3/2)-1}\right]}$

$$= -0.6x^{-5/2}, \quad \text{or} \quad -\dfrac{0.6}{\sqrt{x^5}}$$

Matched Problem 4 Find

(A) $f'(x)$ for $f(x) = 4x^5$

(B) $\dfrac{dy}{dt}$ for $y = \dfrac{t^4}{12}$

(C) y' for $y = \dfrac{1}{3x^3}$

(D) $\dfrac{d}{dx}\dfrac{0.9}{\sqrt[3]{x}}$

Sum and Difference Properties

Let $f(x) = u(x) + v(x)$, where $u'(x)$ and $v'(x)$ exist. Using the four-step process, we have the following:

Step 1 $f(x + h) = u(x + h) + v(x + h)$

Step 2 $f(x + h) - f(x) = u(x + h) + v(x + h) - [u(x) + v(x)]$

$$= u(x + h) - u(x) + v(x + h) - v(x)$$

Step 3 $\dfrac{f(x + h) - f(x)}{h} = \dfrac{u(x + h) - u(x) + v(x + h) - v(x)}{h}$

$$= \dfrac{u(x + h) - u(x)}{h} + \dfrac{v(x + h) - v(x)}{h}$$

Step 4 $f'(x) = \lim\limits_{h \to 0} \dfrac{f(x + h) - f(x)}{h}$

$$= \lim\limits_{h \to 0}\left[\dfrac{u(x + h) - u(x)}{h} + \dfrac{v(x + h) - v(x)}{h}\right]$$

$$\lim\limits_{x \to c}[g(x) + h(x)] = \lim\limits_{x \to c} g(x) + \lim\limits_{x \to c} h(x)$$

$$= \lim\limits_{h \to 0}\dfrac{u(x + h) - u(x)}{h} + \lim\limits_{h \to 0}\dfrac{v(x + h) - v(x)}{h}$$

$$= u'(x) + v'(x)$$

Therefore,

> **The derivative of the sum of two differentiable functions is the sum of the derivatives of the functions.**

Similarly, we can show that

> **The derivative of the difference of two differentiable functions is the difference of the derivatives of the functions.**

Together, we have the **sum and difference property** for differentiation:

THEOREM 4   Sum and Difference Property

If $y = f(x) = u(x) \pm v(x)$, then

$$f'(x) = u'(x) \pm v'(x)$$

Also,

$$y' = u' \pm v' \qquad \frac{dy}{dx} = \frac{du}{dx} \pm \frac{dv}{dx}$$

Note: This rule generalizes to the sum and difference of any given number of functions.

With Theorems 1 through 4, we can compute the derivatives of all polynomials and a variety of other functions.

EXAMPLE 5   **Differentiating Sums and Differences**

(A) If $f(x) = 3x^2 + 2x$, then

$$f'(x) \;\boxed{= (3x^2)' + (2x)' = 3(2x) + 2(1)} = 6x + 2$$

(B) If $y = 4 + 2x^3 - 3x^{-1}$, then

$$y' \;\boxed{= (4)' + (2x^3)' - (3x^{-1})' = 0 + 2(3x^2) - 3(-1)x^{-2}} = 6x^2 + 3x^{-2}$$

(C) If $y = \sqrt[3]{w} - 3w$, then

$$\frac{dy}{dw} = \frac{d}{dw}w^{1/3} - \frac{d}{dw}3w = \frac{1}{3}w^{-2/3} - 3 = \frac{1}{3w^{2/3}} - 3$$

(D)

$$\frac{d}{dx}\left(\frac{5}{3x^2} - \frac{2}{x^4} + \frac{x^3}{9}\right) \;\boxed{= \frac{d}{dx}\frac{5}{3}x^{-2} - \frac{d}{dx}2x^{-4} + \frac{d}{dx}\frac{1}{9}x^3}$$

$$= \frac{5}{3}(-2)x^{-3} - 2(-4)x^{-5} + \frac{1}{9}\cdot 3x^2$$

$$= -\frac{10}{3x^3} + \frac{8}{x^5} + \frac{1}{3}x^2$$

Matched Problem 5   Find

(A) $f'(x)$ for $f(x) = 3x^4 - 2x^3 + x^2 - 5x + 7$

(B) y' for $y = 3 - 7x^{-2}$

(C) $\dfrac{dy}{dv}$ for $y = 5v^3 - \sqrt[4]{v}$

(D) $\dfrac{d}{dx}\left(-\dfrac{3}{4x} + \dfrac{4}{x^3} - \dfrac{x^4}{8}\right)$

Applications

EXAMPLE 6   **Instantaneous Velocity** An object moves along the y axis (marked in feet) so that its position at time x (in seconds) is

$$f(x) = x^3 - 6x^2 + 9x$$

(A) Find the instantaneous velocity function v.

(B) Find the velocity at $x = 2$ and $x = 5$ seconds.

(C) Find the time(s) when the velocity is 0.

SOLUTION

(A) $v = f'(x) \boxed{= (x^3)' - (6x^2)' + (9x)'} = 3x^2 - 12x + 9$

(B) $f'(2) = 3(2)^2 - 12(2) + 9 = -3$ feet per second

$f'(5) = 3(5)^2 - 12(5) + 9 = 24$ feet per second

(C) $v = f'(x) = 3x^2 - 12x + 9 = 0$ Factor 3 out of each term.

$3(x^2 - 4x + 3) = 0$ Factor the quadratic term.

$3(x - 1)(x - 3) = 0$ Use the zero property.

$x = 1, 3$

So, $v = 0$ at $x = 1$ and $x = 3$ seconds.

Matched Problem 6   Repeat Example 6 for $f(x) = x^3 - 15x^2 + 72x$.

EXAMPLE 7   **Tangents** Let $f(x) = x^4 - 6x^2 + 10$.

(A) Find $f'(x)$.

(B) Find the equation of the tangent line at $x = 1$.

(C) Find the values of x where the tangent line is horizontal.

SOLUTION

(A) $f'(x) \boxed{= (x^4)' - (6x^2)' + (10)'}$

$= 4x^3 - 12x$

(B) $y - y_1 = m(x - x_1)$ $y_1 = f(x_1) = f(1) = (1)^4 - 6(1)^2 + 10 = 5$

$y - 5 = -8(x - 1)$ $m = f'(x_1) = f'(1) = 4(1)^3 - 12(1) = -8$

$y = -8x + 13$ Tangent line at $x = 1$

(C) Since a horizontal line has 0 slope, we must solve $f'(x) = 0$ for x:

$f'(x) = 4x^3 - 12x = 0$ Factor $4x$ out of each term.

$4x(x^2 - 3) = 0$ Factor the difference of two squares.

$4x(x + \sqrt{3})(x - \sqrt{3}) = 0$ Use the zero property.

$x = 0, -\sqrt{3}, \sqrt{3}$

Matched Problem 7   Repeat Example 7 for $f(x) = x^4 - 8x^3 + 7$.

Exercises 3-5

A

Find the indicated derivatives in Problems 1–18.

1. $f'(x)$ for $f(x) = 7$

2. $\dfrac{d}{dx}3$

3. $\dfrac{dy}{dx}$ for $y = x^9$

4. y' for $y = x^6$

5. $\dfrac{d}{dx}x^3$

6. $g'(x)$ for $g(x) = x^5$

7. y' for $y = x^{-4}$

8. $\dfrac{dy}{dx}$ for $y = x^{-8}$

9. $g'(x)$ for $g(x) = x^{8/3}$

10. $f'(x)$ for $f(x) = x^{9/2}$

11. $\dfrac{dy}{dx}$ for $y = \dfrac{1}{x^{10}}$

12. y' for $y = \dfrac{1}{x^{12}}$

13. $f'(x)$ for $f(x) = 5x^2$

14. $\dfrac{d}{dx}(-2x^3)$

15. y' for $y = 0.4x^7$

16. $f'(x)$ for $f(x) = 0.8x^4$

17. $\dfrac{d}{dx}\left(\dfrac{x^3}{18}\right)$

18. $\dfrac{dy}{dx}$ for $y = \dfrac{x^5}{25}$

Problems 19–24 refer to functions f and g that satisfy $f'(2) = 3$ and $g'(2) = -1$. In each problem, find $h'(2)$ for the indicated function h.

19. $h(x) = 4f(x)$

20. $h(x) = 5g(x)$

21. $h(x) = f(x) + g(x)$

22. $h(x) = g(x) - f(x)$

23. $h(x) = 2f(x) - 3g(x) + 7$

24. $h(x) = -4f(x) + 5g(x) - 9$

B

Find the indicated derivatives in Problems 25–48.

25. $\dfrac{d}{dx}(2x - 5)$

26. $\dfrac{d}{dx}(-4x + 9)$

27. $f'(t)$ if $f(t) = 2t^2 - 3t + 1$

28. $\dfrac{dy}{dt}$ if $y = 2 + 5t - 8t^3$

29. y' for $y = 5x^{-2} + 9x^{-1}$

30. $g'(x)$ if $g(x) = 5x^{-7} - 2x^{-4}$

31. $\dfrac{d}{du}(5u^{0.3} - 4u^{2.2})$

32. $\dfrac{d}{du}(2u^{4.5} - 3.1u + 13.2)$

33. $h'(t)$ if $h(t) = 2.1 + 0.5t - 1.1t^3$

34. $F'(t)$ if $F(t) = 0.2t^3 - 3.1t + 13.2$

35. y' if $y = \dfrac{2}{5x^4}$

36. w' if $w = \dfrac{7}{5u^2}$

37. $\dfrac{d}{dx}\left(\dfrac{3x^2}{2} - \dfrac{7}{5x^2}\right)$

38. $\dfrac{d}{dx}\left(\dfrac{5x^3}{4} - \dfrac{2}{5x^3}\right)$

39. $G'(w)$ if $G(w) = \dfrac{5}{9w^4} + 5\sqrt[3]{w}$

40. $H'(w)$ if $H(w) = \dfrac{5}{w^6} - 2\sqrt{w}$

41. $\dfrac{d}{du}(3u^{2/3} - 5u^{1/3})$

42. $\dfrac{d}{du}(8u^{3/4} + 4u^{-1/4})$

43. $h'(t)$ if $h(t) = \dfrac{3}{t^{3/5}} - \dfrac{6}{t^{1/2}}$

44. $F'(t)$ if $F(t) = \dfrac{5}{t^{1/5}} - \dfrac{8}{t^{3/2}}$

45. y' if $y = \dfrac{1}{\sqrt[3]{x}}$

46. w' if $w = \dfrac{10}{\sqrt[5]{u}}$

47. $\dfrac{d}{dx}\left(\dfrac{1.2}{\sqrt{x}} - 3.2x^{-2} + x\right)$

48. $\dfrac{d}{dx}\left(2.8x^{-3} - \dfrac{0.6}{\sqrt[3]{x^2}} + 7\right)$

For Problems 49–52, find

(A) $f'(x)$

(B) The slope of the graph of f at $x = 2$ and $x = 4$

(C) The equations of the tangent lines at $x = 2$ and $x = 4$

(D) The value(s) of x where the tangent line is horizontal

49. $f(x) = 6x - x^2$

50. $f(x) = 2x^2 + 8x$

51. $f(x) = 3x^4 - 6x^2 - 7$

52. $f(x) = x^4 - 32x^2 + 10$

If an object moves along the y axis (marked in feet) so that its position at time x (in seconds) is given by the indicated functions in Problems 53–56, find

(A) The instantaneous velocity function $v = f'(x)$

(B) The velocity when $x = 0$ and $x = 3$ seconds

(C) The time(s) when $v = 0$

53. $f(x) = 176x - 16x^2$

54. $f(x) = 80x - 10x^2$

55. $f(x) = x^3 - 9x^2 + 15x$

56. $f(x) = x^3 - 9x^2 + 24x$

Problems 57–64 require the use of a graphing calculator. For each problem, find $f'(x)$ and approximate (to four decimal places) the value(s) of x where the graph of f has a horizontal tangent line.

57. $f(x) = x^2 - 3x - 4\sqrt{x}$

58. $f(x) = x^2 + x - 10\sqrt{x}$

59. $f(x) = 3\sqrt[3]{x^4} - 1.5x^2 - 3x$

60. $f(x) = 3\sqrt[3]{x^4} - 2x^2 + 4x$

61. $f(x) = 0.05x^4 + 0.1x^3 - 1.5x^2 - 1.6x + 3$

62. $f(x) = 0.02x^4 - 0.06x^3 - 0.78x^2 + 0.94x + 2.2$

63. $f(x) = 0.2x^4 - 3.12x^3 + 16.25x^2 - 28.25x + 7.5$

64. $f(x) = 0.25x^4 - 2.6x^3 + 8.1x^2 - 10x + 9$

65. Let $f(x) = ax^2 + bx + c, a \neq 0$. Recall that the graph of $y = f(x)$ is a parabola. Use the derivative $f'(x)$ to derive a formula for the x coordinate of the vertex of this parabola.

66. Now that you know how to find derivatives, explain why it is no longer necessary for you to memorize the formula for the x coordinate of the vertex of a parabola.

67. Give an example of a cubic polynomial function that has

(A) No horizontal tangents

(B) One horizontal tangent

(C) Two horizontal tangents

68. Can a cubic polynomial function have more than two horizontal tangents? Explain.

C

Find the indicated derivatives in Problems 69–76.

69. $f'(x)$ if $f(x) = (2x - 1)^2$

70. y' if $y = (2x - 5)^2$

71. $\dfrac{d}{dx} \dfrac{10x + 20}{x}$

72. $\dfrac{dy}{dx}$ if $y = \dfrac{x^2 + 25}{x^2}$

73. $\dfrac{dy}{dx}$ if $y = \dfrac{3x - 4}{12x^2}$

74. $f'(x)$ if $f(x) = \dfrac{2x^5 - 4x^3 + 2x}{x^3}$

In Problems 75-80, discuss the validity of each statement. If the statement is always true, explain why. If not, give a counterexample.

75. The derivative of a sum is the sum of the derivatives.

76. The derivative of a difference is the difference of the derivatives.

77. The derivative of a product is the product of the derivatives.

78. The derivative of a quotient is the quotient of the derivatives.

79. The derivative of a constant is 0.

80. The derivative of a constant times a function is 0.

Applications

81. Sales analysis. A company's total sales (in millions of dollars) t months from now are given by

$$S(t) = 0.03t^3 + 0.5t^2 + 2t + 3$$

(A) Find $S'(t)$.

(B) Find $S(5)$ and $S'(5)$ (to two decimal places). Write a brief verbal interpretation of these results.

(C) Find $S(10)$ and $S'(10)$ (to two decimal places). Write a brief verbal interpretation of these results.

82. Sales analysis. A company's total sales (in millions of dollars) t months from now are given by

$$S(t) = 0.015t^4 + 0.4t^3 + 3.4t^2 + 10t - 3$$

(A) Find $S'(t)$.

(B) Find $S(4)$ and $S'(4)$ (to two decimal places). Write a brief verbal interpretation of these results.

(C) Find $S(8)$ and $S'(8)$ (to two decimal places). Write a brief verbal interpretation of these results.

83. Advertising. A marine manufacturer will sell $N(x)$ power boats after spending $\$x$ thousand on advertising, as given by

$$N(x) = 1,000 - \frac{3,780}{x} \qquad 5 \le x \le 30$$

(see figure).

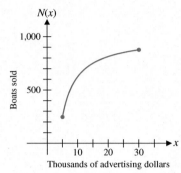

Figure for 83

(A) Find $N'(x)$.

(B) Find $N'(10)$ and $N'(20)$. Write a brief verbal interpretation of these results.

84. Price–demand equation. Suppose that, in a given gourmet food store, people are willing to buy x pounds of chocolate candy per day at $\$p$ per quarter pound, as given by the price–demand equation

$$x = 10 + \frac{180}{p} \qquad 2 \le p \le 10$$

This function is graphed in the figure. Find the demand and the instantaneous rate of change of demand with respect to price when the price is $\$5$. Write a brief verbal interpretation of these results.

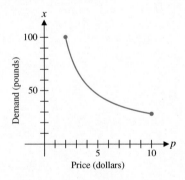

Figure for 84

85. College enrollment. The percentages of male high-school graduates who enrolled in college are given in the second column of Table 1.

Table 1 College enrollment percentages

Year	Male	Female
1970	55.2	48.5
1980	46.7	51.8
1990	58.0	62.2
2000	59.9	66.2
2006	65.8	66.1

(A) Let x represent time (in years) since 1970, and let y represent the corresponding percentage of male high-school graduates who enrolled in college. Enter the data in a graphing calculator and find a cubic regression equation for the data.

(B) If $y = M(x)$ denotes the regression equation found in part A, find $M(46)$ and $M'(46)$ (to the nearest tenth), and write a brief verbal interpretation of these results.

86. College enrollment. The percentages of female high-school graduates who enrolled in college are given in the third column of Table 1.

(A) Let x represent time (in years) since 1970, and let y represent the corresponding percentage of female high-school graduates who enrolled in college. Enter the data in a graphing calculator and find a cubic regression equation for the data.

(B) If $y = F(x)$ denotes the regression equation found in part A, find $F(46)$ and $F'(46)$ (to the nearest tenth), and write a brief verbal interpretation of these results.

87. Medicine. A person x inches tall has a pulse rate of y beats per minute, as given approximately by

$$y = 590x^{-1/2} \qquad 30 \le x \le 75$$

What is the instantaneous rate of change of pulse rate at the

(A) 36-inch level?

(B) 64-inch level?

88. Ecology. A coal-burning electrical generating plant emits sulfur dioxide into the surrounding air. The concentration $C(x)$, in parts per million, is given approximately by

$$C(x) = \frac{0.1}{x^2}$$

where x is the distance from the plant in miles. Find the instantaneous rate of change of concentration at

(A) $x = 1$ mile

(B) $x = 2$ miles

89. Learning. Suppose that a person learns y items in x hours, as given by

$$y = 50\sqrt{x} \qquad 0 \le x \le 9$$

(see figure). Find the rate of learning at the end of

(A) 1 hour   (B) 9 hours

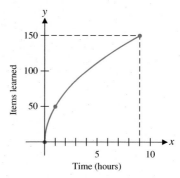

Figure for 89

90. Learning. If a person learns y items in x hours, as given by

$$y = 21\sqrt[3]{x^2} \qquad 0 \le x \le 8$$

find the rate of learning at the end of

(A) 1 hour   (B) 8 hours

Answers to Matched Problems

1. All are 0.

2. (A) $6x^5$ (B) $30x^{29}$
  (C) $-2t^{-3} = -2/t^3$ (D) $\frac{3}{2}x^{1/2}$

3. (A) $-x^{-2}$, or $-1/x^2$ (B) $\frac{2}{3}u^{-1/3}$, or $2/(3\sqrt[3]{u})$
  (C) $-\frac{1}{2}x^{-3/2}$, or $-1/(2\sqrt{x^3})$

4. (A) $20x^4$ (B) $t^3/3$
  (C) $-x^{-4}$, or $-1/x^4$ (D) $-0.3x^{-4/3}$, or $-0.3/\sqrt[3]{x^4}$

5. (A) $12x^3 - 6x^2 + 2x - 5$
  (B) $14x^{-3}$, or $14/x^3$
  (C) $15v^2 - \frac{1}{4}v^{-3/4}$, or $15v^2 - 1/(4v^{3/4})$
  (D) $3/(4x^2) - (12/x^4) - (x^3/2)$

6. (A) $v = 3x^2 - 30x + 72$
  (B) $f'(2) = 24$ ft/s; $f'(5) = -3$ ft/s
  (C) $x = 4$ and $x = 6$ seconds

7. (A) $f'(x) = 4x^3 - 24x^2$
  (B) $y = -20x + 20$
  (C) $x = 0$ and $x = 6$

3-6 Differentials

- Increments
- Differentials
- Approximations Using Differentials

In this section, we introduce increments and differentials. Increments are useful and they provide an alternative notation for defining the derivative. Differentials are often easier to compute than increments and can be used to approximate increments.

Increments

In Section 3-4, we defined the derivative of f at x as the limit of the difference quotient

$$f'(x) = \lim_{h \to 0} \frac{f(x + h) - f(x)}{h}$$

We considered various interpretations of this limit, including slope, velocity, and instantaneous rate of change. Increment notation enables us to interpret the numerator and denominator of the difference quotient separately.

Given $y = f(x) = x^3$, if x changes from 2 to 2.1, then y will change from $y = f(2) = 2^3 = 8$ to $y = f(2.1) = 2.1^3 = 9.261$. The change in x is called the *increment in x* and is denoted by Δx (read as "delta x").* Similarly, the change in y is called the *increment in y* and is denoted by Δy. In terms of the given example, we write

$$\Delta x = 2.1 - 2 = 0.1 \qquad \textit{Change in x}$$
$$\Delta y = f(2.1) - f(2) \qquad \textit{f(x) = x}^3$$
$$= 2.1^3 - 2^3 \qquad \textit{Use a calculator.}$$
$$= 9.261 - 8$$
$$= 1.261 \qquad \textit{Corresponding change in y}$$

CONCEPTUAL INSIGHT

The symbol Δx does not represent the product of Δ and x but is the symbol for a single quantity: the *change in x*. Likewise, the symbol Δy represents a single quantity: the *change in y*.

DEFINITION   Increments

For $y = f(x)$, $\quad \Delta x = x_2 - x_1$, $\quad$ so $\qquad x_2 = x_1 + \Delta x$, $\quad$ and

$$\Delta y = y_2 - y_1$$
$$= f(x_2) - f(x_1)$$
$$= f(x_1 + \Delta x) - f(x_1)$$

Δy represents the change in y corresponding to a change Δx in x.
Δx can be either positive or negative.

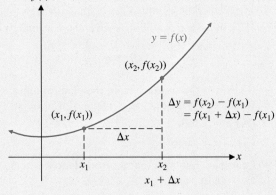

[**Note:** Δy depends on the function f, the input x_1, and the increment Δx.]

EXAMPLE 1   **Increments** Given the function $y = f(x) = \dfrac{x^2}{2}$,

(A) Find Δx, Δy, and $\Delta y/\Delta x$ for $x_1 = 1$ and $x_2 = 2$.

(B) Find $\dfrac{f(x_1 + \Delta x) - f(x_1)}{\Delta x}$ for $x_1 = 1$ and $\Delta x = 2$.

SOLUTION   (A) $\Delta x = x_2 - x_1 = 2 - 1 = 1$
$$\Delta y = f(x_2) - f(x_1)$$
$$= f(2) - f(1) = \frac{4}{2} - \frac{1}{2} = \frac{3}{2}$$

$$\frac{\Delta y}{\Delta x} = \frac{f(x_2) - f(x_1)}{x_2 - x_1} = \frac{\frac{3}{2}}{1} = \frac{3}{2}$$

*Δ is the symbol for the Greek letter delta.

(B) $\dfrac{f(x_1 + \Delta x) - f(x_1)}{\Delta x} = \dfrac{f(1 + 2) - f(1)}{2}$

$= \dfrac{f(3) - f(1)}{2} = \dfrac{\frac{9}{2} - \frac{1}{2}}{2} = \dfrac{4}{2} = 2$

Matched Problem 1 Given the function $y = f(x) = x^2 + 1$,

(A) Find Δx, Δy, and $\Delta y / \Delta x$ for $x_1 = 2$ and $x_2 = 3$.

(B) Find $\dfrac{f(x_1 + \Delta x) - f(x_1)}{\Delta x}$ for $x_1 = 1$ and $\Delta x = 2$.

In Example 1, we observe another notation for the difference quotient

$$\frac{f(x + h) - f(x)}{h} \tag{1}$$

It is common to refer to h, the change in x, as Δx. Then the difference quotient (1) takes on the form

$$\frac{f(x + \Delta x) - f(x)}{\Delta x} \qquad \text{or} \qquad \frac{\Delta y}{\Delta x} \qquad \Delta y = f(x + \Delta x) - f(x)$$

and the derivative is defined by

$$f'(x) = \lim_{\Delta x \to 0} \frac{f(x + \Delta x) - f(x)}{\Delta x}$$

or

$$f'(x) = \lim_{\Delta x \to 0} \frac{\Delta y}{\Delta x} \tag{2}$$

if the limit exists.

EXPLORE & DISCUSS 1 Suppose that $y = f(x)$ defines a function whose domain is the set of all real numbers. If every increment Δy is equal to 0, then what is the range of f?

Differentials

Assume that the limit in equation (2) exists. Then, for small Δx, the difference quotient $\Delta y / \Delta x$ provides a good approximation for $f'(x)$. Also, $f'(x)$ provides a good approximation for $\Delta y / \Delta x$. We write

$$\frac{\Delta y}{\Delta x} \approx f'(x) \qquad \Delta x \text{ is small, but} \neq 0 \tag{3}$$

Multiplying both sides of (3) by Δx gives us

$$\Delta y \approx f'(x)\,\Delta x \qquad \Delta x \text{ is small, but} \neq 0 \tag{4}$$

From equation (4), we see that $f'(x)\Delta x$ provides a good approximation for Δy when Δx is small.

Because of the practical and theoretical importance of $f'(x)\,\Delta x$, we give it the special name **differential** and represent it with the special symbol *dy* or *df*:

$$dy = f'(x)\Delta x \qquad \text{or} \qquad df = f'(x)\Delta x$$

For example,

$$d(2x^3) = (2x^3)'\,\Delta x = 6x^2\,\Delta x$$

$$d(x) = (x)'\,\Delta x = 1\,\Delta x = \Delta x$$

In the second example, we usually drop the parentheses in $d(x)$ and simply write

$$dx = \Delta x$$

In summary, we have the following:

> **DEFINITION Differentials**
>
> If $y = f(x)$ defines a differentiable function, then the **differential dy, or df,** is defined as the product of $f'(x)$ and dx, where $dx = \Delta x$. Symbolically,
>
> $$dy = f'(x)\,dx, \qquad \text{or} \qquad df = f'(x)\,dx$$
>
> where
>
> $$dx = \Delta x$$
>
> **Note:** The differential dy (or df) is actually a function involving two independent variables, x and dx. A change in either one or both will affect dy (or df).

EXAMPLE 2 **Differentials** Find dy for $f(x) = x^2 + 3x$. Evaluate dy for

(A) $x = 2$ and $dx = 0.1$

(B) $x = 3$ and $dx = 0.1$

(C) $x = 1$ and $dx = 0.02$

SOLUTION $dy = f'(x)\,dx$

$\qquad = (2x + 3)\,dx$

(A) When $x = 2$ and $dx = 0.1$,   (B) When $x = 3$ and $dx = 0.1$,

$\qquad dy = [2(2) + 3]0.1 = 0.7$ $dy = [2(3) + 3]0.1 = 0.9$

(C) When $x = 1$ and $dx = 0.02$,

$\qquad dy = [2(1) + 3]0.02 = 0.1$

Matched Problem 2 Find dy for $f(x) = \sqrt{x} + 3$. Evaluate dy for

(A) $x = 4$ and $dx = 0.1$

(B) $x = 9$ and $dx = 0.12$

(C) $x = 1$ and $dx = 0.01$

We now have two interpretations of the symbol dy/dx. Referring to the function $y = f(x) = x^2 + 3x$ in Example 2 with $x = 2$ and $dx = 0.1$, we have

$$\frac{dy}{dx} = f'(2) = 7 \qquad \textit{Derivative}$$

and

$$\frac{dy}{dx} = \frac{0.7}{0.1} = 7 \qquad \textit{Ratio of differentials}$$

Approximations Using Differentials

Earlier, we noted that for small Δx,

$$\frac{\Delta y}{\Delta x} \approx f'(x) \qquad \text{and} \qquad \Delta y \approx f'(x)\Delta x$$

Also, since

$$dy = f'(x)\,dx$$

it follows that

$$\Delta y \approx dy$$

and dy can be used to approximate Δy.

To interpret this result geometrically, we need to recall a basic property of the slope. The vertical change in a line is equal to the product of the slope and the horizontal change, as shown in Figure 1.

Now consider the line tangent to the graph of $y = f(x)$, as shown in Figure 2. Since $f'(x)$ is the slope of the tangent line and dx is the horizontal change in the tangent line, it follows that the vertical change in the tangent line is given by $dy = f'(x)\,dx$, as indicated in Figure 2.

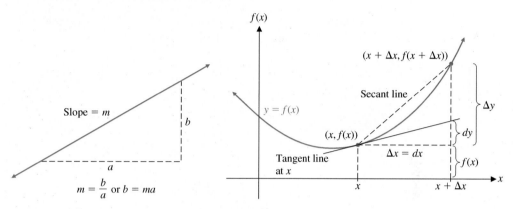

$$m = \frac{b}{a} \text{ or } b = ma$$

Figure 1

Figure 2

EXAMPLE 3 **Comparing Increments and Differentials** Let $y = f(x) = 6x - x^2$.

(A) Find Δy and dy when $x = 2$.

(B) Graph Δy and dy from part A for $-1 \le \Delta x \le 1$.

(C) Compare Δy and dy from part A for $\Delta x = 0.1, 0.2,$ and 0.3.

SOLUTION (A) $\Delta y = f(2 + \Delta x) - f(2)$

$\qquad = 6(2 + \Delta x) - (2 + \Delta x)^2 - (6 \cdot 2 - 2^2)$ *Remove parentheses.*

$\qquad = 12 + 6\Delta x - 4 - 4\Delta x - \Delta x^2 - 12 + 4$ *Collect like terms.*

$\qquad = 2\Delta x - \Delta x^2$

Since $f'(x) = 6 - 2x$, $f'(2) = 2$, and $dx = \Delta x$, $dy = f'(2)\,dx = 2\Delta x$

(B) The graphs of $\Delta y = 2\Delta x - \Delta x^2$ and $dy = 2\Delta x$ are shown in Figure 3. Examining the graphs, we conclude that the differential provides a linear approximation of the increments and that the approximation is better for values of $\Delta x = dx$ close to 0.

(C) Table 1 compares the values of Δx and dy for the indicated values of Δx.

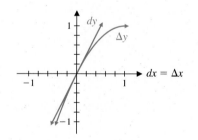

Figure 3 $\Delta y = 2\Delta x - \Delta x^2,\ dy = 2\Delta x$

Table 1

Δx	Δy	dy
0.1	0.19	0.2
0.2	0.36	0.4
0.3	0.51	0.6

Matched Problem 3 Repeat Example 3 for $x = 4$ and $\Delta x = dx = -0.1, -0.2,$ and -0.3.

CONCEPTUAL INSIGHT

The error in the approximation $\Delta y \approx dy$ is usually small when $\Delta x = dx$ is small (see Example 3C), but it can be quite substantial in some cases.

EXAMPLE 4 **Cost–Revenue** A company manufactures and sells x transistor radios per week. If the weekly cost and revenue equations are

$$C(x) = 5{,}000 + 2x \qquad R(x) = 10x - \frac{x^2}{1{,}000} \qquad 0 \le x \le 8{,}000$$

then find the approximate changes in revenue and profit if production is increased from 2,000 to 2,010 units per week.

SOLUTION We will approximate ΔR and ΔP with dR and dP, respectively, using $x = 2{,}000$ and $dx = 2{,}010 - 2{,}000 = 10$.

$$R(x) = 10x - \frac{x^2}{1{,}000} \qquad\qquad P(x) = R(x) - C(x) = 10x - \frac{x^2}{1{,}000} - 5{,}000 - 2x$$

$$dR = R'(x)\,dx \qquad\qquad\qquad\qquad\qquad = 8x - \frac{x^2}{1{,}000} - 5{,}000$$

$$= \left(10 - \frac{x}{500}\right)dx \qquad\qquad dP = P'(x)\,dx$$

$$= \left(10 - \frac{2{,}000}{500}\right)10 \qquad\qquad\quad = \left(8 - \frac{x}{500}\right)dx$$

$$= \$60 \text{ per week} \qquad\qquad\qquad = \left(8 - \frac{2{,}000}{500}\right)10$$

$$\qquad\qquad\qquad\qquad\qquad\qquad\quad = \$40 \text{ per week}$$

Matched Problem 4 Repeat Example 4 with production increasing from 6,000 to 6,010.

Comparing the results in Example 4 and Matched Problem 4, we see that an increase in production results in a revenue and profit increase at the 2,000 production level but a revenue and profit loss at the 6,000 production level.

Exercises 3-6

A

In Problems 1–6, find the indicated quantities for
$y = f(x) = 3x^2$.

1. Δx, Δy, and $\Delta y/\Delta x$; given $x_1 = 1$ and $x_2 = 4$

2. Δx, Δy, and $\Delta y/\Delta x$; given $x_1 = 2$ and $x_2 = 5$

3. $\dfrac{f(x_1 + \Delta x) - f(x_1)}{\Delta x}$; given $x_1 = 1$ and $\Delta x = 2$

4. $\dfrac{f(x_1 + \Delta x) - f(x_1)}{\Delta x}$; given $x_1 = 2$ and $\Delta x = 1$

5. $\Delta y/\Delta x$; given $x_1 = 1$ and $x_2 = 3$

6. $\Delta y/\Delta x$; given $x_1 = 2$ and $x_2 = 3$

In Problems 7–12, find dy for each function.

7. $y = 30 + 12x^2 - x^3$

8. $y = 200x - \dfrac{x^2}{30}$

9. $y = x^2\left(1 - \dfrac{x}{9}\right)$

10. $y = x^3(60 - x)$

11. $y = \dfrac{590}{\sqrt{x}}$

12. $y = 52\sqrt{x}$

B

In Problems 13 and 14, find the indicated quantities for
$y = f(x) = 3x^2$.

13. (A) $\dfrac{f(2 + \Delta x) - f(2)}{\Delta x}$ (simplify)

(B) What does the quantity in part (A) approach as Δx approaches 0?

14. (A) $\dfrac{f(3 + \Delta x) - f(3)}{\Delta x}$ (simplify)

(B) What does the quantity in part (A) approach as Δx approaches 0?

In Problems 15–18, find dy for each function.

15. $y = (2x + 1)^2$

16. $y = (3x + 5)^2$

17. $y = \dfrac{x^2 + 9}{x}$

18. $y = \dfrac{(x - 1)^2}{x^2}$

In Problems 19–22, evaluate dy and Δy for each function for the indicated values.

19. $y = f(x) = x^2 - 3x + 2; x = 5, dx = \Delta x = 0.2$

20. $y = f(x) = 30 + 12x^2 - x^3; x = 2, dx = \Delta x = 0.1$

21. $y = f(x) = 75\left(1 - \dfrac{2}{x}\right); x = 5, dx = \Delta x = -0.5$

22. $y = f(x) = 100\left(x - \dfrac{4}{x^2}\right); x = 2, dx = \Delta x = -0.1$

23. A cube with 10-inch sides is covered with a coat of fiberglass 0.2 inch thick. Use differentials to estimate the volume of the fiberglass shell.

24. A sphere with a radius of 5 centimeters is coated with ice 0.1 centimeter thick. Use differentials to estimate the volume of the ice. [Recall that $V = \frac{4}{3}\pi r^3$.]

C

In Problems 25–28,

(A) Find Δy and dy for the function f at the indicated value of x.

(B) Graph Δy and dy from part A.

(C) Compare the values of Δy and dy from part A at the indicated values of Δx.

25. $f(x) = x^2 + 2x + 3; x = -0.5, \Delta x = dx = 0.1, 0.2, 0.3$

26. $f(x) = x^2 + 2x + 3; x = -2, \Delta x = dx = -0.1, -0.2, -0.3$

27. $f(x) = x^3 - 2x^2; x = 1, \Delta x = dx = 0.05, 0.10, 0.15$

28. $f(x) = x^3 - 2x^2; x = 2, \Delta x = dx = -0.05, -0.10, -0.15$

In Problems 29–32, discuss the validity of each statement. If the statement is always true, explain why. If not, give a counterexample.

29. If the graph of the function $y = f(x)$ is a line, then the functions Δy and dy (of the independent variable $\Delta x = dx$) for $f(x)$ at $x = 3$ are identical.

30. If the graph of the function $y = f(x)$ is a parabola, then the functions Δy and dy (of the independent variable $\Delta x = dx$) for $f(x)$ at $x = 0$ are identical.

31. Suppose that $y = f(x)$ defines a differentiable function whose domain is the set of all real numbers. If every differential dy at $x = 2$ is equal to 0, then $f(x)$ is a constant function.

32. Suppose that $y = f(x)$ defines a function whose domain is the set of all real numbers. If every increment at $x = 2$ is equal to 0, then $f(x)$ is a constant function.

33. Find dy if $y = (1 - 2x)\sqrt[3]{x^2}$.

34. Find dy if $y = (2x^2 - 4)\sqrt{x}$.

35. Find dy and Δy for $y = 52\sqrt{x}$, $x = 4$, and $\Delta x = dx = 0.3$.

36. Find dy and Δy for $y = 590/\sqrt{x}$, $x = 64$, and $\Delta x = dx = 1$.

Applications

Use differential approximations in the following problems.

37. **Advertising.** A company will sell N units of a product after spending $\$x$ thousand in advertising, as given by

$$N = 60x - x^2 \qquad 5 \leq x \leq 30$$

Approximately what increase in sales will result by increasing the advertising budget from $\$10,000$ to $\$11,000$? From $\$20,000$ to $\$21,000$?

38. **Price–demand.** Suppose that the daily demand (in pounds) for chocolate candy at $\$x$ per pound is given by

$$D = 1,000 - 40x^2 \qquad 1 \leq x \leq 5$$

If the price is increased from $\$3.00$ per pound to $\$3.20$ per pound, what is the approximate change in demand?

39. **Average cost.** For a company that manufactures tennis rackets, the average cost per racket $\overline{C}$ is

$$\overline{C} = \frac{400}{x} + 5 + \frac{1}{2}x \qquad x \geq 1$$

where x is the number of rackets produced per hour. What will the approximate change in average cost per racket be if production is increased from 20 per hour to 25 per hour? From 40 per hour to 45 per hour?

40. **Revenue and profit.** A company manufactures and sells x televisions per month. If the cost and revenue equations are

$$C(x) = 72,000 + 60x$$

$$R(x) = 200x - \frac{x^2}{30} \qquad 0 \leq x \leq 6,000$$

what will the approximate changes in revenue and profit be if production is increased from 1,500 to 1,510? From 4,500 to 4,510?

41. **Pulse rate.** The average pulse rate y (in beats per minute) of a healthy person x inches tall is given approximately by

$$y = \frac{590}{\sqrt{x}} \qquad 30 \leq x \leq 75$$

Approximately how will the pulse rate change for a change in height from 36 to 37 inches? From 64 to 65 inches?

42. **Measurement.** An egg of a particular bird is nearly spherical. If the radius to the inside of the shell is 5 millimeters and the radius to the outside of the shell is 5.3 millimeters, approximately what is the volume of the shell? [Remember that $V = \frac{4}{3}\pi r^3$.]

43. **Medicine.** A drug is given to a patient to dilate her arteries. If the radius of an artery is increased from 2 to 2.1 millimeters, approximately how much is the cross-sectional area increased? [Assume that the cross section of the artery is circular; that is, $A = \pi r^2$.]

44. **Drug sensitivity.** One hour after x milligrams of a particular drug are given to a person, the change in body temperature T (in degrees Fahrenheit) is given by

$$T = x^2\left(1 - \frac{x}{9}\right) \qquad 0 \leq x \leq 6$$

Approximate the changes in body temperature produced by the following changes in drug dosages:

(A) From 2 to 2.1 milligrams

(B) From 3 to 3.1 milligrams

(C) From 4 to 4.1 milligrams

45. Learning. A particular person learning to type has an achievement record given approximately by

$$N = 75\left(1 - \frac{2}{t}\right) \qquad 3 \le t \le 20$$

where N is the number of words per minute typed after t weeks of practice. What is the approximate improvement from 5 to 5.5 weeks of practice?

46. Learning. If a person learns y items in x hours, as given approximately by

$$y = 52\sqrt{x} \qquad 0 \le x \le 9$$

what is the approximate increase in the number of items learned when x changes from 1 to 1.1 hours? From 4 to 4.1 hours?

47. Politics. In a new city, the voting population (in thousands) is given by

$$N(t) = 30 + 12t^2 - t^3 \qquad 0 \le t \le 8$$

where t is time in years. Find the approximate change in votes for the following changes in time:

(A) From 1 to 1.1 years

(B) From 4 to 4.1 years

(C) From 7 to 7.1 years

1. (A) $\Delta x = 1, \Delta y = 5, \Delta y/\Delta x = 5$

  (B) 4

2. $dy = \dfrac{1}{2\sqrt{x}}\, dx$

  (A) 0.025

  (B) 0.02

  (C) 0.005

3. (A) $\Delta y = -2\Delta x - \Delta x^2; dy = -2\Delta x$

  (B)

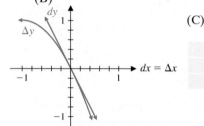

  (C)

Δx	Δy	dy
-0.1	0.19	0.2
-0.2	0.36	0.4
-0.3	0.51	0.6

4. $dR = -\$20/\text{wk}; dP = -\$40/\text{wk}$

3-7 Marginal Analysis in Business and Economics

- Marginal Cost, Revenue, and Profit
- Application
- Marginal Average Cost, Revenue, and Profit

Marginal Cost, Revenue, and Profit

One important application of calculus to business and economics involves *marginal analysis*. In economics, the word *marginal* refers to a rate of change — that is, to a derivative. Thus, if $C(x)$ is the total cost of producing x items, then $C'(x)$ is called the *marginal cost* and represents the instantaneous rate of change of total cost with respect to the number of items produced. Similarly, the *marginal revenue* is the derivative of the total revenue function, and the *marginal profit* is the derivative of the total profit function.

> **DEFINITION Marginal Cost, Revenue, and Profit**
>
> If x is the number of units of a product produced in some time interval, then
>
> $$\text{total cost} = C(x)$$
>
> $$\textbf{marginal cost} = C'(x)$$
>
> $$\text{total revenue} = R(x)$$
>
> $$\textbf{marginal revenue} = R'(x)$$
>
> $$\text{total profit} = P(x) = R(x) - C(x)$$
>
> $$\textbf{marginal profit} = P'(x) = R'(x) - C'(x)$$
>
> $$= (\text{marginal revenue}) - (\text{marginal cost})$$
>
> Marginal cost (or revenue or profit) is the instantaneous rate of change of cost (or revenue or profit) relative to production at a given production level.

To begin our discussion, we consider a cost function $C(x)$. It is important to remember that $C(x)$ represents the *total* cost of producing x items, not the cost of producing a *single* item. To find the cost of producing a single item, we use the difference of two successive values of $C(x)$:

$$\text{Total cost of producing } x + 1 \text{ items} = C(x + 1)$$
$$\text{Total cost of producing } x \text{ items} = C(x)$$
$$\text{Exact cost of producing the } (x + 1)\text{st item} = C(x + 1) - C(x)$$

EXAMPLE 1   **Cost Analysis** A company manufactures fuel tanks for cars. The total weekly cost (in dollars) of producing x tanks is given by

$$C(x) = 10,000 + 90x - 0.05x^2$$

(A) Find the marginal cost function.

(B) Find the marginal cost at a production level of 500 tanks per week.

(C) Interpret the results of part B.

(D) Find the exact cost of producing the 501st item.

SOLUTION   (A) $C'(x) = 90 - 0.1x$

(B) $C'(500) = 90 - 0.1(500) = \$40$ Marginal cost

(C) At a production level of 500 tanks per week, the total production costs are increasing at the rate of $40 per tank.

(D)
$$C(501) = 10,000 + 90(501) - 0.05(501)^2$$
$$= \$42,539.95 \quad \text{Total cost of producing 501 tanks per week}$$
$$C(500) = 10,000 + 90(500) - 0.05(500)^2$$
$$= \$42,500.00 \quad \text{Total cost of producing 500 tanks per week}$$
$$C(501) - C(500) = 42,539.95 - 42,500.00$$
$$= \$39.95 \quad \text{Exact cost of producing the 501st tank}$$

Matched Problem 1   A company manufactures automatic transmissions for cars. The total weekly cost (in dollars) of producing x transmissions is given by

$$C(x) = 50,000 + 600x - 0.75x^2$$

(A) Find the marginal cost function.

(B) Find the marginal cost at a production level of 200 transmissions per week.

(C) Interpret the results of part B.

(D) Find the exact cost of producing the 201st transmission.

In Example 1, we found that the cost of the 501st tank and the marginal cost at a production level of 500 tanks differ by only a nickel. Increments and differentials will help us understand the relationship between marginal cost and the cost of a single item. If $C(x)$ is any total cost function, then

$$C'(x) \approx \frac{C(x + \Delta x) - C(x)}{\Delta x} \quad \text{See Section 3-6}$$

$$C'(x) \approx C(x + 1) - C(x) \quad \Delta x = 1$$

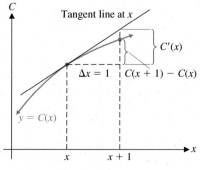

Figure 1 $C'(x) \approx C(x + 1) - C(x)$

We see that the marginal cost $C'(x)$ approximates $C(x + 1) - C(x)$, the exact cost of producing the $(x + 1)$st item. These observations are summarized next and are illustrated in Figure 1.

> **THEOREM 1   Marginal Cost and Exact Cost**
>
> If $C(x)$ is the total cost of producing x items, then the marginal cost function approximates the exact cost of producing the $(x + 1)$st item:
>
> Marginal cost   Exact cost
>
> $$C'(x) \approx C(x + 1) - C(x)$$
>
> Similar statements can be made for total revenue functions and total profit functions.

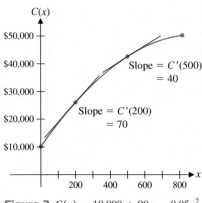

$C(x)$

$50,000

$40,000

Slope $= C'(500)$
$= 40$

$30,000

$20,000   Slope $= C'(200)$
$= 70$

$10,000

200   400   600   800 x

Figure 2 $C(x) = 10,000 + 90x - 0.05x^2$

> **CONCEPTUAL INSIGHT**
>
> Theorem 1 states that the marginal cost at a given production level x approximates the cost of producing the $(x + 1)$st, or *next,* item. In practice, the marginal cost is used more frequently than the exact cost. One reason for this is that the marginal cost is easily visualized when one is examining the graph of the total cost function. Figure 2 shows the graph of the cost function discussed in Example 1, with tangent lines added at $x = 200$ and $x = 500$. The graph clearly shows that as production increases, the slope of the tangent line decreases. Thus, the cost of producing the next tank also decreases, a desirable characteristic of a total cost function. We will have much more to say about graphical analysis in Chapter 5.

Application

Now we discuss how price, demand, revenue, cost, and profit are tied together in typical applications. Although either price or demand can be used as the independent variable in a price–demand equation, it is common to use demand as the independent variable when marginal revenue, cost, and profit are also involved.

EXAMPLE 2   **Production Strategy** A company's market research department recommends the manufacture and marketing of a new headphone set for MP3 players. After suitable test marketing, the research department presents the following **price–demand equation**:

$$x = 10,000 - 1,000p \qquad \text{x is demand at price p.} \qquad (1)$$

Solving (1) for p gives

$$p = 10 - 0.001x \qquad (2)$$

where x is the number of headphones that retailers are likely to buy at $\$p$ per set. The financial department provides the **cost function**

$$C(x) = 7,000 + 2x \qquad (3)$$

where $\$7,000$ is the estimate of fixed costs (tooling and overhead) and $\$2$ is the estimate of variable costs per headphone set (materials, labor, marketing, transportation, storage, etc.).

(A) Find the domain of the function defined by the price–demand equation (2).

(B) Find and interpret the marginal cost function $C'(x)$.

(C) Find the revenue function as a function of x and find its domain.

(D) Find the marginal revenue at $x = 2,000$, $5,000$, and $7,000$. Interpret these results.

(E) Graph the cost function and the revenue function in the same coordinate system. Find the intersection points of these two graphs and interpret the results.

(F) Find the profit function and its domain and sketch the graph of the function.

(G) Find the marginal profit at $x = 1,000$, $4,000$, and $6,000$. Interpret these results.

SOLUTION   (A) Since price p and demand x must be non-negative, we have $x \geq 0$ and

$$p = 10 - 0.001x \geq 0$$
$$10 \geq 0.001x$$
$$10,000 \geq x$$

Thus, the permissible values of x are $0 \leq x \leq 10,000$.

(B) The marginal cost is $C'(x) = 2$. Since this is a constant, it costs an additional $2 to produce one more headphone set at any production level.

(C) The **revenue** is the amount of money R received by the company for manufacturing and selling x headphone sets at $$p$ per set and is given by

$$R = \text{(number of headphone sets sold)(price per headphone set)} = xp$$

In general, the revenue R can be expressed as a function of p using equation (1) or as a function of x using equation (2). As we mentioned earlier, when using marginal functions, we will always use the number of items x as the independent variable. Thus, the **revenue function** is

$$R(x) = xp = x(10 - 0.001x) \quad \text{Using equation (2)} \quad (4)$$
$$= 10x - 0.001x^2$$

Since equation (2) is defined only for $0 \leq x \leq 10,000$, it follows that the domain of the revenue function is $0 \leq x \leq 10,000$.

(D) The **marginal revenue** is

$$R'(x) = 10 - 0.002x$$

For production levels of $x = 2,000, 5,000,$ and $7,000$, we have

$$R'(2,000) = 6 \qquad R'(5,000) = 0 \qquad R'(7,000) = -4$$

This means that at production levels of 2,000, 5,000, and 7,000, the respective approximate changes in revenue per unit change in production are $6, $0, and $-$4. That is, at the 2,000 output level, revenue increases as production increases; at the 5,000 output level, revenue does not change with a "small" change in production; and at the 7,000 output level, revenue decreases with an increase in production.

(E) Graphing $R(x)$ and $C(x)$ in the same coordinate system results in Figure 3. The intersection points are called the **break-even points**, because revenue equals cost at these production levels. The company neither makes nor loses money, but just breaks even. The break-even points are obtained as follows:

$$C(x) = R(x)$$
$$7,000 + 2x = 10x - 0.001x^2$$
$$0.001x^2 - 8x + 7,000 = 0 \quad \text{Solve by the quadratic formula}$$
$$x^2 - 8,000x + 7,000,000 = 0 \quad \text{(see Appendix A-7).}$$
$$x = \frac{8,000 \pm \sqrt{8,000^2 - 4(7,000,000)}}{2}$$
$$= \frac{8,000 \pm \sqrt{36,000,000}}{2}$$
$$= \frac{8,000 \pm 6,000}{2}$$
$$= 1,000, \quad 7,000$$

$$R(1,000) = 10(1,000) - 0.001(1,000)^2 = 9,000$$

$$C(1,000) = 7,000 + 2(1,000) = 9,000$$

$$R(7,000) = 10(7,000) - 0.001(7,000)^2 = 21,000$$

$$C(7,000) = 7,000 + 2(7,000) = 21,000$$

The break-even points are (1,000, 9,000) and (7,000, 21,000), as shown in Figure 3. Further examination of the figure shows that cost is greater than revenue for production levels between 0 and 1,000 and also between 7,000 and 10,000. Consequently, the company incurs a loss at these levels. By contrast, for production levels between 1,000 and 7,000, revenue is greater than cost, and the company makes a profit.

(F) The **profit function** is

$$P(x) = R(x) - C(x)$$
$$= (10x - 0.001x^2) - (7,000 + 2x)$$
$$= -0.001x^2 + 8x - 7,000$$

The domain of the cost function is $x \geq 0$, and the domain of the revenue function is $0 \leq x \leq 10,000$. The domain of the profit function is the set of x values for which both functions are defined—that is, $0 \leq x \leq 10,000$. The graph of the profit function is shown in Figure 4. Notice that the x coordinates of the break-even points in Figure 3 are the x intercepts of the profit function. Furthermore, the intervals on which cost is greater than revenue and on which revenue is greater than cost correspond, respectively, to the intervals on which profit is negative and on which profit is positive.

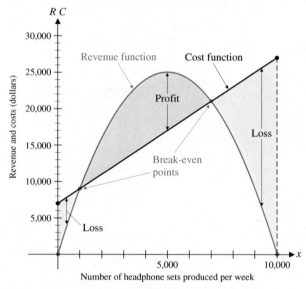

Figure 3

(G) The **marginal profit** is

$$P'(x) = -0.002x + 8$$

For production levels of 1,000, 4,000, and 6,000, we have

$$P'(1,000) = 6 \qquad P'(4,000) = 0 \qquad P'(6,000) = -4$$

This means that at production levels of 1,000, 4,000, and 6,000, the respective approximate changes in profit per unit change in production are $6, $0, and −$4. That is, at the 1,000 output level, profit will be increased if production is increased; at the 4,000 output level, profit does not change for "small" changes in production; and at the 6,000 output level, profits will decrease if production is increased. It seems that the best production level to produce a maximum profit is 4,000.

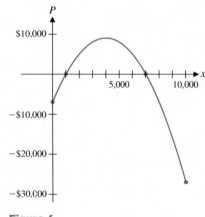

Figure 4

Example 2 requires careful study since a number of important ideas in economics and calculus are involved. In the next chapter, we will develop a systematic procedure for finding the production level (and, using the demand equation, the selling price) that will maximize profit.

Matched Problem 2   Refer to the revenue and profit functions in Example 2.

(A) Find $R'(3,000)$ and $R'(6,000)$. Interpret the results.

(B) Find $P'(2,000)$ and $P'(7,000)$. Interpret the results.

Marginal Average Cost, Revenue, and Profit

Sometimes it is desirable to carry out marginal analysis relative to **average cost (cost per unit)**, **average revenue (revenue per unit)**, and **average profit (profit per unit)**.

DEFINITION **Marginal Average Cost, Revenue, and Profit**

If x is the number of units of a product produced in some time interval, then

Cost per unit: average cost $= \overline{C}(x) = \dfrac{C(x)}{x}$

  marginal average cost $= \overline{C}'(x) = \dfrac{d}{dx}\overline{C}(x)$

Revenue per unit: average revenue $= \overline{R}(x) = \dfrac{R(x)}{x}$

  marginal average revenue $= \overline{R}'(x) = \dfrac{d}{dx}\overline{R}(x)$

Profit per unit: average profit $= \overline{P}(x) = \dfrac{P(x)}{x}$

  marginal average profit $= \overline{P}'(x) = \dfrac{d}{dx}\overline{P}(x)$

EXAMPLE 3   **Cost Analysis** A small machine shop manufactures drill bits used in the petroleum industry. The manager estimates that the total daily cost (in dollars) of producing x bits is

$$C(x) = 1,000 + 25x - 0.1x^2$$

(A) Find $\overline{C}(x)$ and $\overline{C}'(x)$.

(B) Find $\overline{C}(10)$ and $\overline{C}'(10)$. Interpret these quantities.

(C) Use the results in part (B) to estimate the average cost per bit at a production level of 11 bits per day.

SOLUTION   (A) $\overline{C}(x) = \dfrac{C(x)}{x} = \dfrac{1,000 + 25x - 0.1x^2}{x}$

  $= \dfrac{1,000}{x} + 25 - 0.1x$ *Average cost function*

  $\overline{C}'(x) = \dfrac{d}{dx}\overline{C}(x) = -\dfrac{1,000}{x^2} - 0.1$ *Marginal average cost function*

(B) $\overline{C}(10) = \dfrac{1,000}{10} + 25 - 0.1(10) = \$124$

  $\overline{C}'(10) = -\dfrac{1,000}{10^2} - 0.1 = -\$10.10$

At a production level of 10 bits per day, the average cost of producing a bit is $124. This cost is decreasing at the rate of $10.10 per bit.

(C) If production is increased by 1 bit, then the average cost per bit will decrease by approximately $10.10. So, the average cost per bit at a production level of 11 bits per day is approximately $124 − $10.10 = $113.90.

Matched Problem 3   Consider the cost function for the production of headphone sets from Example 2:

$$C(x) = 7,000 + 2x$$

(A) Find $\overline{C}(x)$ and $\overline{C}'(x)$.

(B) Find $\overline{C}(100)$ and $\overline{C}'(100)$. Interpret these quantities.

(C) Use the results in part (B) to estimate the average cost per headphone set at a production level of 101 headphone sets.

EXPLORE & DISCUSS 1   A student produced the following solution to Matched Problem 3:

$$C(x) = 7,000 + 2x \quad \text{Cost}$$
$$C'(x) = 2 \quad\quad\quad \text{Marginal cost}$$
$$\frac{C'(x)}{x} = \frac{2}{x} \quad\quad \text{“Average” of the marginal cost}$$

Explain why the last function is not the same as the marginal average cost function.

 CAUTION

1. The marginal average cost function is computed by first finding the average cost function and then finding its derivative. As Explore & Discuss 1 illustrates, reversing the order of these two steps produces a different function that does not have any useful economic interpretations.

2. Recall that the marginal cost function has two interpretations: the usual interpretation of any derivative as an instantaneous rate of change and the special interpretation as an approximation to the exact cost of the $(x + 1)$st item. This special interpretation does not apply to the marginal average cost function. Referring to Example 3, we would be incorrect to interpret $\overline{C}'(10) = -\$10.10$ to mean that the average cost of the next bit is approximately $-\$10.10$. In fact, the phrase “average cost of the next bit” does not even make sense. Averaging is a concept applied to a collection of items, not to a single item.

These remarks also apply to revenue and profit functions.

Exercises 3-7

In Problems 1–4, find the marginal cost function.

1. $C(x) = 175 + 0.8x$

2. $C(x) = 4,500 + 9.5x$

3. $C(x) = 210 + 4.6x - 0.01x^2$

4. $C(x) = 790 + 13x - 0.2x^2$

In Problems 5–8, find the marginal revenue function.

5. $R(x) = 4x - 0.01x^2$

6. $R(x) = 36x - 0.03x^2$

7. $R(x) = x(12 - 0.04x)$

8. $R(x) = x(25 - 0.05x)$

In Problems 9-12, find the marginal profit function if the cost and revenue, respectively, are those in the indicated problems.

9. Problem 1 and Problem 5

10. Problem 2 and Problem 6

11. Problem 3 and Problem 7

12. Problem 4 and Problem 8

B

In Problems 13–20, find the indicated function if cost and revenue are given by $C(x) = 145 + 1.1x$ and $R(x) = 5x - 0.02x^2$, respectively.

13. Average cost function

14. Average revenue function

15. Marginal average cost function

16. Marginal average revenue function

17. Profit function

18. Marginal profit function

19. Average profit function

20. Marginal average profit function

C

In Problems 21–24, discuss the validity of each statement. If the statement is always true, explain why. If not, give a counterexample.

21. If a cost function is linear, then the marginal cost is a constant.

22. If a price–demand equation is linear, then the marginal revenue function is linear.

23. Marginal profit is equal to marginal cost minus marginal revenue.

24. Marginal average cost is equal to average marginal cost.

Applications

25. **Cost analysis.** The total cost (in dollars) of producing x food processors is
$$C(x) = 2,000 + 50x - 0.5x^2$$
   (A) Find the exact cost of producing the 21st food processor.
   (B) Use marginal cost to approximate the cost of producing the 21st food processor.

26. **Cost analysis.** The total cost (in dollars) of producing x electric guitars is
$$C(x) = 1,000 + 100x - 0.25x^2$$
   (A) Find the exact cost of producing the 51st guitar.
   (B) Use marginal cost to approximate the cost of producing the 51st guitar.

27. **Cost analysis.** The total cost (in dollars) of manufacturing x auto body frames is
$$C(x) = 60,000 + 300x$$
   (A) Find the average cost per unit if 500 frames are produced.
   (B) Find the marginal average cost at a production level of 500 units and interpret the results.
   (C) Use the results from parts (A) and (B) to estimate the average cost per frame if 501 frames are produced.

28. **Cost analysis.** The total cost (in dollars) of printing x dictionaries is
$$C(x) = 20,000 + 10x$$
   (A) Find the average cost per unit if 1,000 dictionaries are produced.
   (B) Find the marginal average cost at a production level of 1,000 units and interpret the results.
   (C) Use the results from parts (A) and (B) to estimate the average cost per dictionary if 1,001 dictionaries are produced.

29. **Profit analysis.** The total profit (in dollars) from the sale of x skateboards is
$$P(x) = 30x - 0.3x^2 - 250 \qquad 0 \le x \le 100$$
   (A) Find the exact profit from the sale of the 26th skateboard.
   (B) Use marginal profit to approximate the profit from the sale of the 26th skateboard.

30. **Profit analysis.** The total profit (in dollars) from the sale of x calendars is
$$P(x) = 22x - 0.2x^2 - 400 \qquad 0 \le x \le 100$$
   (A) Find the exact profit from the sale of the 41st calendar.
   (B) Use the marginal profit to approximate the profit from the sale of the 41st calendar.

31. **Profit analysis.** The total profit (in dollars) from the sale of x DVDs is
$$P(x) = 5x - 0.005x^2 - 450 \qquad 0 \le x \le 1,000$$
   Evaluate the marginal profit at the given values of x, and interpret the results.
   (A) $x = 450$ (B) $x = 750$

32. **Profit analysis.** The total profit (in dollars) from the sale of x cameras is
$$P(x) = 12x - 0.02x^2 - 1,000 \qquad 0 \le x \le 600$$
   Evaluate the marginal profit at the given values of x, and interpret the results.
   (A) $x = 200$ (B) $x = 350$

33. **Profit analysis.** The total profit (in dollars) from the sale of x lawn mowers is
$$P(x) = 30x - 0.03x^2 - 750 \qquad 0 \le x \le 1,000$$
   (A) Find the average profit per mower if 50 mowers are produced.
   (B) Find the marginal average profit at a production level of 50 mowers and interpret the results.
   (C) Use the results from parts (A) and (B) to estimate the average profit per mower if 51 mowers are produced.

34. **Profit analysis.** The total profit (in dollars) from the sale of x gas grills is
$$P(x) = 20x - 0.02x^2 - 320 \qquad 0 \le x \le 1,000$$
   (A) Find the average profit per grill if 40 grills are produced.
   (B) Find the marginal average profit at a production level of 40 grills and interpret the results.
   (C) Use the results from parts (A) and (B) to estimate the average profit per grill if 41 grills are produced.

35. **Revenue analysis.** The price p (in dollars) and the demand x for a brand of running shoes are related by the equation
$$x = 4,000 - 40p$$
   (A) Express the price p in terms of the demand x, and find the domain of this function.
   (B) Find the revenue $R(x)$ from the sale of x pairs of running shoes. What is the domain of R?
   (C) Find the marginal revenue at a production level of 1,600 pairs and interpret the results.
   (D) Find the marginal revenue at a production level of 2,500 pairs, and interpret the results.

36. Revenue analysis. The price p (in dollars) and the demand x for a particular steam iron are related by the equation

$$x = 1{,}000 - 20p$$

(A) Express the price p in terms of the demand x, and find the domain of this function.

(B) Find the revenue $R(x)$ from the sale of x steam irons. What is the domain of R?

(C) Find the marginal revenue at a production level of 400 steam irons and interpret the results.

(D) Find the marginal revenue at a production level of 650 steam irons and interpret the results.

37. Revenue, cost, and profit. The price–demand equation and the cost function for the production of table saws are given, respectively, by

$$x = 6{,}000 - 30p \quad \text{and} \quad C(x) = 72{,}000 + 60x$$

where x is the number of saws that can be sold at a price of $\$p$ per saw and $C(x)$ is the total cost (in dollars) of producing x saws.

(A) Express the price p as a function of the demand x, and find the domain of this function.

(B) Find the marginal cost.

(C) Find the revenue function and state its domain.

(D) Find the marginal revenue.

(E) Find $R'(1{,}500)$ and $R'(4{,}500)$ and interpret these quantities.

(F) Graph the cost function and the revenue function on the same coordinate system for $0 \le x \le 6{,}000$. Find the break-even points, and indicate regions of loss and profit.

(G) Find the profit function in terms of x.

(H) Find the marginal profit.

(I) Find $P'(1{,}500)$ and $P'(3{,}000)$ and interpret these quantities.

38. Revenue, cost, and profit. The price–demand equation and the cost function for the production of HDTVs are given, respectively, by

$$x = 9{,}000 - 30p \quad \text{and} \quad C(x) = 150{,}000 + 30x$$

where x is the number of HDTVs that can be sold at a price of $\$p$ per TV and $C(x)$ is the total cost (in dollars) of producing x TVs.

(A) Express the price p as a function of the demand x, and find the domain of this function.

(B) Find the marginal cost.

(C) Find the revenue function and state its domain.

(D) Find the marginal revenue.

(E) Find $R'(3{,}000)$ and $R'(6{,}000)$ and interpret these quantities.

(F) Graph the cost function and the revenue function on the same coordinate system for $0 \le x \le 9{,}000$. Find the break-even points, and indicate regions of loss and profit.

(G) Find the profit function in terms of x.

(H) Find the marginal profit.

(I) Find $P'(1{,}500)$ and $P'(4{,}500)$ and interpret these quantities.

39. Revenue, cost, and profit. A company is planning to manufacture and market a new two-slice electric toaster. After conducting extensive market surveys, the research department provides the following estimates: a weekly demand of 200 toasters at a price of $16 per toaster and a weekly demand of 300 toasters at a price of $14 per toaster. The financial department estimates that weekly fixed costs will be $1,400 and variable costs (cost per unit) will be $4.

(A) Assume that the relationship between price p and demand x is linear. Use the research department's estimates to express p as a function of x and find the domain of this function.

(B) Find the revenue function in terms of x and state its domain.

(C) Assume that the cost function is linear. Use the financial department's estimates to express the cost function in terms of x.

(D) Graph the cost function and revenue function on the same coordinate system for $0 \le x \le 1{,}000$. Find the break-even points and indicate regions of loss and profit.

(E) Find the profit function in terms of x.

(F) Evaluate the marginal profit at $x = 250$ and $x = 475$ and interpret the results.

40. Revenue, cost, and profit. The company in Problem 39 is also planning to manufacture and market a four-slice toaster. For this toaster, the research department's estimates are a weekly demand of 300 toasters at a price of $25 per toaster and a weekly demand of 400 toasters at a price of $20. The financial department's estimates are fixed weekly costs of $5,000 and variable costs of $5 per toaster.

(A) Assume that the relationship between price p and demand x is linear. Use the research department's estimates to express p as a function of x, and find the domain of this function.

(B) Find the revenue function in terms of x and state its domain.

(C) Assume that the cost function is linear. Use the financial department's estimates to express the cost function in terms of x.

(D) Graph the cost function and revenue function on the same coordinate system for $0 \le x \le 800$. Find the break-even points and indicate regions of loss and profit.

(E) Find the profit function in terms of x.

(F) Evaluate the marginal profit at $x = 325$ and $x = 425$ and interpret the results.

41. Revenue, cost, and profit. The total cost and the total revenue (in dollars) for the production and sale of x ski jackets are given, respectively, by

$$C(x) = 24x + 21{,}900 \quad \text{and} \quad R(x) = 200x - 0.2x^2$$
$$0 \le x \le 1{,}000$$

(A) Find the value of x where the graph of $R(x)$ has a horizontal tangent line.

(B) Find the profit function $P(x)$.

(C) Find the value of x where the graph of $P(x)$ has a horizontal tangent line.

(D) Graph $C(x)$, $R(x)$, and $P(x)$ on the same coordinate system for $0 \le x \le 1{,}000$. Find the break-even points. Find the x intercepts of the graph of $P(x)$.

42. Revenue, cost, and profit. The total cost and the total revenue (in dollars) for the production and sale of x hair dryers are given, respectively, by

$$C(x) = 5x + 2{,}340 \quad \text{and} \quad R(x) = 40x - 0.1x^2$$
$$0 \le x \le 400$$

(A) Find the value of x where the graph of $R(x)$ has a horizontal tangent line.

(B) Find the profit function $P(x)$.

(C) Find the value of x where the graph of $P(x)$ has a horizontal tangent line.

(D) Graph $C(x)$, $R(x)$, and $P(x)$ on the same coordinate system for $0 \le x \le 400$. Find the break-even points. Find the x intercepts of the graph of $P(x)$.

43. Break-even analysis. The price–demand equation and the cost function for the production of garden hoses are given, respectively, by

$$p = 20 - \sqrt{x} \quad \text{and} \quad C(x) = 500 + 2x$$

where x is the number of garden hoses that can be sold at a price of $\$p$ per unit and $C(x)$ is the total cost (in dollars) of producing x garden hoses.

(A) Express the revenue function in terms of x.

(B) Graph the cost function and revenue function in the same viewing window for $0 \le x \le 400$. Use approximation techniques to find the break-even points correct to the nearest unit.

44. Break-even analysis. The price–demand equation and the cost function for the production of handwoven silk scarves are given, respectively, by

$$p = 60 - 2\sqrt{x} \quad \text{and} \quad C(x) = 3{,}000 + 5x$$

where x is the number of scarves that can be sold at a price of $\$p$ per unit and $C(x)$ is the total cost (in dollars) of producing x scarves.

(A) Express the revenue function in terms of x.

(B) Graph the cost function and the revenue function in the same viewing window for $0 \le x \le 900$. Use approximation techniques to find the break-even points correct to the nearest unit.

45. Break-even analysis. Table 2 contains price–demand and total cost data for the production of projectors, where p is the wholesale price (in dollars) of a projector for an annual demand of x projectors and C is the total cost (in dollars) of producing x projectors.

Table 2		
x	p($)	C($)
3,190	581	1,130,000
4,570	405	1,241,000
5,740	181	1,410,000
7,330	85	1,620,000

(A) Find a quadratic regression equation for the price–demand data, using x as the independent variable.

(B) Find a linear regression equation for the cost data, using x as the independent variable. Use this equation to estimate the fixed costs and variable costs per projector. Round answers to the nearest dollar.

(C) Find the break-even points. Round answers to the nearest integer.

(D) Find the price range for which the company will make a profit. Round answers to the nearest dollar.

46. Break-even analysis. Table 3 contains price–demand and total cost data for the production of treadmills, where p is the wholesale price (in dollars) of a treadmill for an annual demand of x treadmills and C is the total cost (in dollars) of producing x treadmills.

Table 3		
x	p($)	C($)
2,910	1,435	3,650,000
3,415	1,280	3,870,000
4,645	1,125	4,190,000
5,330	910	4,380,000

(A) Find a linear regression equation for the price–demand data, using x as the independent variable.

(B) Find a linear regression equation for the cost data, using x as the independent variable. Use this equation to estimate the fixed costs and variable costs per treadmill. Round answers to the nearest dollar.

(C) Find the break-even points. Round answers to the nearest integer.

(D) Find the price range for which the company will make a profit. Round answers to the nearest dollar.

Answers to Matched Problems

1. (A) $C'(x) = 600 - 1.5x$

(B) $C'(200) = 300$. At a production level of 200 transmissions, total costs are increasing at the rate of $300 per transmission.

(C) $C(201) - C(200) = \$299.25$

2. (A) $R'(3{,}000) = 4$. At a production level of 3,000, a unit increase in production will increase revenue by approximately $4.
$R'(6{,}000) = -2$. At a production level of 6,000, a unit increase in production will decrease revenue by approximately $2.

(B) $P'(2{,}000) = 4$. At a production level of 2,000, a unit increase in production will increase profit by approximately $4.
$P'(7{,}000) = -6$. At a production level of 7,000, a unit increase in production will decrease profit by approximately $6.

3. (A) $\overline{C}(x) = \dfrac{7{,}000}{x} + 2; \overline{C}'(x) = -\dfrac{7{,}000}{x^2}$

(B) $\overline{C}(100) = \$72; \overline{C}'(100) = -\$0.70$. At a production level of 100 headphone sets, the average cost per headphone set is $72. This average cost is decreasing at a rate of $0.70 per headphone set.

(C) Approx. $71.30.

Chapter 3   Review

Important Terms, Symbols, and Concepts

3-1 Introduction to Limits

- The graph of the function $y = f(x)$ is the graph of the set of all ordered pairs $(x, f(x))$.
- The limit of the function $y = f(x)$ as x approaches c is L, written as $\lim_{x \to c} f(x) = L$, if the functional value $f(x)$ is close to the single real number L whenever x is close, but not equal, to c (on either side of c).
- The limit of the function $y = f(x)$ as x approaches c from the left is K, written as $\lim_{x \to c^-} f(x) = K$, if $f(x)$ is close to K whenever x is close to, but to the left of, c on the real-number line.
- The limit of the function $y = f(x)$ as x approaches c from the right is L, written as $\lim_{x \to c^+} f(x) = L$, if $f(x)$ is close to L whenever x is close to, but to the right of, c on the real-number line.
- The limit of the difference quotient $[f(a + h) - f(a)]/h$ always results in a $0/0$ indeterminate form. Algebraic simplification is often required to evaluate this type of limit.

3-2 Infinite Limits and Limits at Infinity

- If $f(x)$ increases or decreases without bound as x approaches a from either side of a, then the line $x = a$ is a **vertical asymptote** of the graph of $y = f(x)$.
- If $f(x)$ gets close to L as x increases without bound or decreases without bound, then L is called the limit of f at ∞ or $-\infty$.
- The end behavior of a polynomial is described in terms of limits at infinity.
- If $f(x)$ approaches L as $x \to \infty$ or as $x \to -\infty$, then the line $y = L$ is a **horizontal asymptote** of the graph of $y = f(x)$. Polynomial functions never have horizontal asymptotes. A rational function can have at most one.

3-3 Continuity

- Intuitively, the graph of a continuous function can be drawn without lifting a pen off the paper. Algebraically, a function f is **continuous at c** if

  1. $\lim_{x \to c} f(x)$ exists,   2. $f(c)$ exists, and   3. $\lim_{x \to c} f(x) = f(c)$

- Continuity properties are useful for determining where a function is continuous and where it is discontinuous.
- Continuity properties are also useful for solving inequalities.

3-4 The Derivative

- Given a function $y = f(x)$, the **average rate of change** is the ratio of the change in y to the change in x.
- The **instantaneous rate of change** is the limit of the average rate of change as the change in x approaches 0.
- The slope of the secant line through two points on the graph of a function $y = f(x)$ is the ratio of the change in y to the change in x. The slope of the tangent line at the point $(a, f(a))$ is the limit of the slope of the secant line through the points $(a, f(a))$ and $(a + h, f(a + h))$ as h approaches 0.
- The **derivative of $y = f(x)$ at x**, denoted as $f'(x)$, is the limit of the difference quotient $[f(x + h) - f(x)]/h$ as $h \to 0$ (if the limit exists).
- The four-step method is used to find derivatives.
- If the limit of the difference quotient does not exist at $x = a$, then f is nondifferentiable at a and $f'(a)$ does not exist.

3-5 Basic Differentiation Properties

- The derivative of a constant function is 0.
- For any real number n, the derivative of $f(x) = x^n$ is nx^{n-1}.
- If f is a differential function, then the derivative of $kf(x)$ is $kf'(x)$.
- The derivative of the sum or difference of two differential functions is the sum or difference of the derivatives of the functions.

3-6 Differentials

- Given the function $y = f(x)$, the change in x is also called the **increment of x** and is denoted as Δx. The corresponding change in y is called the **increment of y** and is given by $\Delta y = f(x + \Delta x) - f(x)$.

- If $y = f(x)$ is differentiable at x, then the **differential of x** is $dx = \Delta x$ and the **differential of $y = f(x)$** is $dy = f'(x)dx$, or $df = f'(x)dx$. In this context, x and dx are both independent variables.

Ex. 1, p. 188
Ex. 2, p. 190
Ex. 3, p. 191

3-7 Marginal Analysis in Business and Economics

- If $y = C(x)$ is the total cost of producing x items, then $y = C'(x)$ is the **marginal cost** and $C(x + 1) - C(x)$ is the exact cost of producing item $x + 1$. Furthermore, $C'(x) \approx C(x + 1) - C(x)$. Similar statements can be made regarding total revenue and total profit functions.

Ex. 1, p. 195
Ex. 2, p. 196

- If $y = C(x)$ is the total cost of producing x items, then the **average cost**, or cost per unit, is $\overline{C}(x) = \dfrac{C(x)}{x}$ and the **marginal average cost** is $\overline{C}'(x) = \dfrac{d}{dx}\overline{C}(x)$. Similar statements can be made regarding total revenue and total profit functions.

Ex. 3, p. 199

Review Exercises

Work through all the problems in this chapter review, and check your answers in the back of the book. Answers to all review problems are there, along with section numbers in italics to indicate where each type of problem is discussed. Where weaknesses show up, review appropriate sections of the text.

Many of the problems in this exercise set ask you to find a derivative. Most of the answers to these problems contain both an unsimplified form and a simplified form of the derivative. When checking your work, first check that you applied the rules correctly, and then check that you performed the algebraic simplification correctly.

A

1. Find the indicated quantities for $y = f(x) = 2x^2 + 5$:

   (A) The change in y if x changes from 1 to 3

   (B) The average rate of change of y with respect to x if x changes from 1 to 3

   (C) The slope of the secant line through the points $(1, f(1))$ and $(3, f(3))$ on the graph of $y = f(x)$

   (D) The instantaneous rate of change of y with respect to x at $x = 1$

   (E) The slope of the line tangent to the graph of $y = f(x)$ at $x = 1$

   (F) $f'(1)$

2. Use the four-step process to find $f'(x)$ for $f(x) = -3x + 2$.

3. If $\lim\limits_{x \to 1} f(x) = 2$ and $\lim\limits_{x \to 1} g(x) = 4$, find

   (A) $\lim\limits_{x \to 1}(5f(x) + 3g(x))$

   (B) $\lim\limits_{x \to 1}[f(x)g(x)]$

   (C) $\lim\limits_{x \to 1}\dfrac{g(x)}{f(x)}$

   (D) $\lim\limits_{x \to 1}[5 + 2x - 3g(x)]$

In Problems 4–10, use the graph of f to estimate the indicated limits and function values.

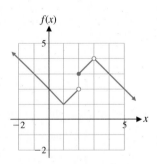

Figure for 4–10

4. $f(1.5)$

5. $f(2.5)$

6. $f(2.75)$

7. $f(3.25)$

8. (A) $\lim\limits_{x \to 1^-} f(x)$ (B) $\lim\limits_{x \to 1^+} f(x)$

   (C) $\lim\limits_{x \to 1} f(x)$ (D) $f(1)$

9. (A) $\lim\limits_{x \to 2^-} f(x)$ (B) $\lim\limits_{x \to 2^+} f(x)$

   (C) $\lim\limits_{x \to 2} f(x)$ (D) $f(2)$

10. (A) $\lim\limits_{x \to 3^-} f(x)$ (B) $\lim\limits_{x \to 3^+} f(x)$

    (C) $\lim\limits_{x \to 3} f(x)$ (D) $f(3)$

In Problems 11–13, use the graph of the function f shown in the figure to answer each question.

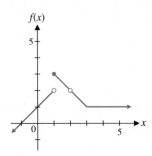

Figure for 11–13

11. (A) $\lim\limits_{x \to 1} f(x) = ?$ (B) $f(1) = ?$
(C) Is f continuous at $x = 1$?

12. (A) $\lim\limits_{x \to 2} f(x) = ?$ (B) $f(2) = ?$
(C) Is f continuous at $x = 2$?

13. (A) $\lim\limits_{x \to 3} f(x) = ?$ (B) $f(3) = ?$
(C) Is f continuous at $x = 3$?

In Problems 14–23, refer to the following graph of $y = f(x)$:

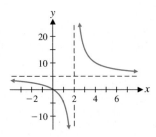

Figure for 14–23

14. $\lim\limits_{x \to \infty} f(x) = ?$ **15.** $\lim\limits_{x \to -\infty} f(x) = ?$

16. $\lim\limits_{x \to 2^+} f(x) = ?$ **17.** $\lim\limits_{x \to 2^-} f(x) = ?$

18. $\lim\limits_{x \to 0^-} f(x) = ?$ **19.** $\lim\limits_{x \to 0^+} f(x) = ?$

20. $\lim\limits_{x \to 0} f(x) = ?$

21. Identify any vertical asymptotes.

22. Identify any horizontal asymptotes.

23. Where is $y = f(x)$ discontinuous?

24. Use the four-step process to find $f'(x)$ for $f(x) = 5x^2$.

25. If $f(5) = 4$, $f'(5) = -1$, $g(5) = 2$, and $g'(5) = -3$, then find $h'(5)$ for each of the following functions:
(A) $h(x) = 3f(x)$
(B) $h(x) = -2g(x)$
(C) $h(x) = 2f(x) + 5$
(D) $h(x) = -g(x) - 1$
(E) $h(x) = 2f(x) + 3g(x)$

In Problems 26–31, find $f'(x)$ and simplify.

26. $f(x) = \dfrac{1}{3}x^3 - 5x^2 + 1$ **27.** $f(x) = 2x^{1/2} - 3x$

28. $f(x) = 5$ **29.** $f(x) = \dfrac{3}{2x} + \dfrac{5x^3}{4}$

30. $f(x) = \dfrac{0.5}{x^4} + 0.25x^4$

31. $f(x) = (3x^3 - 2)(x + 1)$ (*Hint:* Multiply and then differentiate.)

In Problems 32–35, find the indicated quantities for $y = f(x) = x^2 + x$.

32. Δx, Δy, and $\Delta y / \Delta x$ for $x_1 = 1$ and $x_2 = 3$.

33. $[f(x_1 + \Delta x) - f(x_1)]/\Delta x$ for $x_1 = 1$ and $\Delta x = 2$.

34. dy for $x_1 = 1$ and $x_2 = 3$.

35. Δy and dy for $x = 1$, $\Delta x = dx = 0.2$.

B

Problems 36–38 refer to the function.

$$f(x) = \begin{cases} x^2 & \text{if } 0 \le x < 2 \\ 8 - x & \text{if } x \ge 2 \end{cases}$$

which is graphed in the figure.

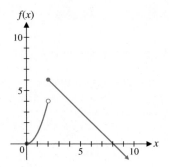

Figure for 36–38

36. (A) $\lim\limits_{x \to 2^-} f(x) = ?$ (B) $\lim\limits_{x \to 2^+} f(x) = ?$
(C) $\lim\limits_{x \to 2} f(x) = ?$ (D) $f(2) = ?$
(E) Is f continuous at $x = 2$?

37. (A) $\lim\limits_{x \to 5^-} f(x) = ?$ (B) $\lim\limits_{x \to 5^+} f(x) = ?$
(C) $\lim\limits_{x \to 5} f(x) = ?$ (D) $f(5) = ?$
(E) Is f continuous at $x = 5$?

38. Solve each inequality. Express answers in interval notation.
(A) $f(x) < 0$ (B) $f(x) \ge 0$

In Problems 39–41, solve each inequality. Express the answer in interval notation. Use a graphing calculator in Problem 41 to approximate partition numbers to four decimal places.

39. $x^2 - x < 12$ **40.** $\dfrac{x - 5}{x^2 + 3x} > 0$

41. $x^3 + x^2 - 4x - 2 > 0$

42. Let $f(x) = 0.5x^2 - 5$.
(A) Find the slope of the secant line through $(2, f(2))$ and $(4, f(4))$.
(B) Find the slope of the secant line through $(2, f(2))$ and $(2 + h, f(2 + h))$, $h \ne 0$.
(C) Find the slope of the tangent line at $x = 2$.

In Problems 43–46, find the indicated derivative and simplify.

43. $\dfrac{dy}{dx}$ for $y = \dfrac{1}{3}x^{-3} - 5x^{-2} + 1$

44. y' for $y = \dfrac{3\sqrt{x}}{2} + \dfrac{5}{3\sqrt{x}}$

45. $g'(x)$ for $g(x) = 1.8\sqrt[3]{x} + \dfrac{0.9}{\sqrt[3]{x}}$

46. $\dfrac{dy}{dx}$ for $y = \dfrac{2x^3 - 3}{5x^3}$

47. For $y = f(x) = x^2 + 4$, find

    (A) The slope of the graph at $x = 1$

    (B) The equation of the tangent line at $x = 1$ in the form $y = mx + b$

In Problems 48 and 49, find the value(s) of x where the tangent line is horizontal.

48. $f(x) = 10x - x^2$

49. $f(x) = x^3 + 3x^2 - 45x - 135$

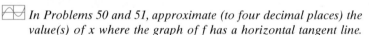 In Problems 50 and 51, approximate (to four decimal places) the value(s) of x where the graph of f has a horizontal tangent line.

50. $f(x) = x^4 - 2x^3 - 5x^2 + 7x$

51. $f(x) = x^5 - 10x^3 - 5x + 10$

52. If an object moves along the y axis (scale in feet) so that it is at $y = f(x) = 8x^2 - 4x + 1$ at time x (in seconds), find

    (A) The instantaneous velocity function

    (B) The velocity at time $x = 3$ seconds

53. An object moves along the y axis (scale in feet) so that at time x (in seconds) it is at $y = f(x) = -5x^2 + 16x + 3$. Find

    (A) The instantaneous velocity function

    (B) The time(s) when the velocity is 0

54. Let $f(x) = x^3$, $g(x) = (x - 4)^3$, and $h(x) = (x + 3)^3$.

    (A) How are the graphs of f, g, and h related? Illustrate your conclusion by graphing f, g, and h on the same co-ordinate axes.

    (B) How would you expect the graphs of the derivatives of these functions to be related? Illustrate your conclusion by graphing f', g', and h' on the same coordinate axes.

In Problems 55–59, determine where f is continuous. Express the answer in interval notation.

55. $f(x) = x^2 - 4$ **56.** $f(x) = \dfrac{x + 1}{x - 2}$

57. $f(x) = \dfrac{x + 4}{x^2 + 3x - 4}$ **58.** $f(x) = \sqrt[3]{4 - x^2}$

59. $f(x) = \sqrt{4 - x^2}$

In Problems 60–69, evaluate the indicated limits if they exist.

60. Let $f(x) = \dfrac{2x}{x^2 - 3x}$. Find

    (A) $\lim\limits_{x \to 1} f(x)$ (B) $\lim\limits_{x \to 3} f(x)$ (C) $\lim\limits_{x \to 0} f(x)$

61. Let $f(x) = \dfrac{x + 1}{(3 - x)^2}$. Find

    (A) $\lim\limits_{x \to 1} f(x)$ (B) $\lim\limits_{x \to -1} f(x)$ (C) $\lim\limits_{x \to 3} f(x)$

62. Let $f(x) = \dfrac{|x - 4|}{x - 4}$. Find

    (A) $\lim\limits_{x \to 4^-} f(x)$ (B) $\lim\limits_{x \to 4^+} f(x)$ (C) $\lim\limits_{x \to 4} f(x)$

63. Let $f(x) = \dfrac{x - 3}{9 - x^2}$. Find

    (A) $\lim\limits_{x \to 3} f(x)$ (B) $\lim\limits_{x \to -3} f(x)$ (C) $\lim\limits_{x \to 0} f(x)$

64. Let $f(x) = \dfrac{x^2 - x - 2}{x^2 - 7x + 10}$. Find

    (A) $\lim\limits_{x \to -1} f(x)$ (B) $\lim\limits_{x \to 2} f(x)$ (C) $\lim\limits_{x \to 5} f(x)$

65. Let $f(x) = \dfrac{2x}{3x - 6}$. Find

    (A) $\lim\limits_{x \to \infty} f(x)$ (B) $\lim\limits_{x \to -\infty} f(x)$ (C) $\lim\limits_{x \to 2} f(x)$

66. Let $f(x) = \dfrac{2x^3}{3(x - 2)^2}$. Find

    (A) $\lim\limits_{x \to \infty} f(x)$ (B) $\lim\limits_{x \to -\infty} f(x)$ (C) $\lim\limits_{x \to 2} f(x)$

67. Let $f(x) = \dfrac{2x}{3(x - 2)^3}$. Find

    (A) $\lim\limits_{x \to \infty} f(x)$ (B) $\lim\limits_{x \to -\infty} f(x)$ (C) $\lim\limits_{x \to 2} f(x)$

68. $\lim\limits_{h \to 0} \dfrac{f(2 + h) - f(2)}{h}$ for $f(x) = x^2 + 4$

69. $\lim\limits_{h \to 0} \dfrac{f(x + h) - f(x)}{h}$ for $f(x) = \dfrac{1}{x + 2}$

In Problems 70 and 71, use the definition of the derivative and the four-step process to find f'(x).

70. $f(x) = x^2 - x$ **71.** $f(x) = \sqrt{x} - 3$

C

Problems 72–77 refer to the function f in the figure. Determine whether f is differentiable at the indicated value of x.

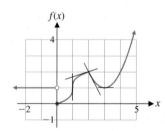

72. $x = -1$ **73.** $x = 0$

74. $x = 1$ **75.** $x = 2$

76. $x = 3$ **77.** $x = 4$

In Problems 78–82, find all horizontal and vertical asymptotes.

78. $f(x) = \dfrac{5x}{x - 7}$ **79.** $f(x) = \dfrac{-2x + 5}{(x - 4)^2}$

80. $f(x) = \dfrac{x^2 + 9}{x - 3}$ **81.** $f(x) = \dfrac{x^2 - 9}{x^2 + x - 2}$

82. $f(x) = \dfrac{x^3 - 1}{x^3 - x^2 - x + 1}$

83. The domain of the power function $f(x) = x^{1/5}$ is the set of all real numbers. Find the domain of the derivative $f'(x)$. Discuss the nature of the graph of $y = f(x)$ for any x values excluded from the domain of $f'(x)$.

84. Let f be defined by

$$f(x) = \begin{cases} x^2 - m & \text{if } x \le 1 \\ -x^2 + m & \text{if } x > 1 \end{cases}$$

where m is a constant.

(A) Graph f for $m = 0$, and find

$$\lim_{x \to 1^-} f(x) \quad \text{and} \quad \lim_{x \to 1^+} f(x)$$

(B) Graph f for $m = 2$, and find

$$\lim_{x \to 1^-} f(x) \quad \text{and} \quad \lim_{x \to 1^+} f(x)$$

(C) Find m so that

$$\lim_{x \to 1^-} f(x) = \lim_{x \to 1^+} f(x)$$

and graph f for this value of m.

(D) Write a brief verbal description of each graph. How does the graph in part (C) differ from the graphs in parts (A) and (B)?

85. Let $f(x) = 1 - |x - 1|, 0 \le x \le 2$ (see the figure).

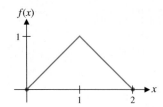

Figure for 85

(A) $\displaystyle\lim_{h \to 0^-} \dfrac{f(1 + h) - f(1)}{h} = ?$

(B) $\displaystyle\lim_{h \to 0^+} \dfrac{f(1 + h) - f(1)}{h} = ?$

(C) $\displaystyle\lim_{h \to 0} \dfrac{f(1 + h) - f(1)}{h} = ?$

(D) Does $f'(1)$ exist?

Applications

86. Natural-gas rates. Table 1 shows the winter rates for natural gas charged by the Bay State Gas Company. The customer charge is a fixed monthly charge, independent of the amount of gas used per month.

Table 1 Natural Gas Rates	
Monthly customer charge	$7.47
First 90 therms	$0.4000 per therm
All usage over 90 therms	$0.2076 per therm

(A) Write a piecewise definition of the monthly charge $S(x)$ for a customer who uses x therms in a winter month.

(B) Graph $S(x)$.

(C) Is $S(x)$ continuous at $x = 90$? Explain.

87. Cost analysis. The total cost (in dollars) of producing x HDTVs is

$$C(x) = 10{,}000 + 200x - 0.1x^2$$

(A) Find the exact cost of producing the 101st TV.

(B) Use the marginal cost to approximate the cost of producing the 101st TV.

88. Cost analysis. The total cost (in dollars) of producing x bicycles is

$$C(x) = 5{,}000 + 40x + 0.05x^2$$

(A) Find the total cost and the marginal cost at a production level of 100 bicycles and interpret the results.

(B) Find the average cost and the marginal average cost at a production level of 100 bicycles and interpret the results.

89. Cost analysis. The total cost (in dollars) of producing x laser printers per week is shown in the figure. Which is greater, the approximate cost of producing the 201st printer or the approximate cost of producing the 601st printer? Does this graph represent a manufacturing process that is becoming more efficient or less efficient as production levels increase? Explain.

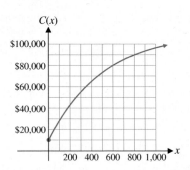

Figure for 89

90. Cost analysis. Let

$$p = 25 - 0.01x \quad \text{and} \quad C(x) = 2x + 9{,}000$$
$$0 \le x \le 2{,}500$$

be the price–demand equation and cost function, respectively, for the manufacture of umbrellas.

(A) Find the marginal cost, average cost, and marginal average cost functions.

(B) Express the revenue in terms of x, and find the marginal revenue, average revenue, and marginal average revenue functions.

(C) Find the profit, marginal profit, average profit, and marginal average profit functions.

(D) Find the break-even point(s).

(E) Evaluate the marginal profit at $x = 1{,}000, 1{,}150$, and $1{,}400$, and interpret the results.

(F) Graph $R = R(x)$ and $C = C(x)$ on the same coordinate system, and locate regions of profit and loss.

91. Employee training. A company producing computer components has established that, on average, a new employee can assemble $N(t)$ components per day after t days of on-the-job training, as given by

$$N(t) = \frac{40t - 80}{t}, t \geq 2$$

(A) Find the average rate of change of $N(t)$ from 2 days to 5 days.

(B) Find the instantaneous rate of change of $N(t)$ at 2 days.

92. Sales analysis. The total number of swimming pools, N (in thousands), sold during a year is given by

$$N(t) = 2t + \frac{1}{3}t^{3/2}$$

where t is the number of months since the beginning of the year. Find $N(9)$ and $N'(9)$, and interpret these quantities.

93. Natural-gas consumption. The data in Table 2 give the U.S. consumption of natural gas in trillions of cubic feet.

Table 2

Year	Natural-Gas Consumption
1960	12.0
1970	21.1
1980	19.9
1990	18.7
2000	21.9

(A) Let x represent time (in years), with $x = 0$ corresponding to 1960, and let y represent the corresponding U.S. consumption of natural gas. Enter the data set in a graphing calculator and find a cubic regression equation for the data.

(B) If $y = N(x)$ denotes the regression equation found in part (A), find $N(50)$ and $N'(50)$, and write a brief verbal interpretation of these results.

94. Break-even analysis. Table 3 contains price–demand and total cost data from a bakery for the production of kringles (a Danish pastry), where p is the price (in dollars) of a kringle for a daily demand of x kringles and C is the total cost (in dollars) of producing x kringles.

Table 3

x	$p(\$)$	$C(\$)$
125	9	740
140	8	785
170	7	850
200	6	900

(A) Find a linear regression equation for the price–demand data, using x as the independent variable.

(B) Find a linear regression equation for the cost data, using x as the independent variable. Use this equation to estimate the fixed costs and variable costs per kringle.

(C) Find the break-even points.

(D) Find the price range for which the bakery will make a profit.

95. Pollution. A sewage treatment plant uses a pipeline that extends 1 mile toward the center of a large lake. The concentration of effluent $C(x)$ in parts per million, x meters from the end of the pipe is given approximately by

$$C(x) = \frac{500}{x^2}, x \geq 1$$

What is the instantaneous rate of change of concentration at 10 meters? At 100 meters?

96. Medicine. The body temperature (in degrees Fahrenheit) of a patient t hours after taking a fever-reducing drug is given by

$$F(t) = 0.16t^2 - 1.6t + 102$$

Find $F(4)$ and $F'(4)$. Write a brief verbal interpretation of these quantities.

97. Learning. If a person learns N items in t hours, as given by

$$N(t) = 20\sqrt{t}$$

find the rate of learning after

(A) 1 hour   (B) 4 hours

98. Physics: The coefficient of thermal expansion (CTE) is a measure of the expansion of an object subjected to extreme temperatures. We want to use a Michaelis–Menten function of the form

$$C(T) = \frac{C_{max}T}{M + T}$$

where C = CTE, T is temperature in K (degrees Kelvin), and C_{max} and M are constants. Table 4 lists the coefficients of thermal expansion for titanium at various temperatures.

Table 4   Coefficients of Thermal Expansion

T (K)	Titanium
100	4.5
200	7.4
293	8.6
500	9.9
800	11.1
1100	11.7

(A) Plot the points in columns 1 and 2 of Table 4 on graph paper and estimate C_{max} to the nearest integer. To estimate M, add the horizontal line CTE = $\frac{C_{max}}{2}$ to your graph, connect successive points on the graph with straight-line segments, and estimate the value of T (to the nearest multiple of fifty) that satisfies

$$C(T) = \frac{C_{max}}{2}.$$

(B) Use the constants $\frac{C_{max}}{2}$ and M from part (A) to form a Michaelis–Menten function for the CTE of titanium.

(C) Use the function from part (B) to estimate the CTE of titanium at 600 K and to estimate the temperature when the CTE of titanium is 10.

Additional Derivative Topics

Introduction

In this chapter, we develop techniques for finding derivatives of a wide variety of functions, including exponential and logarithmic functions. There are straightforward procedures—the product rule, quotient rule, and chain rule—for writing down the derivative of any function that is the product, quotient, or composite of functions whose derivatives are known. With the ability to calculate derivatives easily, we consider a wealth of applications involving rates of change. For example, we apply the derivative to study population growth, radioactive decay, elasticity of demand, and environmental crises (see Problem 31 in Section 4-6 or Problem 71 in Section 4-7). Before starting this chapter, you may find it helpful to review the basic properties of exponential and logarithmic functions in Sections 2-5 and 2-6.

4-1   The Constant *e* and Continuous Compound Interest

- The Constant *e*
- Continuous Compound Interest

In Chapter 2, both the exponential function with base *e* and continuous compound interest were introduced informally. Now, with an understanding of limit concepts, we can give precise definitions of *e* and continuous compound interest.

The Constant *e*

The irrational number *e* is a particularly suitable base for both exponential and logarithmic functions. The reasons for choosing this number as a base will become clear as we develop differentiation formulas for the exponential function e^x and the natural logarithmic function ln *x*.

In precalculus treatments (Chapter 2), the number *e* is defined informally as the irrational number that can be approximated by the expression $[1 + (1/n)]^n$ for *n* sufficiently large. Now we will use the limit concept to formally define *e* as either of the following two limits. [*Note:* If $s = 1/n$, then as $n \to \infty$, $s \to 0$.]

DEFINITION   The Number *e*

$$e = \lim_{n \to \infty} \left(1 + \frac{1}{n}\right)^n \qquad \text{or, alternatively,} \qquad e = \lim_{s \to 0}(1 + s)^{1/s}$$

Both limits are equal to $e = 2.718\ 281\ 828\ 459\ldots$

Proof that the indicated limits exist and represent an irrational number between 2 and 3 is not easy and is omitted.

CONCEPTUAL INSIGHT

The two limits used to define *e* are unlike any we have encountered so far. Some people reason (incorrectly) that both limits are 1, since $1 + s \to 1$ as $s \to 0$ and 1 to any power is 1. An ordinary scientific calculator with a y^x key can convince you otherwise. Consider the following table of values for *s* and $f(s) = (1 + s)^{1/s}$ and Figure 1 for *s* close to 0. Compute the table values with a calculator yourself, and try several values of *s* even closer to 0. Note that the function is discontinuous at $s = 0$.

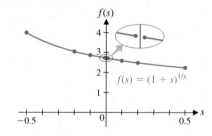

Figure 1

s approaches 0 from the left → 0 ← *s approaches 0 from the right*

s	−0.5	−0.2	−0.1	−0.01 → 0 ← 0.01	0.1	0.2	0.5
$(1 + s)^{1/s}$	4.0000	3.0518	2.8680	2.7320 → e ← 2.7048	2.5937	2.4883	2.2500

Continuous Compound Interest

Now we can see how *e* appears quite naturally in the important application of compound interest. Let us start with simple interest, move on to compound interest, and then proceed on to continuous compound interest.

On one hand, if a principal P is borrowed at an annual rate r,* then after t years at simple interest, the borrower will owe the lender an amount A given by

$$A = P + Prt = P(1 + rt) \quad \text{Simple interest} \tag{1}$$

On the other hand, if interest is compounded n times a year, then the borrower will owe the lender an amount A given by

$$A = P\left(1 + \frac{r}{n}\right)^{nt} \quad \text{Compound interest} \tag{2}$$

where r/n is the interest rate per compounding period and nt is the number of compounding periods. Suppose that $P, r,$ and t in equation (2) are held fixed and n is increased. Will the amount A increase without bound, or will it tend to approach some limiting value?

Let us perform a calculator experiment before we attack the general limit problem. If $P = \$100$, $r = 0.06$, and $t = 2$ years, then

$$A = 100\left(1 + \frac{0.06}{n}\right)^{2n}$$

We compute A for several values of n in Table 1. The biggest gain appears in the first step, then the gains slow down as n increases. The amount A appears to approach $\$112.75$ as n gets larger and larger.

Table 1

Compounding Frequency	n	$A = 100\left(1 + \dfrac{0.06}{n}\right)^{2n}$
Annually	1	\$112.3600
Semiannually	2	112.5509
Quarterly	4	112.6493
Monthly	12	112.7160
Weekly	52	112.7419
Daily	365	112.7486
Hourly	8,760	112.7496

Keeping $P, r,$ and t fixed in equation (2), we compute the following limit and observe an interesting and useful result:

$$\lim_{n \to \infty} P\left(1 + \frac{r}{n}\right)^{nt} = P \lim_{n \to \infty} \left(1 + \frac{r}{n}\right)^{(n/r)rt} \quad \text{Insert } r/r \text{ in the exponent and}$$
$$\text{let } s = r/n. \text{ Note that}$$
$$n \to \infty \text{ implies } s \to 0.$$
$$= P \lim_{s \to 0} [(1 + s)^{1/s}]^{rt} \quad \text{Use a limit property.}^\dagger$$
$$= P[\lim_{s \to 0} (1 + s)^{1/s}]^{rt} \quad \lim_{s \to 0} (1 + s)^{1/s} = e$$
$$= Pe^{rt}$$

The resulting formula is called the **continuous compound interest formula**, a widely used formula in business and economics.

THEOREM 1 Continuous Compound Interest Formula
If a principal P is invested at an annual rate r (expressed as a decimal) compounded continuously, then the amount A in the account at the end of t years is given by

$$A = Pe^{rt}$$

---

*If r is the interest rate written as a decimal, then $100r\%$ is the rate in percent. For example, if $r = 0.12$, then $100r\% = 100(0.12)\% = 12\%$. The expressions 0.12 and 12% are equivalent. Unless stated otherwise, all formulas in this book use r in decimal form.

†The following new limit property is used: If $\lim_{x \to c} f(x)$ exists, then $\lim_{x \to c}[f(x)]^p = [\lim_{x \to c} f(x)]^p$, provided that the last expression names a real number.

EXAMPLE 1   **Computing Continuously Compounded Interest** If $100 is invested at 6% compounded continuously,* what amount will be in the account after 2 years? How much interest will be earned?

SOLUTION

$$A = Pe^{rt}$$
$$= 100e^{(0.06)(2)} \qquad \textit{6\% is equivalent to r = 0.06.}$$
$$\approx \$112.7497$$

Compare this result with the values calculated in Table 1. The interest earned is $112.7497 − $100 = $12.7497.

Matched Problem 1   What amount (to the nearest cent) will be in an account after 5 years if $100 is invested at an annual nominal rate of 8% compounded annually? Semiannually? Continuously?

EXAMPLE 2   **Graphing the Growth of an Investment** Union Savings Bank offers a 5-year certificate of deposit (CD) that earns 5.75% compounded continuously. If $1,000 is invested in one of these CDs, graph the amount in the account as a function of time for a period of 5 years.

SOLUTION   We want to graph

$$A = 1,000e^{0.0575t} \qquad 0 \le t \le 5$$

Using a calculator, we construct a table of values (Table 2). Then we graph the points from the table and join the points with a smooth curve (Fig. 2).

Table 2

t	$A(\$)$
0	1,000
1	1,059
2	1,122
3	1,188
4	1,259
5	1,333

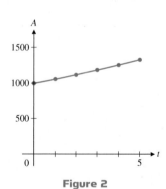

Figure 2

CONCEPTUAL INSIGHT

Depending on the domain, the graph of an exponential function can appear to be linear. Table 2 shows that the graph in Figure 2 is *not* linear. The slope determined by the first two points (for $t = 0$ and $t = 1$) is 59 but the slope determined by the first and third points (for $t = 0$ and $t = 2$) is 61. For a linear graph, the slope determined by any two points is constant.

Matched Problem 2   If $5,000 is invested in a Union Savings Bank 4-year CD that earns 5.61% compounded continuously, graph the amount in the account as a function of time for a period of 4 years.

---
*Following common usage, we will often write "at 6% compounded continuously," understanding that this means "at an annual nominal rate of 6% compounded continuously."

EXAMPLE 3   **Computing Growth Time** How long will it take an investment of $5,000 to grow to $8,000 if it is invested at 5% compounded continuously?

SOLUTION   Starting with the continous compound interest formula $A = Pe^{rt}$, we must solve for t:

$$A = Pe^{rt}$$
$$8,000 = 5,000e^{0.05t}$$
$$e^{0.05t} = 1.6$$
$$\ln e^{0.05t} = \ln 1.6$$
$$0.05t = \ln 1.6$$
$$t = \frac{\ln 1.6}{0.05}$$
$$t \approx 9.4 \text{ years}$$

Divide both sides by 5,000 and reverse the equation.

Take the natural logarithm of both sides—recall that $\log_b b^x = x$.

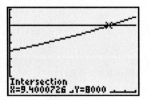

Figure 3
$y_1 = 5,000e^{0.05x}$
$y_2 = 8,000$

   Figure 3 shows an alternative method for solving Example 3 on a graphing calculator.

Matched Problem 3   How long will it take an investment of $10,000 to grow to $15,000 if it is invested at 9% compounded continuously?

EXAMPLE 4   **Computing Doubling Time** How long will it take money to double if it is invested at 6.5% compounded continuously?

SOLUTION   Starting with the continuous compound interest formula $A = Pe^{rt}$, we solve for t, given $A = 2P$ and $R = 0.065$:

$$2P = Pe^{0.065t}$$
$$e^{0.065t} = 2$$
$$\ln e^{0.065t} = \ln 2$$
$$0.065t = \ln 2$$
$$t = \frac{\ln 2}{0.065}$$
$$t \approx 10.66 \text{ years}$$

Divide both sides by P and reverse the equation.
Take the natural logarithm of both sides.

Matched Problem 4   How long will it take money to triple if it is invested at 5.5% compounded continuously?

EXPLORE & DISCUSS 1   You are considering three options for investing $10,000: at 7% compounded annually, at 6% compounded monthly, and at 5% compounded continuously.

(A) Which option would be the best for investing $10,000 for 8 years?

(B) How long would you need to invest your money for the third option to be the best?

Exercises 4-1

A

Use a calculator to evaluate A to the nearest cent in Problems 1 and 2.

1. $A = \$1,000e^{0.1t}$ for $t = 2, 5,$ and 8

2. $A = \$5,000e^{0.08t}$ for $t = 1, 4,$ and 10

3. If $6,000 is invested at 10% compounded continuously, graph the amount in the account as a function of time for a period of 8 years.

4. If $4,000 is invested at 8% compounded continuously, graph the amount in the account as a function of time for a period of 6 years.

B

In Problems 5–10, solve for t or r to two decimal places.

5. $2 = e^{0.06t}$
6. $2 = e^{0.03t}$

7. $3 = e^{0.1r}$
8. $3 = e^{0.25t}$

9. $2 = e^{5r}$
10. $3 = e^{10r}$

C

In Problems 11 and 12, use a calculator to complete each table to five decimal places.

11.

n	$[1 + (1/n)]^n$
10	2.593 74
100	
1,000	
10,000	
100,000	
1,000,000	
10,000,000	
↓	↓
∞	$e = 2.718\ 281\ 828\ 459\ldots$

12.

s	$(1 + s)^{1/s}$
0.01	2.704 81
−0.01	
0.001	
−0.001	
0.000 1	
−0.000 1	
0.000 01	
−0.000 01	
↓	↓
0	$e = 2.718\ 281\ 828\ 459\ldots$

13. Use a calculator and a table of values to investigate

$$\lim_{n \to \infty} (1 + n)^{1/n}$$

Do you think this limit exists? If so, what do you think it is?

14. Use a calculator and a table of values to investigate

$$\lim_{s \to 0^+} \left(1 + \frac{1}{s}\right)^s$$

Do you think this limit exists? If so, what do you think it is?

15. It can be shown that the number *e* satisfies the inequality

$$\left(1 + \frac{1}{n}\right)^n < e < \left(1 + \frac{1}{n}\right)^{n+1} \qquad n \geq 1$$

Illustrate this condition by graphing

$$y_1 = (1 + 1/n)^n$$
$$y_2 = 2.718\ 281\ 828 \approx e$$
$$y_3 = (1 + 1/n)^{n+1}$$

in the same viewing window, for $1 \leq n \leq 20$.

16. It can be shown that

$$e^s = \lim_{n \to \infty} \left(1 + \frac{s}{n}\right)^n$$

for any real number *s*. Illustrate this equation graphically for $s = 2$ by graphing

$$y_1 = (1 + 2/n)^n$$
$$y_2 = 7.389\ 056\ 099 \approx e^2$$

in the same viewing window, for $1 \leq n \leq 50$.

Applications

17. **Continuous compound interest.** Provident Bank offers a 10-year CD that earns 4.15% compounded continuously.

(A) If $10,000 is invested in this CD, how much will it be worth in 10 years?

(B) How long will it take for the account to be worth $18,000?

18. **Continuous compound interest.** Provident Bank also offers a 3-year CD that earns 3.64% compounded continuously.

(A) If $10,000 is invested in this CD, how much will it be worth in 3 years?

(B) How long will it take for the account to be worth $11,000?

19. **Present value.** A note will pay $20,000 at maturity 10 years from now. How much should you be willing to pay for the note now if money is worth 5.2% compounded continuously?

20. **Present value.** A note will pay $50,000 at maturity 5 years from now. How much should you be willing to pay for the note now if money is worth 6.4% compounded continuously?

21. **Continuous compound interest.** An investor bought stock for $20,000. Five years later, the stock was sold for $30,000. If interest is compounded continuously, what annual nominal rate of interest did the original $20,000 investment earn?

22. Continuous compound interest. A family paid $99,000 cash for a house. Fifteen years later, the house was sold for $195,000. If interest is compounded continuously, what annual nominal rate of interest did the original $99,000 investment earn?

23. Present value. Solving $A = Pe^{rt}$ for P, we obtain

$$P = Ae^{-rt}$$

which is the present value of the amount A due in t years if money earns interest at an annual nominal rate r compounded continuously.

(A) Graph $P = 10,000e^{-0.08t}, 0 \le t \le 50$.

(B) $\lim_{t \to \infty} 10,000e^{-0.08t} = ?$ [Guess, using part (A).]

[*Conclusion:* The longer the time until the amount A is due, the smaller is its present value, as we would expect.]

24. Present value. Referring to Problem 23, in how many years will the $10,000 be due in order for its present value to be $5,000?

25. Doubling time. How long will it take money to double if it is invested at 4% compounded continuously?

26. Doubling time. How long will it take money to double if it is invested at 5% compounded continuously?

27. Doubling rate. At what nominal rate compounded continuously must money be invested to double in 8 years?

28. Doubling rate. At what nominal rate compounded continuously must money be invested to double in 10 years?

29. Growth time. A man with $20,000 to invest decides to diversify his investments by placing $10,000 in an account that earns 7.2% compounded continuously and $10,000 in an account that earns 8.4% compounded annually. Use graphical approximation methods to determine how long it will take for his total investment in the two accounts to grow to $35,000.

30. Growth time. A woman invests $5,000 in an account that earns 8.8% compounded continuously and $7,000 in an account that earns 9.6% compounded annually. Use graphical approximation methods to determine how long it will take for her total investment in the two accounts to grow to $20,000.

31. Doubling times

(A) Show that the doubling time t (in years) at an annual rate r compounded continuously is given by

$$t = \frac{\ln 2}{r}$$

(B) Graph the doubling-time equation from part (A) for $0.02 \le r \le 0.30$. Is this restriction on r reasonable? Explain.

(C) Determine the doubling times (in years, to two decimal places) for $r = 5\%, 10\%, 15\%, 20\%, 25\%,$ and 30%.

32. Doubling rates

(A) Show that the rate r that doubles an investment at continuously compounded interest in t years is given by

$$r = \frac{\ln 2}{t}$$

(B) Graph the doubling-rate equation from part (A) for $1 \le t \le 20$. Is this restriction on t reasonable? Explain.

(C) Determine the doubling rates for $t = 2, 4, 6, 8, 10,$ and 12 years.

33. Radioactive decay. A mathematical model for the decay of radioactive substances is given by

$$Q = Q_0 e^{rt}$$

where

Q_0 = amount of the substance at time $t = 0$
r = continuous compound rate of decay
t = time in years
Q = amount of the substance at time t

If the continuous compound rate of decay of radium per year is $r = -0.000\,433\,2$, how long will it take a certain amount of radium to decay to half the original amount? (This period is the *half-life* of the substance.)

34. Radioactive decay. The continuous compound rate of decay of carbon-14 per year is $r = -0.000\,123\,8$. How long will it take a certain amount of carbon-14 to decay to half the original amount? (Use the radioactive decay model in Problem 33.)

35. Radioactive decay. A cesium isotope has a half-life of 30 years. What is the continuous compound rate of decay? (Use the radioactive decay model in Problem 33.)

36. Radioactive decay. A strontium isotope has a half-life of 90 years. What is the continuous compound rate of decay? (Use the radioactive decay model in Problem 33.)

37. World population. A mathematical model for world population growth over short intervals is given by

$$P = P_0 e^{rt}$$

where

P_0 = population at time $t = 0$
r = continuous compound rate of growth
t = time in years
P = population at time t

How long will it take world population to double if it continues to grow at its current continuous compound rate of 1.3% per year?

38. U.S. population. How long will it take for the U.S. population to double if it continues to grow at a rate of 0.975% per year?

39. Population growth. Some underdeveloped nations have population doubling times of 50 years. At what continuous compound rate is the population growing? (Use the population growth model in Problem 37.)

40. Population growth. Some developed nations have population doubling times of 200 years. At what continuous compound rate is the population growing? (Use the population growth model in Problem 37.)

3. 4.51 yr

4. 19.97 yr

1. $146.93; $148.02; $149.18

2. $A = 5{,}000e^{0.0561t}$

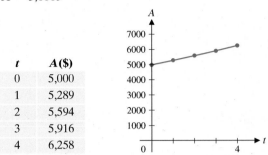

t	A($)
0	5,000
1	5,289
2	5,594
3	5,916
4	6,258

4-2   Derivatives of Exponential and Logarithmic Functions

- The Derivative of e^x
- The Derivative of $\ln x$
- Other Logarithmic and Exponential Functions
- Exponential and Logarithmic Models

In this section, we find formulas for the derivatives of logarithmic and exponential functions. A review of Sections 2–5 and 2–6 may prove helpful. In particular, recall that $f(x) = e^x$ is the exponential function with base $e \approx 2.718$, and the inverse of the function e^x is the natural logarithm function $\ln x$. More generally, if b is a positive real number, $b \neq 1$, then the exponential function b^x with base b, and the logarithmic function $\log_b x$ with base b, are inverses of each other.

The Derivative of e^x

In the process of finding the derivative of e^x, we use (without proof) the fact that

$$\lim_{h \to 0} \frac{e^h - 1}{h} = 1 \tag{1}$$

EXPLORE & DISCUSS 1

Complete Table 1.

Table 1

h	−0.1	−0.01	−0.001	→ 0 ←	0.001	0.01	0.1
$\dfrac{e^h - 1}{h}$							

Do your calculations make it reasonable to conclude that

$$\lim_{h \to 0} \frac{e^h - 1}{h} = 1?$$

Discuss.

We now apply the four-step process (Section 3-4) to the exponential function $f(x) = e^x$.

Step 1 Find $f(x + h)$.
$$f(x + h) = e^{x+h} = e^x e^h \qquad \textit{See Section 2-4.}$$

Step 2 Find $f(x + h) - f(x)$.
$$f(x + h) - f(x) = e^x e^h - e^x \qquad \textit{Factor out } e^x.$$
$$= e^x(e^h - 1)$$

Step 3 Find $\dfrac{f(x + h) - f(x)}{h}$.

$$\frac{f(x + h) - f(x)}{h} = \frac{e^x(e^h - 1)}{h} = e^x\left(\frac{e^h - 1}{h}\right)$$

Step 4 Find $f'(x) = \lim\limits_{h \to 0} \dfrac{f(x + h) - f(x)}{h}$.

$$f'(x) = \lim_{h \to 0} \frac{f(x + h) - f(x)}{h}$$

$$= \lim_{h \to 0} e^x\left(\frac{e^h - 1}{h}\right)$$

$$= e^x \lim_{h \to 0}\left(\frac{e^h - 1}{h}\right) \qquad \text{Use the limit in (1).}$$

$$= e^x \cdot 1 = e^x$$

Therefore,

$$\frac{d}{dx}e^x = e^x \qquad \text{The derivative of the exponential function is the exponential function.}$$

EXAMPLE 1 **Finding Derivatives** Find $f'(x)$ for

(A) $f(x) = 5e^x - 3x^4 + 9x + 16$ (B) $f(x) = -7x^e + 2e^x + e^2$

SOLUTIONS (A) $f'(x) = 5e^x - 12x^3 + 9$ (B) $f'(x) = -7ex^{e-1} + 2e^x$

Remember that e is a real number, so the power rule (Section 3–5) is used to find the derivative of x^e. The derivative of the exponential function e^x, however, is e^x. Note that $e^2 \approx 7.389$ is a constant, so its derivative is 0.

Matched Problem 1 Find $f'(x)$ for

(A) $f(x) = 4e^x + 8x^2 + 7x - 14$ (B) $f(x) = x^7 - x^5 + e^3 - x + e^x$

⚠ **CAUTION**

$$\frac{d}{dx}e^x \neq xe^{x-1} \qquad \frac{d}{dx}e^x = e^x$$

The power rule cannot be used to differentiate the exponential function. The power rule applies to exponential forms x^n, where the exponent is a constant and the base is a variable. In the exponential form e^x, the base is a constant and the exponent is a variable.

The Derivative of ln x

We summarize some important facts about logarithmic functions from Section 2–6:

SUMMARY

Recall that the inverse of an exponential function is called a **logarithmic function**. For $b > 0$ and $b \neq 1$,

Logarithmic form		Exponential form
$y = \log_b x$	is equivalent to	$x = b^y$
Domain: $(0, \infty)$		Domain: $(-\infty, \infty)$
Range: $(-\infty, \infty)$		Range: $(0, \infty)$

The graphs of $y = \log_b x$ and $y = b^x$ are symmetric with respect to the line $y = x$. (See Figure 1.)

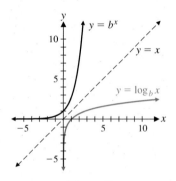

Figure 1

Of all the possible bases for logarithmic functions, the two most widely used are

$$\log x = \log_{10} x \quad \text{Common logarithm (base 10)}$$

$$\ln x = \log_e x \quad \text{Natural logarithm (base e)}$$

We are now ready to use the definition of the derivative and the four-step process discussed in Section 3-4 to find a formula for the derivative of $\ln x$. Later we will extend this formula to include $\log_b x$ for any base b.

Let $f(x) = \ln x$, $x > 0$.

Step 1   Find $f(x + h)$.

$$f(x + h) = \ln(x + h) \quad \text{ln}(x + h) \text{ cannot be simplified.}$$

Step 2   Find $f(x + h) - f(x)$.

$$f(x + h) - f(x) = \ln(x + h) - \ln x \qquad \text{Use ln } A - \text{ln } B = \text{ln } \frac{A}{B}.$$

$$= \ln \frac{x + h}{x}$$

Step 3   Find $\dfrac{f(x + h) - f(x)}{h}$.

$$\frac{f(x + h) - f(x)}{h} = \frac{\ln(x + h) - \ln x}{h}$$

$$= \frac{1}{h} \ln \frac{x + h}{x}$$

$$= \frac{x}{x} \cdot \frac{1}{h} \ln \frac{x + h}{x} \qquad \text{Multiply by } 1 = x/x \text{ to change form.}$$

$$= \frac{1}{x}\left[\frac{x}{h}\ln\left(1 + \frac{h}{x}\right)\right] \qquad \text{Use } p \ln A = \ln A^p.$$

$$= \frac{1}{x}\ln\left(1 + \frac{h}{x}\right)^{x/h}$$

Step 4 Find $f'(x) = \lim_{h\to 0}\dfrac{f(x + h) - f(x)}{h}$.

$$f'(x) = \lim_{h\to 0}\frac{f(x + h) - f(x)}{h}$$

$$= \lim_{h\to 0}\left[\frac{1}{x}\ln\left(1 + \frac{h}{x}\right)^{x/h}\right] \qquad \begin{array}{l}\text{Let } s = h/x. \text{ Note that } h \to 0 \\ \text{implies } s \to 0.\end{array}$$

$$= \frac{1}{x}\lim_{s\to 0}\left[\ln(1 + s)^{1/s}\right] \qquad \text{Use a new limit property.*}$$

$$= \frac{1}{x}\ln\left[\lim_{s\to 0}(1 + s)^{1/s}\right] \qquad \text{Use the definition of } e.$$

$$= \frac{1}{x}\ln e \qquad \ln e = \log_e e = 1$$

$$= \frac{1}{x}$$

Therefore,

$$\frac{d}{dx}\ln x = \frac{1}{x}$$

CONCEPTUAL INSIGHT

In finding the derivative of ln x, we used the following properties of logarithms:

$$\ln\frac{A}{B} = \ln A - \ln B \qquad \ln A^p = p\ln A$$

We also noted that there is no property that simplifies $\ln(A + B)$. (See Theorem 1 in Section 2-6 for a list of properties of logarithms.)

EXAMPLE 2 **Finding Derivatives** Find y' for

(A) $y = 3e^x + 5\ln x$ \qquad (B) $y = x^4 - \ln x^4$

SOLUTIONS (A) $y' = 3e^x + \dfrac{5}{x}$

(B) Before taking the derivative, we use a property of logarithms (see Theorem 1, Section 2-6) to rewrite y.

$$y = x^4 - \ln x^4 \qquad \text{Use } \ln M^p = p\ln M.$$

$$y = x^4 - 4\ln x \qquad \text{Now take the derivative of both sides.}$$

$$y' = 4x^3 - \frac{4}{x}$$

Matched Problem 2 Find y' for

(A) $y = 10x^3 - 100\ln x$ \qquad (B) $y = \ln x^5 + e^x - \ln e^2$

---

*The following new limit property is used: If $\lim_{x\to c} f(x)$ exists and is positive, then $\lim_{x\to c}[\ln f(x)] = \ln[\lim_{x\to c} f(x)]$.

Other Logarithmic and Exponential Functions

In most applications involving logarithmic or exponential functions, the number e is the preferred base. However, in some situations it is convenient to use a base other than e. Derivatives of $y = \log_b x$ and $y = b^x$ can be obtained by expressing these functions in terms of the natural logarithmic and exponential functions.

We begin by finding a relationship between $\log_b x$ and $\ln x$ for any base b such that $b > 0$ and $b \neq 1$.

$$y = \log_b x \qquad \text{Change to exponential form.}$$
$$b^y = x \qquad \text{Take the natural logarithm of both sides.}$$
$$\ln b^y = \ln x \qquad \text{Recall that } \ln b^y = y \ln b.$$
$$y \ln b = \ln x \qquad \text{Solve for y.}$$
$$y = \frac{1}{\ln b} \ln x$$

Therefore,

$$\log_b x = \frac{1}{\ln b} \ln x \qquad \text{Change-of-base formula for logarithms*} \qquad (2)$$

Similarly, we can find a relationship between b^x and e^x for any base b such that $b > 0, b \neq 1$.

$$y = b^x \qquad \text{Take the natural logarithm of both sides.}$$
$$\ln y = \ln b^x \qquad \text{Recall that } \ln b^x = x \ln b.$$
$$\ln y = x \ln b \qquad \text{Take the exponential function of both sides.}$$
$$y = e^{x \ln b}$$

Therefore,

$$b^x = e^{x \ln b} \qquad \text{Change-of-base formula for exponential functions} \qquad (3)$$

Differentiating both sides of equation (2) gives

$$\frac{d}{dx} \log_b x = \frac{1}{\ln b} \frac{d}{dx} \ln x = \frac{1}{\ln b}\left(\frac{1}{x}\right)$$

It can be shown that the derivative of the function e^{cx}, where c is a constant, is the function ce^{cx} (see Problems 49–50 in Exercise 4-2 or the more general results of Section 4–4). Therefore, differentiating both sides of equation (3), we have

$$\frac{d}{dx} b^x = e^{x \ln b} \ln b = b^x \ln b$$

For convenience, we list the derivative formulas for exponential and logarithmic functions:

Derivatives of Exponential and Logarithmic Functions
For $b > 0, b \neq 1$,

$$\frac{d}{dx} e^x = e^x \qquad \frac{d}{dx} b^x = b^x \ln b$$

$$\frac{d}{dx} \ln x = \frac{1}{x} \qquad \frac{d}{dx} \log_b x = \frac{1}{\ln b}\left(\frac{1}{x}\right)$$

---

*Equation (2) is a special case of the **general change-of-base formula** for logarithms (which can be derived in the same way): $\log_b x = (\log_a x)/(\log_a b)$.

EXAMPLE 3   **Finding Derivatives** Find $g'(x)$ for

(A) $g(x) = 2^x - 3^x$ (B) $g(x) = \log_4 x^5$

SOLUTIONS   (A) $g'(x) = 2^x \ln 2 - 3^x \ln 3$

(B) First, use a property of logarithms to rewrite $g(x)$.

$$g(x) = \log_4 x^5 \qquad \text{Use } \log_b M^p = p \log_b M.$$
$$g(x) = 5 \log_4 x \qquad \text{Take the derivative of both sides.}$$
$$g'(x) = \frac{5}{\ln 4}\left(\frac{1}{x}\right)$$

Matched Problem 3   Find $g'(x)$ for

(A) $g(x) = x^{10} + 10^x$ (B) $g(x) = \log_2 x - 6 \log_5 x$

EXPLORE & DISCUSS 2

(A) The graphs of $f(x) = \log_2 x$ and $g(x) = \log_4 x$ are shown in Figure 2. Which graph belongs to which function?

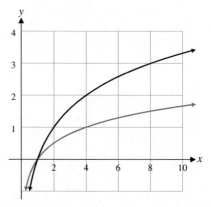

Figure 2

(B) Sketch graphs of $f'(x)$ and $g'(x)$.

(C) The function $f(x)$ is related to $g(x)$ in the same way that $f'(x)$ is related to $g'(x)$. What is that relationship?

Exponential and Logarithmic Models

EXAMPLE 4   **Price–Demand Model** An Internet store sells Australian wool blankets. If the store sells x blankets at a price of $\$p$ per blanket, then the price–demand equation is $p = 350(0.999)^x$. Find the rate of change of price with respect to demand when the demand is 800 blankets and interpret the result.

SOLUTION $\dfrac{dp}{dx} = 350(0.999)^x \ln 0.999$

If $x = 800$, then

$$\frac{dp}{dx} = 350(0.999)^{800} \ln 0.999 \approx -0.157, \text{ or } -\$0.16$$

When the demand is 800 blankets, the price is decreasing by $0.16 per blanket.

Matched Problem 4   The store in Example 4 also sells a reversible fleece blanket. If the price–demand equation for reversible fleece blankets is $p = 200(0.998)^x$, find the rate of change of price with respect to demand when the demand is 400 blankets and interpret the result.

EXAMPLE 5   **Cable TV Subscribers**   A statistician used data from the U.S. Census Bureau to construct the model

$$S(t) = 21 \ln t + 2$$

where $S(t)$ is the number of cable TV subscribers (in millions) in year t ($t = 0$ corresponds to 1980). Use this model to estimate the number of cable TV subscribers in 2015 and the rate of change of the number of subscribers in 2015. Round both to the nearest tenth of a million. Interpret these results.

SOLUTION   Since 2015 corresponds to $t = 35$, we must find $S(35)$ and $S'(35)$.

$$S(35) = 21 \ln 35 + 2 = 76.7 \text{ million}$$

$$S'(t) = 21\frac{1}{t} = \frac{21}{t}$$

$$S'(35) = \frac{21}{35} = 0.6 \text{ million}$$

In 2015 there will be approximately 76.7 million subscribers, and this number is growing at the rate of 0.6 million subscribers per year.

Matched Problem 5   A model for newspaper circulation is

$$C(t) = 83 - 9 \ln t$$

where $C(t)$ is newspaper circulation (in millions) in year t ($t = 0$ corresponds to 1980). Use this model to estimate the circulation and the rate of change of circulation in 2015. Round both to the nearest tenth of a million. Interpret these results.

CONCEPTUAL INSIGHT

On most graphing calculators, exponential regression produces a function of the form $y = a \cdot b^x$. Formula (3) on page 221 allows you to change the base b (chosen by the graphing calculator) to the more familiar base e:

$$y = a \cdot b^x = a \cdot e^{x \ln b}$$

On most graphing calculators, logarithmic regression produces a function of the form $y = a + b \ln x$. Formula (2) on page 221 allows you to write the function in terms of logarithms to any base d that you may prefer:

$$y = a + b \ln x = a + b(\ln d) \log_d x$$

Exercises 4-2

A

In Problems 1–14, find $f'(x)$.

1. $f(x) = 5e^x + 3x + 1$

2. $f(x) = -7e^x - 2x + 5$

3. $f(x) = -2 \ln x + x^2 - 4$

4. $f(x) = 6 \ln x - x^3 + 2$

5. $f(x) = x^3 - 6e^x$

6. $f(x) = 9e^x + 2x^2$

7. $f(x) = e^x + x - \ln x$

8. $f(x) = \ln x + 2e^x - 3x^2$

9. $f(x) = \ln x^3$

10. $f(x) = \ln x^8$

11. $f(x) = 5x - \ln x^5$

12. $f(x) = 4 + \ln x^9$

13. $f(x) = \ln x^2 + 4e^x$

14. $f(x) = \ln x^{10} + 2 \ln x$

B

In Problems 15–22, find the equation of the line tangent to the graph of f at the indicated value of x.

15. $f(x) = 3 + \ln x; x = 1$

16. $f(x) = 2 \ln x; x = 1$

17. $f(x) = 3e^x; x = 0$

18. $f(x) = e^x + 1; x = 0$

19. $f(x) = \ln x^3; x = e$

20. $f(x) = 1 + \ln x^4; x = e$

21. $f(x) = 2 + e^x; x = 1$

22. $f(x) = 5e^x; x = 1$

23. A student claims that the line tangent to the graph of $f(x) = e^x$ at $x = 3$ passes through the point $(2, 0)$ (see the figure). Is she correct? Will the line tangent at $x = 4$ pass through $(3, 0)$? Explain.

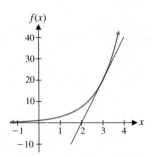

Figure for 23

24. Refer to Problem 23. Does the line tangent to the graph of $f(x) = e^x$ at $x = 1$ pass through the origin? Are there any other lines tangent to the graph of f that pass through the origin? Explain.

25. A student claims that the line tangent to the graph of $g(x) = \ln x$ at $x = 3$ passes through the origin (see the figure). Is he correct? Will the line tangent at $x = 4$ pass through the origin? Explain.

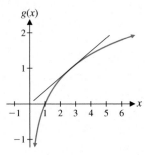

Figure for 25

26. Refer to Problem 25. Does the line tangent to the graph of $f(x) = \ln x$ at $x = e$ pass through the origin? Are there any other lines tangent to the graph of f that pass through the origin? Explain.

In Problems 27–30, first use appropriate properties of logarithms to rewrite f(x), and then find $f'(x)$.

27. $f(x) = 10x + \ln 10x$

28. $f(x) = 2 + 3 \ln \dfrac{1}{x}$

29. $f(x) = \ln \dfrac{4}{x^3}$

30. $f(x) = x + 5 \ln 6x$

C

In Problems 31–42, find $\dfrac{dy}{dx}$ for the indicated function y.

31. $y = \log_2 x$

32. $y = 3 \log_5 x$

33. $y = 3^x$

34. $y = 4^x$

35. $y = 2x - \log x$

36. $y = \log x + 4x^2 + 1$

37. $y = 10 + x + 10^x$

38. $y = x^5 - 5^x$

39. $y = 3 \ln x + 2 \log_3 x$

40. $y = -\log_2 x + 10 \ln x$

41. $y = 2^x + e^2$

42. $y = e^3 - 3^x$

In Problems 43–48, use graphical approximation methods to find the points of intersection of f(x) and g(x) (to two decimal places).

43. $f(x) = e^x; g(x) = x^4$

[Note that there are three points of intersection and that e^x is greater than x^4 for large values of x.]

44. $f(x) = e^x; g(x) = x^5$

[Note that there are two points of intersection and that e^x is greater than x^5 for large values of x.]

45. $f(x) = (\ln x)^2; g(x) = x$

46. $f(x) = (\ln x)^3; g(x) = \sqrt{x}$

47. $f(x) = \ln x; g(x) = x^{1/5}$

48. $f(x) = \ln x; g(x) = x^{1/4}$

49. Explain why $\lim\limits_{h \to 0} \dfrac{e^{ch} - 1}{h} = c$.

50. Use the result of Problem 49 and the four-step process to show that if $f(x) = e^{cx}$, then $f'(x) = ce^{cx}$.

Applications

51. **Salvage value.** The estimated salvage value S (in dollars) of a company airplane after t years is given by

$$S(t) = 300{,}000(0.9)^t$$

What is the rate of depreciation (in dollars per year) after 1 year? 5 years? 10 years?

52. **Resale value.** The estimated resale value R (in dollars) of a company car after t years is given by

$$R(t) = 20{,}000(0.86)^t$$

What is the rate of depreciation (in dollars per year) after 1 year? 2 years? 3 years?

53. **Bacterial growth.** A single cholera bacterium divides every 0.5 hour to produce two complete cholera bacteria. If we start with a colony of 5,000 bacteria, then after t hours, there will be

$$A(t) = 5{,}000 \cdot 2^{2t} = 5{,}000 \cdot 4^t$$

bacteria. Find $A'(t)$, $A'(1)$, and $A'(5)$, and interpret the results.

54. **Bacterial growth.** Repeat Problem 53 for a starting colony of 1,000 bacteria such that a single bacterium divides every 0.25 hour.

55. **Blood pressure.** An experiment was set up to find a relationship between weight and systolic blood pressure in children. Using hospital records for 5,000 children, the experimenters found that the systolic blood pressure was given approximately by

$$P(x) = 17.5(1 + \ln x) \qquad 10 \le x \le 100$$

where $P(x)$ is measured in millimeters of mercury and x is measured in pounds. What is the rate of change of blood pressure with respect to weight at the 40-pound weight level? At the 90-pound weight level?

56. **Blood pressure.** Refer to Problem 55. Find the weight (to the nearest pound) at which the rate of change of blood pressure with respect to weight is 0.3 millimeter of mercury per pound.

57. **Psychology: stimulus/response.** In psychology, the Weber–Fechner law for the response to a stimulus is

$$R = k \ln \frac{S}{S_0}$$

where R is the response, S is the stimulus, and S_0 is the lowest level of stimulus that can be detected. Find dR/dS.

58. **Psychology: learning.** A mathematical model for the average of a group of people learning to type is given by

$$N(t) = 10 + 6 \ln t \qquad t \ge 1$$

where $N(t)$ is the number of words per minute typed after t hours of instruction and practice (2 hours per day, 5 days per week). What is the rate of learning after 10 hours of instruction and practice? After 100 hours?

Answers to Matched Problems

1. (A) $4e^x + 16x + 7$

(B) $7x^6 - 5x^4 - 1 + e^x$

2. (A) $30x^2 - \dfrac{100}{x}$

(B) $\dfrac{5}{x} + e^x$

3. (A) $10x^9 + 10^x \ln 10$

(B) $\left(\dfrac{1}{\ln 2} - \dfrac{6}{\ln 5} \right) \dfrac{1}{x}$

4. The price is decreasing at the rate of $0.18 per blanket.

5. The circulation in 2015 is approximately 51.0 million and is decreasing at the rate of 0.3 million per year.

4-3 Derivatives of Products and Quotients

- Derivatives of Products
- Derivatives of Quotients

The derivative properties discussed in Section 3-5 add substantially to our ability to compute and apply derivatives to many practical problems. In this and the next two sections, we add a few more properties that will increase this ability even further.

Derivatives of Products

In Section 3-5, we found that the derivative of a sum is the sum of the derivatives. Is the derivative of a product the product of the derivatives?

EXPLORE & DISCUSS 1 — Let $F(x) = x^2$, $S(x) = x^3$, and $f(x) = F(x)S(x) = x^5$. Which of the following is $f'(x)$?

(A) $F'(x)S'(x)$ (B) $F(x)S'(x)$

(C) $F'(x)S(x)$ (D) $F(x)S'(x) + F'(x)S(x)$

Comparing the various expressions computed in Explore & Discuss 1, we see that the derivative of a product is not the product of the derivatives.

Using the definition of the derivative and the four-step process, we can show that

The derivative of the product of two functions is the first function times the derivative of the second function, plus the second function times the derivative of the first function.

THEOREM 1 Product Rule

If

$$y = f(x) = F(x)S(x)$$

and if $F'(x)$ and $S'(x)$ exist, then

$$f'(x) = F(x)S'(x) + S(x)F'(x)$$

Using simplified notation,

$$y' = FS' + SF' \qquad \text{or} \qquad \frac{dy}{dx} = F\frac{dS}{dx} + S\frac{dF}{dx}$$

EXAMPLE 1 **Differentiating a Product** Use two different methods to find $f'(x)$ for

$$f(x) = 2x^2(3x^4 - 2).$$

SOLUTION **Method 1.** Use the product rule:

$$f'(x) = 2x^2(3x^4 - 2)' + (3x^4 - 2)(2x^2)' \qquad \text{First times derivative of}$$
$$= 2x^2(12x^3) + (3x^4 - 2)(4x) \qquad \text{second, plus second times}$$
$$= 24x^5 + 12x^5 - 8x \qquad \text{derivative of first}$$
$$= 36x^5 - 8x$$

Method 2. Multiply first; then take derivatives:

$$f(x) = 2x^2(3x^4 - 2) = 6x^6 - 4x^2$$
$$f'(x) = 36x^5 - 8x$$

Matched Problem 1 Use two different methods to find $f'(x)$ for $f(x) = 3x^3(2x^2 - 3x + 1)$.

Some products we encounter can be differentiated by either method illustrated in Example 1. In other situations, the product rule *must* be used. Unless instructed otherwise, you should use the product rule to differentiate all products in this section in order to gain experience with this important differentiation rule.

EXAMPLE 2   **Tangent Lines** Let $f(x) = (2x - 9)(x^2 + 6)$.

(A) Find the equation of the line tangent to the graph of $f(x)$ at $x = 3$.

(B) Find the value(s) of x where the tangent line is horizontal.

SOLUTION   (A) First, find $f'(x)$:

$$f'(x) = (2x - 9)(x^2 + 6)' + (x^2 + 6)(2x - 9)'$$
$$= (2x - 9)(2x) + (x^2 + 6)(2)$$

Then, find $f(3)$ and $f'(3)$:

$$f(3) = [2(3) - 9](3^2 + 6) = (-3)(15) = -45$$
$$f'(3) = [2(3) - 9]2(3) + (3^2 + 6)(2) = -18 + 30 = 12$$

Now, find the equation of the tangent line at $x = 3$:

$$y - y_1 = m(x - x_1) \qquad y_1 = f(x_1) = f(3) = -45$$
$$y - (-45) = 12(x - 3) \qquad m = f'(x_1) = f'(3) = 12$$
$$y = 12x - 81 \qquad \text{Tangent line at } x = 3$$

(B) The tangent line is horizontal at any value of x such that $f'(x) = 0$, so

$$f'(x) = (2x - 9)2x + (x^2 + 6)2 = 0$$
$$6x^2 - 18x + 12 = 0$$
$$x^2 - 3x + 2 = 0$$
$$(x - 1)(x - 2) = 0$$
$$x = 1, 2$$

The tangent line is horizontal at $x = 1$ and at $x = 2$.

Matched Problem 2   Repeat Example 2 for $f(x) = (2x + 9)(x^2 - 12)$.

CONCEPTUAL INSIGHT

As Example 2 illustrates, the way we write $f'(x)$ depends on what we want to do. If we are interested only in evaluating $f'(x)$ at specified values of x, then the form in part (A) is sufficient. However, if we want to solve $f'(x) = 0$, we must multiply and collect like terms, as we did in part (B).

EXAMPLE 3   **Finding Derivatives** Find $f'(x)$ for

(A) $f(x) = 2x^3 e^x$ (B) $f(x) = 6x^4 \ln x$

SOLUTIONS   (A) $f'(x) = 2x^3(e^x)' + e^x(2x^3)'$ (B) $f'(x) = 6x^4(\ln x)' + (\ln x)(6x^4)'$
$\qquad = 2x^3 e^x + e^x(6x^2)$ $\qquad = 6x^4 \dfrac{1}{x} + (\ln x)(24x^3)$
$\qquad = 2x^2 e^x(x + 3)$ $\qquad = 6x^3 + 24x^3 \ln x$
$\qquad\qquad\qquad\qquad = 6x^3(1 + 4\ln x)$

Matched Problem 3   Find $f'(x)$ for

(A) $f(x) = 5x^8 e^x$ (B) $f(x) = x^7 \ln x$

Derivatives of Quotients

The derivative of a quotient of two functions is not the quotient of the derivatives of the two functions.

EXPLORE & DISCUSS 2

Let $T(x) = x^5$, $B(x) = x^2$, and

$$f(x) = \frac{T(x)}{B(x)} = \frac{x^5}{x^2} = x^3$$

Which of the following is $f'(x)$?

(A) $\dfrac{T'(x)}{B'(x)}$ (B) $\dfrac{T'(x)B(x)}{[B(x)]^2}$ (C) $\dfrac{T(x)B'(x)}{[B(x)]^2}$

(D) $\dfrac{T'(x)B(x)}{[B(x)]^2} - \dfrac{T(x)B'(x)}{[B(x)]^2} = \dfrac{T'(x)B(x) - T(x)B'(x)}{[B(x)]^2}$

The expressions in Explore & Discuss 2 suggest that the derivative of a quotient leads to a more complicated quotient than expected.

If $T(x)$ and $B(x)$ are any two differentiable functions and

$$f(x) = \frac{T(x)}{B(x)}$$

then

$$f'(x) = \frac{B(x)T'(x) - T(x)B'(x)}{[B(x)]^2}$$

Therefore,

The derivative of the quotient of two functions is the denominator function times the derivative of the numerator function, minus the numerator function times the derivative of the denominator function, divided by the denominator function squared.

THEOREM 2   Quotient Rule

If

$$y = f(x) = \frac{T(x)}{B(x)}$$

and if $T'(x)$ and $B'(x)$ exist, then

$$f'(x) = \frac{B(x)T'(x) - T(x)B'(x)}{[B(x)]^2}$$

Using simplified notation,

$$y' = \frac{BT' - TB'}{B^2} \qquad \text{or} \qquad \frac{dy}{dx} = \frac{B\dfrac{dT}{dx} - T\dfrac{dB}{dx}}{B^2}$$

EXAMPLE 4   **Differentiating Quotients**

(A) If $f(x) = \dfrac{x^2}{2x-1}$, find $f'(x)$.   (B) If $y = \dfrac{t^2-t}{t^3+1}$, find y'.

(C) Find $\dfrac{d}{dx}\dfrac{x^2-3}{x^2}$ by using the quotient rule and also by splitting the fraction into two fractions.

SOLUTION   (A) $f'(x) = \dfrac{(2x-1)(x^2)' - x^2(2x-1)'}{(2x-1)^2}$

The denominator times the derivative of the numerator, minus the numerator times the derivative of the denominator, divided by the square of the denominator

$$= \dfrac{(2x-1)(2x) - x^2(2)}{(2x-1)^2}$$

$$= \dfrac{4x^2 - 2x - 2x^2}{(2x-1)^2}$$

$$= \dfrac{2x^2 - 2x}{(2x-1)^2}$$

(B) $y' = \dfrac{(t^3+1)(t^2-t)' - (t^2-t)(t^3+1)'}{(t^3+1)^2}$

$$= \dfrac{(t^3+1)(2t-1) - (t^2-t)(3t^2)}{(t^3+1)^2}$$

$$= \dfrac{2t^4 - t^3 + 2t - 1 - 3t^4 + 3t^3}{(t^3+1)^2}$$

$$= \dfrac{-t^4 + 2t^3 + 2t - 1}{(t^3+1)^2}$$

(C) **Method 1.** Use the quotient rule:

$$\dfrac{d}{dx}\dfrac{x^2-3}{x^2} = \dfrac{x^2\dfrac{d}{dx}(x^2-3) - (x^2-3)\dfrac{d}{dx}x^2}{(x^2)^2}$$

$$= \dfrac{x^2(2x) - (x^2-3)2x}{x^4}$$

$$= \dfrac{2x^3 - 2x^3 + 6x}{x^4} = \dfrac{6x}{x^4} = \dfrac{6}{x^3}$$

Method 2. Split into two fractions:

$$\dfrac{x^2-3}{x^2} = \dfrac{x^2}{x^2} - \dfrac{3}{x^2} = 1 - 3x^{-2}$$

$$\dfrac{d}{dx}(1 - 3x^{-2}) = 0 - 3(-2)x^{-3} = \dfrac{6}{x^3}$$

Comparing methods 1 and 2, we see that it often pays to change an expression algebraically before choosing a differentiation formula.

Matched Problem 4   Find

(A) $f'(x)$ for $f(x) = \dfrac{2x}{x^2+3}$ (B) y' for $y = \dfrac{t^3-3t}{t^2-4}$

(C) $\dfrac{d}{dx}\dfrac{2+x^3}{x^3}$ in two ways

EXAMPLE 5 Finding Derivatives Find $f'(x)$ for

(A) $f(x) = \dfrac{3e^x}{1 + e^x}$

(B) $f(x) = \dfrac{\ln x}{2x + 5}$

SOLUTIONS (A) $f'(x) = \dfrac{(1 + e^x)(3e^x)' - 3e^x(1 + e^x)'}{(1 + e^x)^2}$

$= \dfrac{(1 + e^x)3e^x - 3e^xe^x}{(1 + e^x)^2}$

$= \dfrac{3e^x}{(1 + e^x)^2}$

(B) $f'(x) = \dfrac{(2x + 5)(\ln x)' - (\ln x)(2x + 5)'}{(2x + 5)^2}$

$= \dfrac{(2x + 5) \cdot \dfrac{1}{x} - (\ln x)(2)}{(2x + 5)^2}$ Multiply by $\dfrac{x}{x}$

$= \dfrac{2x + 5 - 2x \ln x}{x(2x + 5)^2}$

Matched Problem 5 Find $f'(x)$ for

(A) $f(x) = \dfrac{x^3}{e^x + 2}$

(B) $f(x) = \dfrac{4x}{1 + \ln x}$

EXAMPLE 6 Sales Analysis The total sales S (in thousands of games) of a video game t months after the game is introduced are given by

$$S(t) = \dfrac{125t^2}{t^2 + 100}$$

(A) Find $S'(t)$.

(B) Find $S(10)$ and $S'(10)$. Write a brief interpretation of these results.

(C) Use the results from part (B) to estimate the total sales after 11 months.

SOLUTION (A) $S'(t) = \dfrac{(t^2 + 100)(125t^2)' - 125t^2(t^2 + 100)'}{(t^2 + 100)^2}$

$= \dfrac{(t^2 + 100)(250t) - 125t^2(2t)}{(t^2 + 100)^2}$

$= \dfrac{250t^3 + 25{,}000t - 250t^3}{(t^2 + 100)^2}$

$= \dfrac{25{,}000t}{(t^2 + 100)^2}$

(B) $S(10) = \dfrac{125(10)^2}{10^2 + 100} = 62.5$ and $S'(10) = \dfrac{25{,}000(10)}{(10^2 + 100)^2} = 6.25.$

Total sales after 10 months are 62,500 games, and sales are increasing at the rate of 6,250 games per month.

(C) Total sales will increase by approximately 6,250 games during the next month, so the estimated total sales after 11 months are 62,500 + 6,250 = 68,750 games.

Matched Problem 6 Refer to Example 6. Suppose that the total sales S (in thousands of games) t months after the game is introduced are given by

$$S(t) = \frac{150t}{t + 3}$$

(A) Find $S'(t)$.

(B) Find $S(12)$ and $S'(12)$. Write a brief interpretation of these results.

(C) Use the results from part (B) to estimate the total sales after 13 months.

Exercises 4-3

Answers to most of the problems in this exercise set contain both an unsimplified form and a simplified form of the derivative. When checking your work, first check that you applied the rules correctly and then check that you performed the algebraic simplification correctly. Unless instructed otherwise, when differentiating a product, use the product rule rather than performing the multiplication first.

A

In Problems 1–26, find $f'(x)$ and simplify.

1. $f(x) = 2x^3(x^2 - 2)$
2. $f(x) = 5x^2(x^3 + 2)$

3. $f(x) = (x - 3)(2x - 1)$

4. $f(x) = (3x + 2)(4x - 5)$

5. $f(x) = \dfrac{x}{x - 3}$

6. $f(x) = \dfrac{3x}{2x + 1}$
7. $f(x) = \dfrac{2x + 3}{x - 2}$

8. $f(x) = \dfrac{3x - 4}{2x + 3}$
9. $f(x) = 3xe^x$

10. $f(x) = x^2 e^x$
11. $f(x) = x^3 \ln x$

12. $f(x) = 5x \ln x$

13. $f(x) = (x^2 + 1)(2x - 3)$

14. $f(x) = (3x + 5)(x^2 - 3)$

15. $f(x) = (0.4x + 2)(0.5x - 5)$

16. $f(x) = (0.5x - 4)(0.2x + 1)$

17. $f(x) = \dfrac{x^2 + 1}{2x - 3}$
18. $f(x) = \dfrac{3x + 5}{x^2 - 3}$

19. $f(x) = (x^2 + 2)(x^2 - 3)$

20. $f(x) = (x^2 - 4)(x^2 + 5)$

21. $f(x) = \dfrac{x^2 + 2}{x^2 - 3}$
22. $f(x) = \dfrac{x^2 - 4}{x^2 + 5}$

23. $f(x) = \dfrac{e^x}{x^2 + 1}$
24. $f(x) = \dfrac{1 - e^x}{1 + e^x}$

25. $f(x) = \dfrac{\ln x}{1 + x}$
26. $f(x) = \dfrac{2x}{1 + \ln x}$

In Problems 27–38, find $h'(x)$, where $f(x)$ is an unspecified differentiable function.

27. $h(x) = xf(x)$
28. $h(x) = x^2 f(x)$

29. $h(x) = x^3 f(x)$
30. $h(x) = \dfrac{f(x)}{x}$

31. $h(x) = \dfrac{f(x)}{x^2}$
32. $h(x) = \dfrac{f(x)}{x^3}$

33. $h(x) = \dfrac{x}{f(x)}$
34. $h(x) = \dfrac{x^2}{f(x)}$

35. $h(x) = e^x f(x)$
36. $h(x) = \dfrac{e^x}{f(x)}$

37. $h(x) = \dfrac{\ln x}{f(x)}$
38. $h(x) = \dfrac{f(x)}{\ln x}$

B

In Problems 39–48, find the indicated derivatives and simplify.

39. $f'(x)$ for $f(x) = (2x + 1)(x^2 - 3x)$

40. y' for $y = (x^3 + 2x^2)(3x - 1)$

41. $\dfrac{dy}{dt}$ for $y = (2.5t - t^2)(4t + 1.4)$

42. $\dfrac{d}{dt}[(3 - 0.4t^3)(0.5t^2 - 2t)]$

43. y' for $y = \dfrac{5x - 3}{x^2 + 2x}$

44. $f'(x)$ for $f(x) = \dfrac{3x^2}{2x - 1}$

45. $\dfrac{d}{dw}\dfrac{w^2 - 3w + 1}{w^2 - 1}$

46. $\dfrac{dy}{dw}$ for $y = \dfrac{w^4 - w^3}{3w - 1}$

47. y' for $y = (1 + x - x^2)e^x$

48. $\dfrac{dy}{dt}$ for $y = (1 + e^t)\ln t$

In Problems 49–54, find $f'(x)$ and find the equation of the line tangent to the graph of f at $x = 2$.

49. $f(x) = (1 + 3x)(5 - 2x)$

50. $f(x) = (7 - 3x)(1 + 2x)$

51. $f(x) = \dfrac{x - 8}{3x - 4}$

52. $f(x) = \dfrac{2x - 5}{2x - 3}$

53. $f(x) = \dfrac{x}{2^x}$

54. $f(x) = (x - 2) \ln x$

In Problems 55–58, find $f'(x)$ and find the value(s) of x where $f'(x) = 0$.

55. $f(x) = (2x - 15)(x^2 + 18)$

56. $f(x) = (2x - 3)(x^2 - 6)$

57. $f(x) = \dfrac{x}{x^2 + 1}$

58. $f(x) = \dfrac{x}{x^2 + 9}$

In Problems 59–62, find $f'(x)$ in two ways: (1) using the product or quotient rule and (2) simplifying first.

59. $f(x) = x^3(x^4 - 1)$

60. $f(x) = x^4(x^3 - 1)$

61. $f(x) = \dfrac{x^3 + 9}{x^3}$

62. $f(x) = \dfrac{x^4 + 4}{x^4}$

C

In Problems 63–82, find each indicated derivative and simplify.

63. $f(w) = (w + 1)2^w$

64. $g(w) = (w - 5) \log_3 w$

65. $\dfrac{d}{dx} \dfrac{3x^2 - 2x + 3}{4x^2 + 5x - 1}$

66. y' for $y = \dfrac{x^3 - 3x + 4}{2x^2 + 3x - 2}$

67. $\dfrac{dy}{dx}$ for $y = 9x^{1/3}(x^3 + 5)$

68. $\dfrac{d}{dx}[(4x^{1/2} - 1)(3x^{1/3} + 2)]$

69. y' for $y = \dfrac{\log_2 x}{1 + x^2}$

70. $\dfrac{dy}{dx}$ for $y = \dfrac{10^x}{1 + x^4}$

71. $f'(x)$ for $f(x) = \dfrac{6\sqrt[3]{x}}{x^2 - 3}$

72. y' for $y = \dfrac{2\sqrt{x}}{x^2 - 3x + 1}$

73. $g'(t)$ if $g(t) = \dfrac{0.2t}{3t^2 - 1}$

74. $h'(t)$ if $h(t) = \dfrac{-0.05t^2}{2t + 1}$

75. $\dfrac{d}{dx}[4x \log x^5]$

76. $\dfrac{d}{dt}[10^t \log t]$

77. $\dfrac{d}{dx} \dfrac{x^3 - 2x^2}{\sqrt[3]{x^2}}$

78. $\dfrac{dy}{dx}$ for $y = \dfrac{x^2 - 3x + 1}{\sqrt[4]{x}}$

79. $f'(x)$ for $f(x) = \dfrac{(2x^2 - 1)(x^2 + 3)}{x^2 + 1}$

80. y' for $y = \dfrac{2x - 1}{(x^3 + 2)(x^2 - 3)}$

81. $\dfrac{dy}{dt}$ for $y = \dfrac{t \ln t}{e^t}$

82. $\dfrac{dy}{du}$ for $y = \dfrac{u^2 e^u}{1 + \ln u}$

Applications

83. Sales analysis. The total sales S (in thousands of DVDs) of a DVD are given by

$$S(t) = \dfrac{90t^2}{t^2 + 50}$$

where t is the number of months since the release of the DVD.

(A) Find $S'(t)$.

(B) Find $S(10)$ and $S'(10)$. Write a brief interpretation of these results.

(C) Use the results from part (B) to estimate the total sales after 11 months.

84. Sales analysis. A communications company has installed a new cable television system in a city. The total number N (in thousands) of subscribers t months after the installation of the system is given by

$$N(t) = \dfrac{180t}{t + 4}$$

(A) Find $N'(t)$.

(B) Find $N(16)$ and $N'(16)$. Write a brief interpretation of these results.

(C) Use the results from part (B) to estimate the total number of subscribers after 17 months.

85. Price–demand equation. According to economic theory, the demand x for a quantity in a free market decreases as the price p increases (see the figure). Suppose that the number x of DVD players people are willing to buy per week from a retail chain at a price of $\$p$ is given by

$$x = \dfrac{4,000}{0.1p + 1} \qquad 10 \le p \le 70$$

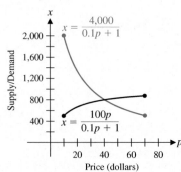

Figure for 85 and 86

(A) Find dx/dp.

(B) Find the demand and the instantaneous rate of change of demand with respect to price when the price is $40. Write a brief interpretation of these results.

(C) Use the results from part (B) to estimate the demand if the price is increased to $41.

86. Price–supply equation. According to economic theory, the supply x of a quantity in a free market increases as the price p increases (see the figure). Suppose that the number x of DVD players a retail chain is willing to sell per week at a price of $\$p$ is given by

$$x = \frac{100p}{0.1p + 1} \qquad 10 \le p \le 70$$

(A) Find dx/dp.

(B) Find the supply and the instantaneous rate of change of supply with respect to price when the price is $40. Write a brief verbal interpretation of these results.

(C) Use the results from part (B) to estimate the supply if the price is increased to $41.

87. Medicine. A drug is injected into a patient's bloodstream through her right arm. The drug concentration (in milligrams per cubic centimeter) in the bloodstream of the left arm t hours after the injection is given by

$$C(t) = \frac{0.14t}{t^2 + 1}$$

(A) Find $C'(t)$.

(B) Find $C'(0.5)$ and $C'(3)$, and interpret the results.

88. Drug sensitivity. One hour after a dose of x milligrams of a particular drug is administered to a person, the change in body temperature $T(x)$, in degrees Fahrenheit, is given approximately by

$$T(x) = x^2\left(1 - \frac{x}{9}\right) \qquad 0 \le x \le 7$$

The rate $T'(x)$ at which T changes with respect to the size of the dosage x is called the *sensitivity* of the body to the dosage.

(A) Use the product rule to find $T'(x)$.

(B) Find $T'(1), T'(3)$, and $T'(6)$.

89. Learning. In the early twentieth century, L. L. Thurstone found that a given person successfully accomplished $N(x)$ acts after x practice acts, as given by

$$N(x) = \frac{100x + 200}{x + 32}$$

(A) Find the instantaneous rate of change of learning, $N'(x)$, with respect to the number of practice acts, x.

(B) Find $N'(4)$ and $N'(68)$.

Answers to Matched Problems

1. $30x^4 - 36x^3 + 9x^2$

2. (A) $y = 84x - 297$

(B) $x = -4, x = 1$

3. (A) $5x^8 e^x + e^x(40x^7) = 5x^7(x + 8)e^x$

(B) $x^7 \cdot \dfrac{1}{x} + \ln x\,(7x^6) = x^6\,(1 + 7 \ln x)$

4. (A) $\dfrac{(x^2 + 3)2 - (2x)(2x)}{(x^2 + 3)^2} = \dfrac{6 - 2x^2}{(x^2 + 3)^2}$

(B) $\dfrac{(t^2 - 4)(3t^2 - 3) - (t^3 - 3t)(2t)}{(t^2 - 4)^2} = \dfrac{t^4 - 9t^2 + 12}{(t^2 - 4)^2}$

(C) $-\dfrac{6}{x^4}$

5. (A) $\dfrac{(e^x + 2)\,3x^2 - x^3 e^x}{(e^x + 2)^2}$

(B) $\dfrac{(1 + \ln x)\,4 - 4x\dfrac{1}{x}}{(1 + \ln x)^2} = \dfrac{4 \ln x}{(1 + \ln x)^2}$

6. (A) $S'(t) = \dfrac{450}{(t + 3)^2}$

(B) $S(12) = 120; S'(12) = 2$. After 12 months, the total sales are 120,000 games, and sales are increasing at the rate of 2,000 games per month.

(C) 122,000 games

4-4   The Chain Rule

- Composite Functions
- General Power Rule
- The Chain Rule

The word *chain* in the name "chain rule" comes from the fact that a function formed by composition involves a chain of functions—that is, a function of a function. The *chain rule* enables us to compute the derivative of a composite function in terms of the derivatives of the functions making up the composition. In this section, we review composite functions, introduce the chain rule by means of a special case known as the *general power rule,* and then discuss the chain rule itself.

Composite Functions

The function $m(x) = (x^2 + 4)^3$ is a combination of a quadratic function and a cubic function. To see this more clearly, let

$$y = f(u) = u^3 \qquad \text{and} \qquad u = g(x) = x^2 + 4$$

We can express y as a function of x:

$$y = f(u) = f[g(x)] = [x^2 + 4]^3 = m(x)$$

The function m is the *composite* of the two functions f and g.

DEFINITION   Composite Functions

A function m is a **composite** of functions f and g if

$$m(x) = f[g(x)]$$

The domain of m is the set of all numbers x such that x is in the domain of g, and $g(x)$ is in the domain of f.

EXAMPLE 1   **Composite Functions** Let $f(u) = e^u$ and $g(x) = -3x$. Find $f[g(x)]$ and $g[f(u)]$.

SOLUTION
$$f[g(x)] = f(-3x) = e^{-3x}$$
$$g[f(u)] = g(e^u) = -3e^u$$

Matched Problem 1   Let $f(u) = 2u$ and $g(x) = e^x$. Find $f[g(x)]$ and $g[f(u)]$.

EXAMPLE 2   **Composite Functions** Write each function as a composition of two simpler functions.

(A) $y = 100e^{0.04x}$ (B) $y = \sqrt{4 - x^2}$

SOLUTION   (A) Let

$$y = f(u) = 100e^u$$
$$u = g(x) = 0.04x$$

Check: $y = f[g(x)] = 100e^{g(x)} = 100e^{0.04x}$

(B) Let

$$y = f(u) = \sqrt{u}$$
$$u = g(x) = 4 - x^2$$

Check: $y = f[g(x)] = \sqrt{g(x)} = \sqrt{4 - x^2}$

Matched Problem 2   Write each function as a composition of two simpler functions.

(A) $y = 50e^{-2x}$ (B) $y = \sqrt[3]{1 + x^3}$

CONCEPTUAL INSIGHT

There can be more than one way to express a function as a composition of simpler functions. Choosing $y = f(u) = 100u$ and $u = g(x) = e^{0.04x}$ in Example 2A produces the same result:

$$y = f[g(x)] = 100g(x) = 100e^{0.04x}$$

Since we will be using composition as a means to an end (finding a derivative), usually it will not matter what functions you choose for the composition.

General Power Rule

We have already made extensive use of the power rule,

$$\frac{d}{dx}x^n = nx^{n-1} \tag{1}$$

Now we can generalize this rule in order to differentiate composite functions of the form $[u(x)]^n$, where $u(x)$ is a differentiable function. Is rule (1) still valid if we replace x with a function $u(x)$?

Let $u(x) = 2x^2$ and $f(x) = [u(x)]^3 = 8x^6$. Which of the following is $f'(x)$?

(A) $3[u(x)]^2$ (B) $3[u'(x)]^2$ (C) $3[u(x)]^2u'(x)$

The calculations in Explore & Discuss 1 show that we cannot generalize the power rule simply by replacing x with $u(x)$ in equation (1).

How can we find a formula for the derivative of $[u(x)]^n$, where $u(x)$ is an arbitrary differentiable function? Let's begin by considering the derivatives of $[u(x)]^2$ and $[u(x)]^3$ to see if a general pattern emerges. Since $[u(x)]^2 = u(x)u(x)$, we use the product rule to write

$$\frac{d}{dx}[u(x)]^2 = \frac{d}{dx}[u(x)u(x)]$$
$$= u(x)u'(x) + u(x)u'(x)$$
$$= 2u(x)u'(x) \tag{2}$$

Because $[u(x)]^3 = [u(x)]^2u(x)$, we use the product rule and the result in equation (2) to write

$$\frac{d}{dx}[u(x)]^3 = \frac{d}{dx}\{[u(x)]^2u(x)\}$$
$$= [u(x)]^2\frac{d}{dx}u(x) + u(x)\frac{d}{dx}[u(x)]^2$$
$$= [u(x)]^2u'(x) + u(x)[2u(x)u'(x)]$$
$$= 3[u(x)]^2u'(x)$$

Use equation (2) to substitute for $\frac{d}{dx}[u(x)]^2$.

Continuing in this fashion, we can show that

$$\frac{d}{dx}[u(x)]^n = n[u(x)]^{n-1}u'(x) \qquad n \text{ a positive integer} \tag{3}$$

Using more advanced techniques, we can establish formula (3) for all real numbers n, obtaining the **general power rule**.

THEOREM 1   General Power Rule

If $u(x)$ is a differentiable function, n is any real number, and

$$y = f(x) = [u(x)]^n$$

then

$$f'(x) = n[u(x)]^{n-1}u'(x)$$

Using simplified notation,

$$y' = nu^{n-1}u' \qquad \text{or} \qquad \frac{d}{dx}u^n = nu^{n-1}\frac{du}{dx} \qquad \text{where } u = u(x)$$

EXAMPLE 3 **Using the General Power Rule** Find the indicated derivatives:

(A) $f'(x)$ if $f(x) = (3x + 1)^4$ (B) y' if $y = (x^3 + 4)^7$

(C) $\dfrac{d}{dt}\dfrac{1}{(t^2 + t + 4)^3}$ (D) $\dfrac{dh}{dw}$ if $h(w) = \sqrt{3 - w}$

SOLUTION

(A) $f(x) = (3x + 1)^4$ Let $u = 3x + 1, n = 4$.

$f'(x) = 4(3x + 1)^3(3x + 1)'$ $nu^{n-1}\dfrac{du}{dx}$

$= 4(3x + 1)^3 \, 3$ $\dfrac{du}{dx} = 3$

$= 12(3x + 1)^3$

(B) $y = (x^3 + 4)^7$ Let $u = (x^3 + 4), n = 7$.

$y' = 7(x^3 + 4)^6(x^3 + 4)'$ $nu^{n-1}\dfrac{du}{dx}$

$= 7(x^3 + 4)^6 \, 3x^2$ $\dfrac{du}{dx} = 3x^2$

$= 21x^2(x^3 + 4)^6$

(C) $\dfrac{d}{dt}\dfrac{1}{(t^2 + t + 4)^3}$

$= \dfrac{d}{dt}(t^2 + t + 4)^{-3}$ Let $u = t^2 + t + 4, n = -3$.

$= -3(t^2 + t + 4)^{-4}(t^2 + t + 4)'$ $nu^{n-1}\dfrac{du}{dt}$

$= -3(t^2 + t + 4)^{-4}(2t + 1)$ $\dfrac{du}{dt} = 2t + 1$

$= \dfrac{-3(2t + 1)}{(t^2 + t + 4)^4}$

(D) $h(w) = \sqrt{3 - w} = (3 - w)^{1/2}$ Let $u = 3 - w, n = \dfrac{1}{2}$.

$\dfrac{dh}{dw} = \dfrac{1}{2}(3 - w)^{-1/2}(3 - w)'$ $nu^{n-1}\dfrac{du}{dw}$

$= \dfrac{1}{2}(3 - w)^{-1/2}(-1)$ $\dfrac{du}{dw} = -1$

$= -\dfrac{1}{2(3 - w)^{1/2}}$ or $-\dfrac{1}{2\sqrt{3 - w}}$

Matched Problem 3 Find the indicated derivatives:

(A) $h'(x)$ if $h(x) = (5x + 2)^3$ (B) y' if $y = (x^4 - 5)^5$

(C) $\dfrac{d}{dt}\dfrac{1}{(t^2 + 4)^2}$ (D) $\dfrac{dg}{dw}$ if $g(w) = \sqrt{4 - w}$

Notice that we used two steps to differentiate each function in Example 3. First, we applied the general power rule, and then we found du/dx. As you gain experience with the general power rule, you may want to combine these two steps. If you do this, be certain to multiply by du/dx. For example,

$\dfrac{d}{dx}(x^5 + 1)^4 = 4(x^5 + 1)^3 5x^4$ Correct

$\dfrac{d}{dx}(x^5 + 1)^4 \neq 4(x^5 + 1)^3$ $du/dx = 5x^4$ is missing

CONCEPTUAL INSIGHT

If we let $u(x) = x$, then $du/dx = 1$, and the general power rule reduces to the (ordinary) power rule discussed in Section 3-5. Compare the following:

$$\frac{d}{dx}x^n = nx^{n-1} \qquad \text{Yes—power rule}$$

$$\frac{d}{dx}u^n = nu^{n-1}\frac{du}{dx} \qquad \text{Yes—general power rule}$$

$$\frac{d}{dx}u^n \neq nu^{n-1} \qquad \text{Unless } u(x) = x + k, \text{ so that } du/dx = 1$$

The Chain Rule

We have used the general power rule to find derivatives of composite functions of the form $f(g(x))$, where $f(u) = u^n$ is a power function. But what if f is not a power function? Then a more general rule, the *chain rule,* enables us to compute the derivatives of many composite functions of the form $f(g(x))$.

Suppose that

$$y = m(x) = f[g(x)]$$

is a composite of f and g, where

$$y = f(u) \qquad \text{and} \qquad u = g(x)$$

To express the derivative dy/dx in terms of the derivatives of f and g, we use the definition of a derivative (see Section 3-4).

$$\frac{dy}{dx} = \lim_{h\to 0}\frac{m(x+h) - m(x)}{h} \qquad \begin{array}{l}\text{Substitute } m(x+h) = f[g(x+h)] \\ \text{and } m(x) = f[g(x)].\end{array}$$

$$= \lim_{h\to 0}\frac{f[g(x+h)] - f[g(x)]}{h} \qquad \text{Multiply by } 1 = \frac{g(x+h) - g(x)}{g(x+h) - g(x)}.$$

$$= \lim_{h\to 0}\left[\frac{f[g(x+h)] - f[g(x)]}{h} \cdot \frac{g(x+h) - g(x)}{g(x+h) - g(x)}\right]$$

$$= \lim_{h\to 0}\left[\frac{f[g(x+h)] - f[g(x)]}{g(x+h) - g(x)} \cdot \frac{g(x+h) - g(x)}{h}\right] \qquad (4)$$

We recognize the second factor in equation (4) as the difference quotient for $g(x)$. To interpret the first factor as the difference quotient for $f(u)$, we let $k = g(x+h) - g(x)$. Since $u = g(x)$, we write

$$u + k = g(x) + g(x+h) - g(x) = g(x+h)$$

Substituting in equation (1), we have

$$\frac{dy}{dx} = \lim_{h\to 0}\left[\frac{f(u+k) - f(u)}{k} \cdot \frac{g(x+h) - g(x)}{h}\right] \qquad (5)$$

If we assume that $k = [g(x+h) - g(x)] \to 0$ as $h \to 0$, we can find the limit of each difference quotient in equation (5):

$$\frac{dy}{dx} = \left[\lim_{k\to 0}\frac{f(u+k) - f(u)}{k}\right]\left[\lim_{h\to 0}\frac{g(x+h) - g(x)}{h}\right]$$

$$= f'(u)g'(x)$$

$$= \frac{dy}{du}\frac{du}{dx}$$

This result is correct under general conditions and is called the *chain rule,* but our "derivation" is superficial because it ignores some hidden problems. Since a formal proof of the chain rule is beyond the scope of this book, we simply state it as follows:

THEOREM 2   Chain Rule

If $y = f(u)$ and $u = g(x)$ define the composite function

$$y = m(x) = f[g(x)]$$

then

$$\frac{dy}{dx} = \frac{dy}{du}\frac{du}{dx} \qquad \text{provided that } \frac{dy}{du} \text{ and } \frac{du}{dx} \text{ exist}$$

or, equivalently,

$$m'(x) = f'[g(x)]g'(x) \qquad \text{provided that } f'[g(x)] \text{ and } g'(x) \text{ exist}$$

EXAMPLE 4   **Using the Chain Rule** Find $dy/du, du/dx,$ and dy/dx (express dy/dx as a function of x) for

(A) $y = u^{3/2}$ and $u = 3x^2 + 1$

(B) $y = e^u$ and $u = 2x^3 + 5$

(C) $y = \ln u$ and $u = x^2 - 4x + 2$

SOLUTION   (A) $\dfrac{dy}{du} = \dfrac{3}{2}u^{1/2}$ and $\dfrac{du}{dx} = 6x$ Basic derivative rules

$\dfrac{dy}{dx} = \dfrac{dy}{du}\dfrac{du}{dx}$ Chain rule

$= \dfrac{3}{2}u^{1/2}(6x) = 9x(3x^2 + 1)^{1/2}$ Since $u = 3x^2 + 1$

(B) $\dfrac{dy}{du} = e^u$ and $\dfrac{du}{dx} = 6x^2$ Basic derivative rules

$\dfrac{dy}{dx} = \dfrac{dy}{du}\dfrac{du}{dx}$ Chain rule

$= e^u(6x^2) = 6x^2 e^{2x^3+5}$ Since $u = 2x^3 + 5$

(C) $\dfrac{dy}{du} = \dfrac{1}{u}$ and $\dfrac{du}{dx} = 2x - 4$ Basic derivative rules

$\dfrac{dy}{dx} = \dfrac{dy}{du}\dfrac{du}{dx}$ Chain rule

$= \dfrac{1}{u}(2x - 4) = \dfrac{2x - 4}{x^2 - 4x + 2}$ Since $u = x^2 - 4x + 2$

Matched Problem 4   Find $dy/du, du/dx,$ and dy/dx (express dy/dx as a function of x) for

(A) $y = u^{-5}$ and $u = 2x^3 + 4$

(B) $y = e^u$ and $u = 3x^4 + 6$

(C) $y = \ln u$ and $u = x^2 + 9x + 4$

EXPLORE & DISCUSS 2

Let $m(x) = f[g(x)]$. Use the chain rule and Figures 1 and 2 to find

(A) $f(4)$　　　(B) $g(6)$　　　(C) $m(6)$

(D) $f'(4)$　　　(E) $g'(6)$　　　(F) $m'(6)$

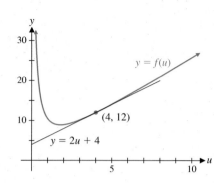
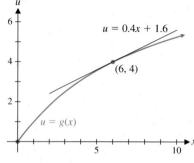

Figure 1　　　　　　　　　　　　　　Figure 2

The chain rule can be extended to compositions of three or more functions. For example, if $y = f(w)$, $w = g(u)$, and $u = h(x)$, then

$$\frac{dy}{dx} = \frac{dy}{dw}\frac{dw}{du}\frac{du}{dx}$$

EXAMPLE 5　**Using the Chain Rule**　For $y = h(x) = e^{1+(\ln x)^2}$, find dy/dx.

SOLUTION　Note that h is of the form $y = e^w$, where $w = 1 + u^2$ and $u = \ln x$.

$$\frac{dy}{dx} = \frac{dy}{dw}\frac{dw}{du}\frac{du}{dx}$$

$$= e^w(2u)\left(\frac{1}{x}\right)$$

$$= e^{1+u^2}(2u)\left(\frac{1}{x}\right) \qquad \text{Since } w = 1 + u^2$$

$$= e^{1+(\ln x)^2}(2\ln x)\left(\frac{1}{x}\right) \qquad \text{Since } u = \ln x$$

$$= \frac{2}{x}(\ln x)e^{1+(\ln x)^2}$$

Matched Problem 5　For $y = h(x) = [\ln(1 + e^x)]^3$, find dy/dx.

The chain rule generalizes basic derivative rules. We list three general derivative rules here for convenient reference [the first, equation (6), is the general power rule of Theorem 1].

General Derivative Rules

$$\frac{d}{dx}[f(x)]^n = n[f(x)]^{n-1}f'(x) \tag{6}$$

$$\frac{d}{dx}\ln[f(x)] = \frac{1}{f(x)}f'(x) \tag{7}$$

$$\frac{d}{dx}e^{f(x)} = e^{f(x)}f'(x) \tag{8}$$

Unless directed otherwise, you now have a choice between the chain rule and the general derivative rules. However, practicing with the chain rule will help prepare you for concepts that appear later in the text. Examples 4 and 5 illustrate the chain rule method, and the next example illustrates the general derivative rules method.

EXAMPLE 6 Using General Derivative Rules

(A) $\dfrac{d}{dx}e^{2x} = e^{2x}\dfrac{d}{dx}2x$ Using equation (5)

$\qquad = e^{2x}(2) = 2e^{2x}$

(B) $\dfrac{d}{dx}\ln(x^2 + 9) = \dfrac{1}{x^2 + 9}\dfrac{d}{dx}(x^2 + 9)$ Using equation (4)

$\qquad = \dfrac{1}{x^2 + 9}2x = \dfrac{2x}{x^2 + 9}$

(C) $\dfrac{d}{dx}(1 + e^{x^2})^3 = 3(1 + e^{x^2})^2\dfrac{d}{dx}(1 + e^{x^2})$ Using equation (3)

$\qquad = 3(1 + e^{x^2})^2 e^{x^2}\dfrac{d}{dx}x^2$ Using equation (5)

$\qquad = 3(1 + e^{x^2})^2 e^{x^2}(2x)$

$\qquad = 6xe^{x^2}(1 + e^{x^2})^2$

Matched Problem 6 Find

(A) $\dfrac{d}{dx}\ln(x^3 + 2x)$ (B) $\dfrac{d}{dx}e^{3x^2+2}$ (C) $\dfrac{d}{dx}(2 + e^{-x^2})^4$

Exercises 4-4

For many of the problems in this exercise set, the answers in the back of the book include both an unsimplified form and a simplified form. When checking your work, first check that you applied the rules correctly, and then check that you performed the algebraic simplification correctly.

A

In Problems 1–4, find f[g(x)].

1. $f(u) = u^3$; $g(x) = 3x^2 + 2$
2. $f(u) = u^4$; $g(x) = 1 - 4x^3$
3. $f(u) = e^u$; $g(x) = -x^2$
4. $g(u) = e^u$; $g(x) = 3x^3$

In Problems 5–8, write each composite function in the form $y = f(u)$ and $u = g(x)$.

5. $y = (3x^2 - x + 5)^4$
6. $y = (2x^3 + x + 3)^5$
7. $y = e^{1+x+x^2}$
8. $y = e^{x^4+2x^2+5}$

In Problems 9–16, replace ? with an expression that will make the indicated equation valid.

9. $\dfrac{d}{dx}(3x + 4)^4 = 4(3x + 4)^3$ __?__
10. $\dfrac{d}{dx}(5 - 2x)^6 = 6(5 - 2x)^5$ __?__
11. $\dfrac{d}{dx}(4 - 2x^2)^3 = 3(4 - 2x^2)^2$ __?__
12. $\dfrac{d}{dx}(3x^2 + 7)^5 = 5(3x^2 + 7)^4$ __?__
13. $\dfrac{d}{dx}e^{x^2+1} = e^{x^2+1}$ __?__
14. $\dfrac{d}{dx}e^{4x-2} = e^{4x-2}$ __?__
15. $\dfrac{d}{dx}\ln(x^4 + 1) = \dfrac{1}{x^4 + 1}$ __?__
16. $\dfrac{d}{dx}\ln(x - x^3) = \dfrac{1}{x - x^3}$ __?__

In Problems 17–42, find f'(x) and simplify.

17. $f(x) = (x + 3)^2$

18. $f(x) = (x - 6)^3$

19. $f(x) = (2x + 5)^3$

20. $f(x) = (3x - 7)^5$

21. $f(x) = (5 - 2x)^4$

22. $f(x) = (9 - 5x)^2$

23. $f(x) = (4 + 0.2x)^5$

24. $f(x) = (6 - 0.5x)^4$

25. $f(x) = (3x^2 + 5)^5$

26. $f(x) = (5x^2 - 3)^6$

27. $f(x) = 5e^x$

28. $f(x) = 10 - 4e^x$

29. $f(x) = e^{5x}$

30. $f(x) = 6e^{-2x}$

31. $f(x) = 3e^{-6x}$

32. $f(x) = e^{x^2 + 3x + 1}$

33. $f(x) = (2x - 5)^{1/2}$

34. $f(x) = (4x + 3)^{1/2}$

35. $f(x) = (x^4 + 1)^{-2}$

36. $f(x) = (x^5 + 2)^{-3}$

37. $f(x) = 4 - 2 \ln x$

38. $f(x) = 8 \ln x$

39. $f(x) = 3 \ln(1 + x^2)$

40. $f(x) = 2 \ln(x^2 - 3x + 4)$

41. $f(x) = (1 + \ln x)^3$

42. $f(x) = (x - 2 \ln x)^4$

In Problems 43–48, find f'(x) and the equation of the line tangent to the graph of f at the indicated value of x. Find the value(s) of x where the tangent line is horizontal.

43. $f(x) = (2x - 1)^3;\quad x = 1$

44. $f(x) = (3x - 1)^4;\quad x = 1$

45. $f(x) = (4x - 3)^{1/2};\quad x = 3$

46. $f(x) = (2x + 8)^{1/2};\quad x = 4$

47. $f(x) = 5e^{x^2 - 4x + 1};\quad x = 0$

48. $f(x) = \ln(1 - x^2 + 2x^4);\quad x = 1$

B

In Problems 49–64, find the indicated derivative and simplify.

49. y' if $y = 3(x^2 - 2)^4$

50. y' if $y = 2(x^3 + 6)^5$

51. $\dfrac{d}{dt} 2(t^2 + 3t)^{-3}$

52. $\dfrac{d}{dt} 3(t^3 + t^2)^{-2}$

53. $\dfrac{dh}{dw}$ if $h(w) = \sqrt{w^2 + 8}$

54. $\dfrac{dg}{dw}$ if $g(w) = \sqrt[3]{3w - 7}$

55. $g'(x)$ if $g(x) = 4xe^{3x}$

56. $h'(x)$ if $h(x) = \dfrac{e^{2x}}{x^2 + 9}$

57. $\dfrac{d}{dx} \dfrac{\ln(1 + x)}{x^3}$

58. $\dfrac{d}{dx} [x^4 \ln(1 + x^4)]$

59. $F'(t)$ if $F(t) = (e^{t^2 + 1})^3$

60. $G'(t)$ if $G(t) = (1 - e^{2t})^2$

61. y' if $y = \ln(x^2 + 3)^{3/2}$

62. y' if $y = [\ln(x^2 + 3)]^{3/2}$

63. $\dfrac{d}{dw} \dfrac{1}{(w^3 + 4)^5}$

64. $\dfrac{d}{dw} \dfrac{1}{(w^2 - 2)^6}$

In Problems 65–70, find f'(x) and find the equation of the line tangent to the graph of f at the indicated value of x.

65. $f(x) = x(4 - x)^3;\quad x = 2$

66. $f(x) = x^2(1 - x)^4;\quad x = 2$

67. $f(x) = \dfrac{x}{(2x - 5)^3};\quad x = 3$

68. $f(x) = \dfrac{x^4}{(3x - 8)^2};\quad x = 4$

69. $f(x) = \sqrt{\ln x};\quad x = e$

70. $f(x) = e^{\sqrt{x}};\quad x = 1$

In Problems 71–76, find f'(x) and find the value(s) of x where the tangent line is horizontal.

71. $f(x) = x^2(x - 5)^3$

72. $f(x) = x^3(x - 7)^4$

73. $f(x) = \dfrac{x}{(2x + 5)^2}$

74. $f(x) = \dfrac{x - 1}{(x - 3)^3}$

75. $f(x) = \sqrt{x^2 - 8x + 20}$

76. $f(x) = \sqrt{x^2 + 4x + 5}$

77. A student reasons that the functions $f(x) = \ln[5(x^2 + 3)^4]$ and $g(x) = 4 \ln(x^2 + 3)$ must have the same derivative since he has entered $f(x)$, $g(x)$, $f'(x)$, and $g'(x)$ into a graphing calculator, but only three graphs appear (see the figure). Is his reasoning correct? Are $f'(x)$ and $g'(x)$ the same function? Explain.

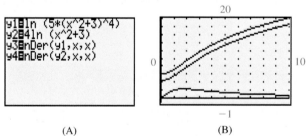

(A)   (B)

Figure for 77

78. A student reasons that the functions $f(x) = (x + 1) \ln(x + 1) - x$ and $g(x) = (x + 1)^{1/3}$ must have the same derivative since she has entered $f(x)$, $g(x)$, $f'(x)$, and $g'(x)$ into a graphing calculator, but only three graphs appear (see the figure). Is her reasoning correct? Are $f'(x)$ and $g'(x)$ the same function? Explain.

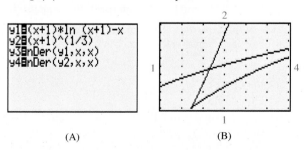

(A)   (B)

Figure for 78

C

In Problems 79–90, find each derivative and simplify.

79. $\dfrac{d}{dx}[3x(x^2 + 1)^3]$

80. $\dfrac{d}{dx}[2x^2(x^3 - 3)^4]$

81. $\dfrac{d}{dx}\dfrac{(x^3 - 7)^4}{2x^3}$

82. $\dfrac{d}{dx}\dfrac{3x^2}{(x^2 + 5)^3}$

83. $\dfrac{d}{dx}\log_2(3x^2 - 1)$

84. $\dfrac{d}{dx}\log(x^3 - 1)$

85. $\dfrac{d}{dx}10^{x^2+x}$

86. $\dfrac{d}{dx}8^{1-2x^2}$

87. $\dfrac{d}{dx}\log_3(4x^3 + 5x + 7)$

88. $\dfrac{d}{dx}\log_5(5^{x^2-1})$

89. $\dfrac{d}{dx}2^{x^3-x^2+4x+1}$

90. $\dfrac{d}{dx}10^{\ln x}$

Applications

91. Cost function. The total cost (in hundreds of dollars) of producing x cell phones per day is

$$C(x) = 10 + \sqrt{2x + 16} \qquad 0 \le x \le 50$$

(see the figure).

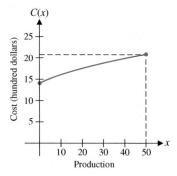

Figure for 91

(A) Find $C'(x)$.

(B) Find $C'(24)$ and $C'(42)$. Interpret the results.

92. Cost function. The total cost (in hundreds of dollars) of producing x cameras per week is

$$C(x) = 6 + \sqrt{4x + 4} \qquad 0 \le x \le 30$$

(A) Find $C'(x)$.

(B) Find $C'(15)$ and $C'(24)$. Interpret the results.

93. Price–supply equation. The number x of bicycle helmets a retail chain is willing to sell per week at a price of $\$p$ is given by

$$x = 80\sqrt{p + 25} - 400 \qquad 20 \le p \le 100$$

(see the figure).

(A) Find dx/dp.

(B) Find the supply and the instantaneous rate of change of supply with respect to price when the price is $75. Write a brief interpretation of these results.

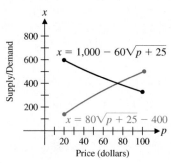

Figure for 93 and 94

94. Price–demand equation. The number x of bicycle helmets people are willing to buy per week from a retail chain at a price of $\$p$ is given by

$$x = 1,000 - 60\sqrt{p + 25} \qquad 20 \le p \le 100$$

(see the figure).

(A) Find dx/dp.

(B) Find the demand and the instantaneous rate of change of demand with respect to price when the price is $75. Write a brief interpretation of these results.

95. Drug concentration. The drug concentration in the bloodstream t hours after injection is given approximately by

$$C(t) = 4.35e^{-t} \qquad 0 \le t \le 5$$

where $C(t)$ is concentration in milligrams per milliliter.

(A) What is the rate of change of concentration after 1 hour? After 4 hours?

(B) Graph C.

96. Water pollution. The use of iodine crystals is a popular way of making small quantities of water safe to drink. Crystals placed in a 1-ounce bottle of water will dissolve until the solution is saturated. After saturation, half of the solution is poured into a quart container of water, and after about an hour, the water is usually safe to drink. The half-empty 1-ounce bottle is then refilled, to be used again in the same way. Suppose that the concentration of iodine in the 1-ounce bottle t minutes after the crystals are introduced can be approximated by

$$C(t) = 250(1 - e^{-t}) \qquad t \ge 0$$

where $C(t)$ is the concentration of iodine in micrograms per milliliter.

(A) What is the rate of change of the concentration after 1 minute? After 4 minutes?

(B) Graph C for $0 \le t \le 5$.

97. Blood pressure and age. A research group using hospital records developed the following mathematical model relating systolic blood pressure and age:

$$P(x) = 40 + 25\ln(x + 1) \qquad 0 \le x \le 65$$

$P(x)$ is pressure, measured in millimeters of mercury, and x is age in years. What is the rate of change of pressure at the end of 10 years? At the end of 30 years? At the end of 60 years?

98. Biology. A yeast culture at room temperature (68°F) is placed in a refrigerator set at a constant temperature of 38°F. After t hours, the temperature T of the culture is given approximately by

$$T = 30e^{-0.58t} + 38 \qquad t \geq 0$$

What is the rate of change of temperature of the culture at the end of 1 hour? At the end of 4 hours?

99. Learning. In 1930, L. L. Thurstone developed the following formula to indicate how learning time T depends on the length of a list n:

$$T = f(n) = \frac{c}{k}n\sqrt{n-a}$$

Here, a, c, and k are empirical constants. Suppose that, for a particular person, the time T (in minutes) required to learn a list of length n is

$$T = f(n) = 2n\sqrt{n-2}$$

(A) Find dT/dn.

(B) Find $f'(11)$ and $f'(27)$. Interpret the results.

Answers to Matched Problems

1. $f[g(x)] = 2e^x$, $g[f(u)] = e^{2u}$
2. (A) $f(u) = 50e^u$, $u = -2x$
   (B) $f(u) = \sqrt[3]{u}$, $u = 1 + x^3$

   [*Note:* There are other correct answers.]
3. (A) $15(5x+2)^2$
   (B) $20x^3(x^4-5)^4$
   (C) $-4t/(t^2+4)^3$
   (D) $-1/(2\sqrt{4-w})$
4. (A) $\frac{dy}{dx} = -5u^{-4}, \frac{du}{dx} = 6x^2, \frac{dy}{dx} = -30x^2(2x^3+4)^{-6}$
   (B) $\frac{dy}{du} = e^u, \frac{du}{dx} = 12x^3, \frac{dy}{dx} = 12x^3 e^{3x^4+6}$
   (C) $\frac{dy}{du} = \frac{1}{u}, \frac{du}{dx} = 2x+9, \frac{dy}{dx} = \frac{2x+9}{x^2+9x+4}$
5. $\dfrac{3e^x[\ln(1+e^x)]^2}{1+e^x}$
6. (A) $\dfrac{3x^2+2}{x^3+2x}$ (B) $6xe^{3x^2+2}$ (C) $-8xe^{-x^2}(2+e^{-x^2})^3$

4-5 Implicit Differentiation

- Special Function Notation
- Implicit Differentiation

Special Function Notation

The equation

$$y = 2 - 3x^2 \tag{1}$$

defines a function f with y as a dependent variable and x as an independent variable. Using function notation, we would write

$$y = f(x) \qquad \text{or} \qquad f(x) = 2 - 3x^2$$

In order to minimize the number of symbols, we will often write equation (1) in the form

$$y = 2 - 3x^2 = y(x)$$

where y is *both* a dependent variable and a function symbol. This is a convenient notation, and no harm is done as long as one is aware of the double role of y. Other examples are

$$x = 2t^2 - 3t + 1 = x(t)$$
$$z = \sqrt{u^2 - 3u} = z(u)$$
$$r = \frac{1}{(s^2 - 3s)^{2/3}} = r(s)$$

Until now, we have considered functions involving only one independent variable. There is no reason to stop there: The concept can be generalized to functions involving two or more independent variables, and this will be done in detail in

Chapter 8. For now, we will "borrow" the notation for a function involving two independent variables. For example,

$$F(x, y) = x^2 - 2xy + 3y^2 - 5$$

specifies a function F involving two independent variables.

Implicit Differentiation

Consider the equation

$$3x^2 + y - 2 = 0 \qquad (2)$$

and the equation obtained by solving equation (2) for y in terms of x,

$$y = 2 - 3x^2 \qquad (3)$$

Both equations define the same function with x as the independent variable and y as the dependent variable. For equation (3), we write

$$y = f(x)$$

where

$$f(x) = 2 - 3x^2 \qquad (4)$$

and we have an **explicit** (directly stated) rule that enables us to determine y for each value of x. On the other hand, the y in equation (2) is the same y as in equation (3), and equation (2) **implicitly** gives (implies, though does not directly express) y as a function of x. We say that equations (3) and (4) define the function f explicitly and equation (2) defines f implicitly.

The direct use of an equation that defines a function implicitly to find the derivative of the dependent variable with respect to the independent variable is called **implicit differentiation**. Let's differentiate equation (2) implicitly and equation (3) directly, and compare results.

Starting with

$$3x^2 + y - 2 = 0$$

we think of y as a function of x and write

$$3x^2 + y(x) - 2 = 0$$

Then we differentiate both sides with respect to x:

$$\frac{d}{dx}[(3x^2 + y(x) - 2)] = \frac{d}{dx}0$$

$$\frac{d}{dx}3x^2 + \frac{d}{dx}y(x) - \frac{d}{dx}2 = 0$$

$$6x + y' - 0 = 0$$

Since y is a function of x, but is not explicitly given, we simply write $\frac{d}{dx}y(x) = y'$ to indicate its derivative.

Now we solve for y':

$$y' = -6x$$

Note that we get the same result if we start with equation (3) and differentiate directly:

$$y = 2 - 3x^2$$
$$y' = -6x$$

Why are we interested in implicit differentiation? Why not solve for y in terms of x and differentiate directly? The answer is that there are many equations of the form

$$F(x, y) = 0 \qquad (5)$$

that are either difficult or impossible to solve for y explicitly in terms of x (try it for $x^2y^5 - 3xy + 5 = 0$ or for $e^y - y = 3x$, for example). But it can be shown that, under fairly general conditions on F, equation (5) will define one or more functions in which y is a dependent variable and x is an independent variable. To find y' under these conditions, we differentiate equation (5) implicitly.

EXPLORE & DISCUSS 1

(A) How many tangent lines are there to the graph in Figure 1 when $x = 0$? When $x = 1$? When $x = 2$? When $x = 4$? When $x = 6$?

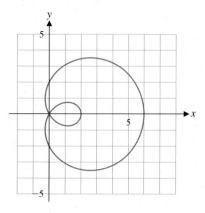

Figure 1

(B) Sketch the tangent lines referred to in part (A), and estimate each of their slopes.

(C) Explain why the graph in Figure 1 is not the graph of a function.

EXAMPLE 1   **Differentiating Implicitly** Given

$$F(x, y) = x^2 + y^2 - 25 = 0 \qquad (6)$$

find y' and the slope of the graph at $x = 3$.

SOLUTION   We start with the graph of $x^2 + y^2 - 25 = 0$ (a circle, as shown in Fig. 2) so that we can interpret our results geometrically. From the graph, it is clear that equation (6) does not define a function. But with a suitable restriction on the variables, equation (6) can define two or more functions. For example, the upper half and the lower half of the circle each define a function. On each half-circle, a point that corresponds to $x = 3$ is found by substituting $x = 3$ into equation (6) and solving for y:

$$x^2 + y^2 - 25 = 0$$
$$(3)^2 + y^2 = 25$$
$$y^2 = 16$$
$$y = \pm 4$$

The point $(3, 4)$ is on the upper half-circle, and the point $(3, -4)$ is on the lower half-circle. We will use these results in a moment. We now differentiate equation (6) implicitly, treating y as a function of x [i.e., $y = y(x)$]:

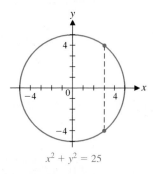

$$x^2 + y^2 = 25$$

Figure 2

$$x^2 + y^2 - 25 = 0$$

$$x^2 + [y(x)]^2 - 25 = 0$$

$$\frac{d}{dx}\{x^2 + [y(x)]^2 - 25\} = \frac{d}{dx}0$$

$$\frac{d}{dx}x^2 + \frac{d}{dx}[y(x)]^2 - \frac{d}{dx}25 = 0 \qquad \text{Use the chain rule.}$$

$$2x + 2[y(x)]^{2-1}y'(x) - 0 = 0$$

$$2x + 2yy' = 0 \qquad \text{Solve for } y' \text{ in terms of } x \text{ and } y.$$

$$y' = -\frac{2x}{2y}$$

$$y' = -\frac{x}{y} \qquad \text{Leave the answer in terms of } x \text{ and } y.$$

We have found y' without first solving $x^2 + y^2 - 25 = 0$ for y in terms of x. And by leaving y' in terms of x and y, we can use $y' = -x/y$ to find y' for *any* point on the graph of $x^2 + y^2 - 25 = 0$ (except where $y = 0$). In particular, for $x = 3$, we found that $(3, 4)$ and $(3, -4)$ are on the graph. The slope of the graph at $(3, 4)$ is

$$y'|_{(3,4)} = -\frac{3}{4} \qquad \text{The slope of the graph at } (3, 4)$$

and the slope at $(3, -4)$ is

$$y'|_{(3,-4)} = -\frac{3}{-4} = \frac{3}{4} \qquad \text{The slope of the graph at } (3, -4)$$

The symbol

$$y'|_{(a,b)}$$

is used to indicate that we are evaluating y' at $x = a$ and $y = b$.

The results are interpreted geometrically in Figure 3 on the original graph.

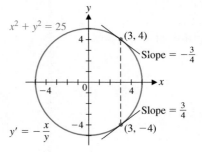

Figure 3

Matched Problem 1   Graph $x^2 + y^2 - 169 = 0$, find y' by implicit differentiation, and find the slope of the graph when $x = 5$.

CONCEPTUAL INSIGHT

When differentiating implicitly, the derivative of y^2 is $2yy'$, not just $2y$. This is because y represents a function of x, so the chain rule applies. Suppose, for example, that y represents the function $y = 5x + 4$. Then

$$(y^2)' = [(5x + 4)^2]' = 2(5x + 4) \cdot 5 = 2yy'$$

So, when differenting implicitly, the derivative of y is y', the derivative of y^2 is $2yy'$, the derivative of y^3 is $3y^2y'$, and so on.

EXAMPLE 2   **Differentiating Implicitly**   Find the equation(s) of the tangent line(s) to the graph of

$$y - xy^2 + x^2 + 1 = 0 \qquad\qquad (7)$$

at the point(s) where $x = 1$.

SOLUTION   We first find y when $x = 1$:

$$y - xy^2 + x^2 + 1 = 0$$
$$y - (1)y^2 + (1)^2 + 1 = 0$$
$$y - y^2 + 2 = 0$$
$$y^2 - y - 2 = 0$$
$$(y - 2)(y + 1) = 0$$
$$y = -1, 2$$

So there are two points on the graph of (7) where $x = 1$, namely, $(1, -1)$ and $(1, 2)$. We next find the slope of the graph at these two points by differentiating equation (7) implicitly:

$$y - xy^2 + x^2 + 1 = 0$$

$$\frac{d}{dx}y - \frac{d}{dx}xy^2 + \frac{d}{dx}x^2 + \frac{d}{dx}1 = \frac{d}{dx}0$$ *Use the product rule and the chain rule for $\frac{d}{dx}xy^2$.*

$$y' - (x \cdot 2yy' + y^2) + 2x = 0$$

$$y' - 2xyy' - y^2 + 2x = 0$$ *Solve for y' by getting all terms involving y' on one side.*

$$y' - 2xyy' = y^2 - 2x$$

$$(1 - 2xy)y' = y^2 - 2x$$

$$y' = \frac{y^2 - 2x}{1 - 2xy}$$

Now find the slope at each point:

$$y'|_{(1,-1)} = \frac{(-1)^2 - 2(1)}{1 - 2(1)(-1)} = \frac{1 - 2}{1 + 2} = \frac{-1}{3} = -\frac{1}{3}$$

$$y'|_{(1,2)} = \frac{(2)^2 - 2(1)}{1 - 2(1)(2)} = \frac{4 - 2}{1 - 4} = \frac{2}{-3} = -\frac{2}{3}$$

Equation of tangent line at $(1, -1)$:

$$y - y_1 = m(x - x_1)$$
$$y + 1 = -\tfrac{1}{3}(x - 1)$$
$$y + 1 = -\tfrac{1}{3}x + \tfrac{1}{3}$$
$$y = -\tfrac{1}{3}x - \tfrac{2}{3}$$

Equation of tangent line at $(1, 2)$:

$$y - y_1 = m(x - x_1)$$
$$y - 2 = -\tfrac{2}{3}(x - 1)$$
$$y - 2 = -\tfrac{2}{3}x + \tfrac{2}{3}$$
$$y = -\tfrac{2}{3}x + \tfrac{8}{3}$$

Matched Problem 2   Repeat Example 2 for $x^2 + y^2 - xy - 7 = 0$ at $x = 1$.

EXAMPLE 3   **Differentiating Implicitly**   Find x' for $x = x(t)$ defined implicitly by

$$t \ln x = xe^t - 1$$

and evaluate x' at $(t, x) = (0, 1)$.

SOLUTION   It is important to remember that x is the dependent variable and t is the independent variable. Therefore, we differentiate both sides of the equation with respect to t (using product and chain rules where appropriate) and then solve for x':

$$t \ln x = xe^t - 1 \qquad \text{Differentiate implicitly with respect to } t.$$

$$\frac{d}{dt}(t \ln x) = \frac{d}{dt}(xe^t) - \frac{d}{dt}1$$

$$t\frac{x'}{x} + \ln x = xe^t + x'e^t \qquad \text{Clear fractions.}$$

$$\boxed{x \cdot t\frac{x'}{x} + x \cdot \ln x = x \cdot xe^t + x \cdot e^t x'} \qquad x \neq 0$$

$$tx' + x \ln x = x^2 e^t + xe^t x' \qquad \text{Solve for } x'.$$

$$tx' - xe'x' = x^2 e^t - x \ln x \qquad \text{Factor out } x'.$$

$$(t - xe^t)x' = x^2 e^t - x \ln x$$

$$x' = \frac{x^2 e^t - x \ln x}{t - xe^t}$$

Now we evaluate x' at $(t, x) = (0, 1)$, as requested:

$$x'|_{(0,1)} = \frac{(1)^2 e^0 - 1 \ln 1}{0 - 1e^0}$$

$$= \frac{1}{-1} = -1$$

Matched Problem 3   Find x' for $x = x(t)$ defined implicitly by

$$1 + x \ln t = te^x$$

and evaluate x' at $(t, x) = (1, 0)$.

Exercises 4-5

A

In Problems 1–4, find y' in two ways:

(A) Differentiate the given equation implicitly and then solve for y'.

(B) Solve the given equation for y and then differentiate directly.

1. $3x + 5y + 9 = 0$

2. $-2x + 6y - 4 = 0$

3. $3x^2 - 4y - 18 = 0$

4. $2x^3 + 5y - 2 = 0$

In Problems 5–22, use implicit differentiation to find y' and evaluate y' at the indicated point.

5. $y - 5x^2 + 3 = 0;\ (1, 2)$

6. $5x^3 - y - 1 = 0;\ (1, 4)$

7. $x^2 - y^3 - 3 = 0;\ (2, 1)$

8. $y^2 + x^3 + 4 = 0;\ (-2, 2)$

9. $y^2 + 2y + 3x = 0;\ (-1, 1)$

10. $y^2 - y - 4x = 0;\ (0, 1)$

B

11. $xy - 6 = 0;\ (2, 3)$

12. $3xy - 2x - 2 = 0;\ (2, 1)$

13. $2xy + y + 2 = 0;\ (-1, 2)$

14. $2y + xy - 1 = 0;\ (-1, 1)$

15. $x^2 y - 3x^2 - 4 = 0;\ (2, 4)$

16. $2x^3 y - x^3 + 5 = 0;\ (-1, 3)$

17. $e^y = x^2 + y^2;\ (1, 0)$

18. $x^2 - y = 4e^y;\ (2, 0)$

19. $x^3 - y = \ln y;\ (1, 1)$

20. $\ln y = 2y^2 - x;\ (2, 1)$

21. $x \ln y + 2y = 2x^3;\ (1, 1)$

22. $xe^y - y = x^2 - 2;\ (2, 0)$

In Problems 23 and 24, find x' for $x = x(t)$ defined implicitly by the given equation. Evaluate x' at the indicated point.

23. $x^2 - t^2 x + t^3 + 11 = 0;\ (-2, 1)$

24. $x^3 - tx^2 - 4 = 0;\ (-3, -2)$

Problems 25 and 26 refer to the equation and graph shown in the 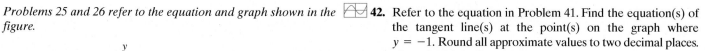 *figure.*

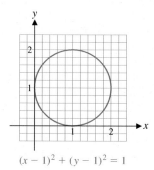

$$(x - 1)^2 + (y - 1)^2 = 1$$

Figure for 25 and 26

25. Use implicit differentiation to find the slopes of the tangent lines at the points on the graph where $x = 1.6$. Check your answers by visually estimating the slopes on the graph in the figure.

26. Find the slopes of the tangent lines at the points on the graph where $x = 0.2$. Check your answers by visually estimating the slopes on the graph in the figure.

In Problems 27–30, find the equation(s) of the tangent line(s) to the graphs of the indicated equations at the point(s) with the given value of x.

27. $xy - x - 4 = 0; x = 2$

28. $3x + xy + 1 = 0; x = -1$

29. $y^2 - xy - 6 = 0; x = 1$

30. $xy^2 - y - 2 = 0; x = 1$

31. If $xe^y = 1$, find y' in two ways, first by differentiating implicitly and then by solving for y explicitly in terms of x. Which method do you prefer? Explain.

32. Explain the difficulty that arises in solving $x^3 + y + xe^y = 1$ for y as an explicit function of x. Find the slope of the tangent line to the graph of the equation at the point $(0, 1)$.

C

In Problems 33–40, find y' and the slope of the tangent line to the graph of each equation at the indicated point.

33. $(1 + y)^3 + y = x + 7; (2, 1)$

34. $(y - 3)^4 - x = y; (-3, 4)$

35. $(x - 2y)^3 = 2y^2 - 3; (1, 1)$

36. $(2x - y)^4 - y^3 = 8; (-1, -2)$

37. $\sqrt{7 + y^2} - x^3 + 4 = 0; (2, 3)$

38. $6\sqrt{y^3 + 1} - 2x^{3/2} - 2 = 0; (4, 2)$

39. $\ln(xy) = y^2 - 1; (1, 1)$

40. $e^{xy} - 2x = y + 1; (0, 0)$

41. Find the equation(s) of the tangent line(s) at the point(s) on the graph of the equation

$$y^3 - xy - x^3 = 2$$

where $x = 1$. Round all approximate values to two decimal places.

42. Refer to the equation in Problem 41. Find the equation(s) of the tangent line(s) at the point(s) on the graph where $y = -1$. Round all approximate values to two decimal places.

Applications

For the demand equations in Problems 43–46, find the rate of change of p with respect to x by differentiating implicitly (x is the number of items that can be sold at a price of $p).

43. $x = p^2 - 2p + 1,000$ **44.** $x = p^3 - 3p^2 + 200$

45. $x = \sqrt{10,000 - p^2}$ **46.** $x = \sqrt[3]{1,500 - p^3}$

47. Biophysics. In biophysics, the equation

$$(L + m)(V + n) = k$$

is called the *fundamental equation of muscle contraction,* where m, n, and k are constants and V is the velocity of the shortening of muscle fibers for a muscle subjected to a load L. Find dL/dV by implicit differentiation.

48. Biophysics. In Problem 47, find dV/dL by implicit differentiation.

49. Speed of sound. The speed of sound in air is given by the formula

$$v = k\sqrt{T}$$

where v is the velocity of sound, T is the temperature of the air, and k is a constant. Use implicit differentiation to find $\dfrac{dT}{dv}$.

50. Gravity. The equation

$$F = G\frac{m_1 m_2}{r^2}$$

is Newton's law of universal gravitation. G is a constant and F is the gravitational force between two objects having masses m_1 and m_2 that are a distance r from each other. Use implicit differentiation to find $\dfrac{dr}{dF}$. Assume that m_1 and m_2 are constant.

51. Speed of sound. Refer to Problem 49. Find $\dfrac{dv}{dT}$ and discuss the connection between $\dfrac{dv}{dT}$ and $\dfrac{dT}{dv}$.

52. Gravity. Refer to Problem 50. Find $\dfrac{dF}{dr}$ and discuss the connection between $\dfrac{dF}{dr}$ and $\dfrac{dr}{dF}$.

Answers to Matched Problems

1. $y' = -x/y$. When $x = 5$, $y = \pm 12$; thus, $y'|_{(5,12)} = -\frac{5}{12}$ and $y'|_{(5,-12)} = \frac{5}{12}$

2. $y' = \dfrac{y - 2x}{2y - x}$; $y = \frac{4}{5}x - \frac{14}{5}, y = \frac{1}{5}x + \frac{14}{5}$

3. $x' = \dfrac{te^x - x}{t \ln t - t^2 e^x}$; $x'|_{(1,0)} = -1$

4-6   Related Rates

Union workers are concerned that the rate at which wages are increasing is lagging behind the rate of increase in the company's profits. An automobile dealer wants to predict how badly an anticipated increase in interest rates will decrease his rate of sales. An investor is studying the connection between the rate of increase in the Dow Jones average and the rate of increase in the gross domestic product over the past 50 years.

In each of these situations, there are two quantities—wages and profits, for example—that are changing with respect to time. We would like to discover the precise relationship between the rates of increase (or decrease) of the two quantities. We begin our discussion of such *related rates* by considering familiar situations in which the two quantities are distances and the two rates are velocities.

EXAMPLE 1   **Related Rates and Motion** A 26-foot ladder is placed against a wall (Fig. 1). If the top of the ladder is sliding down the wall at 2 feet per second, at what rate is the bottom of the ladder moving away from the wall when the bottom of the ladder is 10 feet away from the wall?

SOLUTION   Many people think that since the ladder is a constant length, the bottom of the ladder will move away from the wall at the rate that the top of the ladder is moving down the wall. This is not the case, however.

At any moment in time, let x be the distance of the bottom of the ladder from the wall and let y be the distance of the top of the ladder from the ground (see Fig. 1). Both x and y are changing with respect to time and can be thought of as functions of time; that is, $x = x(t)$ and $y = y(t)$. Furthermore, x and y are related by the Pythagorean relationship:

$$x^2 + y^2 = 26^2 \tag{1}$$

26 ft

Figure 1

Differentiating equation (1) implicitly with respect to time t and using the chain rule where appropriate, we obtain

$$2x\frac{dx}{dt} + 2y\frac{dy}{dt} = 0 \tag{2}$$

The rates dx/dt and dy/dt are related by equation (2). This is a **related-rates problem**.

Our problem is to find dx/dt when $x = 10$ feet, given that $dy/dt = -2$ (y is decreasing at a constant rate of 2 feet per second). We have all the quantities we need in equation (2) to solve for dx/dt, except y. When $x = 10$, y can be found from equation (1):

$$10^2 + y^2 = 26^2$$
$$y = \sqrt{26^2 - 10^2} = 24 \text{ feet}$$

Substitute $dy/dt = -2$, $x = 10$, and $y = 24$ into (2). Then solve for dx/dt:

$$2(10)\frac{dx}{dt} + 2(24)(-2) = 0$$

$$\frac{dx}{dt} = \frac{-2(24)(-2)}{2(10)} = 4.8 \text{ feet per second}$$

The bottom of the ladder is moving away from the wall at a rate of 4.8 feet per second.

CONCEPTUAL INSIGHT

In the solution to Example 1, we used equation (1) in two ways: first, to find an equation relating dy/dt and dx/dt, and second, to find the value of y when $x = 10$. These steps must be done in this order. Substituting $x = 10$ and then differentiating does not produce any useful results:

$$x^2 + y^2 = 26^2$$ Substituting 10 for x has the effect of

$$100 + y^2 = 26^2$$ stopping the ladder.

$$0 + 2yy' = 0$$ The rate of change of a stationary

$$y' = 0$$ object is always 0, but that is not the rate of change of the moving ladder.

Matched Problem 1   Again, a 26-foot ladder is placed against a wall (Fig. 1). If the bottom of the ladder is moving away from the wall at 3 feet per second, at what rate is the top moving down when the top of the ladder is 24 feet above ground?

EXPLORE & DISCUSS 1   (A) For which values of x and y in Example 1 is dx/dt equal to 2 (i.e., the same rate that the ladder is sliding down the wall)?

(B) When is dx/dt greater than 2? Less than 2?

DEFINITION   Suggestions for Solving Related-Rates Problems

Step 1   Sketch a figure if helpful.

Step 2   Identify all relevant variables, including those whose rates are given and those whose rates are to be found.

Step 3   Express all given rates and rates to be found as derivatives.

Step 4   Find an equation connecting the variables identified in step 2.

Step 5   Implicitly differentiate the equation found in step 4, using the chain rule where appropriate, and substitute in all given values.

Step 6   Solve for the derivative that will give the unknown rate.

EXAMPLE 2   **Related Rates and Motion** Suppose that two motorboats leave from the same point at the same time. If one travels north at 15 miles per hour and the other travels east at 20 miles per hour, how fast will the distance between them be changing after 2 hours?

SOLUTION   First, draw a picture, as shown in Figure 2.

All variables, x, y, and z, are changing with time. They can be considered as functions of time: $x = x(t)$, $y = y(t)$, and $z = z(t)$, given implicitly. It now makes sense to take derivatives of each variable with respect to time. From the Pythagorean theorem,

$$z^2 = x^2 + y^2 \qquad (3)$$

We also know that

$$\frac{dx}{dt} = 20 \text{ miles per hour} \qquad \text{and} \qquad \frac{dy}{dt} = 15 \text{ miles per hour}$$

Figure 2

We want to find dz/dt at the end of 2 hours—that is, when $x = 40$ miles and $y = 30$ miles. To do this, we differentiate both sides of equation (3) with respect to t and solve for dz/dt:

$$2z\frac{dz}{dt} = 2x\frac{dx}{dt} + 2y\frac{dy}{dt} \qquad (4)$$

We have everything we need except z. From equation (3), when $x = 40$ and $y = 30$, we find z to be 50. Substituting the known quantities into equation (4), we obtain

$$2(50)\frac{dz}{dt} = 2(40)(20) + 2(30)(15)$$

$$\frac{dz}{dt} = 25 \text{ miles per hour}$$

The boats will be separating at a rate of 25 miles per hour.

Matched Problem 2   Repeat Example 2 for the same situation at the end of 3 hours.

EXAMPLE 3   **Related Rates and Motion** Suppose that a point is moving along the graph of $x^2 + y^2 = 25$ (Fig. 3). When the point is at $(-3, 4)$, its x coordinate is increasing at the rate of 0.4 unit per second. How fast is the y coordinate changing at that moment?

SOLUTION   Since both x and y are changing with respect to time, we can consider each as a function of time, namely,

$$x = x(t) \qquad \text{and} \qquad y = y(t)$$

but restricted so that

$$x^2 + y^2 = 25 \qquad (5)$$

We want to find dy/dt, given $x = -3$, $y = 4$, and $dx/dt = 0.4$. Implicitly differentiating both sides of equation (5) with respect to t, we have

$$x^2 + y^2 = 25$$

$$2x\frac{dx}{dt} + 2y\frac{dy}{dt} = 0 \qquad \textit{Divide both sides by 2.}$$

$$x\frac{dx}{dt} + y\frac{dy}{dt} = 0 \qquad \textit{Substitute x = −3, y = 4, and dx/dt = 0.4, and solve for dy/dt.}$$

$$(-3)(0.4) + 4\frac{dy}{dt} = 0$$

$$\frac{dy}{dt} = 0.3 \text{ unit per second}$$

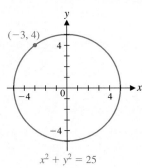

$x^2 + y^2 = 25$

Figure 3

Matched Problem 3   A point is moving on the graph of $y^3 = x^2$. When the point is at $(-8, 4)$, its y coordinate is decreasing by 2 units per second. How fast is the x coordinate changing at that moment?

EXAMPLE 4   **Related Rates and Business** Suppose that for a company manufacturing flash drives, the cost, revenue, and profit equations are given by

$$C = 5{,}000 + 2x \qquad \textit{Cost equation}$$

$$R = 10x - 0.001x^2 \qquad \textit{Revenue equation}$$

$$P = R - C \qquad \textit{Profit equation}$$

where the production output in 1 week is x flash drives. If production is increasing at the rate of 500 flash drives per week when production is 2,000 flash drives, find the rate of increase in

(A) Cost   (B) Revenue   (C) Profit

SOLUTION If production x is a function of time (it must be, since it is changing with respect to time), then C, R, and P must also be functions of time. These functions are given implicitly (rather than explicitly). Letting t represent time in weeks, we differentiate both sides of each of the preceding three equations with respect to t and then substitute $x = 2{,}000$ and $dx/dt = 500$ to find the desired rates.

(A) $C = 5{,}000 + 2x$ Think: $C = C(t)$ and $x = x(t)$.

$$\frac{dC}{dt} = \frac{d}{dt}(5{,}000) + \frac{d}{dt}(2x)$$ Differentiate both sides with respect to t.

$$\frac{dC}{dt} = 0 + 2\frac{dx}{dt} = 2\frac{dx}{dt}$$

Since $dx/dt = 500$ when $x = 2{,}000$,

$$\frac{dC}{dt} = 2(500) = \$1{,}000 \text{ per week}$$

Cost is increasing at a rate of $1,000 per week.

(B) $R = 10x - 0.001x^2$

$$\frac{dR}{dt} = \frac{d}{dt}(10x) - \frac{d}{dt}0.001x^2$$

$$\frac{dR}{dt} = 10\frac{dx}{dt} - 0.002x\frac{dx}{dt}$$

$$\frac{dR}{dt} = (10 - 0.002x)\frac{dx}{dt}$$

Since $dx/dt = 500$ when $x = 2{,}000$,

$$\frac{dR}{dt} = [10 - 0.002(2{,}000)](500) = \$3{,}000 \text{ per week}$$

Revenue is increasing at a rate of $3,000 per week.

(C) $P = R - C$

$$\frac{dP}{dt} = \frac{dR}{dt} - \frac{dC}{dt}$$ Results from parts (A) and (B)

$$= \$3{,}000 - \$1{,}000$$

$$= \$2{,}000 \text{ per week}$$

Profit is increasing at a rate of $2,000 per week.

Matched Problem 4   Repeat Example 4 for a production level of 6,000 flash drives per week.

Exercises 4-6

A

In Problems 1–6, assume that $x = x(t)$ and $y = y(t)$. Find the indicated rate, given the other information.

1. $y = x^2 + 2$; $dx/dt = 3$ when $x = 5$; find dy/dt

2. $y = x^3 - 3$; $dx/dt = -2$ when $x = 2$; find dy/dt

3. $x^2 + y^2 = 1$; $dy/dt = -4$ when $x = -0.6$ and $y = 0.8$; find dx/dt

4. $x^2 + y^2 = 4$; $dy/dt = 5$ when $x = 1.2$ and $y = -1.6$; find dx/dt

5. $x^2 + 3xy + y^2 = 11$; $dx/dt = 2$ when $x = 1$ and $y = 2$; find dy/dt

6. $x^2 - 2xy - y^2 = 7$; $dy/dt = -1$ when $x = 2$ and $y = -1$; find dx/dt

B

7. A point is moving on the graph of $xy = 36$. When the point is at $(4, 9)$, its x coordinate is increasing by 4 units per second. How fast is the y coordinate changing at that moment?

8. A point is moving on the graph of $4x^2 + 9y^2 = 36$. When the point is at $(3, 0)$, its y coordinate is decreasing by 2 units per second. How fast is its x coordinate changing at that moment?

9. A boat is being pulled toward a dock as shown in the figure. If the rope is being pulled in at 3 feet per second, how fast is the distance between the dock and the boat decreasing when it is 30 feet from the dock?

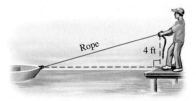

Rope

4 ft

Figure for 9 and 10

10. Refer to Problem 9. Suppose that the distance between the boat and the dock is decreasing by 3.05 feet per second. How fast is the rope being pulled in when the boat is 10 feet from the dock?

11. A rock thrown into a still pond causes a circular ripple. If the radius of the ripple is increasing by 2 feet per second, how fast is the area changing when the radius is 10 feet? [Use $A = \pi R^2$, $\pi \approx 3.14$.]

12. Refer to Problem 11. How fast is the circumference of a circular ripple changing when the radius is 10 feet? [Use $C = 2\pi R$, $\pi \approx 3.14$.]

13. The radius of a spherical balloon is increasing at the rate of 3 centimeters per minute. How fast is the volume changing when the radius is 10 centimeters? [Use $V = \frac{4}{3}\pi R^3$, $\pi \approx 3.14$.]

14. Refer to Problem 13. How fast is the surface area of the sphere increasing when the radius is 10 centimeters? [Use $S = 4\pi R^2$, $\pi \approx 3.14$.]

15. Boyle's law for enclosed gases states that if the volume is kept constant, the pressure P and temperature T are related by the equation

$$\frac{P}{T} = k$$

where k is a constant. If the temperature is increasing at 3 kelvins per hour, what is the rate of change of pressure when the temperature is 250 kelvins and the pressure is 500 pounds per square inch?

16. Boyle's law for enclosed gases states that if the temperature is kept constant, the pressure P and volume V of a gas are related by the equation

$$VP = k$$

where k is a constant. If the volume is decreasing by 5 cubic inches per second, what is the rate of change of pressure when the volume is 1,000 cubic inches and the pressure is 40 pounds per square inch?

17. A 10-foot ladder is placed against a vertical wall. Suppose that the bottom of the ladder slides away from the wall at a constant rate of 3 feet per second. How fast is the top of the ladder sliding down the wall (negative rate) when the bottom is 6 feet from the wall? [*Hint:* Use the Pythagorean theorem, $a^2 + b^2 = c^2$, where c is the length of the hypotenuse of a right triangle and a and b are the lengths of the two shorter sides.]

18. A weather balloon is rising vertically at the rate of 5 meters per second. An observer is standing on the ground 300 meters from where the balloon was released. At what rate is the distance between the observer and the balloon changing when the balloon is 400 meters high?

C

19. A streetlight is on top of a 20-foot pole. A person who is 5 feet tall walks away from the pole at the rate of 5 feet per second. At what rate is the tip of the person's shadow moving away from the pole when he is 20 feet from the pole?

20. Refer to Problem 19. At what rate is the person's shadow growing when he is 20 feet from the pole?

21. Helium is pumped into a spherical balloon at a constant rate of 4 cubic feet per second. How fast is the radius increasing after 1 minute? After 2 minutes? Is there any time at which the radius is increasing at a rate of 100 feet per second? Explain.

22. A point is moving along the x axis at a constant rate of 5 units per second. At which point is its distance from $(0, 1)$ increasing at a rate of 2 units per second? At 4 units per second? At 5 units per second? At 10 units per second? Explain.

23. A point is moving on the graph of $y = e^x + x + 1$ in such a way that its x coordinate is always increasing at a rate of 3 units per second. How fast is the y coordinate changing when the point crosses the x axis?

24. A point is moving on the graph of $x^3 + y^2 = 1$ in such a way that its y coordinate is always increasing at a rate of 2 units per second. At which point(s) is the x coordinate increasing at a rate of 1 unit per second?

Applications

25. Cost, revenue, and profit rates. Suppose that for a company manufacturing calculators, the cost, revenue, and profit equations are given by

$$C = 90,000 + 30x \qquad R = 300x - \frac{x^2}{30}$$

$$P = R - C$$

where the production output in 1 week is x calculators. If production is increasing at a rate of 500 calculators per week when production output is 6,000 calculators, find the rate of increase (decrease) in

(A) Cost   (B) Revenue   (C) Profit

26. Cost, revenue, and profit rates. Repeat Problem 25 for

$$C = 72,000 + 60x \qquad R = 200x - \frac{x^2}{30}$$

$$P = R - C$$

where production is increasing at a rate of 500 calculators per week at a production level of 1,500 calculators.

27. Advertising. A retail store estimates that weekly sales s and weekly advertising costs x (both in dollars) are related by

$$s = 60,000 - 40,000e^{-0.0005x}$$

The current weekly advertising costs are $2,000, and these costs are increasing at the rate of $300 per week. Find the current rate of change of sales.

28. Advertising. Repeat Problem 27 for

$$s = 50,000 - 20,000e^{-0.0004x}$$

29. Price–demand. The price p (in dollars) and demand x for a product are related by

$$2x^2 + 5xp + 50p^2 = 80,000$$

(A) If the price is increasing at a rate of $2 per month when the price is $30, find the rate of change of the demand.

(B) If the demand is decreasing at a rate of 6 units per month when the demand is 150 units, find the rate of change of the price.

30. Price–demand. Repeat Problem 29 for

$$x^2 + 2xp + 25p^2 = 74,500$$

31. Pollution. An oil tanker aground on a reef is forming a circular oil slick about 0.1 foot thick (see the figure). To estimate the rate dV/dt (in cubic feet per minute) at which the oil is leaking from the tanker, it was found that the radius of the slick was increasing at 0.32 foot per minute ($dR/dt = 0.32$) when the radius R was 500 feet. Find dV/dt, using $\pi \approx 3.14$.

Tanker

R

Oil slick

$A = \pi R^2$
$V = 0.1\, A$

Figure for 31

32. Learning. A person who is new on an assembly line performs an operation in T minutes after x performances of the operation, as given by

$$T = 6\left(1 + \frac{1}{\sqrt{x}}\right)$$

If $dx/dt = 6$ operations per hours, where t is time in hours, find dT/dt after 36 performances of the operation.

Answers to Matched Problems

1. $dy/dt = -1.25$ ft/sec
2. $dz/dt = 25$ mi/hr
3. $dx/dt = 6$ units/sec
4. (A) $dC/dt = $1,000/wk$
   (B) $dR/dt = -$1,000/wk$
   (C) $dP/dt = -$2,000/wk$

4-7   Elasticity of Demand

- Relative Rate of Change
- Elasticity of Demand

When will a price increase lead to an increase in revenue? To answer this question and study relationships among price, demand, and revenue, economists use the notion of *elasticity of demand*. In this section, we define the concepts of *relative rate of change*, *percentage rate of change*, and *elasticity of demand*.

Relative Rate of Change

EXPLORE & DISCUSS 1

A broker is trying to sell you two stocks: Biotech and Comstat. The broker estimates that Biotech's earnings will increase $2 per year over the next several years, while Comstat's earnings will increase only $1 per year. Is this sufficient information for you to choose between the two stocks? What other information might you request from the broker to help you decide?

Interpreting rates of change is a fundamental application of calculus. In Explore & Discuss 1, Biotech's earnings are increasing at twice the rate of Comstat's, but that does not automatically make Biotech the better buy. The obvious information that is missing is the cost of each stock. If Biotech costs $100 a share and Comstat costs $25 share, then which stock is the better buy? To answer this question, we introduce two new concepts: *relative rate of change* and *percentage rate of change*.

DEFINITION **Relative and Percentage Rates of Change**

The **relative rate of change** of a function $f(x)$ is $\dfrac{f'(x)}{f(x)}$.

The **percentage rate of change** is $100 \times \dfrac{f'(x)}{f(x)}$.

Because

$$\frac{d}{dx} \ln f(x) = \frac{f'(x)}{f(x)}$$

the relative rate of change of $f(x)$ is the derivative of the logarithm of $f(x)$. This is also referred to as the **logarithmic derivative** of $f(x)$. Returning to Explore & Discuss 1, we can now write

	Relative rate of change		Percentage rate of change
Biotech	$\dfrac{2}{100} = 0.02$	or	2%
Comstat	$\dfrac{1}{25} = 0.04$	or	4%

EXAMPLE 1 **Percentage Rate of Change** Table 1 lists the GDP (gross domestic product expressed in billions of 2005 dollars) and U.S. population from 2000 to 2008. A model for the GDP is

$$f(t) = 280t + 11{,}147$$

where t is years since 2000. Find and graph the percentage rate of change of $f(t)$ for $0 \le t \le 8$.

Table 1

Year	Real GDP (billions of 2005 dollars)	Population (in millions)
2000	$11,226	282.2
2002	$11,553	287.7
2004	$12,264	292.9
2006	$12,976	298.4
2008	$13,312	304.1

SOLUTION If $p(t)$ is the percentage rate of change of $f(t)$, then

$$p(t) = 100 \times \frac{d}{dx} \ln(280t + 11{,}147)$$

$$= \frac{28{,}000}{280t + 11{,}147}$$

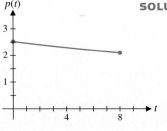

Figure 1

The graph of $p(t)$ is shown in Figure 1 (graphing details omitted). Notice that $p(t)$ is decreasing, even though the GDP is increasing.

Matched Problem 1   A model for the population data in Table 1 is

$$f(t) = 2.7t + 282$$

where t is years since 2000. Find and graph $p(t)$, the percentage rate of change of $f(t)$ for $0 \le t \le 8$.

Elasticity of Demand

Economists use logarithmic derivatives and relative rates of change to study the relationship among price changes, demand, and revenue. Suppose the price \$$p$ and the demand x for a certain product are related by the price–demand equation

$$x + 500p = 10{,}000 \tag{1}$$

In problems involving revenue, cost, and profit, it is customary to use the demand equation to express price as a function of demand. Since we want to know the effects that changes in price have on demand, it is more convenient to express demand as a function of price. Solving (1) for x, we have

$$x = 10{,}000 - 500p$$

$$= 500(20 - p) \quad \textit{Demand as a function of price}$$

or

$$x = f(p) = 500(20 - p) \qquad 0 \le p \le 20 \tag{2}$$

Since x and p both represent nonnegative quantities, we must restrict p so that $0 \le p \le 20$. For most products, demand is assumed to be a decreasing function of price. That is, price increases result in lower demand, and price decreases result in higher demand (see Figure 2).

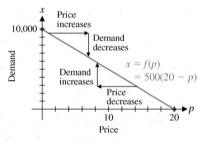

Figure 2

Economists use the *elasticity of demand* to study the relationship between changes in price and changes in demand. The **elasticity of demand** is the negative of the ratio of the relative rate of change of demand to the relative rate of change of price. If price and demand are related by a price–demand equation of the form $x = f(p)$, then the elasticity of demand can be expressed as

$$-\frac{\text{relative rate of change of demand}}{\text{relative rate of change of price}} = -\frac{\dfrac{d}{dp}\ln f(p)}{\dfrac{d}{dp}\ln p}$$

$$= -\frac{\dfrac{f'(p)}{f(p)}}{\dfrac{1}{p}}$$

$$= -\frac{pf'(p)}{f(p)}$$

THEOREM 1   Elasticity of Demand

If price and demand are related by $x = f(p)$, then the elasticity of demand is given by

$$E(p) = -\frac{pf'(p)}{f(p)}$$

CONCEPTUAL INSIGHT

Since p and $f(p)$ are nonnegative and $f'(p)$ is negative (remember, demand is usually a decreasing function of price), $E(p)$ is nonnegative. This is why elasticity of demand is defined as the negative of a ratio.

The next example illustrates interpretations of the elasticity of demand.

EXAMPLE 2   **Elasticity of Demand** Find $E(p)$ for the price–demand equation

$$x = f(p) = 500(20 - p)$$

Find and interpret each of the following:

(A) $E(4)$ (B) $E(16)$ (C) $E(10)$

SOLUTION $E(p) = -\dfrac{pf'(p)}{f(p)} = -\dfrac{p(-500)}{500(20 - p)} = \dfrac{p}{20 - p}$

In order to interpret values of $E(p)$, we must recall the definition of elasticity:

$$E(p) = -\frac{\text{relative rate of change of demand}}{\text{relative rate of change of price}}$$

or

$$-\left(\begin{array}{c}\text{relative rate of} \\ \text{change of demand}\end{array}\right) \approx E(p)\left(\begin{array}{c}\text{relative rate of} \\ \text{change of price}\end{array}\right)$$

(A) $E(4) = \frac{4}{16} = 0.25 < 1$. If the \$4 price changes by 10%, then the demand will change by approximately $0.25(10\%) = 2.5\%$.

(B) $E(16) = \frac{16}{4} = 4 > 1$. If the \$16 price changes by 10%, then the demand will change by approximately $4(10\%) = 40\%$.

(C) $E(10) = \frac{10}{10} = 1$. If the \$10 price changes by 10%, then the demand will also change by approximately 10%.

CONCEPTUAL INSIGHT

Do not be concerned with the omission of any negative signs in these interpretations. We already know that if price increases, then demand decreases, and vice versa (Fig. 2 on page 257). $E(p)$ is a measure of *how much* the demand changes for a given change in price.

Matched Problem 2   Find $E(p)$ for the price–demand equation

$$x = f(p) = 1,000(40 - p)$$

Find and interpret each of the following:

(A) $E(8)$ (B) $E(30)$ (C) $E(20)$

The three cases illustrated in the solution to Example 2 are referred to as **inelastic demand, elastic demand**, and **unit elasticity**, as indicated in Table 2.

Table 2

$E(p)$	Demand	Interpretation
$0 < E(p) < 1$	Inelastic	Demand is not sensitive to changes in price. A change in price produces a smaller change in demand.
$E(p) > 1$	Elastic	Demand is sensitive to changes in price. A change in price produces a larger change in demand.
$E(p) = 1$	Unit	A change in price produces the same change in demand.

Now we want to see how revenue and elasticity are related. We have used the following model for revenue many times before:

$$\text{Revenue} = (\text{demand}) \times (\text{price})$$

Since we are looking for a connection between $E(p)$ and revenue, we will use a price–demand equation written in the form $x = f(p)$, where x is demand and p is price.

$$R(p) = xp = pf(p) \qquad \textit{Revenue as a function of price}$$
$$R'(p) = pf'(p) + f(p)$$
$$= f(p)\left[\frac{pf'(p)}{f(p)} + 1\right] \qquad E(p) = -\frac{pf'(p)}{f(p)}$$
$$= f(p)[1 - E(p)]$$

Since $x = f(p) > 0$, it follows that $R'(p)$ and $[1 - E(p)]$ always have the same sign (see Table 3).

Table 3 Revenue and Elasticity of Demand

All Are True or All Are False	**All Are True or All Are False**
$R'(p) > 0$	$R'(p) < 0$
$E(p) < 1$	$E(p) > 1$
Demand is inelastic	Demand is elastic

These facts are interpreted in the following summary and in Figure 3:

SUMMARY   Revenue and Elasticity of Demand

When demand is inelastic,

   A price increase will increase revenue.
   A price decrease will decrease revenue.

When demand is elastic,

   A price increase will decrease revenue.
   A price decrease will increase revenue.

CONCEPTUAL INSIGHT

We know that a price increase will decrease demand at all price levels (Fig. 2). As Figure 3 illustrates, the effects of a price increase on revenue depends on the price level. If demand is elastic, then a price increase decreases revenue. If demand is inelastic, then a price increase increases revenue.

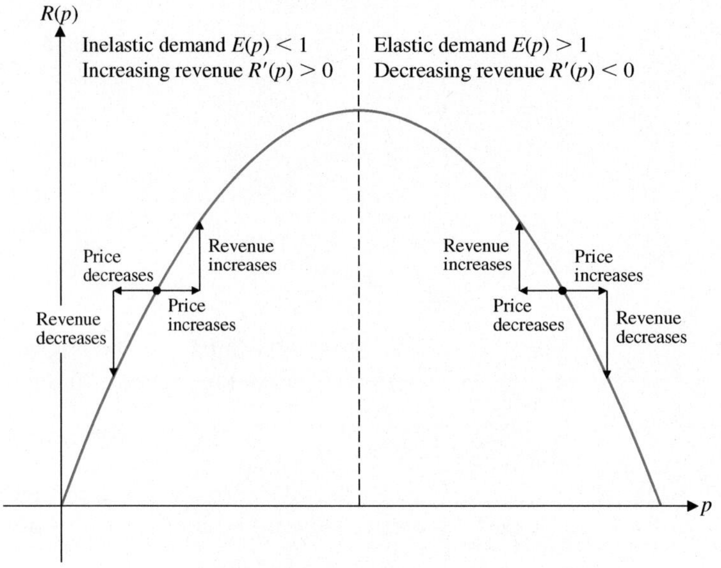

Figure 3 Revenue and elasticity

EXAMPLE 3   **Elasticity and Revenue** A manufacturer of sunglasses currently sells one type for $15 a pair. The price p and the demand x for these glasses are related by

$$x = f(p) = 9{,}500 - 250p$$

If the current price is increased, will revenue increase or decrease?

SOLUTION

$$E(p) = -\frac{pf'(p)}{f(p)}$$

$$= -\frac{p(-250)}{9{,}500 - 250p}$$

$$= \frac{p}{38 - p}$$

$$E(15) = \frac{15}{23} \approx 0.65$$

At the $15 price level, demand is inelastic and a price increase will increase revenue.

Matched Problem 3   Repeat Example 3 if the current price for sunglasses is $21 a pair.

Exercises 4-7

A

In Problems 1–6, find the relative rate of change of f(x).

1. $f(x) = 35x - 0.4x^2$

2. $f(x) = 60x - 1.2x^2$

3. $f(x) = 7 + 4e^{-x}$

4. $f(x) = 15 - 3e^{-0.5x}$

5. $f(x) = 12 + 5 \ln x$

6. $f(x) = 25 - 2 \ln x$

In Problems 7–16, find the relative rate of change of f(x) at the indicated value of x. Round to three decimal places.

7. $f(x) = 45; x = 100$

8. $f(x) = 580; x = 300$

9. $f(x) = 420 - 5x; x = 25$

10. $f(x) = 500 - 6x; x = 40$

11. $f(x) = 420 - 5x; x = 55$

12. $f(x) = 500 - 6x; x = 75$

13. $f(x) = 4x^2 - \ln x; x = 2$

14. $f(x) = 9x - 5 \ln x; x = 3$

15. $f(x) = 4x^2 - \ln x; x = 5$

16. $f(x) = 9x - 5 \ln x; x = 7$

In Problems 17–24, find the percentage rate of change of f(x) at the indicated value of x. Round to the nearest tenth of a percent.

17. $f(x) = 225 + 65x; x = 5$

18. $f(x) = 75 + 110x; x = 4$

19. $f(x) = 225 + 65x; x = 15$

20. $f(x) = 75 + 110x; x = 16$

21. $f(x) = 5,100 - 3x^2; x = 35$

22. $f(x) = 3,000 - 8x^2; x = 12$

23. $f(x) = 5,100 - 3x^2; x = 41$

24. $f(x) = 3,000 - 8x^2; x = 18$

In Problems 25–30, use the price–demand equation to find E(p), the elasticity of demand.

25. $x = f(p) = 25,000 - 450p$

26. $x = f(p) = 10,000 - 190p$

27. $x = f(p) = 4,800 - 4p^2$

28. $x = f(p) = 8,400 - 7p^2$

29. $x = f(p) = 98 - 0.6e^p$

30. $x = f(p) = 160 - 35 \ln p$

B

In Problems 31–34, use the price–demand equation to determine whether demand is elastic, is inelastic, or has unit elasticity at the indicated values of p.

31. $x = f(p) = 12,000 - 10p^2$

    (A) $p = 10$ (B) $p = 20$

    (C) $p = 30$

32. $x = f(p) = 1,875 - p^2$

    (A) $p = 15$ (B) $p = 25$

    (C) $p = 40$

33. $x = f(p) = 950 - 2p - 0.1p^2$

    (A) $p = 30$ (B) $p = 50$

    (C) $p = 70$

34. $x = f(p) = 875 - p - 0.05p^2$

    (A) $p = 50$ (B) $p = 70$

    (C) $p = 100$

35. Given the price–demand equation

$$p + 0.005x = 30$$

(A) Express the demand x as a function of the price p.

(B) Find the elasticity of demand, $E(p)$.

(C) What is the elasticity of demand when $p = \$10$? If this price is increased by 10%, what is the approximate change in demand?

(D) What is the elasticity of demand when $p = \$25$? If this price is increased by 10%, what is the approximate change in demand?

(E) What is the elasticity of demand when $p = \$15$? If this price is increased by 10%, what is the approximate change in demand?

36. Given the price–demand equation

$$p + 0.01x = 50$$

(A) Express the demand x as a function of the price p.

(B) Find the elasticity of demand, $E(p)$.

(C) What is the elasticity of demand when $p = \$10$? If this price is decreased by 5%, what is the approximate change in demand?

(D) What is the elasticity of demand when $p = \$45$? If this price is decreased by 5%, what is the approximate change in demand?

(E) What is the elasticity of demand when $p = \$25$? If this price is decreased by 5%, what is the approximate change in demand?

37. Given the price–demand equation

$$0.02x + p = 60$$

(A) Express the demand x as a function of the price p.

(B) Express the revenue R as a function of the price p.

(C) Find the elasticity of demand, $E(p)$.

(D) For which values of p is demand elastic? Inelastic?

(E) For which values of p is revenue increasing? Decreasing?

(F) If $p = \$10$ and the price is decreased, will revenue increase or decrease?

(G) If $p = \$40$ and the price is decreased, will revenue increase or decrease?

38. Repeat Problem 37 for the price–demand equation

$$0.025x + p = 50$$

In Problems 39–46, use the price–demand equation to find the values of p for which demand is elastic and the values for which demand is inelastic. Assume that price and demand are both positive.

39. $x = f(p) = 210 - 30p$

40. $x = f(p) = 480 - 8p$

41. $x = f(p) = 3,125 - 5p^2$

42. $x = f(p) = 2,400 - 6p^2$

43. $x = f(p) = \sqrt{144 - 2p}$

44. $x = f(p) = \sqrt{324 - 2p}$

45. $x = f(p) = \sqrt{2,500 - 2p^2}$

46. $x = f(p) = \sqrt{3,600 - 2p^2}$

In Problems 47–52, use the demand equation to find the revenue function. Sketch the graph of the revenue function, and indicate the regions of inelastic and elastic demand on the graph.

47. $x = f(p) = 20(10 - p)$

48. $x = f(p) = 10(16 - p)$

49. $x = f(p) = 40(p - 15)^2$

50. $x = f(p) = 10(p - 9)^2$

51. $x = f(p) = 30 - 10\sqrt{p}$

52. $x = f(p) = 30 - 5\sqrt{p}$

C

If a price–demand equation is solved for p, then price is expressed as $p = g(x)$ and x becomes the independent variable. In this case, it can be shown that the elasticity of demand is given by

$$E(x) = -\frac{g(x)}{xg'(x)}$$

In Problems 53–56, use the price–demand equation to find E(x) at the indicated value of x.

53. $p = g(x) = 50 - 0.1x, x = 200$

54. $p = g(x) = 30 - 0.05x, x = 400$

55. $p = g(x) = 50 - 2\sqrt{x}, x = 400$

56. $p = g(x) = 20 - \sqrt{x}, x = 100$

In Problems 57–60, use the price–demand equation to find the values of x for which demand is elastic and for which demand is inelastic.

57. $p = g(x) = 180 - 0.3x$

58. $p = g(x) = 640 - 0.4x$

59. $p = g(x) = 90 - 0.1x^2$

60. $p = g(x) = 540 - 0.2x^2$

61. Find $E(p)$ for $x = f(p) = Ap^{-k}$, where A and k are positive constants.

62. Find $E(p)$ for $x = f(p) = Ae^{-kp}$, where A and k are positive constants.

Applications

63. Rate of change of cost. A fast-food restaurant can produce a hamburger for $2.50. If the restaurant's daily sales are increasing at the rate of 30 hamburgers per day, how fast is its daily cost for hamburgers increasing?

64. Rate of change of cost. The fast-food restaurant in Problem 63 can produce an order of fries for $0.80. If the restaurant's daily sales are increasing at the rate of 45 orders of fries per day, how fast is its daily cost for fries increasing?

65. Revenue and elasticity. The price–demand equation for hamburgers at a fast-food restaurant is

$$x + 400p = 3,000$$

Currently, the price of a hamburger is $3.00. If the price is increased by 10%, will revenue increase or decrease?

66. Revenue and elasticity. Refer to Problem 65. If the current price of a hamburger is $4.00, will a 10% price increase cause revenue to increase or decrease?

67. Revenue and elasticity. The price–demand equation for an order of fries at a fast-food restaurant is

$$x + 1,000p = 2,500$$

Currently, the price of an order of fries is $0.99. If the price is decreased by 10%, will revenue increase or decrease?

68. Revenue and elasticity. Refer to Problem 67. If the current price of an order of fries is $1.29, will a 10% price decrease cause revenue to increase or decrease?

69. Maximum revenue. Refer to Problem 65. What price will maximize the revenue from selling hamburgers?

70. Maximum revenue. Refer to Problem 67. What price will maximize the revenue from selling fries?

71. Population growth. A model for Canada's population growth (Table 4) is

$$f(t) = 0.31t + 18.5$$

where t is years since 1960. Find and graph the percentage rate of change of $f(t)$ for $0 \le t \le 50$.

72. Population growth. A model for Mexico's population growth (Table 4) is

Table 4	Population Growth	
Year	Canada (millions)	Mexico (millions)
1960	18	39
1970	22	53
1980	25	68
1990	28	85
2000	31	100
2010	34	112

$$f(t) = 1.49t + 38.8$$

where t is years since 1960. Find and graph the percentage rate of change of $f(t)$ for $0 \le t \le 50$.

73. Crime. A model for the number of robberies in the United States (Table 5) is

$$r(t) = 9.7 - 2.7 \ln t$$

where t is years since 1990. Find the relative rate of change for robberies in 2008.

Table 5	Number of Victimizations per 1,000 Population Age 12 and Over	
	Robbery	Aggravated Assault
1995	5.4	9.5
1997	4.3	8.6
1999	3.6	6.7
2001	2.8	5.3
2003	2.5	4.6
2005	2.6	4.3

74. Crime. A model for the number of assaults in the United States (Table 5) is

$$a(t) = 18.2 - 5.2 \ln t$$

where t is years since 1990. Find the relative rate of change for assaults in 2008.

Answers to Matched Problems

1. $p(t) = \dfrac{270}{2.7t + 282}$

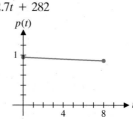

2. $E(p) = \dfrac{p}{40 - p}$

(A) $E(8) = 0.25$; demand is inelastic.

(B) $E(30) = 3$; demand is elastic.

(C) $E(20) = 1$; demand has unit elasticity.

3. $E(21) = \dfrac{21}{17} \approx 1.2$; demand is elastic. Increasing price will decrease revenue.

Chapter 4   Review

Important Terms, Symbols, and Concepts

4-1 The Constant e and Continuous Compound Interest

EXAMPLES

• The number e is defined as

$$\lim_{x \to \infty} \left(1 + \frac{1}{n}\right)^n = \lim_{x \to 0}(1 + s)^{1/s} = 2.718\ 281\ 828\ 459\ldots$$

• If a principal P is invested at an annual rate r (expressed as a decimal) compounded continuously, then the amount A in the account at the end of t years is given by the **compound interest formula**

$$A = Pe^{rt}$$

Ex. 1, p. 213
Ex. 2, p. 213
Ex. 3, p. 214
Ex. 4, p. 214

4-2 Derivatives of Exponential and Logarithmic Functions

• For $b > 0, b \neq 1$,

$$\frac{d}{dx}e^x = e^x \qquad \frac{d}{dx}b^x = b^x \ln b$$

$$\frac{d}{dx}\ln x = \frac{1}{x} \qquad \frac{d}{dx}\log_b x = \frac{1}{\ln b}\frac{1}{x}$$

Ex. 1, p. 218
Ex. 2, p. 220
Ex. 3, p. 222
Ex. 4, p. 222
Ex. 5, p. 223

• The **change-of-base formulas** allow conversion from base e to any base $b, b > 0, b \neq 1$:

$$b^x = e^{x \ln b} \qquad \log_b x = \frac{\ln x}{\ln b}$$

4-3 Derivatives of Products and Quotients

• Product rule. If $y = f(x) = F(x)\,S(x)$, then $f'(x) = F(x)S'(x) + S(x)F'(x)$, provided that both $F'(x)$ and $S'(x)$ exist.

Ex. 1, p. 226
Ex. 2, p. 227
Ex. 3, p. 227

• Quotient rule. If $y = f(x) = \dfrac{T(x)}{B(x)}$, then $f'(x) = \dfrac{B(x)\,T'(x) - T(x)\,B'(x)}{\left[B(x)\right]^2}$ provided that both $T'(x)$ and $B'(x)$ exist.

Ex. 4, p. 229
Ex. 5, p. 230
Ex. 6, p. 230

4-4 The Chain Rule

• A function m is a **composite** of functions f and g if $m(x) = f[g(x)]$.

• The **chain rule** gives a formula for the derivative of the composite function $m(x) = f[g(x)]$:

$$m'(x) = f'[g(x)]g'(x)$$

Ex. 1, p. 234
Ex. 2, p. 234
Ex. 4, p. 238
Ex. 5, p. 239
Ex. 3, p. 236

• A special case of the chain rule is called the **general power rule:**

$$\frac{d}{dx}[f(x)]^n = n[f(x)]^{n-1}f'(x)$$

• Other special cases of the chain rule are the following **general derivative rules:**

Ex. 6, p. 240

$$\frac{d}{dx}\ln[f(x)] = \frac{1}{f(x)}f'(x)$$

$$\frac{d}{dx}e^{f(x)} = e^{f(x)}f'(x)$$

4-5 Implicit Differentiation

- If $y = y(x)$ is a function defined by the equation $F(x, y) = 0$, then we use **implicit differentiation** to find an equation in $x, y,$ and y'.

4-6 Related Rates

- If x and y represent quantities that are changing with respect to time and are related by the equation $F(x, y) = 0$, then implicit differentiation produces an equation that relates $x, y, dy/dt,$ and dx/dt. Problems of this type are called **related-rates problems**.
- Suggestions for solving related-rates problems are given on page 251.

4-7 Elasticity of Demand

- The **relative rate of change**, or the **logarithmic derivative**, of a function $f(x)$ is $f'(x)/f(x)$, and the **percentage rate of change** is $100 \times [f'(x)/f(x)]$.
- If price and demand are related by $x = f(p)$, then the **elasticity of demand** is given by

$$E(p) = -\frac{pf'(p)}{f(p)} = -\frac{\text{relative rate of change of demand}}{\text{relative rate of change of price}}$$

- **Demand is inelastic** if $0 < E(p) < 1$. (Demand is not sensitive to changes in price; a change in price produces a smaller change in demand.) **Demand is elastic** if $E(p) > 1$. (Demand is sensitive to changes in price; a change in price produces a larger change in demand.) **Demand has unit elasticity** if $E(p) = 1$. (A change in price produces the same change in demand.)
- If $R(p) = pf(p)$ is the revenue function, then $R'(p)$ and $[1 - E(p)]$ always have the same sign.

Review Exercises

Work through all the problems in this chapter review, and check your answers in the back of the book. Answers to all review problems are there, along with section numbers in italics to indicate where each type of problem is discussed. Where weaknesses show up, review appropriate sections of the text.

A

1. Use a calculator to evaluate $A = 2{,}000e^{0.09t}$ to the nearest cent for $t = 5, 10,$ and 20.

Find the indicated derivatives in Problems 2–4.

2. $\dfrac{d}{dx}(2 \ln x + 3e^x)$

3. $\dfrac{d}{dx}e^{2x-3}$

4. y' for $y = \ln(2x + 7)$

5. Let $y = \ln u$ and $u = 3 + e^x$.
   (A) Express y in terms of x.
   (B) Use the chain rule to find dy/dx, and then express dy/dx in terms of x.

6. Find y' for $y = y(x)$ defined implicitly by the equation $2y^2 - 3x^3 - 5 = 0$, and evaluate at $(x, y) = (1, 2)$.

7. For $y = 3x^2 - 5$, where $x = x(t)$ and $y = y(t)$, find dy/dt if $dx/dt = 3$ when $x = 12$.

8. Given the demand equation $25p + x = 1{,}000$,
   (A) Express the demand x as a function of the price p.
   (B) Find the elasticity of demand, $E(p)$.
   (C) Find $E(15)$ and interpret.
   (D) Express the revenue function as a function of price p.
   (E) If $p = \$25$, what is the effect of a price cut on revenue?

B

9. Find the slope of the line tangent to $y = 100e^{-0.1x}$ when $x = 0$.

 10. Use a calculator and a table of values to investigate

$$\lim_{n \to \infty} \left(1 + \frac{2}{n}\right)^n$$

Do you think the limit exists? If so, what do you think it is?

Find the indicated derivatives in Problems 11–16.

11. $\dfrac{d}{dz}[(\ln z)^7 + \ln z^7]$

12. $\dfrac{d}{dx}(x^6 \ln x)$

13. $\dfrac{d}{dx} \dfrac{e^x}{x^6}$

14. y' for $y = \ln(2x^3 - 3x)$

15. $f'(x)$ for $f(x) = e^{x^3-x^2}$

16. dy/dx for $y = e^{-2x} \ln 5x$

17. Find the equation of the line tangent to the graph of $y = f(x) = 1 + e^{-x}$ at $x = 0$. At $x = -1$.

18. Find y' for $y = y(x)$ defined implicitly by the equation $x^2 - 3xy + 4y^2 = 23$, and find the slope of the graph at $(-1, 2)$.

19. Find x' for $x = x(t)$ defined implicitly by $x^3 - 2t^2x + 8 = 0$, and evaluate at $(t, x) = (-2, 2)$.

20. Find y' for $y = y(x)$ defined implicitly by $x - y^2 = e^y$, and evaluate at $(1, 0)$.

21. Find y' for $y = y(x)$ defined implicitly by $\ln y = x^2 - y^2$, and evaluate at $(1, 1)$.

22. A point is moving on the graph of $y^2 - 4x^2 = 12$ so that its x coordinate is decreasing by 2 units per second when $(x, y) = (1, 4)$. Find the rate of change of the y coordinate.

23. A 17-foot ladder is placed against a wall. If the foot of the ladder is pushed toward the wall at 0.5 foot per second, how fast is the top of the ladder rising when the foot is 8 feet from the wall?

24. Water is leaking onto a floor. The resulting circular pool has an area that is increasing at the rate of 24 square inches per minute. How fast is the radius R of the pool increasing when the radius is 12 inches? $[A = \pi R^2]$

C

25. Find the values of p for which demand is elastic and the values for which demand is inelastic if the price–demand equation is
$$x = f(p) = 20(p - 15)^2 \qquad 0 \le p \le 15$$

26. Graph the revenue function and indicate the regions of inelastic and elastic demand of the graph if the price–demand equation is
$$x = f(p) = 5(20 - p) \qquad 0 \le p \le 20$$

27. Let $y = w^3$, $w = \ln u$, and $u = 4 - e^x$.
(A) Express y in terms of x.
(B) Use the chain rule to find dy/dx, and then express dy/dx in terms of x.

Find the indicated derivatives in Problems 28–30.

28. y' for $y = 5^{x^2-1}$

29. $\dfrac{d}{dx} \log_5(x^2 - x)$ **30.** $\dfrac{d}{dx}\sqrt{\ln(x^2 + x)}$

31. Find y' for $y = y(x)$ defined implicitly by the equation $e^{xy} = x^2 + y + 1$, and evaluate at $(0, 0)$.

32. A rock thrown into a still pond causes a circular ripple. The radius is increasing at a constant rate of 3 feet per second. Show that the area does not increase at a constant rate. When is the rate of increase of the area the smallest? The largest? Explain.

33. A point moves along the graph of $y = x^3$ in such a way that its y coordinate is increasing at a constant rate of 5 units per second. Does the x coordinate ever increase at a faster rate than the y coordinate? Explain.

Applications

34. Doubling time. How long will it take money to double if it is invested at 5% interest compounded
(A) Annually?   (B) Continuously?

35. Continuous compound interest. If $100 is invested at 10% interest compounded continuously, then the amount (in dollars) at the end of t years is given by
$$A = 100e^{0.1t}$$
Find $A'(t)$, $A'(1)$, and $A'(10)$.

36. Marginal analysis. The price–demand equation for 14-cubic-foot refrigerators at an appliance store is
$$p(x) = 1,000e^{-0.02x}$$

where x is the monthly demand and p is the price in dollars. Find the marginal revenue equation.

37. Demand equation. Given the demand equation
$$x = \sqrt{5,000 - 2p^3}$$
find the rate of change of p with respect to x by implicit differentiation (x is the number of items that can be sold at a price of p per item).

38. Rate of change of revenue. A company is manufacturing kayaks and can sell all that it manufactures. The revenue (in dollars) is given by
$$R = 750x - \frac{x^2}{30}$$
where the production output in 1 day is x kayaks. If production is increasing at 3 kayaks per day when production is 40 kayaks per day, find the rate of increase in revenue.

39. Revenue and elasticity. The price–demand equation for home-delivered large pizzas is
$$p = 38.2 - 0.002x$$
where x is the number of pizzas delivered weekly. The current price of one pizza is $21. In order to generate additional revenue from the sale of large pizzas, would you recommend a price increase or a price decrease? Explain.

40. Average income. A model for the average income per household before taxes are paid is
$$f(t) = 1,700t + 20,500$$
where t is years since 1980. Find the relative rate of change of household income in 2015.

41. Drug concentration. The drug concentration in the bloodstream t hours after injection is given approximately by
$$C(t) = 5e^{-0.3t}$$
where $C(t)$ is concentration in milligrams per milliliter. What is the rate of change of concentration after 1 hour? After 5 hours?

42. Wound healing. A circular wound on an arm is healing at the rate of 45 square millimeters per day (the area of the wound is decreasing at this rate). How fast is the radius R of the wound decreasing when $R = 15$ millimeters? $[A = \pi R^2]$

43. Psychology: learning. In a computer assembly plant, a new employee, on the average, is able to assemble
$$N(t) = 10(1 - e^{-0.4t})$$
units after t days of on-the-job training.
(A) What is the rate of learning after 1 day? After 5 days?
(B) Find the number of days (to the nearest day) after which the rate of learning is less than 0.25 unit per day.

44. Learning. A new worker on the production line performs an operation in T minutes after x performances of the operation, as given by
$$T = 2\left(1 + \frac{1}{x^{3/2}}\right)$$
If, after performing the operation 9 times, the rate of improvement is $dx/dt = 3$ operations per hour, find the rate of improvement in time dT/dt in performing each operation.

Graphing and Optimization

Introduction

Since the derivative is associated with the slope of the graph of a function at a point, we might expect that it is also related to other properties of a graph. As we will see in this chapter, the derivative can tell us a great deal about the shape of the graph of a function. In particular, we will study methods for finding absolute maximum and minimum values. Manufacturing companies can use these methods to find production levels that will minimize cost or maximize profit, pharmacologists can use them to find levels of drug dosages that will produce maximum sensitivity, and advertisers can use them to determine the number of ads that will maximize the rate of change of sales (see, for example, Problem 93 in Section 5-2).

5-1   First Derivative and Graphs

- Increasing and Decreasing Functions
- Local Extrema
- First-Derivative Test
- Economics Applications

Increasing and Decreasing Functions

Sign charts will be used throughout this chapter. You may find it helpful to review the terminology and techniques for constructing sign charts in Section 3-2.

Figure 1 shows the graph of $y = f(x)$ and a sign chart for $f'(x)$, where

$$f(x) = x^3 - 3x$$

and

$$f'(x) = 3x^2 - 3 = 3(x + 1)(x - 1)$$

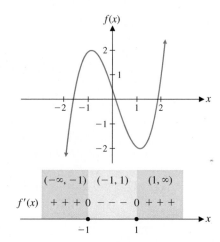

Figure 1

Discuss the relationship between the graph of f and the sign of $f'(x)$ over each interval on which $f'(x)$ has a constant sign. Also, describe the behavior of the graph of f at each partition number for f'.

As they are scanned from left to right, graphs of functions generally have rising and falling sections. If you scan the graph of $f(x) = x^3 - 3x$ in Figure 1 from left to right, you will observe the following:

- On the interval $(-\infty, -1)$, the graph of f is rising, $f(x)$ is increasing,* and the slope of the graph is positive $[f'(x) > 0]$.
- On the interval $(-1, 1)$, the graph of f is falling, $f(x)$ is decreasing, and the slope of the graph is negative $[f'(x) < 0]$.
- On the interval $(1, \infty)$, the graph of f is rising, $f(x)$ is increasing, and the slope of the graph is positive $[f'(x) > 0]$.
- At $x = -1$ and $x = 1$, the slope of the graph is 0 $[f'(x) = 0]$.

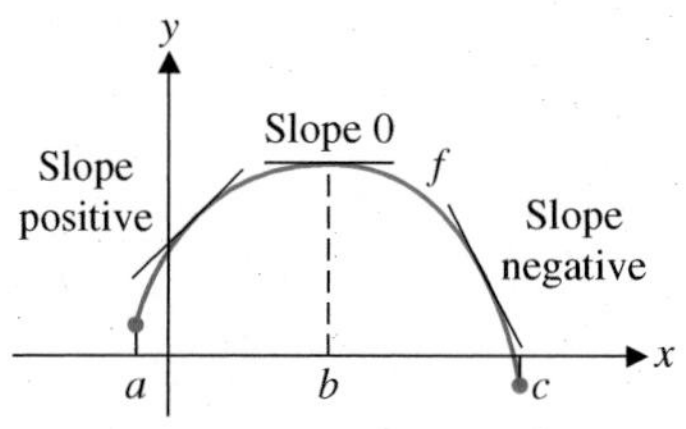

If $f'(x) > 0$ (is positive) on the interval (a, b) (Fig. 2), then $f(x)$ increases ($\nearrow$) and the graph of f rises as we move from left to right over the interval. If $f'(x) < 0$ (is negative) on an interval (a, b), then $f(x)$ decreases ($\searrow$) and the graph of f falls as we move from left to right over the interval. We summarize these important results in Theorem 1.

Slope positive   Slope 0 f Slope negative

a b c

Figure 2

---

*Formally, we say that the function f is **increasing** on an interval (a, b) if $f(x_2) > f(x_1)$ whenever $a < x_1 < x_2 < b$, and f is **decreasing** on (a, b) if $f(x_2) < f(x_1)$ whenever $a < x_1 < x_2 < b$.

> **THEOREM 1 Increasing and Decreasing Functions**
> For the interval (a, b),
>
> | $f'(x)$ | $f(x)$ | Graph of f | Examples |
> |---------|--------|--------------|----------|
> | $+$ | Increases ↗ | Rises ↗ | |
> | $-$ | Decreases ↘ | Falls ↘ | |

EXAMPLE 1 **Finding Intervals on Which a Function Is Increasing or Decreasing** Given the function $f(x) = 8x - x^2$,

(A) Which values of x correspond to horizontal tangent lines?

(B) For which values of x is $f(x)$ increasing? Decreasing?

(C) Sketch a graph of f. Add any horizontal tangent lines.

SOLUTION (A) $f'(x) = 8 - 2x = 0$

$$x = 4$$

So, a horizontal tangent line exists at $x = 4$ only.

(B) We will construct a sign chart for $f'(x)$ to determine which values of x make $f'(x) > 0$ and which values make $f'(x) < 0$. Recall from Section 3-2 that the partition numbers for a function are the points where the function is 0 or discontinuous. When constructing a sign chart for $f'(x)$, we must locate all points where $f'(x) = 0$ or $f'(x)$ is discontinuous. From part (A), we know that $f'(x) = 8 - 2x = 0$ at $x = 4$. Since $f'(x) = 8 - 2x$ is a polynomial, it is continuous for all x. So, 4 is the only partition number. We construct a sign chart for the intervals $(-\infty, 4)$ and $(4, \infty)$, using test numbers 3 and 5:

	$(-\infty, 4)$	$(4, \infty)$
$f'(x)$	$+ + + +$	$0 - - - -$
		4
$f(x)$	Increasing	Decreasing

Test Numbers	
x	$f'(x)$
3	2 (+)
5	−2 (−)

Therefore, $f(x)$ is increasing on $(-\infty, 4)$ and decreasing on $(4, \infty)$.

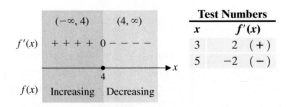

x	$f(x)$
0	0
2	12
4	16
6	12
8	0

Matched Problem 1 Repeat Example 1 for $f(x) = x^2 - 6x + 10$.

As Example 1 illustrates, the construction of a sign chart will play an important role in using the derivative to analyze and sketch the graph of a function f. The partition numbers for f' are central to the construction of these sign charts and also to the analysis of the graph of $y = f(x)$. We already know that if $f'(c) = 0$, then the graph of $y = f(x)$ will have a horizontal tangent line at $x = c$. But the partition numbers for f' also include the numbers c such that $f'(c)$ does not exist.* There are two possibilities at this type of number: (1) $f(c)$ does not exist; or (2) $f(c)$ exists but the slope of the tangent line at $x = c$ is undefined.

> **DEFINITION** **Critical Values**
>
> The values of x in the domain of f where $f'(x) = 0$ or where $f'(x)$ does not exist are called the **critical values** of f.

> **CONCEPTUAL INSIGHT**
>
> The critical values of f are always in the domain of f and are also partition numbers for f', but f' may have partition numbers that are not critical values.
> If f is a polynomial, then both the partition numbers for f' and the critical values of f are the solutions of $f'(x) = 0$.

EXAMPLE 2 **Partition Numbers and Critical Values** Find the critical values of f, the intervals on which f is increasing, and those on which f is decreasing, for $f(x) = 1 + x^3$.

SOLUTION Begin by finding the partition number for $f'(x)$:

$$f'(x) = 3x^2 = 0, \quad \text{only at } x = 0$$

The partition number 0 is in the domain of f, so 0 is the only critical value of f. The sign chart for $f'(x) = 3x^2$ (partition number is 0) is

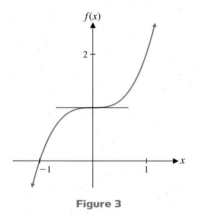

	$(-\infty, 0)$	$(0, \infty)$
$f'(x)$	+ + + + + 0 + + + + +	
$f(x)$	Increasing	Increasing

Test Numbers	
x	$f'(x)$
-1	3 (+)
1	3 (+)

The sign chart indicates that $f(x)$ is increasing on $(-\infty, 0)$ and $(0, \infty)$. Since f is continuous at $x = 0$, it follows that $f(x)$ is increasing for all x. The graph of f is shown in Figure 3.

Figure 3

Matched Problem 2 Find the critical values of f, the intervals on which f is increasing, and those on which f is decreasing, for $f(x) = 1 - x^3$.

EXAMPLE 3 **Partition Numbers and Critical Values** Find the critical values of f, the intervals on which f is increasing, and those on which f is decreasing, for $f(x) = (1 - x)^{1/3}$.

SOLUTION

$$f'(x) = -\frac{1}{3}(1 - x)^{-2/3} = \frac{-1}{3(1 - x)^{2/3}}$$

---

*We are assuming that $f'(c)$ does not exist at any point of discontinuity of f'. There do exist functions f such that f' is discontinuous at $x = c$, yet $f'(c)$ exists. However, we do not consider such functions in this book.

To find partition numbers for f', we note that f' is continuous for all x, except for values of x for which the denominator is 0; that is, $f'(1)$ does not exist and f' is discontinuous at $x = 1$. Since the numerator is the constant -1, $f'(x) \neq 0$ for any value of x. Thus, $x = 1$ is the only partition number for f'. Since 1 is in the domain of f, $x = 1$ is also the only critical value of f. When constructing the sign chart for f' we use the abbreviation ND to note the fact that $f'(x)$ is *not defined* at $x = 1$.

The sign chart for $f'(x) = -1/[3(1 - x)^{2/3}]$ (partition number is 1) is as follows:

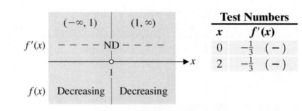

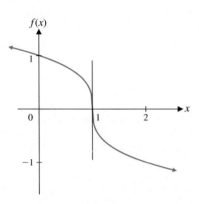

Figure 4

The sign chart indicates that f is decreasing on $(-\infty, 1)$ and $(1, \infty)$. Since f is continuous at $x = 1$, it follows that $f(x)$ is decreasing for all x. **A continuous function can be decreasing (or increasing) on an interval containing values of x where $f'(x)$ does not exist.** The graph of f is shown in Figure 4. Notice that the undefined derivative at $x = 1$ results in a vertical tangent line at $x = 1$. **A vertical tangent will occur at $x = c$ if f is continuous at $x = c$ and if $|f'(x)|$ becomes larger and larger as x approaches c.**

Matched Problem 3 Find the critical values of f, the intervals on which f is increasing, and those on which f is decreasing, for $f(x) = (1 + x)^{1/3}$.

EXAMPLE 4 **Partition Numbers and Critical Values** Find the critical values of f, the intervals on which f is increasing, and those on which f is decreasing, for $f(x) = \dfrac{1}{x - 2}$.

SOLUTION
$$f(x) = \frac{1}{x - 2} = (x - 2)^{-1}$$
$$f'(x) = -(x - 2)^{-2} = \frac{-1}{(x - 2)^2}$$

To find the partition numbers for f', note that $f'(x) \neq 0$ for any x and f' is not defined at $x = 2$. Thus, $x = 2$ is the only partition number for f'. However, $x = 2$ is *not* in the domain of f. Consequently, $x = 2$ is not a critical value of f. This function has no critical values.

The sign chart for $f'(x) = -1/(x - 2)^2$ (partition number is 2) is as follows:

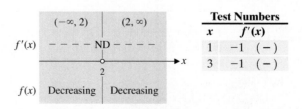

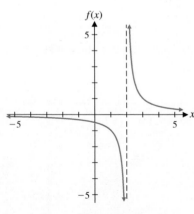

Figure 5

Therefore, f is decreasing on $(-\infty, 2)$ and $(2, \infty)$. The graph of f is shown in Figure 5.

Matched Problem 4 Find the critical values for f, the intervals on which f is increasing, and those on which f is decreasing, for $f(x) = \dfrac{1}{x}$.

EXAMPLE 5 **Partition Numbers and Critical Values** Find the critical values of f, the intervals on which f is increasing, and those on which f is decreasing, for $f(x) = 8 \ln x - x^2$.

SOLUTION The natural logarithm function $\ln x$ is defined on $(0, \infty)$, or $x > 0$, so $f(x)$ is defined only for $x > 0$.

$$f(x) = 8 \ln x - x^2, x > 0$$

$$f'(x) = \frac{8}{x} - 2x \qquad \text{\textit{Find a common denominator.}}$$

$$= \frac{8}{x} - \frac{2x^2}{x} \qquad \text{\textit{Subtract numerators.}}$$

$$= \frac{8 - 2x^2}{x} \qquad \text{\textit{Factor numerator.}}$$

$$= \frac{2(2 - x)(2 + x)}{x}, \quad x > 0$$

Note that $f'(x) = 0$ at -2 and at 2, and $f'(x)$ is discontinuous at 0. These are the partition numbers for $f'(x)$. Since the domain of f is $(0, \infty)$, 0 and -2 are not critical values. The remaining partition number, 2, is the only critical value for $f(x)$.

The sign chart for $f'(x) = \dfrac{2(2 - x)(2 + x)}{x}$, $x > 0$ (partition number is 2), is as follows:

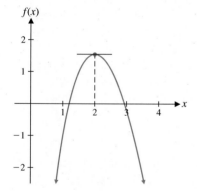

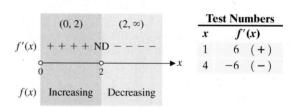

Therefore, f is increasing on $(0, 2)$ and decreasing on $(2, \infty)$. The graph of f is shown in Figure 6.

Figure 6

Matched Problem 5 Find the critical values of f, the intervals on which f is increasing, and those on which f is decreasing, for $f(x) = 5 \ln x - x$.

CONCEPTUAL INSIGHT

Examples 4 and 5 illustrate two important ideas:

1. Do not assume that all partition numbers for the derivative f' are critical values of the function f. To be a critical value, a partition number must also be in the domain of f.

2. The values for which a function is increasing or decreasing must always be expressed in terms of open intervals that are subsets of the domain of the function.

Local Extrema

When the graph of a continuous function changes from rising to falling, a high point, or *local maximum,* occurs. When the graph changes from falling to rising, a low point, or *local minimum,* occurs. In Figure 7, high points occur at c_3 and c_6, and low points occur at c_2 and c_4. In general, we call $f(c)$ a **local maximum** if there exists an interval (m, n) containing c such that

$$f(x) \leq f(c) \qquad \text{for all } x \text{ in } (m, n)$$

Note that this inequality need hold only for values of x near c, which is why we use the term *local.*

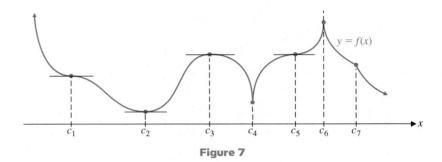

Figure 7

The quantity $f(c)$ is called a **local minimum** if there exists an interval (m, n) containing c such that

$$f(x) \geq f(c) \qquad \text{for all } x \text{ in } (m, n)$$

The quantity $f(c)$ is called a **local extremum** if it is either a local maximum or a local minimum. A point on a graph where a local extremum occurs is also called a **turning point.** In Figure 7 we see that local maxima occur at c_3 and c_6, local minima occur at c_2 and c_4, and all four values produce local extrema. Also, the local maximum $f(c_3)$ is not the highest point on the graph in Figure 7. Later in this chapter, we consider the problem of finding the highest and lowest points on a graph, or absolute extrema. For now, we are concerned only with locating *local* extrema.

EXAMPLE 6 **Analyzing a Graph** Use the graph of f in Figure 8 to find the intervals on which f is increasing, those on which f is decreasing, any local maxima, and any local minima.

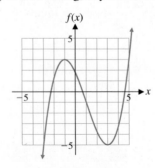

Figure 8

SOLUTION The function f is increasing (the graph is rising) on $(-\infty, -1)$ and on $(3, \infty)$ and is decreasing (the graph is falling) on $(-1, 3)$. Because the graph changes from rising to falling at $x = -1$, $f(-1) = 3$ is a local maximum. Because the graph changes from falling to rising at $x = 3$, $f(3) = -5$ is a local minimum.

Matched Problem 6 Use the graph of g in Figure 9 to find the intervals on which g is increasing, those on which g is decreasing, any local maxima, and any local minima.

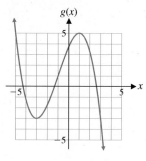

Figure 9

How can we locate local maxima and minima if we are given the equation of a function and not its graph? The key is to examine the critical values of the function. The local extrema of the function f in Figure 7 occur either at points where the derivative is 0 (c_2 and c_3) or at points where the derivative does not exist (c_4 and c_6). In other words, local extrema occur only at critical values of f. Theorem 2 shows that this is true in general.

THEOREM 2   Existence of Local Extrema

If f is continuous on the interval (a, b), c is a number in (a, b), and $f(c)$ is a local extremum, then either $f'(c) = 0$ or $f'(c)$ does not exist (is not defined).

Theorem 2 states that a local extremum can occur only at a critical value, but it does not imply that every critical value produces a local extremum. In Figure 7, c_1 and c_5 are critical values (the slope is 0), but the function does not have a local maximum or local minimum at either of these values.

Our strategy for finding local extrema is now clear: We find all critical values of f and test each one to see if it produces a local maximum, a local minimum, or neither.

First-Derivative Test

If $f'(x)$ exists on both sides of a critical value c, the sign of $f'(x)$ can be used to determine whether the point $(c, f(c))$ is a local maximum, a local minimum, or neither. The various possibilities are summarized in the following box and are illustrated in Figure 10:

PROCEDURE   First-Derivative Test for Local Extrema

Let c be a critical value of f [$f(c)$ is defined and either $f'(c) = 0$ or $f'(c)$ is not defined]. Construct a sign chart for $f'(x)$ close to and on either side of c.

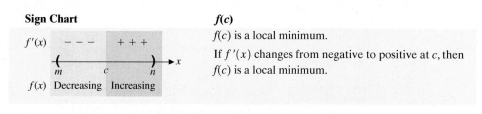

Sign Chart	$f(c)$
$f'(x)$ $+ + +$ $- - -$ $\overset{(}{m} \quad c \quad \overset{)}{n} \to x$ $f(x)$ Increasing Decreasing	$f(c)$ is a local maximum. If $f'(x)$ changes from positive to negative at c, then $f(c)$ is a local maximum.
$f'(x)$ $+ + +$ $+ + +$ $\overset{(}{m} \quad c \quad \overset{)}{n} \to x$ $f(x)$ Increasing Increasing	$f(c)$ is not a local extremum. If $f'(x)$ does not change sign at c, then $f(c)$ is neither a local maximum nor a local minimum.
$f'(x)$ $- - -$ $- - -$ $\overset{(}{m} \quad c \quad \overset{)}{n} \to x$ $f(x)$ Decreasing Decreasing	$f(c)$ is not a local extremum. If $f'(x)$ does not change sign at c, then $f(c)$ is neither a local maximum nor a local minimum.

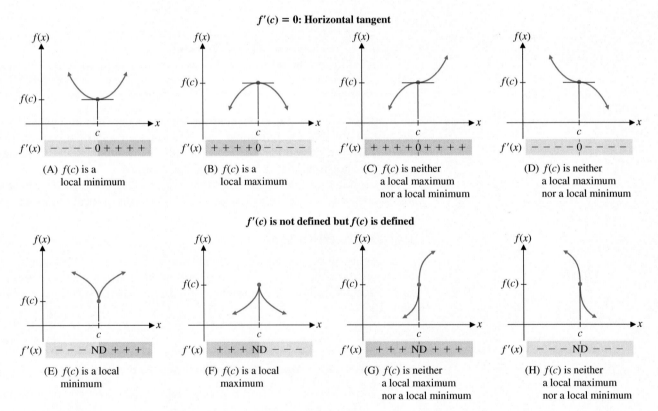

Figure 10 Local extrema

EXAMPLE 7 **Locating Local Extrema** Given $f(x) = x^3 - 6x^2 + 9x + 1$,

(A) Find the critical values of f.

(B) Find the local maxima and minima.

(C) Sketch the graph of f.

SOLUTION (A) Find all numbers x in the domain of f where $f'(x) = 0$ or $f'(x)$ does not exist.

$$f'(x) = 3x^2 - 12x + 9 = 0$$
$$3(x^2 - 4x + 3) = 0$$
$$3(x - 1)(x - 3) = 0$$
$$x = 1 \quad \text{or} \quad x = 3$$

$f'(x)$ exists for all x; the critical values are $x = 1$ and $x = 3$.

(B) The easiest way to apply the first-derivative test for local maxima and minima is to construct a sign chart for $f'(x)$ for all x. Partition numbers for $f'(x)$ are $x = 1$ and $x = 3$ (which also happen to be critical values of f).

Sign chart for $f'(x) = 3(x - 1)(x - 3)$:

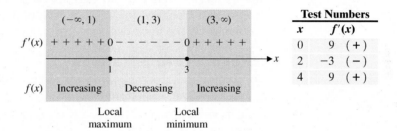

The sign chart indicates that f increases on $(-\infty, 1)$, has a local maximum at $x = 1$, decreases on $(1, 3)$, has a local minimum at $x = 3$, and increases on $(3, \infty)$. These facts are summarized in the following table:

x	$f'(x)$	$f(x)$	Graph of f
$(-\infty, 1)$	+	Increasing	Rising
$x = 1$	0	Local maximum	Horizontal tangent
$(1, 3)$	−	Decreasing	Falling
$x = 3$	0	Local minimum	Horizontal tangent
$(3, \infty)$	+	Increasing	Rising

(C) We sketch a graph of f, using the information from part (B) and point-by-point plotting.

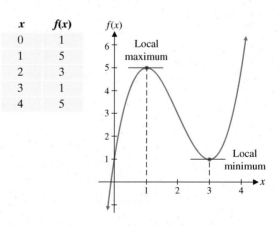

x	$f(x)$
0	1
1	5
2	3
3	1
4	5

Matched Problem 7 Given $f(x) = x^3 - 9x^2 + 24x - 10$,

(A) Find the critical values of f.

(B) Find the local maxima and minima.

(C) Sketch a graph of f.

How can you tell if you have found all the local extrema of a function? In general, this can be a difficult question to answer. However, in the case of a polynomial function, there is an easily determined upper limit on the number of local extrema. Since the local extrema are the x intercepts of the derivative, this limit is a consequence of the number of x intercepts of a polynomial. The relevant information is summarized in the following theorem, which is stated without proof:

THEOREM 3 Intercepts and Local Extrema of Polynomial Functions

If $f(x) = a_n x^n + a_{n-1} x^{n-1} + \cdots + a_1 x + a_0, a_n \neq 0$, is an nth-degree polynomial, then f has at most n x intercepts and at most $n-1$ local extrema.

Theorem 3 does not guarantee that every nth-degree polynomial has exactly $n-1$ local extrema; it says only that there can never be more than $n-1$ local extrema. For example, the third-degree polynomial in Example 7 has two local extrema, while the third-degree polynomial in Example 2 does not have any.

Economics Applications

In addition to providing information for hand-sketching graphs, the derivative is an important tool for analyzing graphs and discussing the interplay between a function and its rate of change. The next two examples illustrate this process in the context of economics applications.

EXAMPLE 8 **Agricultural Exports and Imports** Over the past few decades, the United States has exported more agricultural products than it has imported, maintaining a positive balance of trade in this area. However, the trade balance fluctuated considerably during that period. The graph in Figure 11 approximates the rate of change of the balance of trade over a 15-year period, where $B(t)$ is the balance of trade (in billions of dollars) and t is time (in years).

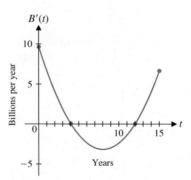

Figure 11 Rate of change of the balance of trade

(A) Write a brief description of the graph of $y = B(t)$, including a discussion of any local extrema.

(B) Sketch a possible graph of $y = B(t)$.

SOLUTION (A) The graph of the derivative $y = B'(t)$ contains the same essential information as a sign chart. That is, we see that $B'(t)$ is positive on $(0, 4)$, 0 at $t = 4$, negative on $(4, 12)$, 0 at $t = 12$, and positive on $(12, 15)$. The trade balance increases for the first 4 years to a local maximum, decreases for the next 8 years to a local minimum, and then increases for the final 3 years.

(B) Without additional information concerning the actual values of $y = B(t)$, we cannot produce an accurate graph. However, we can sketch a possible graph that illustrates the important features, as shown in Figure 12. The absence of a scale on the vertical axis is a consequence of the lack of information about the values of $B(t)$.

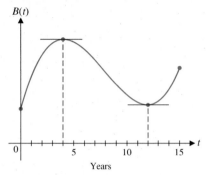

Figure 12 Balance of trade

Matched Problem 8   The graph in Figure 13 approximates the rate of change of the U.S. share of the total world production of motor vehicles over a 20-year period, where $S(t)$ is the U.S. share (as a percentage) and t is time (in years).

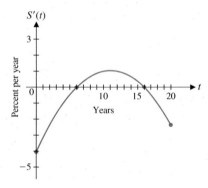

Figure 13

(A) Write a brief description of the graph of $y = S(t)$, including a discussion of any local extrema.

(B) Sketch a possible graph of $y = S(t)$.

EXAMPLE 9   **Revenue Analysis**   The graph of the total revenue $R(x)$ (in dollars) from the sale of x bookcases is shown in Figure 14.

(A) Write a brief description of the graph of the marginal revenue function $y = R'(x)$, including a discussion of any x intercepts.

(B) Sketch a possible graph of $y = R'(x)$.

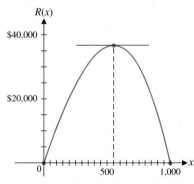

Figure 14 Revenue

SOLUTION (A) The graph of $y = R(x)$ indicates that $R(x)$ increases on $(0, 550)$, has a local maximum at $x = 550$, and decreases on $(550, 1,000)$. Consequently, the marginal revenue function $R'(x)$ must be positive on $(0, 550)$, 0 at $x = 550$, and negative on $(550, 1,000)$.

(B) A possible graph of $y = R'(x)$ illustrating the information summarized in part (A) is shown in Figure 15.

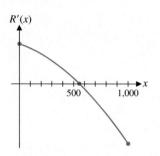

Figure 15 Marginal revenue

Matched Problem 9 The graph of the total revenue $R(x)$ (in dollars) from the sale of x desks is shown in Figure 16.

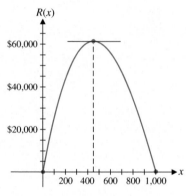

Figure 16

(A) Write a brief description of the graph of the marginal revenue function $y = R'(x)$, including a discussion of any x intercepts.

(B) Sketch a possible graph of $y = R'(x)$.

Comparing Examples 8 and 9, we see that we were able to obtain more information about the function from the graph of its derivative (Example 8) than we were when the process was reversed (Example 9). In the next section, we introduce some ideas that will help us obtain additional information about the derivative from the graph of the function.

Exercises 5-1

A

Problems 1–8 refer to the following graph of $y = f(x)$:

1. Identify the intervals on which $f(x)$ is increasing.

2. Identify the intervals on which $f(x)$ is decreasing.

3. Identify the intervals on which $f'(x) < 0$.

4. Identify the intervals on which $f'(x) > 0$.

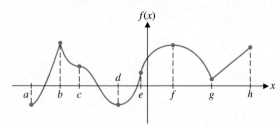

Figure for 1–8

5. Identify the x coordinates of the points where $f'(x) = 0$.

6. Identify the x coordinates of the points where $f'(x)$ does not exist.

7. Identify the x coordinates of the points where $f(x)$ has a local maximum.

8. Identify the x coordinates of the points where $f(x)$ has a local minimum.

In Problems 9 and 10, f(x) is continuous on $(-\infty, \infty)$ and has critical values at $x = a, b, c$, and d. Use the sign chart for $f'(x)$ to determine whether f has a local maximum, a local minimum, or neither at each critical value.

9.
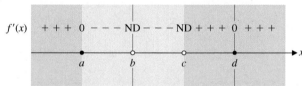

10.
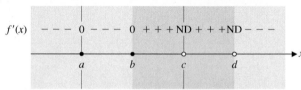

In Problems 11–18, match the graph of f with one of the sign charts a–h in the figure.

11.
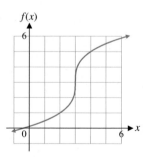

12.
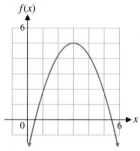

13.
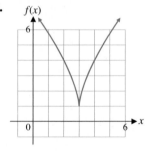

14.
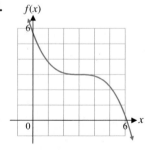

15.
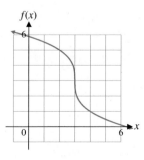

16.
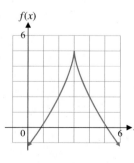

17.
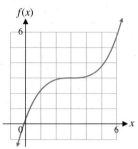

18.
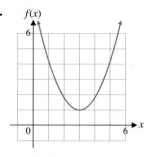

(a)
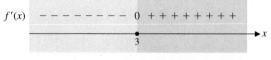

(b)
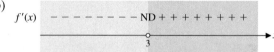

(c)

(d)
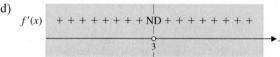

(e)

(f)
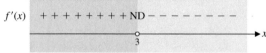

(g)
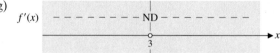

(h)

Figure for 11–18

B

In Problems 19–26, find (A) $f'(x)$, (B) the critical values of f, and (C) the partition numbers for f'.

19. $f(x) = x^3 - 12x + 8$

20. $f(x) = x^3 - 27x + 30$

21. $f(x) = (x + 5)^{1/3}$

22. $f(x) = (x - 9)^{2/3}$

23. $f(x) = \dfrac{6}{x + 2}$

24. $f(x) = \dfrac{5}{x - 4}$

25. $f(x) = |x|$

26. $f(x) = |x + 3|$

In Problems 27–40, find the intervals on which $f(x)$ is increasing, the intervals on which $f(x)$ is decreasing, and the local extrema.

27. $f(x) = 2x^2 - 4x$

28. $f(x) = -3x^2 - 12x$

29. $f(x) = -2x^2 - 16x - 25$

30. $f(x) = -3x^2 + 12x - 5$

31. $f(x) = x^3 + 4x - 5$

32. $f(x) = -x^3 - 4x + 8$

33. $f(x) = 2x^3 - 3x^2 - 36x$

34. $f(x) = -2x^3 + 3x^2 + 120x$

35. $f(x) = 3x^4 - 4x^3 + 5$

36. $f(x) = x^4 + 2x^3 + 5$

37. $f(x) = (x - 1)e^{-x}$

38. $f(x) = x \ln x - x$

39. $f(x) = 4x^{1/3} - x^{2/3}$

40. $f(x) = (x^2 - 9)^{2/3}$

In Problems 41–46, use a graphing calculator to approximate the critical values of $f(x)$ to two decimal places. Find the intervals on which $f(x)$ is increasing, the intervals on which $f(x)$ is decreasing, and the local extrema.

41. $f(x) = x^4 - 4x^3 + 9x$

42. $f(x) = x^4 + 5x^3 - 15x$

43. $f(x) = x \ln x - (x - 2)^3$

44. $f(x) = e^{-x} - 3x^2$

45. $f(x) = e^x - 2x^2$

46. $f(x) = \dfrac{\ln x}{x} - 5x + x^2$

In Problems 47–54, find the intervals on which $f(x)$ is increasing and the intervals on which $f(x)$ is decreasing. Then sketch the graph. Add horizontal tangent lines.

47. $f(x) = 4 + 8x - x^2$

48. $f(x) = 2x^2 - 8x + 9$

49. $f(x) = x^3 - 3x + 1$

50. $f(x) = x^3 - 12x + 2$

51. $f(x) = 10 - 12x + 6x^2 - x^3$

52. $f(x) = x^3 + 3x^2 + 3x$

53. $f(x) = x^4 - 18x^2$

54. $f(x) = -x^4 + 50x^2$

In Problems 55–62, $f(x)$ is continuous on $(-\infty, \infty)$. Use the given information to sketch the graph of f.

55.

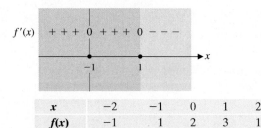

x	-2	-1	0	1	2
$f(x)$	-1	1	2	3	1

56.

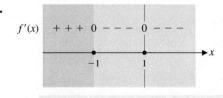

x	-2	-1	0	1	2
$f(x)$	1	3	2	1	-1

57.

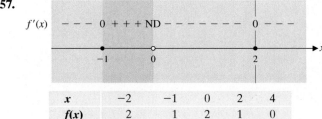

x	-2	-1	0	2	4
$f(x)$	2	1	2	1	0

58.

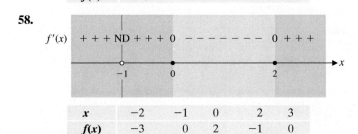

x	-2	-1	0	2	3
$f(x)$	-3	0	2	-1	0

59. $f(-2) = 4, f(0) = 0, f(2) = -4;$

$f'(-2) = 0, f'(0) = 0, f'(2) = 0;$

$f'(x) > 0$ on $(-\infty, -2)$ and $(2, \infty);$

$f'(x) < 0$ on $(-2, 0)$ and $(0, 2)$

60. $f(-2) = -1, f(0) = 0, f(2) = 1;$

$f'(-2) = 0, f'(2) = 0;$

$f'(x) > 0$ on $(-\infty, -2), (-2, 2),$ and $(2, \infty)$

61. $f(-1) = 2, f(0) = 0, f(1) = -2;$

$f'(-1) = 0, f'(1) = 0, f'(0)$ is not defined;

$f'(x) > 0$ on $(-\infty, -1)$ and $(1, \infty);$

$f'(x) < 0$ on $(-1, 0)$ and $(0, 1)$

62. $f(-1) = 2, f(0) = 0, f(1) = 2;$

$f'(-1) = 0, f'(1) = 0, f'(0)$ is not defined;

$f'(x) > 0$ on $(-\infty, -1)$ and $(0, 1);$

$f'(x) < 0$ on $(-1, 0)$ and $(1, \infty)$

Problems 63–68 involve functions f_1–f_6 and their derivatives, g_1–g_6. Use the graphs shown in figures (A) and (B) to match each function f_i with its derivative g_j.

63. f_1 **64.** f_2 **65.** f_3

66. f_4 **67.** f_5 **68.** f_6

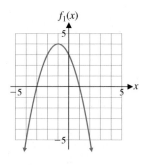
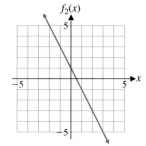

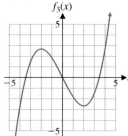
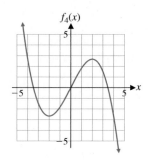

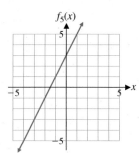
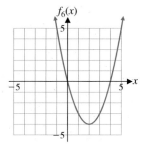

Figure (A) for 63–68

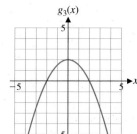
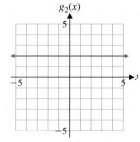

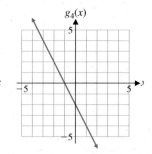

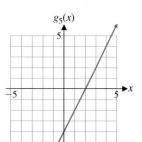
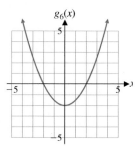

Figure (B) for 63–68

In Problems 69–74, use the given graph of $y = f'(x)$ to find the intervals on which f is increasing, the intervals on which f is decreasing, and the local extrema. Sketch a possible graph of $y = f(x)$.

69.
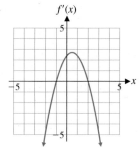

70.
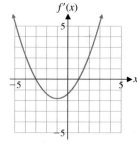

71.
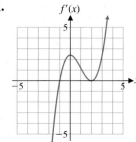

72.
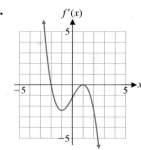

73.
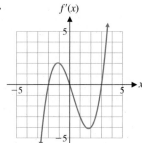

74.
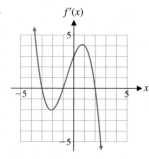

In Problems 75–78, use the given graph of $y = f(x)$ to find the intervals on which $f'(x) > 0$, the intervals on which $f'(x) < 0$, and the values of x for which $f'(x) = 0$. Sketch a possible graph of $y = f'(x)$.

75.
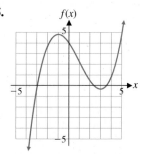

76.
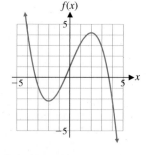

77.

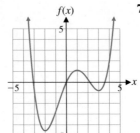

78.

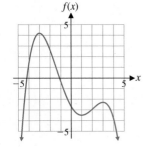

C

In Problems 79–86, find the critical values, the intervals on which f(x) is increasing, the intervals on which f(x) is decreasing, and the local extrema. Do not graph.

79. $f(x) = x + \dfrac{4}{x}$

80. $f(x) = \dfrac{9}{x} + x$

81. $f(x) = 1 + \dfrac{1}{x} + \dfrac{1}{x^2}$

82. $f(x) = 3 - \dfrac{4}{x} - \dfrac{2}{x^2}$

83. $f(x) = \dfrac{x^2}{x - 2}$

84. $f(x) = \dfrac{x^2}{x + 1}$

85. $f(x) = x^4(x - 6)^2$

86. $f(x) = x^3(x - 5)^2$

87. Let $f(x) = x^3 + kx$, where k is a constant. Discuss the number of local extrema and the shape of the graph of f if
   (A) $k > 0$ (B) $k < 0$ (C) $k = 0$

88. Let $f(x) = x^4 + kx^2$, where k is a constant. Discuss the number of local extrema and the shape of the graph of f if
   (A) $k > 0$ (B) $k < 0$ (C) $k = 0$

Applications

89. Profit analysis. The graph of the total profit $P(x)$ (in dollars) from the sale of x cordless electric screwdrivers is shown in the figure.

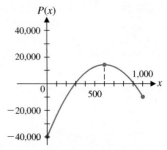

Figure for 89

(A) Write a brief description of the graph of the marginal profit function $y = P'(x)$, including a discussion of any x intercepts.

(B) Sketch a possible graph of $y = P'(x)$.

90. Revenue analysis. The graph of the total revenue $R(x)$ (in dollars) from the sale of x cordless electric screwdrivers is shown in the figure.

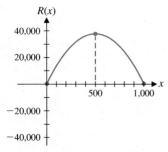

Figure for 90

(A) Write a brief description of the graph of the marginal revenue function $y = R'(x)$, including a discussion of any x intercepts.

(B) Sketch a possible graph of $y = R'(x)$.

91. Price analysis. The figure approximates the rate of change of the price of bacon over a 70-month period, where $B(t)$ is the price of a pound of sliced bacon (in dollars) and t is time (in months).

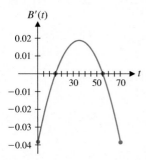

Figure for 91

(A) Write a brief description of the graph of $y = B(t)$, including a discussion of any local extrema.

(B) Sketch a possible graph of $y = B(t)$.

92. Price analysis. The figure approximates the rate of change of the price of eggs over a 70-month period, where $E(t)$ is the price of a dozen eggs (in dollars) and t is time (in months).

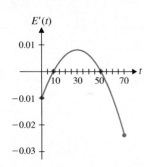

Figure for 92

(A) Write a brief description of the graph of $y = E(t)$, including a discussion of any local extrema.

(B) Sketch a possible graph of $y = E(t)$.

93. Average cost. A manufacturer incurs the following costs in producing x water ski vests in one day, for $0 < x < 150$: fixed costs, \$320; unit production cost, \$20 per vest; equipment maintenance and repairs, $0.05x^2$ dollars. So, the cost of manufacturing x vests in one day is given by

$$C(x) = 0.05x^2 + 20x + 320 \qquad 0 < x < 150$$

(A) What is the average cost $\overline{C}(x)$ per vest if x vests are produced in one day?

(B) Find the critical values of $\overline{C}(x)$, the intervals on which the average cost per vest is decreasing, the intervals on which the average cost per vest is increasing, and the local extrema. Do not graph.

94. Average cost. A manufacturer incurs the following costs in producing x rain jackets in one day for $0 < x < 200$: fixed costs, \$450; unit production cost, \$30 per jacket; equipment maintenance and repairs, $0.08x^2$ dollars.

(A) What is the average cost $\overline{C}(x)$ per jacket if x jackets are produced in one day?

(B) Find the critical values of $\overline{C}(x)$, the intervals on which the average cost per jacket is decreasing, the intervals on which the average cost per jacket is increasing, and the local extrema. Do not graph.

95. Marginal analysis. Show that profit will be increasing over production intervals (a, b) for which marginal revenue is greater than marginal cost. [*Hint:* $P(x) = R(x) - C(x)$]

96. Marginal analysis. Show that profit will be decreasing over production intervals (a, b) for which marginal revenue is less than marginal cost.

97. Medicine. A drug is injected into the bloodstream of a patient through the right arm. The drug concentration in the bloodstream of the left arm t hours after the injection is approximated by

$$C(t) = \frac{0.28t}{t^2 + 4} \qquad 0 < t < 24$$

Find the critical values of $C(t)$, the intervals on which the drug concentration is increasing, the intervals on which the concentration of the drug is decreasing, and the local extrema. Do not graph.

98. Medicine. The concentration $C(t)$, in milligrams per cubic centimeter, of a particular drug in a patient's bloodstream is given by

$$C(t) = \frac{0.3t}{t^2 + 6t + 9} \qquad 0 < t < 12$$

where t is the number of hours after the drug is taken orally. Find the critical values of $C(t)$, the intervals on which the drug concentration is increasing, the intervals on which the drug concentration is decreasing, and the local extrema. Do not graph.

Answers to Matched Problems

1. (A) Horizontal tangent line at $x = 3$.

(B) Decreasing on $(-\infty, 3)$; increasing on $(3, \infty)$

(C)

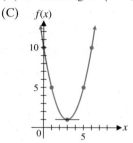

2. Partition number: $x = 0$; critical value: $x = 0$; decreasing for all x

3. Partition number: $x = -1$; critical value: $x = -1$; increasing for all x

4. Partition number: $x = 0$; no critical values; decreasing on $(-\infty, 0)$ and $(0, \infty)$

5. Partition number: $x = 5$; critical value: $x = 5$; increasing on $(0, 5)$; decreasing on $(5, \infty)$

6. Increasing on $(-3, 1)$; decreasing on $(-\infty, -3)$ and $(1, \infty)$; local maximum at $x = 1$; local minimum at $x = -3$

7. (A) Critical values: $x = 2$, $x = 4$

(B) Local maximum at $x = 2$; local minimum at $x = 4$

(C)

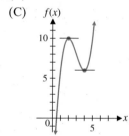

8. (A) The U.S. share of the world market decreases for 6 years to a local minimum, increases for the next 10 years to a local maximum, and then decreases for the final 4 years.

(B)

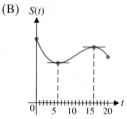

9. (A) The marginal revenue is positive on $(0, 450)$, 0 at $x = 450$, and negative on $(450, 1{,}000)$.

(B)

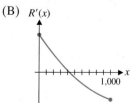

5-2 Second Derivative and Graphs

In Section 5-1, we saw that the derivative can be used when a graph is rising and falling. Now we want to see what the *second derivative* (the derivative of the derivative) can tell us about the shape of a graph.

Using Concavity as a Graphing Tool

Consider the functions

$$f(x) = x^2 \quad \text{and} \quad g(x) = \sqrt{x}$$

for x in the interval $(0, \infty)$. Since

$$f'(x) = 2x > 0 \quad \text{for } 0 < x < \infty$$

and

$$g'(x) = \frac{1}{2\sqrt{x}} > 0 \quad \text{for } 0 < x < \infty$$

both functions are increasing on $(0, \infty)$.

EXPLORE & DISCUSS 1

(A) Discuss the difference in the shapes of the graphs of f and g shown in Figure 1.

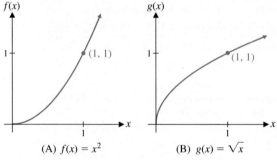

(A) $f(x) = x^2$ (B) $g(x) = \sqrt{x}$

Figure 1

(B) Complete the following table, and discuss the relationship between the values of the derivatives of f and g and the shapes of their graphs:

x	0.25	0.5	0.75	1
$f'(x)$				
$g'(x)$				

We use the term *concave upward* to describe a graph that opens upward and *concave downward* to describe a graph that opens downward. Thus, the graph of f in Figure 1A is concave upward, and the graph of g in Figure 1B is concave downward. Finding a mathematical formulation of concavity will help us sketch and analyze graphs.

We examine the slopes of f and g at various points on their graphs (see Fig. 2) and make two observations about each graph:

1. Looking at the graph of f in Figure 2A, we see that $f'(x)$ (the slope of the tangent line) is *increasing* and that the graph lies *above* each tangent line;

2. Looking at Figure 2B, we see that $g'(x)$ is *decreasing* and that the graph lies *below* each tangent line.

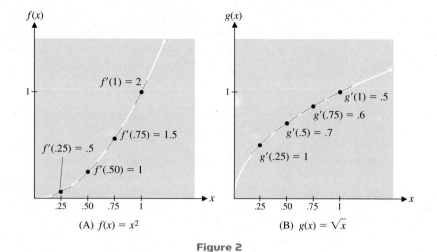

Figure 2

With these ideas in mind, we can state the general definition of concavity.

DEFINITION   Concavity

The graph of a function f is **concave upward** on the interval (a, b) if $f'(x)$ is *increasing* on (a, b) and is **concave downward** on the interval (a, b) if $f'(x)$ is *decreasing* on (a, b).

Geometrically, the graph is concave upward on (a, b) if it lies above its tangent lines in (a, b) and is concave downward on (a, b) if it lies below its tangent lines in (a, b).

How can we determine when $f'(x)$ is increasing or decreasing? In Section 5-1, we used the derivative to determine when a function is increasing or decreasing. To determine when the function $f'(x)$ is increasing or decreasing, we use the derivative of $f'(x)$. The derivative of the derivative of a function is called the *second derivative* of the function. Various notations for the second derivative are given in the following box:

NOTATION   Second Derivative

For $y = f(x)$, the **second derivative** of f, provided that it exists, is

$$f''(x) = \frac{d}{dx}f'(x)$$

Other notations for $f''(x)$ are

$$\frac{d^2y}{dx^2} \quad \text{and} \quad y''$$

Returning to the functions f and g discussed at the beginning of this section, we have

$$f(x) = x^2 \qquad\qquad g(x) = \sqrt{x} = x^{1/2}$$

$$f'(x) = 2x \qquad\qquad g'(x) = \frac{1}{2}x^{-1/2} = \frac{1}{2\sqrt{x}}$$

$$f''(x) = \frac{d}{dx}2x = 2 \qquad g''(x) = \frac{d}{dx}\frac{1}{2}x^{-1/2} = -\frac{1}{4}x^{-3/2} = -\frac{1}{4\sqrt{x^3}}$$

For $x > 0$, we see that $f''(x) > 0$; so, $f'(x)$ is increasing, and the graph of f is concave upward (see Fig. 2A). For $x > 0$, we also see that $g''(x) < 0$; so, $g'(x)$ is decreasing, and the graph of g is concave downward (see Fig. 2B). These ideas are summarized in the following box:

SUMMARY   Concavity

For the interval (a, b),

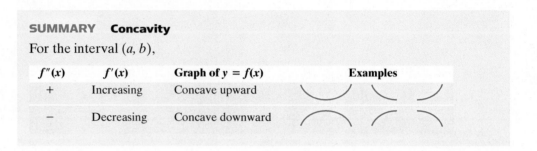

$f''(x)$	$f'(x)$	Graph of $y = f(x)$	Examples
+	Increasing	Concave upward	
−	Decreasing	Concave downward	

CONCEPTUAL INSIGHT

Be careful not to confuse concavity with falling and rising. A graph that is concave upward on an interval may be falling, rising, or both falling and rising on that interval. A similar statement holds for a graph that is concave downward. See Figure 3.

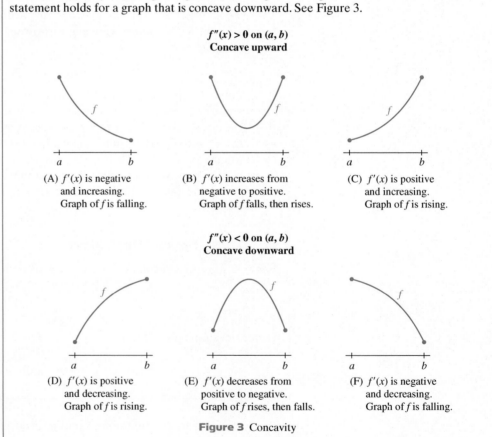

$f''(x) > 0$ on (a, b)
Concave upward

(A) $f'(x)$ is negative and increasing. Graph of f is falling.

(B) $f'(x)$ increases from negative to positive. Graph of f falls, then rises.

(C) $f'(x)$ is positive and increasing. Graph of f is rising.

$f''(x) < 0$ on (a, b)
Concave downward

(D) $f'(x)$ is positive and decreasing. Graph of f is rising.

(E) $f'(x)$ decreases from positive to negative. Graph of f rises, then falls.

(F) $f'(x)$ is negative and decreasing. Graph of f is falling.

Figure 3 Concavity

EXAMPLE 1   **Concavity of Graphs** Determine the intervals on which the graph of each function is concave upward and the intervals on which it is concave downward. Sketch a graph of each function.

(A) $f(x) = e^x$ (B) $g(x) = \ln x$ (C) $h(x) = x^3$

SOLUTION

(A) $f(x) = e^x$

$f'(x) = e^x$

$f''(x) = e^x$

Since $f''(x) > 0$ on $(-\infty, \infty)$, the graph of $f(x) = e^x$ [Fig. 4(A)] is concave upward on $(-\infty, \infty)$.

(B) $g(x) = \ln x$

$g'(x) = \dfrac{1}{x}$

$g''(x) = -\dfrac{1}{x^2}$

The domain of $g(x) = \ln x$ is $(0, \infty)$ and $g''(x) < 0$ on this interval, so the graph of $g(x) = \ln x$ [Fig. 4(B)] is concave downward on $(0, \infty)$.

(C) $h(x) = x^3$

$h'(x) = 3x^2$

$h''(x) = 6x$

Since $h''(x) < 0$ when $x < 0$ and $h''(x) > 0$ when $x > 0$, the graph of $h(x) = x^3$ [Fig. 4(C)] is concave downward on $(-\infty, 0)$ and concave upward on $(0, \infty)$.

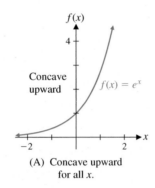

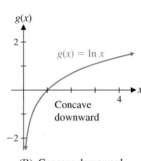

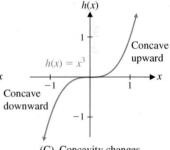

(A) Concave upward for all x.

(B) Concave downward for $x > 0$.

(C) Concavity changes at the origin.

Figure 4

Matched Problem 1 Determine the intervals on which the graph of each function is concave upward and the intervals on which it is cancave downward. Sketch a graph of each function.

(A) $f(x) = -e^{-x}$

(B) $g(x) = \ln \dfrac{1}{x}$

(C) $h(x) = x^{1/3}$

Refer to Example 1. The graphs of $f(x) = e^x$ and $g(x) = \ln x$ never change concavity. But the graph of $h(x) = x^3$ changes concavity at $(0, 0)$. This point is called an *inflection point*.

Finding Inflection Points

An **inflection point** is a point on the graph of the function where the concavity changes (from upward to downward or from downward to upward). For the concavity to change at a point, $f''(x)$ must change sign at that point. But in Section 3-2, we saw that the partition numbers* identify the points where a function can change sign.

> **THEOREM 1 Inflection Points**
> If $y = f(x)$ is continuous on (a, b) and has an inflection point at $x = c$, then either $f''(c) = 0$ or $f''(c)$ does not exist.

---

*As we did with the first derivative, we assume that if f'' is discontinuous at c, then $f''(c)$ does not exist.

Note that inflection points can occur only at partition numbers of f'', but not every partition number of f'' produces an inflection point. Two additional requirements must be satisfied for an inflection point to occur:

A partition number c for f'' produces an inflection point for the graph of f only if

1. $f''(x)$ **changes sign at c and**

2. c **is in the domain of f.**

Figure 5 illustrates several typical cases.

If $f'(c)$ exists and $f''(x)$ changes sign at $x = c$, then the tangent line at an inflection point $(c, f(c))$ will always lie below the graph on the side that is concave upward and above the graph on the side that is concave downward (see Fig. 5A, B, and C).

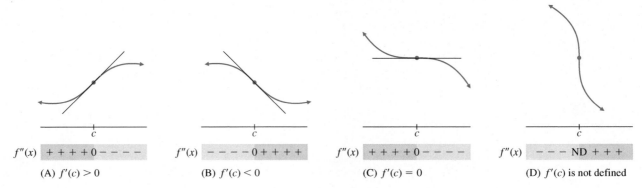

$f''(x)$ $+ + + + 0 - - - -$	$f''(x)$ $- - - - 0 + + + +$	$f''(x)$ $+ + + + 0 - - - -$	$f''(x)$ $- - -$ ND $+ + +$
(A) $f'(c) > 0$	(B) $f'(c) < 0$	(C) $f'(c) = 0$	(D) $f'(c)$ is not defined

Figure 5 Inflection points

EXAMPLE 2   **Locating Inflection Points** Find the inflection point(s) of

$$f(x) = x^3 - 6x^2 + 9x + 1$$

SOLUTION   Since inflection points occur at values of x where $f''(x)$ changes sign, we construct a sign chart for $f''(x)$.

$$f(x) = x^3 - 6x^2 + 9x + 1$$

$$f'(x) = 3x^2 - 12x + 9$$

$$f''(x) = 6x - 12 = 6(x - 2)$$

The sign chart for $f''(x) = 6(x - 2)$ (partition number is 2) is as follows:

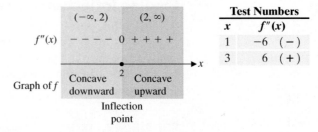

Test Numbers	
x	$f''(x)$
1	-6 $(-)$
3	6 $(+)$

From the sign chart, we see that the graph of f has an inflection point at $x = 2$. That is, the point

$$(2, f(2)) = (2, 3)   \qquad f(2) = 2^3 - 6 \cdot 2^2 + 9 \cdot 2 + 1 = 3$$

is an inflection point on the graph of f.

Matched Problem 2   Find the inflection point(s) of

$$f(x) = x^3 - 9x^2 + 24x - 10$$

EXAMPLE 3   **Locating Inflection Points** Find the inflection point(s) of

$$f(x) = \ln(x^2 - 4x + 5)$$

SOLUTION   First we find the domain of f. Since $\ln x$ is defined only for $x > 0$, f is defined only for

$$x^2 - 4x + 5 > 0 \qquad \text{\textit{Use completing the square (Section 2-3).}}$$
$$(x - 2)^2 + 1 > 0 \qquad \text{\textit{True for all x.}}$$

So the domain of f is $(-\infty, \infty)$. Now we find $f''(x)$ and construct a sign chart for it.

$$f(x) = \ln(x^2 - 4x + 5)$$

$$f'(x) = \frac{2x - 4}{x^2 - 4x + 5}$$

$$f''(x) = \frac{(x^2 - 4x + 5)(2x - 4)' - (2x - 4)(x^2 - 4x + 5)'}{(x^2 - 4x + 5)^2}$$

$$= \frac{(x^2 - 4x + 5)2 - (2x - 4)(2x - 4)}{(x^2 - 4x + 5)^2}$$

$$= \frac{2x^2 - 8x + 10 - 4x^2 + 16x - 16}{(x^2 - 4x + 5)^2}$$

$$= \frac{-2x^2 + 8x - 6}{(x^2 - 4x + 5)^2}$$

$$= \frac{-2(x - 1)(x - 3)}{(x^2 - 4x + 5)^2}$$

The partition numbers for $f''(x)$ are $x = 1$ and $x = 3$.
Sign chart for $f''(x)$:

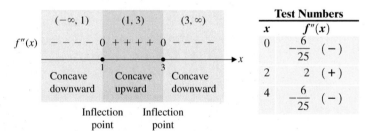

Test Numbers	
x	$f''(x)$
0	$-\dfrac{6}{25}$ $(-)$
2	2 $(+)$
4	$-\dfrac{6}{25}$ $(-)$

The sign chart shows that the graph of f has inflection points at $x = 1$ and $x = 3$.

Matched Problem 3   Find the inflection point(s) of

$$f(x) = \ln(x^2 - 2x + 5)$$

CONCEPTUAL INSIGHT

It is important to remember that the partition numbers for f'' are only *candidates* for inflection points. The function f must be defined at $x = c$, and the second derivative must change sign at $x = c$ in order for the graph to have an inflection point at $x = c$. For example, consider

$$f(x) = x^4 \qquad g(x) = \frac{1}{x}$$

$$f'(x) = 4x^3 \qquad g'(x) = -\frac{1}{x^2}$$

$$f''(x) = 12x^2 \qquad g''(x) = \frac{2}{x^3}$$

In each case, $x = 0$ is a partition number for the second derivative, but neither the graph of $f(x)$ nor the graph of $g(x)$ has an inflection point at $x = 0$. Function f does not have an inflection point at $x = 0$ because $f''(x)$ does not change sign at $x = 0$ (see Fig. 6A). Function g does not have an inflection point at $x = 0$ because $g(0)$ is not defined (see Fig. 6B).

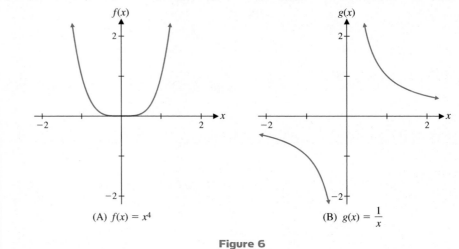

(A) $f(x) = x^4$ (B) $g(x) = \dfrac{1}{x}$

Figure 6

Analyzing Graphs

In the next example, we combine increasing/decreasing properties with concavity properties to analyze the graph of a function.

EXAMPLE 4   **Analyzing a Graph** Figure 7 shows the graph of the derivative of a function f. Use this graph to discuss the graph of f. Include a sketch of a possible graph of f.

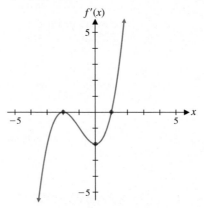

Figure 7

SOLUTION   The sign of the derivative determines where the original function is increasing and decreasing, and the increasing/decreasing properties of the derivative determine the concavity of the original function. The relevant information obtained from the graph of f' is summarized in Table 1, and a possible graph of f is shown in Figure 8.

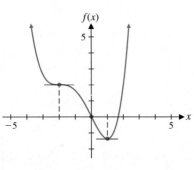

Figure 8

Table 1

x	$f'(x)$ (Fig. 7)	$f(x)$ (Fig. 8)
$-\infty < x < -2$	Negative and increasing	Decreasing and concave upward
$x = -2$	Local maximum	Inflection point
$-2 < x < 0$	Negative and decreasing	Decreasing and concave downward
$x = 0$	Local minimum	Inflection point
$0 < x < 1$	Negative and increasing	Decreasing and concave upward
$x = 1$	x intercept	Local minimum
$1 < x < \infty$	Positive and increasing	Increasing and concave upward

Matched Problem 4   Figure 9 shows the graph of the derivative of a function *f*. Use this graph to discuss the graph of *f*. Include a sketch of a possible graph of *f*.

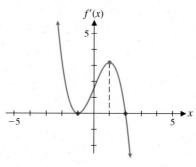

Figure 9

Curve Sketching

Graphing calculators and computers produce the graph of a function by plotting many points. However, important points on a plot many be difficult to identify. Using information gained from the function $f(x)$ and its derivatives, and plotting the important points—intercepts, local extrema, and inflection points—we can sketch by hand a very good representation of the graph of $f(x)$. This graphing process is called **curve sketching**.

PROCEDURE   Graphing Strategy (First Version)*

Step 1   *Analyze f(x).* Find the domain and the intercepts. The *x* intercepts are the solutions of $f(x) = 0$, and the *y* intercept is $f(0)$.

Step 2   *Analyze f'(x).* Find the partition numbers for, and critical values of, $f'(x)$. Construct a sign chart for $f'(x)$, determine the intervals on which *f* is increasing and decreasing, and find local maxima and minima.

Step 3   *Analyze f"(x).* Find the partition numbers for $f''(x)$. Construct a sign chart for $f''(x)$, determine the intervals on which the graph of *f* is concave upward and concave downward, and find inflection points.

Step 4   *Sketch the graph of f.* Locate intercepts, local maxima and minima, and inflection points. Sketch in what you know from steps 1–3. Plot additional points as needed and complete the sketch.

EXAMPLE 5   **Using the Graphing Strategy** Follow the graphing strategy and analyze the function

$$f(x) = x^4 - 2x^3$$

State all the pertinent information and sketch the graph of *f*.

SOLUTION   **Step 1**   *Analyze f(x).* Since *f* is a polynomial, its domain is $(-\infty, \infty)$.

x intercept: $f(x) = 0$

$$x^4 - 2x^3 = 0$$

$$x^3(x - 2) = 0$$

$$x = 0, 2$$

y intercept: $f(0) = 0$

---

*We will modify this summary in Section 5-4 to include additional information about the graph of *f*.

Step 2 *Analyze $f'(x)$.* $f'(x) = 4x^3 - 6x^2 = 4x^2(x - \frac{3}{2})$

Critical values of $f(x)$: 0 and $\frac{3}{2}$

Partition numbers for $f'(x)$: 0 and $\frac{3}{2}$

Sign chart for $f'(x)$:

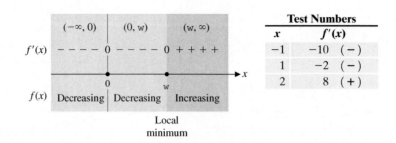

Test Numbers	
x	$f'(x)$
-1	-10 $(-)$
1	-2 $(-)$
2	8 $(+)$

So $f(x)$ is decreasing on $(-\infty, \frac{3}{2})$, is increasing on $(\frac{3}{2}, \infty)$, and has a local minimum at $x = \frac{3}{2}$.

Step 3 *Analyze $f''(x)$.* $f''(x) = 12x^2 - 12x = 12x(x - 1)$

Partition numbers for $f''(x)$: 0 and 1

Sign chart for $f''(x)$:

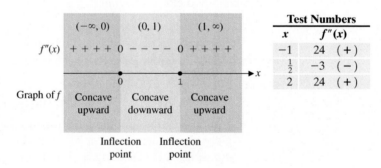

Test Numbers	
x	$f''(x)$
-1	24 $(+)$
$\frac{1}{2}$	-3 $(-)$
2	24 $(+)$

So the graph of f is concave upward on $(-\infty, 0)$ and $(1, \infty)$, is concave downward on $(0, 1)$, and has inflection points at $x = 0$ and $x = 1$.

Step 4 *Sketch the graph of f.*

Test Numbers	
x	$f(x)$
0	0
1	-1
$\frac{3}{2}$	$-\frac{27}{16}$
2	0

Matched Problem 5   Follow the graphing strategy and analyze the function $f(x) = x^4 + 4x^3$. State all the pertinent information and sketch the graph of f.

CONCEPTUAL INSIGHT

Refer to the solution of Example 5. Combining the sign charts for $f'(x)$ and $f''(x)$ (Fig. 10) partitions the real-number line into intervals on which neither $f'(x)$ nor $f''(x)$ changes sign. On each of these intervals, the graph of $f(x)$ must have one of four basic shapes (see also Fig. 3, parts A, C, D, and F on page 286). This reduces sketching the graph of a function to plotting the points identified in the graphing strategy and connecting them with one of the basic shapes.

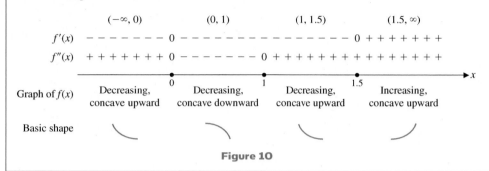

Figure 10

EXAMPLE 6   **Using the Graphing Strategy**   Follow the graphing strategy and analyze the function

$$f(x) = 3x^{5/3} - 20x$$

State all the pertinent information and sketch the graph of f. Round any decimal values to two decimal places.

SOLUTION   **Step 1** *Analyze f(x).* $f(x) = 3x^{5/3} - 20x$

Since x^p is defined for any x and any positive p, the domain of f is $(-\infty, \infty)$.

$$x \text{ intercepts: Solve } f(x) = 0$$

$$3x^{5/3} - 20x = 0$$

$$3x\left(x^{2/3} - \frac{20}{3}\right) = 0 \qquad (a^2 - b^2) = (a - b)(a + b)$$

$$3x\left(x^{1/3} - \sqrt{\frac{20}{3}}\right)\left(x^{1/3} + \sqrt{\frac{20}{3}}\right) = 0$$

The x intercepts of f are

$$x = 0, \quad x = \left(\sqrt{\frac{20}{3}}\right)^3 \approx 17.21, \quad x = \left(-\sqrt{\frac{20}{3}}\right)^3 \approx -17.21$$

y intercept: $f(0) = 0$.

Step 2 Analyze $f'(x)$.

$$f'(x) = 5x^{2/3} - 20$$

$$= 5(x^{2/3} - 4) \qquad \text{Again, } a^2 - b^2 = (a - b)(a + b)$$

$$= 5(x^{1/3} - 2)(x^{1/3} + 2)$$

Critical values of f: $x = 2^3 = 8$ and $x = (-2)^3 = -8$.
Partition numbers for f: $-8, 8$
Sign chart for $f'(x)$:

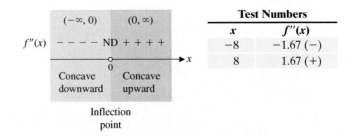

So f is increasing on $(-\infty, -8)$ and $(8, \infty)$ and decreasing on $(-8, 8)$. Therefore, $f(-8)$ is a local maximum, and $f(8)$ is a local minimum.

Step 3 *Analyze $f''(x)$.*

$$f'(x) = 5x^{2/3} - 20$$

$$f''(x) = \frac{10}{3}x^{-1/3} = \frac{10}{3x^{1/3}}$$

Partition number for f'': 0

Sign chart for $f''(x)$:

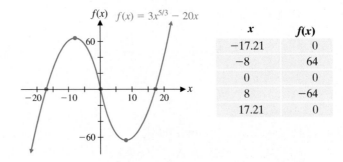

So f is concave downward on $(-\infty, 0)$, is concave upward on $(0, \infty)$, and has an inflection point at $x = 0$.

Step 4 *Sketch the graph of f.*

x	$f(x)$
-17.21	0
-8	64
0	0
8	-64
17.21	0

$f(x) = 3x^{5/3} - 20x$

Matched Problem 6   Follow the graphing strategy and analyze the function $f(x) = 3x^{2/3} - x$. State all the pertinent information and sketch the graph of f. Round any decimal values to two decimal places.

Point of Diminishing Returns

If a company decides to increase spending on advertising, it would expect sales to increase. At first, sales will increase at an increasing rate and then increase at a decreasing rate. The value of x where the rate of change of sales goes from increasing to decreasing is called the **point of diminishing returns**. This is also the point where the rate of change has a maximum value. Money spent after this point may increase sales but at a lower rate.

EXAMPLE 7 **Maximum Rate of Change** Currently, a discount appliance store is selling 200 large-screen television sets monthly. If the store invests $\$x$ thousand in an advertising campaign, the ad company estimates that sales will increase to

$$N(x) = 3x^3 - 0.25x^4 + 200 \qquad 0 \le x \le 9$$

When is the rate of change of sales increasing and when is it decreasing? What is the point of diminishing returns and the maximum rate of change of sales? Graph N and N' on the same coordinate system.

SOLUTION The rate of change of sales with respect to advertising expenditures is

$$N'(x) = 9x^2 - x^3 = x^2(9 - x)$$

To determine when $N'(x)$ is increasing and decreasing, we find $N''(x)$, the derivative of $N'(x)$:

$$N''(x) = 18x - 3x^2 = 3x(6 - x)$$

The information obtained by analyzing the signs of $N'(x)$ and $N''(x)$ is summarized in Table 2 (sign charts are omitted).

Table 2

x	$N''(x)$	$N'(x)$	$N'(x)$	$N(x)$
$0 < x < 6$	+	+	Increasing	Increasing, concave upward
$x = 6$	0	+	Local maximum	Inflection point
$6 < x < 9$	−	+	Decreasing	Increasing, concave downward

Examining Table 2, we see that $N'(x)$ is increasing on $(0, 6)$ and decreasing on $(6, 9)$. The point of diminishing returns is $x = 6$ and the maximum rate of change is $N'(6) = 108$. Note that $N'(x)$ has a local maximum and $N(x)$ has an inflection point at $x = 6$.

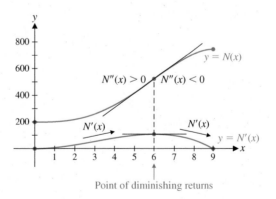

Point of diminishing returns

Matched Problem 7 Repeat Example 7 for

$$N(x) = 4x^3 - 0.25x^4 + 500 \qquad 0 \le x \le 12$$

Exercises 5-2

1. Use the graph of $y = f(x)$ to identify
   (A) Intervals on which the graph of f is concave upward
   (B) Intervals on which the graph of f is concave downward
   (C) Intervals on which $f''(x) < 0$
   (D) Intervals on which $f''(x) > 0$
   (E) Intervals on which $f'(x)$ is increasing
   (F) Intervals on which $f'(x)$ is decreasing
   (G) The x coordinates of inflection points
   (H) The x coordinates of local extrema for $f'(x)$

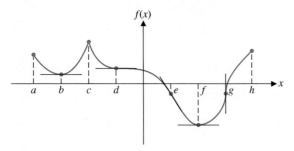

Figure for 1

2. Use the graph of $y = g(x)$ to identify
   (A) Intervals on which the graph of g is concave upward
   (B) Intervals on which the graph of g is concave downward
   (C) Intervals on which $g''(x) < 0$
   (D) Intervals on which $g''(x) > 0$
   (E) Intervals on which $g'(x)$ is increasing
   (F) Intervals on which $g'(x)$ is decreasing
   (G) The x coordinates of inflection points
   (H) The x coordinates of local extrema for $g'(x)$

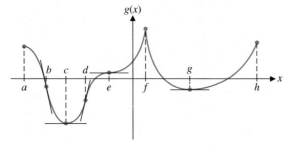

Figure for 2

In Problems 3–6, match the indicated conditions with one of the graphs (A)–(D) shown in the figure.

3. $f'(x) > 0$ and $f''(x) > 0$ on (a, b)

4. $f'(x) > 0$ and $f''(x) < 0$ on (a, b)

5. $f'(x) < 0$ and $f''(x) > 0$ on (a, b)

6. $f'(x) < 0$ and $f''(x) < 0$ on (a, b)

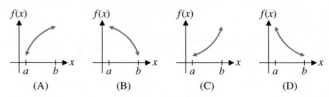

Figure for 3–6

In Problems 7–18, find the indicated derivative for each function.

7. $f''(x)$ for $f(x) = 2x^3 - 4x^2 + 5x - 6$

8. $g''(x)$ for $g(x) = -x^3 + 2x^2 - 3x + 9$

9. $h''(x)$ for $h(x) = 2x^{-1} - 3x^{-2}$

10. $k''(x)$ for $k(x) = -6x^{-2} + 12x^{-3}$

11. d^2y/dx^2 for $y = x^2 - 18x^{1/2}$

12. d^2y/dx^2 for $y = x^3 - 24x^{1/3}$

13. y'' for $y = (x^2 + 9)^4$

14. y'' for $y = (x^2 - 16)^5$

15. $f''(x)$ for $f(x) = e^{-x^2}$

16. $f''(x)$ for $f(x) = xe^{-x}$

17. y'' for $y = \dfrac{\ln x}{x^2}$

18. y'' for $y = x^2 \ln x$

In Problems 19–24, find the x and y coordinates of all inflection points.

19. $f(x) = x^3 + 30x^2$

20. $f(x) = x^3 - 24x^2$

21. $f(x) = x^{5/3} + 2$

22. $f(x) = 5 - x^{4/3}$

23. $f(x) = 1 + x + x^{2/5}$

24. $f(x) = x^{3/5} - 6x + 7$

In Problems 25–34, find the intervals on which the graph of f is concave upward, the intervals on which the graph of f is concave downward, and the inflection points.

25. $f(x) = x^4 + 6x^2$

26. $f(x) = x^4 + 6x$

27. $f(x) = x^3 - 4x^2 + 5x - 2$

28. $f(x) = -x^3 - 5x^2 + 4x - 3$

29. $f(x) = -x^4 + 12x^3 - 12x + 24$

30. $f(x) = x^4 - 2x^3 - 36x + 12$

31. $f(x) = \ln(x^2 - 2x + 10)$

32. $f(x) = \ln(x^2 + 6x + 13)$

33. $f(x) = 8e^x - e^{2x}$

34. $f(x) = e^{3x} - 9e^x$

In Problems 35–42, f(x) is continuous on $(-\infty, \infty)$. Use the given information to sketch the graph of f.

35.

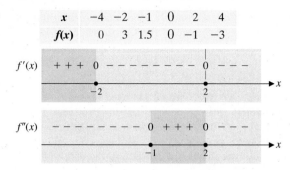

36.

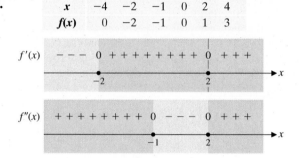

37.

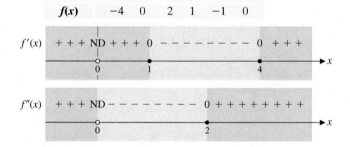

38.

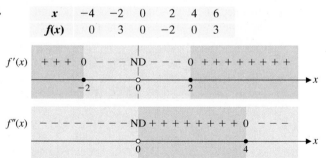

39. $f(0) = 2, f(1) = 0, f(2) = -2$;

$f'(0) = 0, f'(2) = 0$;

$f'(x) > 0$ on $(-\infty, 0)$ and $(2, \infty)$;

$f'(x) < 0$ on $(0, 2)$;

$f''(1) = 0$;

$f''(x) > 0$ on $(1, \infty)$;

$f''(x) < 0$ on $(-\infty, 1)$

40. $f(-2) = -2, f(0) = 1, f(2) = 4$;

$f'(-2) = 0, f'(2) = 0$;

$f'(x) > 0$ on $(-2, 2)$;

$f'(x) < 0$ on $(-\infty, -2)$ and $(2, \infty)$;

$f''(0) = 0$;

$f''(x) > 0$ on $(-\infty, 0)$;

$f''(x) < 0$ on $(0, \infty)$

41. $f(-1) = 0, f(0) = -2, f(1) = 0$;

$f'(0) = 0, f'(-1)$ and $f'(1)$ are not defined;

$f'(x) > 0$ on $(0, 1)$ and $(1, \infty)$;

$f'(x) < 0$ on $(-\infty, -1)$ and $(-1, 0)$;

$f''(-1)$ and $f''(1)$ are not defined;

$f''(x) > 0$ on $(-1, 1)$;

$f''(x) < 0$ on $(-\infty, -1)$ and $(1, \infty)$

42. $f(0) = -2, f(1) = 0, f(2) = 4$;

$f'(0) = 0, f'(2) = 0, f'(1)$ is not defined;

$f'(x) > 0$ on $(0, 1)$ and $(1, 2)$;

$f'(x) < 0$ on $(-\infty, 0)$ and $(2, \infty)$;

$f''(1)$ is not defined;

$f''(x) > 0$ on $(-\infty, 1)$;

$f''(x) < 0$ on $(1, \infty)$

B

In Problems 43–64, summarize the pertinent information obtained by applying the graphing strategy and sketch the graph of $y = f(x)$.

43. $f(x) = (x - 2)(x^2 - 4x - 8)$

44. $f(x) = (x - 3)(x^2 - 6x - 3)$

45. $f(x) = (x + 1)(x^2 - x + 2)$

46. $f(x) = (1 - x)(x^2 + x + 4)$

47. $f(x) = -0.25x^4 + x^3$

48. $f(x) = 0.25x^4 - 2x^3$

49. $f(x) = 16x(x - 1)^3$

50. $f(x) = -4x(x + 2)^3$

51. $f(x) = (x^2 + 3)(9 - x^2)$

52. $f(x) = (x^2 + 3)(x^2 - 1)$

53. $f(x) = (x^2 - 4)^2$

54. $f(x) = (x^2 - 1)(x^2 - 5)$

55. $f(x) = 2x^6 - 3x^5$

56. $f(x) = 3x^5 - 5x^4$

57. $f(x) = 1 - e^{-x}$

58. $f(x) = 2 - 3e^{-2x}$

59. $f(x) = e^{0.5x} + 4e^{-0.5x}$

60. $f(x) = 2e^{0.5x} + e^{-0.5x}$

61. $f(x) = -4 + 2\ln x$

62. $f(x) = 5 - 3 \ln x$

63. $f(x) = \ln(x + 4) - 2$

64. $f(x) = 1 - \ln(x - 3)$

In Problems 65–68, use the graph of $y = f'(x)$ to discuss the graph of $y = f(x)$. Organize your conclusions in a table (see Example 4), and sketch a possible graph of $y = f(x)$.

65.

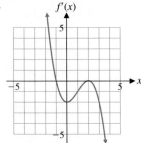

66.

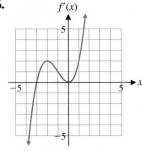

67.

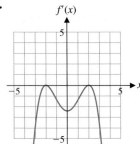

68.

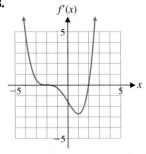

In Problems 69–76, apply steps 1–3 of the graphing strategy to $f(x)$. Use a graphing calculator to approximate (to two decimal places) x intercepts, critical values, and x coordinates of inflection points. Summarize all the pertinent information.

69. $f(x) = x^4 - 5x^3 + 3x^2 + 8x - 5$

70. $f(x) = x^4 + 2x^3 - 5x^2 - 4x + 4$

71. $f(x) = x^4 - 21x^3 + 100x^2 + 20x + 100$

72. $f(x) = x^4 - 12x^3 + 28x^2 + 76x - 50$

73. $f(x) = -x^4 - x^3 + 2x^2 - 2x + 3$

74. $f(x) = -x^4 + x^3 + x^2 + 6$

75. $f(x) = 0.1x^5 + 0.3x^4 - 4x^3 - 5x^2 + 40x + 30$

76. $f(x) = x^5 + 4x^4 - 7x^3 - 20x^2 + 20x - 20$

C

In Problems 77–80, assume that f is a polynomial.

77. Explain how you can locate inflection points for the graph of $y = f(x)$ by examining the graph of $y = f'(x)$.

78. Explain how you can determine where $f'(x)$ is increasing or decreasing by examining the graph of $y = f(x)$.

79. Explain how you can locate local maxima and minima for the graph of $y = f'(x)$ by examining the graph of $y = f(x)$.

80. Explain how you can locate local maxima and minima for the graph of $y = f(x)$ by examining the graph of $y = f'(x)$.

Applications

81. **Inflation.** One commonly used measure of inflation is the annual rate of change of the Consumer Price Index (CPI). A TV news story says that the rate of change of inflation for consumer prices is increasing. What does this say about the shape of the graph of the CPI?

82. **Inflation.** Another commonly used measure of inflation is the annual rate of change of the Producer Price Index (PPI). A government report states that the rate of change of inflation for producer prices is decreasing. What does this say about the shape of the graph of the PPI?

83. **Cost analysis.** A company manufactures a variety of camp stoves at different locations. The total cost $C(x)$ (in dollars) of producing x camp stoves per week at plant A is shown in the figure. Discuss the graph of the marginal cost function $C'(x)$ and interpret the graph of $C'(x)$ in terms of the efficiency of the production process at this plant.

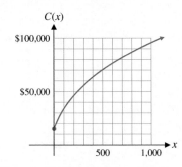

Figure for 83   Production costs at plant A

84. **Cost analysis.** The company in Problem 83 produces the same camp stove at another plant. The total cost $C(x)$ (in dollars) of producing x camp stoves per week at plant B is shown in the figure. Discuss the graph of the marginal cost function $C'(x)$ and interpret the graph of $C'(x)$ in terms of the efficiency of the production process at plant B. Compare the production processes at the two plants.

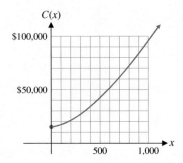

Figure for 84   Production costs at plant B

85. **Revenue.** The marketing research department of a computer company used a large city to test market the firm's new laptop. The department found that the relationship between price p (dollars per unit) and the demand x (units per week) was given approximately by

$$p = 1,296 - 0.12x^2 \qquad 0 < x < 80$$

So, weekly revenue can be approximated by

$$R(x) = xp = 1{,}296x - 0.12x^3 \qquad 0 < x < 80$$

(A) Find the local extrema for the revenue function.

(B) On which intervals is the graph of the revenue function concave upward? Concave downward?

86. Profit. Suppose that the cost equation for the company in Problem 85 is

$$C(x) = 830 + 396x$$

(A) Find the local extrema for the profit function.

(B) On which intervals is the graph of the profit function concave upward? Concave downward?

87. Revenue. A dairy is planning to introduce and promote a new line of organic ice cream. After test marketing the new line in a large city, the marketing research department found that the demand in that city is given approximately by

$$p = 10e^{-x} \qquad 0 \le x \le 5$$

where x thousand quarts were sold per week at a price of $\$p$ each.

(A) Find the local extrema for the revenue function.

(B) On which intervals is the graph of the revenue function concave upward? Concave downward?

88. Revenue. A national food service runs food concessions for sporting events throughout the country. The company's marketing research department chose a particular football stadium to test market a new jumbo hot dog. It was found that the demand for the new hot dog is given approximately by

$$p = 8 - 2\ln x \qquad 5 \le x \le 50$$

where x is the number of hot dogs (in thousands) that can be sold during one game at a price of $\$p$.

(A) Find the local extrema for the revenue function.

(B) On which intervals is the graph of the revenue function concave upward? Concave downward?

89. Production: point of diminishing returns. A T-shirt manufacturer is planning to expand its workforce. It estimates that the number of T-shirts produced by hiring x new workers is given by

$$T(x) = -0.25x^4 + 5x^3 \qquad 0 \le x \le 15$$

When is the rate of change of T-shirt production increasing and when is it decreasing? What is the point of diminishing returns and the maximum rate of change of T-shirt production? Graph T and T' on the same coordinate system.

90. Production: point of diminishing returns. A baseball cap manufacturer is planning to expand its workforce. It estimates that the number of baseball caps produced by hiring x new workers is given by

$$T(x) = -0.25x^4 + 6x^3 \qquad 0 \le x \le 18$$

When is the rate of change of baseball cap production increasing and when is it decreasing? What is the point of diminishing returns and the maximum rate of change of

baseball cap production? Graph T and T' on the same coordinate system.

91. Advertising: point of diminishing returns. A company estimates that it will sell $N(x)$ units of a product after spending $\$x$ thousand on advertising, as given by

$$N(x) = -0.25x^4 + 23x^3 - 540x^2 + 80{,}000 \qquad 24 \le x \le 45$$

When is the rate of change of sales increasing and when is it decreasing? What is the point of diminishing returns and the maximum rate of change of sales? Graph N and N' on the same coordinate system.

92. Advertising: point of diminishing returns. A company estimates that it will sell $N(x)$ units of a product after spending $\$x$ thousand on advertising, as given by

$$N(x) = -0.25x^4 + 13x^3 - 180x^2 + 10{,}000 \qquad 15 \le x \le 24$$

When is the rate of change of sales increasing and when is it decreasing? What is the point of diminishing returns and the maximum rate of change of sales? Graph N and N' on the same coordinate system.

93. Advertising. An automobile dealer uses TV advertising to promote car sales. On the basis of past records, the dealer arrived at the following data, where x is the number of ads placed monthly and y is the number of cars sold that month:

Number of Ads	Number of Cars
x	y
10	325
12	339
20	417
30	546
35	615
40	682
50	795

(A) Enter the data in a graphing calculator and find a cubic regression equation for the number of cars sold monthly as a function of the number of ads.

(B) How many ads should the dealer place each month to maximize the rate of change of sales with respect to the number of ads, and how many cars can the dealer expect to sell with this number of ads? Round answers to the nearest integer.

94. Advertising. A sporting goods chain places TV ads to promote golf club sales. The marketing director used past records to determine the following data, where x is the number of ads placed monthly and y is the number of golf clubs sold that month.

Number of Ads	Number of Golf Clubs
x	y
10	345
14	488
20	746
30	1,228
40	1,671
50	1,955

(A) Enter the data in a graphing calculator and find a cubic regression equation for the number of golf clubs sold monthly as a function of the number of ads.

(B) How many ads should the store manager place each month to maximize the rate of change of sales with respect to the number of ads, and how many golf clubs can the manager expect to sell with this number of ads? Round answers to the nearest integer.

95. Population growth: bacteria. A drug that stimulates reproduction is introduced into a colony of bacteria. After t minutes, the number of bacteria is given approximately by

$$N(t) = 1,000 + 30t^2 - t^3 \qquad 0 \le t \le 20$$

(A) When is the rate of growth, $N'(t)$, increasing? Decreasing?

(B) Find the inflection points for the graph of N.

(C) Sketch the graphs of N and N' on the same coordinate system.

(D) What is the maximum rate of growth?

96. Drug sensitivity. One hour after x milligrams of a particular drug are given to a person, the change in body temperature $T(x)$, in degrees Fahrenheit, is given by

$$T(x) = x^2\left(1 - \frac{x}{9}\right) \qquad 0 \le x \le 6$$

The rate $T'(x)$ at which $T(x)$ changes with respect to the size of the dosage x is called the *sensitivity* of the body to the dosage.

(A) When is $T'(x)$ increasing? Decreasing?

(B) Where does the graph of T have inflection points?

(C) Sketch the graphs of T and T' on the same coordinate system.

(D) What is the maximum value of $T'(x)$?

97. Learning. The time T (in minutes) it takes a person to learn a list of length n is

$$T(n) = 0.08n^3 - 1.2n^2 + 6n \qquad n \ge 0$$

(A) When is the rate of change of T with respect to the length of the list increasing? Decreasing?

(B) Where does the graph of T have inflection points?

(C) Graph T and T' on the same coordinate system.

(D) What is the minimum value of $T'(n)$?

Answers to Matched Problems

1. (A) Concave downward on $(-\infty, \infty)$

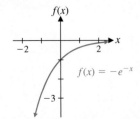

(B) Concave upward on $(0, \infty)$

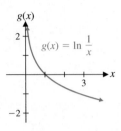

(C) Concave upward on $(-\infty, 0)$ and concave downward on $(0, \infty)$

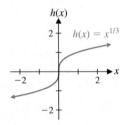

2. The only inflection point is $(3, f(3)) = (3, 8)$.

3. The inflection points are $(-1, f(-1)) = (-1, \ln 8)$ and $(3, f(3)) = (3, \ln 8)$.

4.

x	$f'(x)$	$f(x)$
$-\infty < x < -1$	Positive and decreasing	Increasing and concave downward
$x = -1$	Local minimum	Inflection point
$-1 < x < 1$	Positive and increasing	Increasing and concave upward
$x = 1$	Local maximum	Inflection point
$1 < x < 2$	Positive and decreasing	Increasing and concave downward
$x = 2$	x intercept	Local maximum
$2 < x < \infty$	Negative and decreasing	Decreasing and concave downward

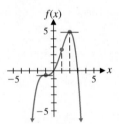

5. x intercepts: $-4, 0$; y intercept: $f(0) = 0$

Decreasing on $(-\infty, -3)$; increasing on $(-3, \infty)$; local minimum at $x = -3$

Concave upward on $(-\infty, -2)$ and $(0, \infty)$; concave downward on $(-2, 0)$

Inflection points at $x = -2$ and $x = 0$

x	$f(x)$
-4	0
-3	-27
-2	-16
0	0

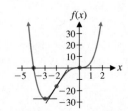

6. x intercepts: $0, 27$; y intercept: $f(0) = 0$

Decreasing on $(-\infty, 0)$ and $(8, \infty)$; increasing on $(0, 8)$; local minimum: $f(0) = 0$; local maximum: $f(8) = 4$

Concave downward on $(-\infty, 0)$ and $(0, \infty)$; no inflection points

x	$f(x)$
0	0
8	4
27	0

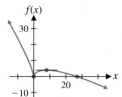

7. $N'(x)$ is increasing on $(0, 8)$ and decreasing on $(8, 12)$. The point of diminishing returns is $x = 8$ and the maximum rate of change is $N'(8) = 256$.

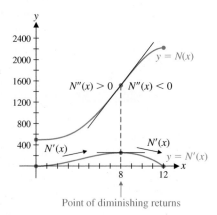

5-3 L'Hôpital's Rule

Introduction

The ability to evaluate a wide variety of different types of limits is one of the skills that are necessary to apply the techniques of calculus successfully. Limits play a fundamental role in the development of the derivative and are an important graphing tool. In order to deal effectively with graphs, we need to develop some more methods for evaluating limits.

In this section, we discuss a powerful technique for evaluating limits of quotients called *L'Hôpital's rule*. The rule is named after the French mathematician Marquis de L'Hôpital (1661–1704). To use L'Hôpital's rule, it is necessary to be familiar with the limit properties of some basic functions. Figure 1 reviews some limits involving powers of x that were discussed earlier.

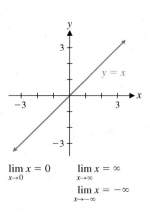

$\lim_{x \to 0} x = 0$ $\lim_{x \to \infty} x = \infty$

$\lim_{x \to -\infty} x = -\infty$

(A) $y = x$

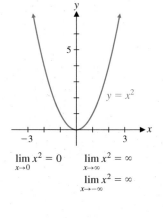

$\lim_{x \to 0} x^2 = 0$ $\lim_{x \to \infty} x^2 = \infty$

$\lim_{x \to -\infty} x^2 = \infty$

(B) $y = x^2$

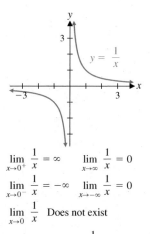

$\lim_{x \to 0^+} \frac{1}{x} = \infty$ $\lim_{x \to \infty} \frac{1}{x} = 0$

$\lim_{x \to 0^-} \frac{1}{x} = -\infty$ $\lim_{x \to -\infty} \frac{1}{x} = 0$

$\lim_{x \to 0} \frac{1}{x}$ Does not exist

(C) $y = \frac{1}{x}$

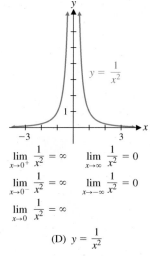

$\lim_{x \to 0^+} \frac{1}{x^2} = \infty$ $\lim_{x \to \infty} \frac{1}{x^2} = 0$

$\lim_{x \to 0^-} \frac{1}{x^2} = \infty$ $\lim_{x \to -\infty} \frac{1}{x^2} = 0$

$\lim_{x \to 0} \frac{1}{x^2} = \infty$

(D) $y = \frac{1}{x^2}$

Figure 1 Limits involving powers of x

The limits in Figure 1 are easily extended to functions of the form $f(x) = (x - c)^n$ and $g(x) = 1/(x - c)^n$. In general, if n is an odd integer, then limits involving $(x - c)^n$ or $1/(x - c)^n$ as x approaches c (or $\pm\infty$) behave, respectively, like the limits of x and $1/x$ as x approaches 0 (or $\pm\infty$). If n is an even integer, then limits involving these expressions behave, respectively, like the limits of x^2 and $1/x^2$ as x approaches 0 (or $\pm\infty$).

EXAMPLE 1   Limits Involving Powers of $x - c$

(A) $\lim\limits_{x\to 2} \dfrac{5}{(x - 2)^4} = \infty$ *Compare with* $\lim\limits_{x\to 0} \dfrac{1}{x^2}$ *in Figure 1.*

(B) $\lim\limits_{x\to -1^-} \dfrac{4}{(x + 1)^3} = -\infty$ *Compare with* $\lim\limits_{x\to 0^-} \dfrac{1}{x}$ *in Figure 1.*

(C) $\lim\limits_{x\to\infty} \dfrac{4}{(x - 9)^6} = 0$ *Compare with* $\lim\limits_{x\to 0^-} \dfrac{1}{x^2}$ *in Figure 1.*

(D) $\lim\limits_{x\to -\infty} 3x^3 = -\infty$ *Compare with* $\lim\limits_{x\to -\infty} x$ *in Figure 1.*

Matched Problem 1   Evaluate each limit.

(A) $\lim\limits_{x\to 3^+} \dfrac{7}{(x - 3)^5}$ (B) $\lim\limits_{x\to -4} \dfrac{6}{(x + 4)^6}$

(C) $\lim\limits_{x\to -\infty} \dfrac{3}{(x + 2)^3}$ (D) $\lim\limits_{x\to\infty} 5x^4$

Figure 2 reviews limits of exponential and logarithmic functions.
    The limits in Figure 2 also generalize to other simple exponential and logarithmic forms.

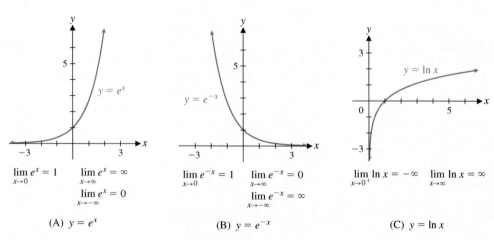

(A) $y = e^x$ (B) $y = e^{-x}$ (C) $y = \ln x$

Figure 2 Limits involving exponential and logarithmic functions

EXAMPLE 2   Limits Involving Exponential and Logarithmic Forms

(A) $\lim\limits_{x\to\infty} 2e^{3x} = \infty$ *Compare with* $\lim\limits_{x\to\infty} e^x$ *in Figure 2.*

(B) $\lim\limits_{x\to\infty} 4e^{-5x} = 0$ *Compare with* $\lim\limits_{x\to\infty} e^{-x}$ *in Figure 2.*

(C) $\lim\limits_{x\to\infty} \ln(x + 4) = \infty$ *Compare with* $\lim\limits_{x\to\infty} \ln x$ *in Figure 2.*

(D) $\lim\limits_{x\to 2^+} \ln(x - 2) = -\infty$ *Compare with* $\lim\limits_{x\to\infty^+} \ln x$ *in Figure 2.*

Matched Problem 2   Evaluate each limit.

(A) $\lim\limits_{x \to -\infty} 2e^{-6x}$ (B) $\lim\limits_{x \to -\infty} 3e^{2x}$

(C) $\lim\limits_{x \to -4^+} \ln(x + 4)$ (D) $\lim\limits_{x \to \infty} \ln(x - 10)$

Now that we have reviewed the limit properties of some basic functions, we are ready to consider the main topic of this section: L'Hôpital's rule.

L'Hôpital's Rule and the Indeterminate Form 0/0

Recall that the limit

$$\lim_{x \to c} \frac{f(x)}{g(x)}$$

is a 0/0 indeterminate form if

$$\lim_{x \to c} f(x) = 0 \quad \text{and} \quad \lim_{x \to c} g(x) = 0$$

The quotient property for limits in Section 3-1 does not apply since $\lim\limits_{x \to c} g(x) = 0$.

If we are dealing with a 0/0 indeterminate form, the limit may or may not exist, and we cannot tell which is true without further investigation.

Each of the following is a 0/0 indeterminate form:

$$\lim_{x \to 2} \frac{x^2 - 4}{x - 2} \quad \text{and} \quad \lim_{x \to 1} \frac{e^x - e}{x - 1}$$

The first limit can be evaluated by performing some algebraic simplifications, such as

$$\lim_{x \to 2} \frac{x^2 - 4}{x - 2} = \lim_{x \to 2} \frac{(x - 2)(x + 2)}{x - 2} = \lim_{x \to 2}(x + 2) = 4$$

The second cannot. Instead, we turn to the powerful **L'Hôpital's rule**, which we now state without proof. This rule can be used whenever a limit is a 0/0 indeterminate form.

THEOREM 1   L'Hôpital's Rule for 0/0 Indeterminate Forms: Version 1
For c a real number,
if $\lim\limits_{x \to c} f(x) = 0$ and $\lim\limits_{x \to c} g(x) = 0$, then

$$\lim_{x \to c} \frac{f(x)}{g(x)} = \lim_{x \to c} \frac{f'(x)}{g'(x)}$$

provided that the second limit exists or is $+\infty$ or $-\infty$.

EXAMPLE 3   **L'Hôpital's Rule** Evaluate $\lim\limits_{x \to 1} \dfrac{e^x - e}{x - 1}$.

SOLUTION   **Step 1** *Check to see if L'Hôpital's rule applies:*

$$\lim_{x \to 1}(e^x - e) = e^1 - e = 0 \quad \text{and} \quad \lim_{x \to 1}(x - 1) = 1 - 1 = 0$$

L'Hôpital's rule does apply.

Step 2 *Apply L'Hôpital's rule:*

0/0 form

$$\lim_{x \to 1} \frac{e^x - e}{x - 1} = \lim_{x \to 1} \frac{\frac{d}{dx}(e^x - e)}{\frac{d}{dx}(x - 1)}$$ Apply L'Hôpital's rule.

$$= \lim_{x \to 1} \frac{e^x}{1}$$ e^x is continuous at $x = 1$.

$$= \frac{e^1}{1} = e$$

Matched Problem 3   Evaluate $\lim\limits_{x \to 4} \dfrac{e^x - e^4}{x - 4}$.

CONCEPTUAL INSIGHT

In L'Hôpital's rule, the symbol $f'(x)/g'(x)$ represents the derivative of $f(x)$ divided by the derivative of $g(x)$, not the derivative of the quotient $f(x)/g(x)$.

When applying L'Hôpital's rule to a 0/0 indeterminate form, be certain that you differentiate the numerator and denominator separately.

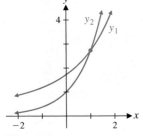

Figure 3

The functions

$$y_1 = \frac{e^x - e}{x - 1} \quad \text{and} \quad y_2 = \frac{e^x}{1}$$

of Example 3 are different functions (see Fig. 3), but both functions have the same limit e as x approaches 1. Although y_1 is undefined at $x = 1$, the graph of y_1 provides a check of the answer to Example 3.

EXAMPLE 4   **L'Hôpital's Rule**   Evaluate $\lim\limits_{x \to 0} \dfrac{\ln(1 + x^2)}{x^4}$.

SOLUTION   **Step 1** *Check to see if L'Hôpital's rule applies:*

$$\lim_{x \to 0} \ln(1 + x^2) = \ln 1 = 0 \quad \text{and} \quad \lim_{x \to 0} x^4 = 0$$

L'Hôpital's rule does apply.

Step 2 *Apply L'Hôpital's rule:*

0/0 form

$$\lim_{x \to 0} \frac{\ln(1 + x^2)}{x^4} = \lim_{x \to 0} \frac{\frac{dx}{dx} \ln(1 + x^2)}{\frac{d}{dx} x^4}$$ Apply L'Hôpital's rule.

$$\lim_{x \to 0} \frac{\ln(1 + x^2)}{x^4} = \lim_{x \to 0} \frac{\frac{2x}{1 + x^2}}{4x^3}$$ Multiply numerator and denominator by $1/4x^3$.

$$= \lim_{x \to 0} \frac{\frac{2x}{1 + x^2} \cdot \frac{1}{4x^3}}{4x^3 \cdot \frac{1}{4x^3}}$$ Simplify.

$$= \lim_{x \to 0} \frac{1}{2x^2(1 + x^2)}$$

Apply Theorem 1 in Section 3-3 and compare with Fig. 1(D).

$$= \infty$$

Matched Problem 4   Evaluate $\lim\limits_{x \to 1} \dfrac{\ln x}{(x - 1)^3}$.

EXAMPLE 5   **L'Hôpital's Rule May Not Be Applicable**   Evaluate $\lim\limits_{x \to 1} \dfrac{\ln x}{x}$.

SOLUTION   **Step 1** *Check to see if L'Hôpital's rule applies:*

$$\lim_{x \to 1} \ln x = \ln 1 = 0, \qquad \text{but} \qquad \lim_{x \to 1} x = 1 \neq 0$$

L'Hôpital's rule does not apply.

Step 2 *Evaluate by another method.* The quotient property for limits from Section 3-1 does apply, and we have

$$\lim_{x \to 1} \frac{\ln x}{x} = \frac{\lim\limits_{x \to 1} \ln x}{\lim\limits_{x \to 1} x} = \frac{\ln 1}{1} = \frac{0}{1} = 0$$

Note that applying L'Hôpital's rule would give us an incorrect result:

$$\lim_{x \to 1} \frac{\ln x}{x} \neq \lim_{x \to 1} \frac{\frac{d}{dx} \ln x}{\frac{d}{dx} x} = \lim_{x \to 1} \frac{1/x}{1} = 1$$

Matched Problem 5   Evaluate $\lim\limits_{x \to 0} \dfrac{x}{e^x}$.

CONCEPTUAL INSIGHT

As Example 5 illustrates, all limits involving quotients are not 0/0 indeterminate forms.

You must always check to see if L'Hôpital's rule applies before you use it.

EXAMPLE 6   **Repeated Application of L'Hôpital's Rule**   Evaluate

$$\lim_{x \to 0} \frac{x^2}{e^x - 1 - x}$$

SOLUTION   **Step 1** *Check to see if L'Hôpital's rule applies:*

$$\lim_{x \to 0} x^2 = 0 \qquad \text{and} \qquad \lim_{x \to 0}(e^x - 1 - x) = 0$$

L'Hôpital's rule does apply.

Step 2   Apply L'Hôpital's rule:

0/0 form

$$\lim_{x \to 0} \frac{x^2}{e^x - 1 - x} = \lim_{x \to 0} \frac{\frac{d}{dx} x^2}{\frac{d}{dx}(e^x - 1 - x)} = \lim_{x \to 0} \frac{2x}{e^x - 1}$$

Since $\lim_{x \to 0} 2x = 0$ and $\lim_{x \to 0}(e^x - 1) = 0$, the new limit obtained is also a 0/0 indeterminate form, and L'Hôpital's rule can be applied again.

Step 3 *Apply L'Hôpital's rule again:*

$$\underset{0/0 \text{ form}}{\lim_{x\to 0}\frac{2x}{e^x-1}} = \lim_{x\to 0}\frac{\frac{d}{dx}2x}{\frac{d}{dx}(e^x-1)} = \lim_{x\to 0}\frac{2}{e^x} = \frac{2}{e^0} = 2$$

Therefore,

$$\lim_{x\to 0}\frac{x^2}{e^x-1-x} = \lim_{x\to 0}\frac{2x}{e^x-1} = \lim_{x\to 0}\frac{2x}{e^x} = 2$$

Matched Problem 6   Evaluate $\lim_{x\to 0}\dfrac{e^{2x}-1-2x}{x^2}$

One-Sided Limits and Limits at ∞

In addition to examining the limit as x approaches c, we have discussed one-sided limits and limits at ∞ in Chapter 3. L'Hôpital's rule is valid in these cases also.

> **THEOREM 2   L'Hôpital's Rule for 0/0 Indeterminate Forms: Version 2 (for one-sided limits and limits at infinity)**
> The first version of L'Hôpital's rule (Theorem 1) remains valid if the symbol $x\to c$ is replaced everywhere it occurs with one of the following symbols:
> $$x\to c^+ \qquad x\to c^- \qquad x\to\infty \qquad x\to-\infty$$

For example, if $\lim_{x\to\infty}f(x) = 0$ and $\lim_{x\to\infty}g(x) = 0$, then

$$\lim_{x\to\infty}\frac{f(x)}{g(x)} = \lim_{x\to\infty}\frac{f'(x)}{g'(x)}$$

provided that the second limit exists or is $+\infty$ or $-\infty$. Similar rules can be written for $x\to c^+$, $x\to c^-$, and $x\to-\infty$.

EXAMPLE 7   **L'Hôpital's Rule for One-Sided Limits**   Evaluate $\lim_{x\to 1^+}\dfrac{\ln x}{(x-1)^2}$.

SOLUTION   **Step 1** *Check to see if L'Hôpital's rule applies:*

$$\lim_{x\to 1^+}\ln x = 0 \qquad \text{and} \qquad \lim_{x\to 1^+}(x-1)^2 = 0$$

L'Hôpital's rule does apply.

Step 2 *Apply L'Hôpital's rule:*

$$\underset{0/0 \text{ form}}{\lim_{x\to 1^+}\frac{\ln x}{(x-1)^2}} = \lim_{x\to 1^+}\frac{\frac{d}{dx}(\ln x)}{\frac{d}{dx}(x-1)^2} \qquad \text{Apply L'Hôpital's rule.}$$

$$= \lim_{x\to 1^+}\frac{1/x}{2(x-1)} \qquad \text{Simplify.}$$

$$= \lim_{x\to 1^+}\frac{1}{2x(x-1)}$$

$$= \infty$$

The limit as $x \to 1^+$ is ∞ because $1/2x(x-1)$ has a vertical asymptote at $x = 1$ (Theorem 1, Section 3-3) and $x(x-1) > 0$ for $x > 1$.

Matched Problem 7 Evaluate $\lim\limits_{x \to 1^-} \dfrac{\ln x}{(x-1)^2}$.

EXAMPLE 8 **L'Hôpital's Rule for Limits at Infinity** Evaluate $\lim\limits_{x \to \infty} \dfrac{\ln(1 + e^{-x})}{e^{-x}}$.

SOLUTION **Step 1** *Check to see if L'Hôpital's rule applies:*

$$\lim_{x \to \infty} \ln(1 + e^{-x}) = \ln(1 + 0) = \ln 1 = 0 \text{ and } \lim_{x \to \infty} e^{-x} = 0$$

L'Hôpital's rule does apply.

Step 2 *Apply L'Hôpital's rule:*

$$\lim_{x \to \infty} \frac{\ln(1 + e^{-x})}{e^{-x}} = \lim_{x \to \infty} \frac{\dfrac{d}{dx}[\ln(1 + e^{-x})]}{\dfrac{d}{dx} e^{-x}} \qquad \text{Apply L'Hôpital's rule.}$$

$$= \lim_{x \to \infty} \frac{-e^{-x}/(1 + e^{-x})}{-e^{-x}} \qquad \text{Multiply numerator and denominator by } -e^x.$$

$$\lim_{x \to \infty} \frac{\ln(1 + e^{-x})}{e^{-x}} = \lim_{x \to \infty} \frac{1}{1 + e^{-x}} \qquad \lim_{x \to \infty} e^{-x} = 0$$

$$= \frac{1}{1 + 0} = 1$$

Matched Problem 8 Evaluate $\lim\limits_{x \to -\infty} \dfrac{\ln(1 + 2e^x)}{e^x}$.

L'Hôpital's Rule and the Indeterminate Form ∞/∞

In Section 3-3, we discussed techniques for evaluating limits of rational functions such as

$$\lim_{x \to \infty} \frac{2x^2}{x^3 + 3} \qquad \lim_{x \to \infty} \frac{4x^3}{2x^2 + 5} \qquad \lim_{x \to \infty} \frac{3x^3}{5x^3 + 6} \qquad (1)$$

Each of these limits is an ∞/∞ *indeterminate form*. In general, if $\lim_{x \to c} f(x) = \pm\infty$ and $\lim_{x \to c} g(x) = \pm\infty$, then

$$\lim_{x \to c} \frac{f(x)}{g(x)}$$

is called an ∞/∞ **indeterminate form**. Furthermore, $x \to c$ can be replaced in all three limits above with $x \to c^+$, $x \to c^-$, $x \to \infty$, or $x \to -\infty$. It can be shown that L'Hôpital's rule also applies to these ∞/∞ indeterminate forms.

THEOREM 3 **L'Hôpital's Rule for the Indeterminate Form ∞/∞: Version 3**
Versions 1 and 2 of L'Hôpital's rule for the indeterminate form $0/0$ are also valid if the limit of f and the limit of g are both infinite; that is, both $+\infty$ and $-\infty$ are permissible for either limit.

For example, if $\lim_{x \to c^+} f(x) = \infty$ and $\lim_{x \to c^+} g(x) = -\infty$, then L'Hôpital's rule can be applied to $\lim_{x \to c^+} [f(x)/g(x)]$.

EXPLORE & DISCUSS 1

Evaluate each of the limits in (1) in two ways:

1. Use Theorem 4 in Section 3-3.
2. Use L'Hôpital's rule.

Given a choice, which method would you choose? Why?

EXAMPLE 9 **L'Hôpital's Rule for the Indeterminate Form ∞/∞** Evaluate $\lim\limits_{x \to \infty} \dfrac{\ln x}{x^2}$.

SOLUTION **Step 1** *Check to see if L'Hôpital's rule applies:*

$$\lim_{x \to \infty} \ln x = \infty \qquad \text{and} \qquad \lim_{x \to \infty} x^2 = \infty$$

L'Hôpital's rule does apply.

Step 2 *Apply L'Hôpital's rule:*

∞/∞ form

$$\lim_{x \to \infty} \frac{\ln x}{x^2} = \lim_{x \to \infty} \frac{\dfrac{d}{dx}(\ln x)}{\dfrac{d}{dx}x^2} \qquad \text{Apply L'Hôpital's rule.}$$

$$= \lim_{x \to \infty} \frac{1/x}{2x} \qquad \text{Simplify.}$$

$$\lim_{x \to \infty} \frac{\ln x}{x^2} = \lim_{x \to \infty} \frac{1}{2x^2} \qquad \text{See Figure 1(D).}$$

$$= 0$$

Matched Problem 9 Evaluate $\lim\limits_{x \to \infty} \dfrac{\ln x}{x}$.

EXAMPLE 10 **L'Hôpital's Rule for the Indeterminate Form ∞/∞** Evaluate $\lim\limits_{x \to \infty} \dfrac{e^x}{x^2}$.

SOLUTION **Step 1** *Check to see if L'Hôpital's rule applies:*

$$\lim_{x \to \infty} e^x = \infty \qquad \text{and} \qquad \lim_{x \to \infty} x^2 = \infty$$

L'Hôpital's rule does apply.

Step 2 *Apply L'Hôpital's rule:*

∞/∞ form

$$\lim_{x \to \infty} \frac{e^x}{x^2} = \lim_{x \to \infty} \frac{\dfrac{d}{dx}e^x}{\dfrac{d}{dx}x^2} = \lim_{x \to \infty} \frac{e^x}{2x}$$

Since $\lim_{x \to \infty} e^x = \infty$ and $\lim_{x \to \infty} 2x = \infty$, this limit is an ∞/∞ indeterminate form and L'Hôpital's rule can be applied again.

Step 3 *Apply L'Hôpital's rule again:*

∞/∞ form

$$\lim_{x \to \infty} \frac{e^x}{2x} = \lim_{x \to \infty} \frac{\dfrac{d}{dx}e^x}{\dfrac{d}{dx}2x} = \lim_{x \to \infty} \frac{e^x}{2} = \infty$$

Therefore,

$$\lim_{x \to \infty} \frac{e^x}{x^2} = \lim_{x \to \infty} \frac{e^x}{2x} = \lim_{x \to \infty} \frac{e^x}{2} = \infty$$

Matched Problem 10   Evaluate $\lim_{x \to \infty} \dfrac{e^{2x}}{x^2}$.

CONCEPTUAL INSIGHT

The three versions of L'Hôpital's rule cover a multitude of limits—far too many to remember case by case. Instead, we suggest you use the following pattern, common to all versions, as a memory aid:

1. All versions involve three limits: $\lim f(x)/g(x)$, $\lim f(x)$, and $\lim g(x)$.
2. The independent variable x must behave the same way in all three limits. The acceptable behaviors are $x \to c$, $x \to c^+$, $x \to c^-$, $x \to \infty$, or $x \to -\infty$.
3. The form of $\lim f(x)/g(x)$ must be $\dfrac{0}{0}$ or $\dfrac{\pm\infty}{\pm\infty}$ and both $\lim f(x)$ and $\lim g(x)$ must approach 0 or both must approach $\pm\infty$.

Exercises 5-3

A

Use L'Hôpital's rule to find each limit in Problems 1–14.

1. $\lim\limits_{x \to 2} \dfrac{x^4 - 16}{x^3 - 8}$

2. $\lim\limits_{x \to 1} \dfrac{x^6 - 1}{x^5 - 1}$

3. $\lim\limits_{x \to 2} \dfrac{x^2 + x - 6}{x^2 + 6x - 16}$

4. $\lim\limits_{x \to 4} \dfrac{x^2 - 8x + 16}{x^2 - 5x + 4}$

5. $\lim\limits_{x \to 0} \dfrac{e^x - 1}{x}$

6. $\lim\limits_{x \to 1} \dfrac{\ln x}{x - 1}$

7. $\lim\limits_{x \to 0} \dfrac{\ln(1 + 4x)}{x}$

8. $\lim\limits_{x \to 0} \dfrac{e^{2x} - 1}{x}$

9. $\lim\limits_{x \to \infty} \dfrac{2x^2 + 7}{5x^3 + 9}$

10. $\lim\limits_{x \to \infty} \dfrac{3x^4 + 6}{2x^2 + 5}$

11. $\lim\limits_{x \to \infty} \dfrac{e^{3x}}{x}$

12. $\lim\limits_{x \to \infty} \dfrac{x}{e^{4x}}$

13. $\lim\limits_{x \to \infty} \dfrac{x^2}{\ln x}$

14. $\lim\limits_{x \to \infty} \dfrac{\ln x}{x^4}$

In Problems 15–18, explain why L'Hôpital's rule does not apply. If the limit exists, find it by other means.

15. $\lim\limits_{x \to 1} \dfrac{x^2 + 5x + 4}{x^3 + 1}$

16. $\lim\limits_{x \to \infty} \dfrac{e^{-x}}{\ln x}$

17. $\lim\limits_{x \to 2} \dfrac{x + 2}{(x - 2)^4}$

18. $\lim\limits_{x \to -3} \dfrac{x^2}{(x + 3)^5}$

In Problems 19–22, the limit can be found in two ways. Use L'Hôpital's rule to find the limit and check your answer using an algebraic simplification.

19. $\lim\limits_{x \to -4} \dfrac{x + 4}{x^2 - 16}$

20. $\lim\limits_{x \to 5} \dfrac{x - 5}{x^2 - 25}$

21. $\lim\limits_{x \to 9} \dfrac{x^2 - x - 72}{x - 9}$

22. $\lim\limits_{x \to 7} \dfrac{x - 7}{x^2 + 6x - 91}$

B

Find each limit in Problems 23–46. Note that L'Hôpital's rule does not apply to every problem, and some problems will require more than one application of L'Hôpital's rule.

23. $\lim\limits_{x \to 0} \dfrac{e^{4x} + 1 - 4x}{x^2}$

24. $\lim\limits_{x \to 0} \dfrac{3x + 1 - e^{3x}}{x^2}$

25. $\lim\limits_{x \to 2} \dfrac{\ln(x - 1)}{x - 1}$

26. $\lim\limits_{x \to -1} \dfrac{\ln(x + 2)}{x + 2}$

27. $\lim\limits_{x \to 0^+} \dfrac{\ln(1 + x^2)}{x^3}$

28. $\lim\limits_{x \to 0^-} \dfrac{\ln(1 + 2x)}{x^2}$

29. $\lim\limits_{x \to 0^+} \dfrac{\ln(1 + \sqrt{x})}{x}$

30. $\lim\limits_{x \to 0^+} \dfrac{\ln(1 + x)}{\sqrt{x}}$

31. $\lim\limits_{x \to -2} \dfrac{x^2 + 2x + 1}{x^2 + x + 1}$

32. $\lim\limits_{x \to 1} \dfrac{2x^3 - 3x^2 + 1}{x^3 - 3x + 2}$

33. $\lim\limits_{x \to -1} \dfrac{x^3 + x^2 - x - 1}{x^3 + 4x^2 + 5x + 2}$

34. $\lim\limits_{x \to 3} \dfrac{x^3 + 3x^2 - x - 3}{x^2 + 6x + 9}$

35. $\lim\limits_{x \to 2^-} \dfrac{x^3 - 12x + 16}{x^3 - 6x^2 + 12x - 8}$

36. $\lim\limits_{x \to 1^+} \dfrac{x^3 + x^2 - x + 1}{x^3 + 3x^2 + 3x - 1}$

37. $\lim\limits_{x \to \infty} \dfrac{3x^2 + 5x}{4x^3 + 7}$

38. $\lim\limits_{x \to \infty} \dfrac{4x^2 + 9x}{5x^2 + 8}$

39. $\lim_{x \to \infty} \dfrac{x^2}{e^{2x}}$

40. $\lim_{x \to \infty} \dfrac{e^{3x}}{x^3}$

41. $\lim_{x \to \infty} \dfrac{1 + e^{-x}}{1 + x^2}$

42. $\lim_{x \to -\infty} \dfrac{1 + e^{-x}}{1 + x^2}$

43. $\lim_{x \to \infty} \dfrac{e^{-x}}{\ln(1 + 4e^{-x})}$

44. $\lim_{x \to \infty} \dfrac{\ln(1 + 2e^{-x})}{\ln(1 + e^{-x})}$

45. $\lim_{x \to 0} \dfrac{e^x - e^{-x} - 2x}{x^3}$

46. $\lim_{x \to 0} \dfrac{e^{2x} - 1 - 2x - 2x^2}{x^3}$

53. $\lim_{x \to \infty} \dfrac{\sqrt{1 + x^2}}{x}$

54. $\lim_{x \to -\infty} \dfrac{x}{\sqrt{4 + x^2}}$

55. $\lim_{x \to -\infty} \dfrac{\sqrt[3]{x^3 + 1}}{x}$

56. $\lim_{x \to \infty} \dfrac{x^2}{\sqrt[3]{(x^3 + 1)^2}}$

C

47. Find $\lim_{x \to 0^+} (x \ln x)$.

[*Hint*: Write $x \ln x = (\ln x)/x^{-1}$.]

48. Find $\lim_{x \to 0^+} (\sqrt{x} \ln x)$.

[*Hint*: Write $\sqrt{x} \ln x = (\ln x)/x^{-1/2}$.]

In Problems 49–52, n is a positive integer. Find each limit.

49. $\lim_{x \to \infty} \dfrac{\ln x}{x^n}$

50. $\lim_{x \to \infty} \dfrac{x^n}{\ln x}$

51. $\lim_{x \to \infty} \dfrac{e^x}{x^n}$

52. $\lim_{x \to \infty} \dfrac{x^n}{e^x}$

In Problems 53–56, show that the repeated application of L'Hôpital's rule does not lead to a solution. Then use algebraic manipulation to evaluate each limit. [Hint: If $x > 0$ and $n > 0$, then $\sqrt[n]{x^n} = x$.]

Answers to Matched Problems

1. (A) ∞
   (B) ∞
   (C) 0
   (D) ∞

2. (A) ∞
   (B) 0
   (C) $-\infty$
   (D) ∞

3. e^4 **4.** ∞ **5.** 0 **6.** 2

7. $-\infty$ **8.** 2 **9.** 0 **10.** ∞

5-4   Curve-Sketching Techniques

- Modifying the Graphing Strategy
- Using the Graphing Strategy
- Modeling Average Cost

When we summarized the graphing strategy in Section 5-2, we omitted one important topic: asymptotes. Polynomial functions do not have any asymptotes. Asymptotes of rational functions were discussed in Section 3-3, but what about all the other functions, such as logarithmic and exponential functions? Since investigating asymptotes always involves limits, we can now use L'Hôpital's rule (Section 5-3) as a tool for finding asymptotes of many different types of functions.

Modifying the Graphing Strategy

The first version of the graphing strategy in Section 5-2 made no mention of asymptotes. Including information about asymptotes produces the following (and final) version of the graphing strategy.

PROCEDURE   Graphing Strategy (Final Version)

Step 1   *Analyze $f(x)$.*

(A)   Find the domain of f.

(B)   Find the intercepts.

(C)   Find asymptotes.

Step 2   *Analyze $f'(x)$.* Find the partition numbers for, and critical values of, $f'(x)$. Construct a sign chart for $f'(x)$, determine the intervals on which f is increasing and decreasing, and find local maxima and minima.

Step 3   *Analyze $f''(x)$.* Find the partition numbers of $f''(x)$. Construct a sign chart for $f''(x)$, determine the intervals on which the graph of f is concave upward and concave downward, and find inflection points.

Step 4   *Sketch the graph of f.* Draw asymptotes and locate intercepts, local maxima and minima, and inflection points. Sketch in what you know from steps 1–3. Plot additional points as needed and complete the sketch.

Using the Graphing Strategy

We will illustrate the graphing strategy with several examples. From now on, you should always use the final version of the graphing strategy. If a function does not have any asymptotes, simply state this fact.

EXAMPLE 1   **Using the Graphing Strategy**   Use the graphing strategy to analyze the function $f(x) = (x - 1)/(x - 2)$. State all the pertinent information and sketch the graph of f.

SOLUTION   **Step 1**   *Analyze $f(x)$.* $f(x) = \dfrac{x - 1}{x - 2}$

(A)   Domain: All real x, except $x = 2$

(B) y intercept: $f(0) = \dfrac{0 - 1}{0 - 2} = \dfrac{1}{2}$

x intercepts: Since a fraction is 0 when its numerator is 0 and its denominator is not 0, the x intercept is $x = 1$.

(C)   Horizontal asymptote: $\dfrac{a_m x^m}{b_n x^n} = \dfrac{x}{x} = 1$

So the line $y = 1$ is a horizontal asymptote.

Vertical asymptote: The denominator is 0 for $x = 2$, and the numerator is not 0 for this value. Therefore, the line $x = 2$ is a vertical asymptote.

Step 2   *Analyze $f'(x)$.* $f'(x) = \dfrac{(x - 2)(1) - (x - 1)(1)}{(x - 2)^2} = \dfrac{-1}{(x - 2)^2}$

Critical values of $f(x)$:   None

Partition number for $f'(x)$: $x = 2$

Sign chart for $f'(x)$:

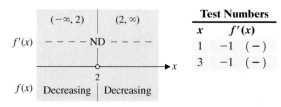

So $f(x)$ is decreasing on $(-\infty, 2)$ and $(2, \infty)$. There are no local extrema.

Step 3   *Analyze $f''(x)$.* $f''(x) = \dfrac{2}{(x - 2)^3}$

Partition number for $f''(x)$: $x = 2$

Sign chart for $f''(x)$:

	$(-\infty, 2)$	$(2, \infty)$
$f''(x)$	$----$ ND	$+++$

Test Numbers

x	$f''(x)$
1	-2 $(-)$
3	2 $(+)$

Graph of f — Concave downward / Concave upward

The graph of f is concave downward on $(-\infty, 2)$ and concave upward on $(2, \infty)$. Since $f(2)$ is not defined, there is no inflection point at $x = 2$, even though $f''(x)$ changes sign at $x = 2$.

Step 4 *Sketch the graph of f.* Insert intercepts and asymptotes, and plot a few additional points (for functions with asymptotes, plotting additional points is often helpful). Then sketch the graph.

x	$f(x)$
-2	$\frac{3}{4}$
0	$\frac{1}{2}$
1	0
$\frac{3}{2}$	-1
$\frac{5}{2}$	3
3	2
4	$\frac{3}{2}$

Matched Problem 1 Follow the graphing strategy and analyze the function $f(x) = 2x/(1 - x)$. State all the pertinent information and sketch the graph of f.

EXAMPLE 2 **Using the Graphing Strategy** Use the graphing strategy to analyze the function

$$g(x) = \frac{2x - 1}{x^2}$$

State all pertinent information and sketch the graph of g.

SOLUTION **Step 1** *Analyze $g(x)$.*

(A) Domain: All real x, except $x = 0$

(B) x intercept: $x = \dfrac{1}{2} = 0.5$

y intercept: Since 0 is not in the domain of g, there is no y intercept.

(C) Horizontal asymptote: $y = 0$ (the x axis)

Vertical asymptote: The denominator of $g(x)$ is 0 at $x = 0$ and the numerator is not. So the line $x = 0$ (the y axis) is a vertical asymptote.

Step 2 *Analyze $g'(x)$.*

$$g(x) = \frac{2x - 1}{x^2} = \frac{2}{x} - \frac{1}{x^2} = 2x^{-1} - x^{-2}$$

$$g'(x) = -2x^{-2} + 2x^{-3} = -\frac{2}{x^2} + \frac{2}{x^3} = \frac{-2x + 2}{x^3}$$

$$= \frac{2(1 - x)}{x^3}$$

Critical values of $g(x)$: $x = 1$

Partition numbers for $g'(x)$: $x = 0, x = 1$

Sign chart for $g'(x)$:

	$(-\infty, 0)$	$(0, 1)$	$(1, \infty)$
$g'(x)$	$- - - -$ ND	$+ + + +$ 0	$- - - -$

Function $f(x)$ is decreasing on $(-\infty, 0)$ and $(1, \infty)$, is increasing on $(0, 1)$, and has a local maximum at $x = 1$.

Step 3 *Analyze $g''(x)$.*

$$g'(x) = -2x^{-2} + 2x^{-3}$$

$$g''(x) = 4x^{-3} - 6x^{-4} = \frac{4}{x^3} - \frac{6}{x^4} = \frac{4x - 6}{x^4} = \frac{2(2x - 3)}{x^4}$$

Partition numbers for $g''(x)$: $x = 0, x = \dfrac{3}{2} = 1.5$

Sign chart for $g''(x)$:

	$(-\infty, 0)$	$(0, 1.5)$	$(1.5, \infty)$
$g''(x)$	$- - - -$ ND	$- - - - - -$ 0	$+ + + +$

Function $g(x)$ is concave downward on $(-\infty, 0)$ and $(0, 1.5)$, is concave upward on $(1.5, \infty)$, and has an inflection point at $x = 1.5$.

Step 4 *Sketch the graph of g.* Plot key points, note that the coordinate axes are asymptotes, and sketch the graph.

x	$g(x)$
-10	-0.21
-1	-3
0.5	0
1	1
1.5	0.89
10	0.19

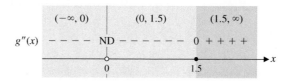

Matched Problem 2 Use the graphing strategy to analyze the function

$$h(x) = \frac{4x + 3}{x^2}$$

State all pertinent information and sketch the graph of h.

EXAMPLE 3 **Graphing Strategy** Follow the steps of the graphing strategy and analyze the function $f(x) = xe^x$. State all the pertinent information and sketch the graph of f.

SOLUTION **Step 1** Analyze $f(x)$: $f(x) = xe^x$.

(A) Domain: All real numbers

(B) y intercept: $f(0) = 0$

x intercept: $xe^x = 0$ for $x = 0$ only, since $e^x > 0$ for all x.

(C) Vertical asymptotes: None

Horizontal asymptotes: We use tables to determine the nature of the graph of f as $x \to \infty$ and $x \to -\infty$:

x	1	5	10	$\to \infty$
$f(x)$	2.72	742.07	220,264.66	$\to \infty$

x	-1	-5	-10	$\to -\infty$
$f(x)$	-0.37	-0.03	$-0.000\,45$	$\to 0$

Step 2 *Analyze $f'(x)$:*

$$f'(x) \;=\; x\frac{d}{dx}e^x + e^x\frac{d}{dx}x$$

$$= xe^x + e^x = e^x(x+1)$$

Critical value of $f(x)$: -1

Partition number for $f'(x)$: -1

Sign chart for $f'(x)$:

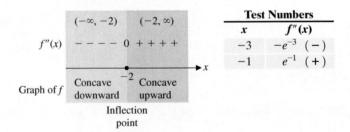

So $f(x)$ decreases on $(-\infty, -1)$, has a local minimum at $x = -1$, and increases on $(-1, \infty)$.

Step 3 *Analyze $f''(x)$:*

$$f''(x) \;=\; e^x\frac{d}{dx}(x+1) + (x+1)\frac{d}{dx}e^x$$

$$= e^x + (x+1)e^x = e^x(x+2)$$

Sign chart for $f''(x)$ (partition number is -2):

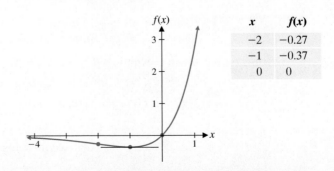

The graph of f is concave downward on $(-\infty, -2)$, has an inflection point at $x = -2$, and is concave upward on $(-2, \infty)$.

Step 4 *Sketch the graph of f, using the information from steps 1 to 3:*

x	$f(x)$
-2	-0.27
-1	-0.37
0	0

Matched Problem 3   Analyze the function $f(x) = xe^{-0.5x}$. State all the pertinent information and sketch the graph of f.

EXPLORE & DISCUSS 1   Refer to the discussion of vertical asymptotes in the solution of Example 3. We used tables of values to estimate limits at infinity and determine horizontal asymptotes. In some cases, the functions involved in these limits can be written in a form that allows us to use L'Hôpital's rule.

$$\overset{-\infty \cdot 0 \ form}{\lim_{x \to -\infty} f(x) = \lim_{x \to -\infty} xe^x} \qquad \textit{Rewrite as a fraction.}$$

$$= \overset{-\infty/\infty \ form}{\lim_{x \to -\infty} \frac{x}{e^{-x}}} \qquad \textit{Apply L'Hôpital's rule.}$$

$$= \lim_{x \to -\infty} \frac{1}{-e^{-x}} \qquad \textit{Simplify.}$$

$$= \lim_{x \to -\infty} (-e^x) \qquad \textit{Property of } e^x$$

$$= 0$$

Use algebraic manipulation and L'Hôpital's rule to verify the value of each of the following limits:

(A) $\lim\limits_{x \to \infty} xe^{-0.5x} = 0$

(B) $\lim\limits_{x \to 0^+} x^2(\ln x - 0.5) = 0$

(C) $\lim\limits_{x \to 0^+} x \ln x = 0$

EXAMPLE 4   **Graphing Strategy** Let $f(x) = x^2 \ln x - 0.5x^2$. Follow the steps in the graphing strategy and analyze this function. State all the pertinent information and sketch the graph of f.

SOLUTION   **Step 1** *Analyze $f(x)$:* $f(x) = x^2 \ln x - 0.5x^2 = x^2(\ln x - 0.5)$.

(A) Domain: $(0, \infty)$

(B) *y* intercept: None [$f(0)$ is not defined.]

   x intercept: Solve $x^2(\ln x - 0.5) = 0$

   $\ln x - 0.5 = 0$ or $x^2 = 0$ *Discard, since 0 is not in the domain of f.*

   $\ln x = 0.5$ *In x = a if and only if x = e^a.*

   $x = e^{0.5}$ *x intercept*

(C) Asymptotes: None. The following tables suggest the nature of the graph as $x \to 0^+$ and as $x \to \infty$:

x	0.1	0.01	0.001	$\to 0^+$	*See Explore &*
$f(x)$	−0.0280	−0.00051	−0.00007	$\to 0$	*Discuss 1(B).*

x	10	100	1,000	$\to \infty$	
$f(x)$	180	41,000	6,400,000	$\to \infty$	

Step 2 *Analyze $f'(x)$:*

$$f'(x) \;\; = x^2 \frac{d}{dx} \ln x + (\ln x) \frac{d}{dx} x^2 - 0.5 \frac{d}{dx} x^2$$

$$= x^2 \frac{1}{x} + (\ln x)\, 2x - 0.5(2x)$$

$$= x + 2x \ln x - x$$

$$= 2x \ln x$$

Critical value of $f(x)$: 1

Partition number for $f'(x)$: 1

Sign chart for $f'(x)$:

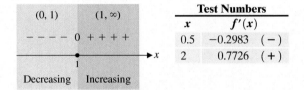

	Test Numbers	
x	*f′(x)*	
0.5	−0.2983	(−)
2	0.7726	(+)

The function $f(x)$ decreases on $(0, 1)$, has a local minimum at $x = 1$, and increases on $(1, \infty)$.

Step 3 *Analyze $f''(x)$:*

$$f''(x) \;\; = 2x \frac{d}{dx} (\ln x) + (\ln x) \frac{d}{dx} (2x)$$

$$= 2x \frac{1}{x} + (\ln x)\, 2$$

$$= 2 + 2 \ln x = 0$$

$$2 \ln x = -2$$

$$\ln x = -1$$

$$x = e^{-1} \approx 0.3679$$

Sign chart for $f'(x)$ (partition number is e^{-1}):

	Test Numbers	
x	*f′(x)*	
0.2	−1.2189	(−)
1	2	(+)

The graph of $f(x)$ is concave downward on $(0, e^{-1})$, has an inflection point at $x = e^{-1}$, and is concave upward on (e^{-1}, ∞).

Step 4 *Sketch the graph of f, using the information from steps 1 to 3:*

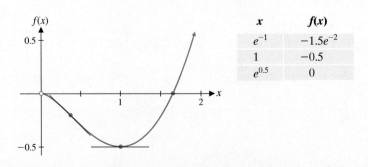

x	*f(x)*
e^{-1}	$-1.5e^{-2}$
1	-0.5
$e^{0.5}$	0

Matched Problem 4 Analyze the function $f(x) = x \ln x$. State all pertinent information and sketch the graph of f.

Modeling Average Cost

EXAMPLE 5 **Average Cost** Given the cost function $C(x) = 5{,}000 + 0.5x^2$, where x is the number of items produced, use the graphing strategy to analyze the graph of the average cost function. State all the pertinent information and sketch the graph of the average cost function. Find the marginal cost function and graph it on the same set of coordinate axes.

SOLUTION The average cost function is

$$\overline{C}(x) = \frac{5{,}000 + 0.5x^2}{x} = \frac{5{,}000}{x} + 0.5x$$

Step 1 *Analyze* $\overline{C}(x)$.

(A) Domain: Since negative values of x do not make sense and $\overline{C}(0)$ is not defined, the domain is the set of positive real numbers.

(B) Intercepts: None

(C) Horizontal asymptote: $\dfrac{a_m x^m}{b_n x^n} = \dfrac{0.5x^2}{x} = 0.5x$

So there is no horizontal asymptote.

Vertical asymptote: The line $x = 0$ is a vertical asymptote since the denominator is 0 and the numerator is not 0 for $x = 0$.

Oblique asymptotes: If a graph approaches a line that is neither horizontal nor vertical as x approaches ∞ or $-\infty$, then that line is called an **oblique asymptote**. If x is a large positive number, then $5{,}000/x$ is very small and

$$\overline{C}(x) = \frac{5{,}000}{x} + 0.5x \approx 0.5x$$

That is,

$$\lim_{x \to \infty} [\overline{C}(x) - 0.5x] = \lim_{x \to \infty} \frac{5{,}000}{x} = 0$$

This implies that the graph of $y = \overline{C}(x)$ approaches the line $y = 0.5x$ as x approaches ∞. That line is an oblique asymptote for the graph of $y = \overline{C}(x)$.*

Step 2 *Analyze* $\overline{C}'(x)$.

$$\overline{C}'(x) = -\frac{5{,}000}{x^2} + 0.5$$

$$= \frac{0.5x^2 - 5{,}000}{x^2}$$

$$= \frac{0.5(x - 100)(x + 100)}{x^2}$$

---

*If $f(x) = n(x)/d(x)$ is a rational function for which the degree of $n(x)$ is 1 more than the degree of $d(x)$, then we can use polynomial long division to write $f(x) = mx + b + r(x)/d(x)$, where the degree of $r(x)$ is less than the degree of $d(x)$. The line $y = mx + b$ is then an oblique asymptote for the graph of $y = f(x)$.

Critical value for $\overline{C}(x)$: 100
Partition numbers for $\overline{C}'(x)$: 0 and 100
Sign chart for $\overline{C}'(x)$:

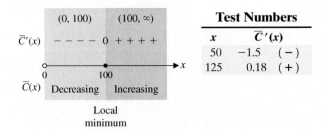

So $\overline{C}(x)$ is decreasing on $(0, 100)$, is increasing on $(100, \infty)$, and has a local minimum at $x = 100$.

Step 3 *Analyze $\overline{C}''(x)$:* $\overline{C}''(x) = \dfrac{10,000}{x^3}$.

$\overline{C}''(x)$ is positive for all positive x, so the graph of $y = \overline{C}(x)$ is concave upward on $(0, \infty)$.

Step 4 *Sketch the graph of $\overline{C}$.* The graph of $\overline{C}$ is shown in Figure 1.

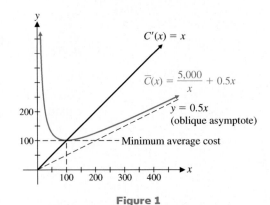

Figure 1

The marginal cost function is $C'(x) = x$. The graph of this linear function is also shown in Figure 1.

Figure 1 illustrates an important principle in economics:

> **The minimum average cost occurs when the average cost is equal to the marginal cost.**

Matched Problem 5 Given the cost function $C(x) = 1,600 + 0.25x^2$, where x is the number of items produced,

(A) Use the graphing strategy to analyze the graph of the average cost function. State all the pertinent information and sketch the graph of the average cost function. Find the marginal cost function and graph it on the same set of coordinate axes. Include any oblique asymptotes.

(B) Find the minimum average cost.

Exercises 5-4

A

1. Use the graph of *f* in the figure to identify the following:

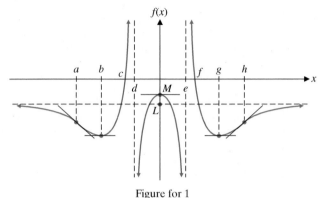

f(x)

Figure for 1

(A) the intervals on which $f'(x) < 0$

(B) the intervals on which $f'(x) > 0$

(C) the intervals on which $f(x)$ is increasing

(D) the intervals on which $f(x)$ is decreasing

(E) the x coordinate(s) of the point(s) where $f(x)$ has a local maximum

(F) the x coordinate(s) of the point(s) where $f(x)$ has a local minimum

(G) the intervals on which $f''(x) < 0$

(H) the intervals on which $f''(x) > 0$

(I) the intervals on which the graph of f is concave upward

(J) the intervals on which the graph of f is concave downward

(K) the x coordinate(s) of the inflection point(s)

(L) the horizontal asymptote(s)

(M) the vertical asymptote(s)

2. Repeat Problem 1 for the following graph of *f*:

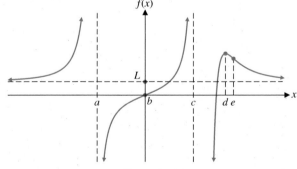

f(x)

Figure for 2

In Problems 3–10, use the given information to sketch the graph of f. Assume that f is continuous on its domain and that all intercepts are included in the table of values.

3. Domain: All real x; $\lim_{x \to \pm\infty} f(x) = 2$

x	-4	-2	0	2	4
$f(x)$	0	-2	0	-2	0

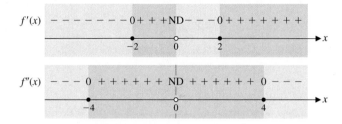

4. Domain: All real x; $\lim_{x \to -\infty} f(x) = -3$; $\lim_{x \to \infty} f(x) = 3$

x	-2	-1	0	1	2
$f(x)$	0	2	0	-2	0

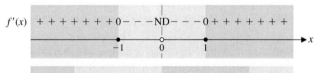

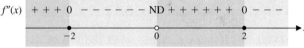

5. Domain: All real x, except $x = -2$;
$\lim_{x \to -2^-} f(x) = \infty$; $\lim_{x \to -2^+} f(x) = -\infty$; $\lim_{x \to \infty} f(x) = 1$

x	-4	0	4	6
$f(x)$	0	0	3	2

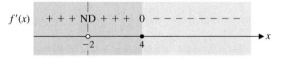

6. Domain: All real x, except
$x = 1$; $\lim_{x \to 1^-} f(x) = \infty$; $\lim_{x \to 1^+} f(x) = \infty$; $\lim_{x \to \infty} f(x) = -2$

x	-4	-2	0	2
$f(x)$	0	-2	0	0

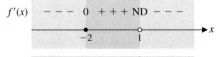

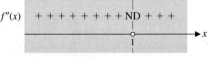

7. Domain: All real x, except $x = -1$;

$f(-3) = 2, f(-2) = 3, f(0) = -1, f(1) = 0$;

$f'(x) > 0$ on $(-\infty, -1)$ and $(-1, \infty)$;

$f''(x) > 0$ on $(-\infty, -1)$; $f''(x) < 0$ on $(-1, \infty)$;

vertical asymptote: $x = -1$;

horizontal asymptote: $y = 1$

8. Domain: All real x, except $x = 1$;

$f(0) = -2, f(2) = 0$;

$f'(x) < 0$ on $(-\infty, 1)$ and $(1, \infty)$;

$f''(x) < 0$ on $(-\infty, 1)$;

$f''(x) > 0$ on $(1, \infty)$;

vertical asymptote: $x = 1$;

horizontal asymptote: $y = -1$

9. Domain: All real x, except $x = -2$ and $x = 2$;

$f(-3) = -1, f(0) = 0, f(3) = 1$;

$f'(x) < 0$ on $(-\infty, -2)$ and $(2, \infty)$;

$f'(x) > 0$ on $(-2, 2)$;

$f''(x) < 0$ on $(-\infty, -2)$ and $(-2, 0)$;

$f''(x) > 0$ on $(0, 2)$ and $(2, \infty)$;

vertical asymptotes: $x = -2$ and $x = 2$;

horizontal asymptote: $y = 0$

10. Domain: All real x, except $x = -1$ and $x = 1$;

$f(-2) = 1, f(0) = 0, f(2) = 1$;

$f'(x) > 0$ on $(-\infty, -1)$ and $(0, 1)$;

$f'(x) < 0$ on $(-1, 0)$ and $(1, \infty)$;

$f''(x) > 0$ on $(-\infty, -1), (-1, 1)$, and $(1, \infty)$;

vertical asymptotes: $x = -1$ and $x = 1$;

horizontal asymptote: $y = 0$

In Problems 11–16, find the domain and intercepts.

11. $f(x) = \sqrt{x + 4}$

12. $f(x) = \sqrt{x + 25}$

13. $f(x) = 75 - 5x$

14. $f(x) = 4x + 52$

15. $f(x) = \dfrac{95}{x - 5}$

16. $f(x) = \dfrac{102}{x + 3}$

In Problems 17–56, summarize the pertinent information obtained by applying the graphing strategy and sketch the graph of $y = f(x)$.

17. $f(x) = \dfrac{x + 3}{x - 3}$

18. $f(x) = \dfrac{2x - 4}{x + 2}$

19. $f(x) = \dfrac{x}{x - 2}$

20. $f(x) = \dfrac{2 + x}{3 - x}$

21. $f(x) = 5 + 5e^{-0.1x}$

22. $f(x) = 3 + 7e^{-0.2x}$

23. $f(x) = 5xe^{-0.2x}$

24. $f(x) = 10xe^{-0.1x}$

25. $f(x) = \ln(1 - x)$

26. $f(x) = \ln(2x + 4)$

27. $f(x) = x - \ln x$

28. $f(x) = \ln(x^2 + 4)$

29. $f(x) = \dfrac{x}{x^2 - 4}$

30. $f(x) = \dfrac{1}{x^2 - 4}$

31. $f(x) = \dfrac{1}{1 + x^2}$

32. $f(x) = \dfrac{x^2}{1 + x^2}$

33. $f(x) = \dfrac{2x}{1 - x^2}$

34. $f(x) = \dfrac{2x}{x^2 - 9}$

35. $f(x) = \dfrac{-5x}{(x - 1)^2}$

36. $f(x) = \dfrac{x}{(x - 2)^2}$

37. $f(x) = \dfrac{x^2 + x - 2}{x^2}$

38. $f(x) = \dfrac{x^2 - 5x - 6}{x^2}$

39. $f(x) = \dfrac{x^2}{x - 1}$

40. $f(x) = \dfrac{x^2}{2 + x}$

41. $f(x) = \dfrac{3x^2 + 2}{x^2 - 9}$

42. $f(x) = \dfrac{2x^2 + 5}{4 - x^2}$

43. $f(x) = \dfrac{x^3}{x - 2}$

44. $f(x) = \dfrac{x^3}{4 - x}$

45. $f(x) = (3 - x)e^x$

46. $f(x) = (x - 2)e^x$

47. $f(x) = e^{-0.5x^2}$

48. $f(x) = e^{-2x^2}$

49. $f(x) = x^2 \ln x$

50. $f(x) = \dfrac{\ln x}{x}$

51. $f(x) = (\ln x)^2$

52. $f(x) = \dfrac{x}{\ln x}$

53. $f(x) = \dfrac{1}{x^2 + 2x - 8}$

54. $f(x) = \dfrac{1}{3 - 2x - x^2}$

55. $f(x) = \dfrac{x^3}{3 - x^2}$

56. $f(x) = \dfrac{x^3}{x^2 - 12}$

In Problems 57–64, show that the line $y = x$ is an oblique asymptote for the graph of $y = f(x)$, summarize all pertinent information obtained by applying the graphing strategy, and sketch the graph of $y = f(x)$.

57. $f(x) = x + \dfrac{4}{x}$

58. $f(x) = x - \dfrac{9}{x}$

59. $f(x) = x - \dfrac{4}{x^2}$

60. $f(x) = x + \dfrac{32}{x^2}$

61. $f(x) = x - \dfrac{9}{x^3}$

62. $f(x) = x + \dfrac{27}{x^3}$

63. $f(x) = x + \dfrac{1}{x} + \dfrac{4}{x^3}$

64. $f(x) = x - \dfrac{16}{x^3}$

In Problems 65–72, summarize all pertinent information obtained by applying the graphing strategy, and sketch the graph of $y = f(x)$. [Note: These rational functions are not reduced to lowest terms.]

65. $f(x) = \dfrac{x^2 + x - 6}{x^2 - 6x + 8}$

66. $f(x) = \dfrac{x^2 + x - 6}{x^2 - x - 12}$

67. $f(x) = \dfrac{2x^2 + x - 15}{x^2 - 9}$

68. $f(x) = \dfrac{2x^2 + 11x + 14}{x^2 - 4}$

69. $f(x) = \dfrac{x^3 - 5x^2 + 6x}{x^2 - x - 2}$

70. $f(x) = \dfrac{x^3 - 5x^2 - 6x}{x^2 + 3x + 2}$

71. $f(x) = \dfrac{x^2 + x - 2}{x^2 - 2x + 1}$

72. $f(x) = \dfrac{x^2 + x - 2}{x^2 + 4x + 4}$

Applications

73. Revenue. The marketing research department for a computer company used a large city to test market the firm's new laptop. The department found that the relationship between price p (dollars per unit) and demand x (units sold per week) was given approximately by

$$p = 1{,}296 - 0.12x^2 \qquad 0 \le x \le 80$$

So, weekly revenue can be approximated by

$$R(x) = xp = 1{,}296x - 0.12x^3 \qquad 0 \le x \le 80$$

Graph the revenue function R.

74. Profit. Suppose that the cost function $C(x)$ (in dollars) for the company in Problem 73 is

$$C(x) = 830 + 396x$$

(A) Write an equation for the profit $P(x)$.

(B) Graph the profit function P.

75. Pollution. In Silicon Valley, a number of computer firms were found to be contaminating underground water supplies with toxic chemicals stored in leaking underground containers. A water quality control agency ordered the companies to take immediate corrective action and contribute to a monetary pool for the testing and cleanup of the underground contamination. Suppose that the required monetary pool (in millions of dollars) is given by

$$P(x) = \frac{2x}{1 - x} \qquad 0 \le x < 1$$

where x is the percentage (expressed as a decimal fraction) of the total contaminant removed.

(A) Where is $P(x)$ increasing? Decreasing?

(B) Where is the graph of P concave upward? Downward?

(C) Find any horizontal and vertical asymptotes.

(D) Find the x and y intercepts.

(E) Sketch a graph of P.

76. Employee training. A company producing dive watches has established that, on average, a new employee can assemble $N(t)$ dive watches per day after t days of on-the-job training, as given by

$$N(t) = \frac{100t}{t + 9} \qquad t \ge 0$$

(A) Where is $N(t)$ increasing? Decreasing?

(B) Where is the graph of N concave upward? Downward?

(C) Find any horizontal and vertical asymptotes.

(D) Find the intercepts.

(E) Sketch a graph of N.

77. Replacement time. An outboard motor has an initial price of $3,200. A service contract costs $300 for the first year and increases $100 per year thereafter. The total cost of the outboard motor (in dollars) after n years is given by

$$C(n) = 3{,}200 + 250n + 50n^2 \qquad n \ge 1$$

(A) Write an expression for the average cost per year, $\overline{C}(n)$, for n years.

(B) Graph the average cost function found in part (A).

(C) When is the average cost per year minimum? (This time is frequently referred to as the **replacement time** for this piece of equipment.)

78. Construction costs. The management of a manufacturing plant wishes to add a fenced-in rectangular storage yard of 20,000 square feet, using a building as one side of the yard (see the figure). If x is the distance (in feet) from the building to the fence, show that the length of the fence required for the yard is given by

$$L(x) = 2x + \frac{20{,}000}{x} \qquad x > 0$$

Storage yard

x

Figure for 78

(A) Graph L.

(B) What are the dimensions of the rectangle requiring the least amount of fencing?

79. Average and marginal costs. The total daily cost (in dollars) of producing x mountain bikes is given by

$$C(x) = 1{,}000 + 5x + 0.1x^2$$

(A) Sketch the graphs of the average cost function and the marginal cost function on the same set of coordinate axes. Include any oblique asymptotes.

(B) Find the minimum average cost.

80. Average and marginal costs. The total daily cost (in dollars) of producing x city bikes is given by

$$C(x) = 500 + 2x + 0.2x^2$$

(A) Sketch the graphs of the average cost function and the marginal cost function on the same set of coordinate axes. Include any oblique asymptotes.

(B) Find the minimum average cost.

81. Minimizing average costs. The table gives the total daily costs y (in dollars) of producing x pepperoni pizzas at various production levels.

Number of Pizzas	Total Costs
x	y
50	395
100	475
150	640
200	910
250	1,140
300	1,450

(A) Enter the data into a graphing calculator and find a quadratic regression equation for the total costs.

(B) Use the regression equation from part (A) to find the minimum average cost (to the nearest cent) and the corresponding production level (to the nearest integer).

82. Minimizing average costs. The table gives the total daily costs y (in dollars) of producing x deluxe pizzas at various production levels.

Number of Pizzas	Total Costs
x	y
50	595
100	755
150	1,110
200	1,380
250	1,875
300	2,410

(A) Enter the data into a graphing calculator and find a quadratic regression equation for the total costs.

(B) Use the regression equation from part (A) to find the minimum average cost (to the nearest cent) and the corresponding production level (to the nearest integer).

83. Medicine. A drug is injected into the bloodstream of a patient through her right arm. The drug concentration in the bloodstream of the left arm t hours after the injection is given by

$$C(t) = \frac{0.14t}{t^2 + 1}$$

Graph C.

84. Physiology. In a study on the speed of muscle contraction in frogs under various loads, researchers found that the speed of contraction decreases with increasing loads. More precisely, they found that the relationship between speed of

contraction, S (in centimeters per second), and load w (in grams) is given approximately by

$$S(w) = \frac{26 + 0.06w}{w} \qquad w \geq 5$$

Graph S.

85. Psychology: retention. Each student in a psychology class is given one day to memorize the same list of 30 special characters. The lists are turned in at the end of the day, and for each succeeding day for 30 days, each student is asked to turn in a list of as many of the symbols as can be recalled. Averages are taken, and it is found that

$$N(t) = \frac{5t + 20}{t} \qquad t \geq 1$$

provides a good approximation of the average number $N(t)$ of symbols retained after t days. Graph N.

Answers to Matched Problems

1. Domain: All real x, except $x = 1$
y intercept: $f(0) = 0$; x intercept: 0
Horizontal asymptote: $y = -2$;
vertical asymptote: $x = 1$
Increasing on $(-\infty, 1)$ and $(1, \infty)$
Concave upward on $(-\infty, 1)$; concave downward on $(1, \infty)$

x	$f(x)$
-1	-1
0	0
$\frac{1}{2}$	2
$\frac{3}{2}$	-6
2	-4
5	$-\frac{5}{2}$

2. Domain: All real x, except $x = 0$
x intercept: $= -\frac{3}{4} = -0.75$
$h(0)$ is not defined
Vertical asymptote: $x = 0$ (the y axis)
Horizontal asymptote: $y = 0$ (the x axis)
Increasing on $(-1.5, 0)$
Decreasing on $(-\infty, -1.5)$ and $(0, \infty)$
Local minimum at $x = 1.5$
Concave upward on $(-2.25, 0)$ and $(0, \infty)$
Concave downward on $(-\infty, -2.25)$
Inflection point at $x = -2.25$

x	$h(x)$
-10	-0.37
-2.25	-1.19
-1.5	-1.33
-0.75	0
2	2.75
10	0.43

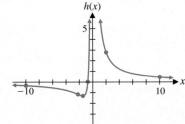

3. Domain: $(-\infty, \infty)$
y intercept: $f(0) = 0$
x intercept: $x = 0$
Horizontal asymptote: $y = 0$ (the x axis)
Increasing on $(-\infty, 2)$
Decreasing on $(2, \infty)$
Local maximum at $x = 2$
Concave downward on $(-\infty, 4)$
Concave upward on $(4, \infty)$
Inflection point at $x = 4$

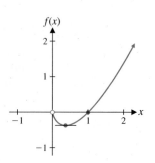

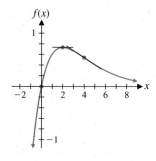

4. Domain: $(0, \infty)$
y intercept: None [$f(0)$ is not defined]
x intercept: $x = 1$
Increasing on (e^{-1}, ∞)
Decreasing on $(0, e^{-1})$
Local minimum at $x = e^{-1} \approx 0.368$
Concave upward on $(0, \infty)$

x	5	10	100	$\to \infty$
$f(x)$	8.05	23.03	460.52	$\to \infty$

x	0.1	0.01	0.001	0.000 1	$\to 0$
$f(x)$	-0.23	-0.046	$-0.006\,9$	$-0.000\,92$	$\to 0$

5. (A) Domain: $(0, \infty)$
Intercepts: None
Vertical asymptote: $x = 0$; oblique asymptote: $y = 0.25x$
Decreasing on $(0, 80)$; increasing on $(80, \infty)$; local minimum at $x = 80$
Concave upward on $(0, \infty)$

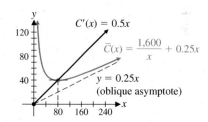

(B) Minimum average cost is 40 at $x = 80$.

5-5 Absolute Maxima and Minima

- Absolute Maxima and Minima
- Second Derivative and Extrema

Now we will consider one of the most important applications of the derivative: finding the absolute maximum or minimum value of a function. An economist may be interested in the price or production level of a commodity that will bring a maximum profit; a doctor may be interested in the time it takes for a drug to reach its maximum concentration in the bloodstream after an injection; and a city planner might be interested in the location of heavy industry in a city in order to produce minimum pollution in residential and business areas. In this section, we develop the procedures needed to find the absolute maximum and absolute minimum values of a function.

Absolute Maxima and Minima

Recall that $f(c)$ is a local maximum value if $f(x) \le f(c)$ for x near c and a local minimum value if $f(x) \ge f(c)$ for x near c. Now we are interested in finding the largest and the smallest values of $f(x)$ throughout its domain.

DEFINITION   Absolute Maxima and Minima

If $f(c) \geq f(x)$ for all x in the domain of f, then $f(c)$ is called the **absolute maximum value** of f.

If $f(c) \leq f(x)$ for all x in the domain of f, then $f(c)$ is called the **absolute minimum value** of f.

Figure 1 illustrates some typical examples.

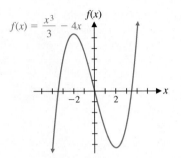

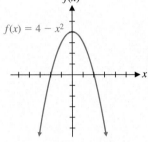

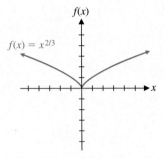

(A) No absolute maximum or minimum
One local maximum at $x = -2$
One local minimum at $x = 2$

(B) Absolute maximum at $x = 0$
No absolute minimum

(C) Absolute minimum at $x = 0$
No absolute maximum

Figure 1

CONCEPTUAL INSIGHT

If $f(c)$ is the absolute maximum value of a function f, then $f(c)$ is obviously a "value" of f. It is common practice to omit "value" and to refer to $f(c)$ as the **absolute maximum** of f. In either usage, note that c is a value of x in the domain of f where the absolute maximum occurs. It is incorrect to refer to c as the absolute maximum. Collectively, the absolute maximum and the absolute minimum are referred to as **absolute extrema**.

In many applications, the domain of a function is restricted because of practical or physical considerations. If the domain is restricted to some closed interval, as is often the case, then Theorem 1 applies.

THEOREM 1   Extreme Value Theorem
A function f that is continuous on a closed interval $[a, b]$ has both an absolute maximum value and an absolute minimum value on that interval.

It is important to understand that the absolute maximum and minimum values depend on both the function f and the interval $[a, b]$. Figure 2 illustrates four cases.

In all four cases illustrated in Figure 2, the absolute maximum value and absolute minimum value occur at a critical value or an endpoint. This property is generalized in Theorem 2. Note that both the absolute maximum value and the absolute minimum value are unique, but each can occur at more than one point in the interval (Fig. 2D).

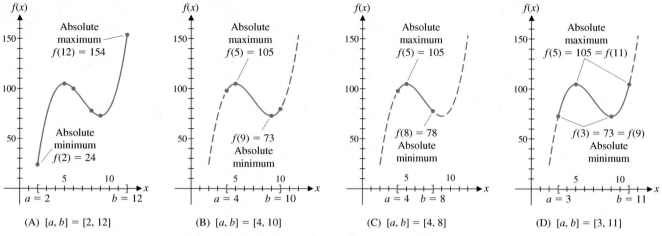

Figure 2 Absolute extrema for $f(x) = x^3 - 21x^2 + 135x - 170$ for various closed intervals

---

THEOREM 2   Locating Absolute Extrema
Absolute extrema (if they exist) must always occur at critical values or at endpoints.

To find the absolute maximum or minimum value of a continuous function on a closed interval, we simply identify the endpoints and critical values in the interval, evaluate the function at each, and then choose the largest and smallest values out of this group.

PROCEDURE Finding Absolute Extrema on a Closed Interval

Step 1   Check to make certain that f is continuous over $[a, b]$.

Step 2   Find the critical values in the interval (a, b).

Step 3   Evaluate f at the endpoints a and b and at the critical values found in step 2.

Step 4   The absolute maximum $f(x)$ on $[a, b]$ is the largest value found in step 3.

Step 5   The absolute minimum $f(x)$ on $[a, b]$ is the smallest value found in step 3.

EXAMPLE 1   **Finding Absolute Extrema** Find the absolute maximum and absolute minimum values of

$$f(x) = x^3 + 3x^2 - 9x - 7$$

on each of the following intervals:

(A) $[-6, 4]$ (B) $[-4, 2]$ (C) $[-2, 2]$

SOLUTION   (A) The function is continuous for all values of x.

$$f'(x) = 3x^2 + 6x - 9 = 3(x - 1)(x + 3)$$

So, $x = -3$ and $x = 1$ are critical values in the interval $(-6, 4)$. Evaluate f at the endpoints and critical values $(-6, -3, 1,$ and $4)$, and choose the maximum and minimum from these:

$$f(-6) = -61 \quad \text{Absolute minimum}$$

$$f(-3) = 20$$

$$f(1) = -12$$

$$f(4) = 69 \quad \text{Absolute maximum}$$

(B) Interval: $[-4, 2]$

x	$f(x)$	
-4	13	
-3	20	Absolute maximum
1	-12	Absolute minimum
2	-5	

(C) Interval: $[-2, 2]$

x	$f(x)$	
-2	15	Absolute maximum
1	-12	Absolute minimum
2	-5	

The critical value x $= -3$ is not included in this table, because it is not in the interval $[-2, 2]$.

Matched Problem 1 Find the absolute maximum and absolute minimum values of

$$f(x) = x^3 - 12x$$

on each of the following intervals:

(A) $[-5, 5]$ (B) $[-3, 3]$ (C) $[-3, 1]$

Now, suppose that we want to find the absolute maximum or minimum value of a function that is continuous on an interval that is not closed. Since Theorem 1 no longer applies, we cannot be certain that the absolute maximum or minimum value exists. Figure 3 illustrates several ways that functions can fail to have absolute extrema.

In general, the best procedure to follow in searching for absolute extrema on an interval that is not of the form [*a*, *b*] is to sketch a graph of the function. However, many applications can be solved with a new tool that does not require any graphing.

Second Derivative and Extrema

The second derivative can be used to classify the local extrema of a function. Suppose that f is a function satisfying $f'(c) = 0$ and $f''(c) > 0$. First, note that if $f''(c) > 0$, then it follows from the properties of limits* that $f''(x) > 0$ in some

---

*Actually, we are assuming that $f''(x)$ is continuous in an interval containing c. It is unlikely that we will encounter a function for which $f''(c)$ exists but $f''(x)$ is not continuous in an interval containing c.

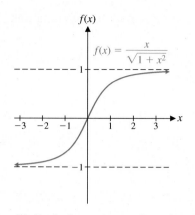

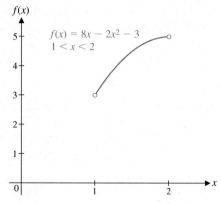

(A) No absolute extrema on $(-\infty, \infty)$:
$-1 < f(x) < 1$ for all x
$[f(x) \neq 1$ or -1 for any $x]$

(B) No absolute extrema on $(1, 2)$:
$3 < f(x) < 5$ for $x \in (1, 2)$
$[f(x) \neq 3$ or 5 for any $x \in (1, 2)]$

(C) No absolute extrema on $(-1, 1)$:
Graph has vertical asymptotes
at $x = -1$ and $x = 1$

Figure 3 Functions with no absolute extrema

interval (m, n) containing c. Thus, the graph of f must be concave upward in this interval. But this implies that $f'(x)$ is increasing in the interval. Since $f'(c) = 0$, $f'(x)$ must change from negative to positive at $x = c$, and $f(c)$ is a local minimum (see Fig. 4). Reasoning in the same fashion, we conclude that if $f'(c) = 0$ and $f''(c) < 0$, then $f(c)$ is a local maximum. Of course, it is possible that both $f'(c) = 0$ and $f''(c) = 0$. In this case, the second derivative cannot be used to determine the shape of the graph around $x = c$; $f(c)$ may be a local minimum, a local maximum, or neither.

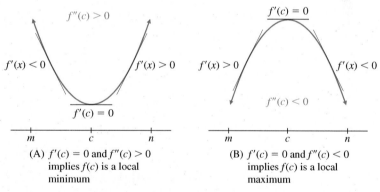

(A) $f'(c) = 0$ and $f''(c) > 0$
implies $f(c)$ is a local
minimum

(B) $f'(c) = 0$ and $f''(c) < 0$
implies $f(c)$ is a local
maximum

Figure 4 Second derivative and local extrema

The sign of the second derivative provides a simple test for identifying local maxima and minima. This test is most useful when we do not want to draw the graph of the function. If we are interested in drawing the graph and have already constructed the sign chart for $f'(x)$, then the first-derivative test can be used to identify the local extrema.

RESULT   Second-Derivative Test

Let c be a critical value of $f(x)$.

$f'(c)$	$f''(c)$	Graph of f is:	$f(c)$	Example
0	+	Concave upward	Local minimum	⌣
0	−	Concave downward	Local maximum	⌢
0	0	?	Test does not apply	

EXAMPLE 2 **Testing Local Extrema** Find the local maxima and minima for each function. Use the second-derivative test when it applies.

(A) $f(x) = x^3 - 6x^2 + 9x + 1$

(B) $f(x) = xe^{-0.2x}$

(C) $f(x) = \frac{1}{6}x^6 - 4x^5 + 25x^4$

SOLUTION (A) Take first and second derivatives and find critical values:

$$f(x) = x^3 - 6x^2 + 9x + 1$$

$$f'(x) = 3x^2 - 12x + 9 = 3(x - 1)(x - 3)$$

$$f''(x) = 6x - 12 = 6(x - 2)$$

Critical values are $x = 1$ and $x = 3$.

$$f''(1) = -6 < 0 \qquad f\text{ has a local maximum at } x = 1.$$

$$f''(3) = 6 > 0 \qquad f\text{ has a local minimum at } x = 3.$$

(B) $$f(x) = xe^{-0.2x}$$

$$f'(x) = e^{-0.2x} + xe^{-0.2x}(-0.2)$$

$$= e^{-0.2x}(1 - 0.2x)$$

$$f''(x) = e^{-0.2x}(-0.2)(1 - 0.2x) + e^{-0.2x}(-0.2)$$

$$= e^{-0.2x}(0.04x - 0.4)$$

Critical value: $x = 1/0.2 = 5$

$f''(5) = e^{-1}(-0.2) < 0$

f has a local maximum at $x = 5$.

(C) $$f(x) = \frac{1}{6}x^6 - 4x^5 + 25x^4$$

$$f'(x) = x^5 - 20x^4 + 100x^3 = x^3(x - 10)^2$$

$$f''(x) = 5x^4 - 80x^3 + 300x^2$$

Critical values are $x = 0$ and $x = 10$.

$$f''(0) = 0 \qquad \text{The second-derivative test fails at both critical values, so}$$

$$f''(10) = 0 \qquad \text{the first-derivative test must be used.}$$

Sign chart for $f'(x) = x^3(x - 10)^2$ (partition numbers are 0 and 10):

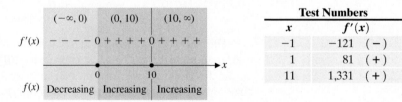

	$(-\infty, 0)$	$(0, 10)$	$(10, \infty)$
$f'(x)$	$- - - - 0$	$+ + + + 0$	$+ + + +$
$f(x)$	Decreasing	Increasing	Increasing

Test Numbers	
x	$f'(x)$
-1	-121 $(-)$
1	81 $(+)$
11	$1,331$ $(+)$

From the chart, we see that $f(x)$ has a local minimum at $x = 0$ and does not have a local extremum at $x = 10$.

Matched Problem 2 Find the local maxima and minima for each function. Use the second-derivative test when it applies.

(A) $f(x) = x^3 - 9x^2 + 24x - 10$

(B) $f(x) = e^x - 5x$

(C) $f(x) = 10x^6 - 24x^5 + 15x^4$

CONCEPTUAL INSIGHT

The second-derivative test does not apply if $f''(c) = 0$ or if $f''(c)$ is not defined. As Example 2C illustrates, if $f''(c) = 0$, then $f(c)$ may or may not be a local extremum. Some other method, such as the first-derivative test, must be used when $f''(c) = 0$ or $f''(c)$ does not exist.

The solution of many optimization problems involves searching for an absolute extremum. If the function in question has only one critical value, then the second-derivative test not only classifies the local extremum but also guarantees that the local extremum is, in fact, the absolute extremum.

THEOREM 3   Second-Derivative Test for Absolute Extremum

Let f be continuous on an interval I with only one critical value c in I.

If $f'(c) = 0$ and $f''(c) > 0$, then $f(c)$ is the absolute minimum of f on I.

If $f'(c) = 0$ and $f''(c) < 0$, then $f(c)$ is the absolute maximum of f on I.

Since the second-derivative test cannot be applied when $f''(c) = 0$ or $f''(c)$ does not exist, Theorem 3 makes no mention of these cases.

EXAMPLE 3   **Finding an Absolute Extremum on an Open Interval** Find the absolute minimum value of each function on $(0, \infty)$.

(A) $f(x) = x + \dfrac{4}{x}$

(B) $f(x) = (\ln x)^2 - 3 \ln x$

SOLUTION   (A) $f(x) = x + \dfrac{4}{x}$

$$f'(x) = 1 - \frac{4}{x^2} = \frac{x^2 - 4}{x^2} = \frac{(x-2)(x+2)}{x^2} \qquad \textit{Critical values are } x = -2 \textit{ and } x = 2.$$

$$f''(x) = \frac{8}{x^3}$$

The only critical value in the interval $(0, \infty)$ is $x = 2$. Since $f''(2) = 1 > 0$, $f(2) = 4$ is the absolute minimum value of f on $(0, \infty)$.

(B) $f(x) = (\ln x)^2 - 3 \ln x$

$$f'(x) = (2 \ln x)\frac{1}{x} - \frac{3}{x} = \frac{2 \ln x - 3}{x} \qquad \textit{Critical value is } x = e^{3/2}.$$

$$f''(x) = \frac{x\dfrac{2}{x} - (2 \ln x - 3)}{x^2} = \frac{5 - 2 \ln x}{x^2}$$

The only critical value in the interval $(0, \infty)$ is $x = e^{3/2}$. Since $f''(e^{3/2}) = 2/e^3 > 0$, $f(e^{3/2}) = -2.25$ is the absolute minimum value of f on $(0, \infty)$.

Matched Problem 3 Find the absolute maximum value of each function on $(0, \infty)$.

(A) $f(x) = 12 - x - \dfrac{5}{x}$ (B) $f(x) = 5 \ln x - x$

Exercises 5-5

A

Problems 1–10 refer to the graph of $y = f(x)$ shown here. Find the absolute minimum and the absolute maximum over the indicated interval.

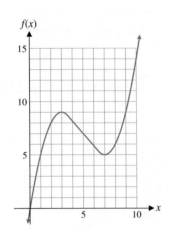

Figure for 1–10

1. $[0, 10]$ 2. $[2, 8]$ 3. $[0, 8]$ 4. $[2, 10]$
5. $[1, 10]$ 6. $[0, 9]$ 7. $[1, 9]$ 8. $[0, 2]$
9. $[2, 5]$ 10. $[5, 8]$

In Problems 11–16, find the absolute maximum and absolute minimum of each function on the given interval.

11. $f(x) = 4x + 9$ on $[2, 3]$ 12. $f(x) = -3x + 20$ on $[-2, 6]$
13. $f(x) = e^{-x}$ on $[-1, 1]$ 14. $f(x) = \ln x$ on $[1, 2]$
15. $f(x) = 9 - x^2$ on $[-4, 4]$
16. $f(x) = x^2 - 6x + 7$ on $[0, 10]$

In Problems 17–32, find the absolute maximum and minimum, if either exists, for each function.

17. $f(x) = x^2 - 2x + 3$ 18. $f(x) = x^2 + 4x - 3$
19. $f(x) = -x^2 - 6x + 9$ 20. $f(x) = -x^2 + 2x + 4$
21. $f(x) = x^3 + x$ 22. $f(x) = -x^3 - 2x$
23. $f(x) = 8x^3 - 2x^4$ 24. $f(x) = x^4 - 4x^3$
25. $f(x) = x + \dfrac{16}{x}$ 26. $f(x) = x + \dfrac{25}{x}$
27. $f(x) = \dfrac{x^2}{x^2 + 1}$ 28. $f(x) = \dfrac{1}{x^2 + 1}$

29. $f(x) = \dfrac{2x}{x^2 + 1}$ 30. $f(x) = \dfrac{-8x}{x^2 + 4}$
31. $f(x) = \dfrac{x^2 - 1}{x^2 + 1}$ 32. $f(x) = \dfrac{9 - x^2}{x^2 + 4}$

B

In Problems 33–56, find the indicated extremum of each function on the given interval.

33. Absolute minimum value on $[0, \infty)$ for
$$f(x) = 2x^2 - 8x + 6$$

34. Absolute maximum value on $[0, \infty)$ for
$$f(x) = 6x - x^2 + 4$$

35. Absolute maximum value on $[0, \infty)$ for
$$f(x) = 3x^2 - x^3$$

36. Absolute minimum value on $[0, \infty)$ for
$$f(x) = x^3 - 6x^2$$

37. Absolute minimum value on $[0, \infty)$ for
$$f(x) = (x + 4)(x - 2)^2$$

38. Absolute minimum value on $[0, \infty)$ for
$$f(x) = (2 - x)(x + 1)^2$$

39. Absolute maximum value on $(0, \infty)$ for
$$f(x) = 2x^4 - 8x^3$$

40. Absolute maximum value on $(0, \infty)$ for
$$f(x) = 4x^3 - 8x^4$$

41. Absolute maximum value on $(0, \infty)$ for
$$f(x) = 20 - 3x - \dfrac{12}{x}$$

42. Absolute minimum value on $(0, \infty)$ for
$$f(x) = 4 + x + \dfrac{9}{x}$$

43. Absolute maximum value on $(0, \infty)$ for
$$f(x) = 10 + 2x + \dfrac{64}{x^2}$$

44. Absolute maximum value on $(0, \infty)$ for
$$f(x) = 20 - 4x - \dfrac{250}{x^2}$$

45. Absolute minimum value on $(0, \infty)$ for

$$f(x) = x + \frac{1}{x} + \frac{30}{x^3}$$

46. Absolute minimum value on $(0, \infty)$ for

$$f(x) = 2x + \frac{5}{x} + \frac{4}{x^3}$$

47. Absolute minimum value on $(0, \infty)$ for

$$f(x) = \frac{e^x}{x^2}$$

48. Absolute maximum value on $(0, \infty)$ for

$$f(x) = \frac{x^4}{e^x}$$

49. Absolute maximum value on $(0, \infty)$ for

$$f(x) = \frac{x^3}{e^x}$$

50. Absolute minimum value on $(0, \infty)$ for

$$f(x) = \frac{e^x}{x}$$

51. Absolute maximum value on $(0, \infty)$ for

$$f(x) = 5x - 2x \ln x$$

52. Absolute minimum value on $(0, \infty)$ for

$$f(x) = 4x \ln x - 7x$$

53. Absolute maximum value on $(0, \infty)$ for

$$f(x) = x^2(3 - \ln x)$$

54. Absolute minimum value on $(0, \infty)$ for

$$f(x) = x^3(\ln x - 2)$$

55. Absolute maximum value on $(0, \infty)$ for

$$f(x) = \ln(xe^{-x})$$

56. Absolute maximum value on $(0, \infty)$ for

$$f(x) = \ln(x^2 e^{-x})$$

In Problems 57–62, find the absolute maximum and minimum, if either exists, for each function on the indicated intervals.

57. $f(x) = x^3 - 6x^2 + 9x - 6$
 (A) $[-1, 5]$ (B) $[-1, 3]$ (C) $[2, 5]$

58. $f(x) = 2x^3 - 3x^2 - 12x + 24$
 (A) $[-3, 4]$ (B) $[-2, 3]$ (C) $[-2, 1]$

59. $f(x) = (x - 1)(x - 5)^3 + 1$
 (A) $[0, 3]$ (B) $[1, 7]$ (C) $[3, 6]$

60. $f(x) = x^4 - 8x^2 + 16$
 (A) $[-1, 3]$ (B) $[0, 2]$ (C) $[-3, 4]$

61. $f(x) = x^4 - 4x^3 + 5$
 (A) $[-1, 2]$ (B) $[0, 4]$ (C) $[-1, 1]$

62. $f(x) = x^4 - 18x^2 + 32$
 (A) $[-4, 4]$ (B) $[-1, 1]$ (C) $[1, 3]$

In Problems 63–70, describe the graph of f at the given point relative to the existence of a local maximum or minimum with one of the following phrases: "Local maximum," "Local minimum," "Neither," or "Unable to determine from the given information." Assume that f(x) is continuous on $(-\infty, \infty)$.

63. $(2, f(2))$ if $f'(2) = 0$ and $f''(2) > 0$

64. $(4, f(4))$ if $f'(4) = 1$ and $f''(4) < 0$

65. $(-3, f(-3))$ if $f'(-3) = 0$ and $f''(-3) = 0$

66. $(-1, f(-1))$ if $f'(-1) = 0$ and $f''(-1) < 0$

67. $(6, f(6))$ if $f'(6) = 1$ and $f''(6)$ does not exist

68. $(5, f(5))$ if $f'(5) = 0$ and $f''(5)$ does not exist

69. $(-2, f(-2))$ if $f'(-2) = 0$ and $f''(-2) < 0$

70. $(1, f(1))$ if $f'(1) = 0$ and $f''(1) > 0$

Answers to Matched Problems

1. (A) Absolute maximum: $f(5) = 65$; absolute minimum: $f(-5) = -65$
 (B) Absolute maximum: $f(-2) = 16$; absolute minimum: $f(2) = -16$
 (C) Absolute maximum: $f(-2) = 16$; absolute minimum: $f(1) = -11$

2. (A) $f(2)$ is a local maximum; $f(4)$ is a local minimum.
 (B) $f(\ln 5) = 5 - 5 \ln 5$ is a local minimum.
 (C) $f(0)$ is a local minimum; there is no local extremum at $x = 1$.

3. (A) $f(\sqrt{5}) = 12 - 2\sqrt{5}$ (B) $f(5) = 5 \ln 5 - 5$

5-6 Optimization

- Area and Perimeter
- Maximizing Revenue and Profit
- Inventory Control

Now we can use calculus to solve **optimization problems**—problems that involve finding the absolute maximum value or the absolute minimum value of a function. As you work through this section, note that the statement of the problem does not usually include the function to be optimized. Often, it is your responsibility to find the function and then to find its absolute extremum.

Area and Perimeter

The techniques used to solve optimization problems are best illustrated through examples.

EXAMPLE 1 **Maximizing Area** A homeowner has $320 to spend on building a fence around a rectangular garden. Three sides of the fence will be constructed with wire fencing at a cost of $2 per linear foot. The fourth side will be constructed with wood fencing at a cost of $6 per linear foot. Find the dimensions and the area of the largest garden that can be enclosed with $320 worth of fencing.

SOLUTION To begin, we draw a figure (Fig. 1), introduce variables, and look for relationships among the variables.

Since we don't know the dimensions of the garden, the lengths of fencing are represented by the variables x and y. The costs of the fencing materials are fixed and are represented by constants.

Now we look for relationships among the variables. The area of the garden is

$$A = xy$$

while the cost of the fencing is

$$C = 2y + 2x + 2y + 6x$$
$$= 8x + 4y$$

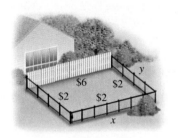

Figure 1

The problem states that the homeowner has $320 to spend on fencing. We assume that enclosing the largest area will use all the money available for fencing. The problem has now been reduced to

Maximize $A = xy$ subject to $8x + 4y = 320$

Before we can use calculus to find the maximum area A, we must express A as a function of a single variable. We use the cost equation to eliminate one of the variables in the area expression (we choose to eliminate y—either will work).

$$8x + 4y = 320$$
$$4y = 320 - 8x$$
$$y = 80 - 2x$$
$$A = xy = x(80 - 2x) = 80x - 2x^2$$

Now we consider the permissible values of x. Because x is one of the dimensions of a rectangle, x must satisfy

$$x \geq 0 \quad \text{Length is always nonnegative.}$$

And because $y = 80 - 2x$ is also a dimension of a rectangle, y must satisfy

$$y = 80 - 2x \geq 0 \quad \text{Width is always nonnegative.}$$
$$80 \geq 2x$$
$$40 \geq x \quad \text{or} \quad x \leq 40$$

We summarize the preceding discussion by stating the following model for this optimization problem:

Maximize $A(x) = 80x - 2x^2$ for $0 \leq x \leq 40$

Next, we find any critical values of A:

$$A'(x) = 80 - 4x = 0$$
$$80 = 4x$$
$$x = \frac{80}{4} = 20 \quad \text{Critical value}$$

Table 1

x	$A(x)$
0	0
20	800
40	0

Since $A(x)$ is continuous on $[0, 40]$, the absolute maximum value of A, if it exists, must occur at a critical value or an endpoint. Evaluating A at these values (Table 1), we see that the maximum area is 800 when

$$x = 20 \quad \text{and} \quad y = 80 - 2(20) = 40$$

Finally, we must answer the questions posed in the problem. The dimensions of the garden with the maximum area of 800 square feet are 20 feet by 40 feet, with one 20-foot side of wood fencing.

Matched Problem 1 Repeat Example 1 if the wood fencing costs $8 per linear foot and all other information remains the same.

We summarize the steps in the solution of Example 1 in the following box:

PROCEDURE Strategy for Solving Optimization Problems

Step 1 Introduce variables, look for relationships among the variables, and construct a mathematical model of the form

Maximize (or minimize) $f(x)$ on the interval I

Step 2 Find the critical values of $f(x)$.

Step 3 Use the procedures developed in Section 5-5 to find the absolute maximum (or minimum) value of $f(x)$ on the interval I and the value(s) of x where this occurs.

Step 4 Use the solution to the mathematical model to answer all the questions asked in the problem.

EXAMPLE 2 **Minimizing Perimeter** Refer to Example 1. The homeowner judges that an area of 800 square feet for the garden is too small and decides to increase the area to 1,250 square feet. What is the minimum cost of building a fence that will enclose a garden with an area of 1,250 square feet? What are the dimensions of this garden? Assume that the cost of fencing remains unchanged.

SOLUTION Refer to Figure 1 and the solution of Example 1. This time we want to minimize the cost of the fencing that will enclose 1,250 square feet. The problem can be expressed as

Minimize $C = 8x + 4y$ subject to $xy = 1,250$

Since x and y represent distances, we know that $x \geq 0$ and $y \geq 0$. But neither variable can equal 0 because their product must be 1,250.

$$xy = 1,250 \qquad \text{Solve the area equation for } y.$$
$$y = \frac{1,250}{x}$$
$$C(x) = 8x + 4\frac{1,250}{x} \qquad \text{Substitute for } y \text{ in the cost equation.}$$
$$= 8x + \frac{5,000}{x} \qquad x > 0$$

The model for this problem is

$$\text{Minimize } C(x) = 8x + \frac{5{,}000}{x} \quad \text{for } x > 0$$

$$= 8x + 5{,}000x^{-1}$$

$$C'(x) = 8 - 5{,}000x^{-2}$$

$$= 8 - \frac{5{,}000}{x^2} = 0$$

$$8 = \frac{5{,}000}{x^2}$$

$$x^2 = \frac{5{,}000}{8} = 625$$

$$x = \sqrt{625} = 25 \quad \text{The negative square root is discarded, since } x > 0.$$

We use the second derivative to determine the behavior at $x = 25$.

$$\boxed{C'(x) = 8 - 5{,}000x^{-2}}$$

$$C''(x) = 0 + 10{,}000x^{-3} = \frac{10{,}000}{x^3}$$

$$C''(25) = \frac{10{,}000}{25^3} = 0.64 > 0$$

The second-derivative test shows that $C(x)$ has a local minimum at $x = 25$, and since $x = 25$ is the only critical value of $x > 0$, then $C(25)$ must be the absolute minimum value of $C(x)$ for $x > 0$. When $x = 25$, the cost is

$$C(25) = 8(25) + \frac{5{,}000}{25} = 200 + 200 = \$400$$

and

$$y = \frac{1{,}250}{25} = 50$$

The minimal cost for enclosing a 1,250-square-foot garden is $400, and the dimensions are 25 feet by 50 feet, with one 25-foot side of wood fencing.

Matched Problem 2 Repeat Example 2 if the homeowner wants to enclose an 1,800-square-foot garden and all other data remain unchanged.

CONCEPTUAL INSIGHT

The restrictions on the variables in the solutions of Examples 1 and 2 are typical of problems involving areas or perimeters (or the cost of the perimeter):

$$8x + 4y = 320 \quad \text{Cost of fencing (Example 1)}$$

$$xy = 1{,}250 \quad \text{Area of garden (Example 2)}$$

The equation in Example 1 restricts the values of x to

$$0 \le x \le 40 \quad \text{or} \quad [0, 40]$$

The endpoints are included in the interval for our convenience (a closed interval is easier to work with than an open one). The area function is defined at each endpoint, so it does no harm to include them.

The equation in Example 2 restricts the values of x to

$$x > 0 \quad \text{or} \quad (0, \infty)$$

Neither endpoint can be included in this interval. We cannot include 0 because the area is not defined when $x = 0$, and we can never include ∞ as an endpoint. Remember, ∞ is not a number; it is a symbol that indicates the interval is unbounded.

Maximizing Revenue and Profit

EXAMPLE 3   **Maximizing Revenue** An office supply company sells x permanent markers per year at $\$p$ per marker. The price–demand equation for these markers is $p = 10 - 0.001x$. What price should the company charge for the markers to maximize revenue? What is the maximum revenue?

SOLUTION

$$\text{Revenue} = \text{price} \times \text{demand}$$

$$R(x) = (10 - 0.001x)x$$

$$= 10x - 0.001x^2$$

Both price and demand must be nonnegative, so

$$x \geq 0 \quad \text{and} \quad p = 10 - 0.001x \geq 0$$

$$10 \geq 0.001x$$

$$10{,}000 \geq x$$

The mathematical model for this problem is

$$\text{Maximize} \quad R(x) = 10x - 0.001x^2 \quad 0 \leq x \leq 10{,}000$$

$$R'(x) = 10 - 0.002x$$

$$10 - 0.002x = 0$$

$$10 = 0.002x$$

$$x = \frac{10}{0.002} = 5{,}000 \qquad \textit{Critical value}$$

Use the second-derivative test for absolute extrema:

$$R''(x) = -0.002 < 0 \quad \text{for all } x$$

$$\text{Max} \quad R(x) = R(5{,}000) = \$25{,}000$$

When the demand is $x = 5{,}000$, the price is

$$10 - 0.001(5{,}000) = \$5 \quad \textit{p = 10 − 0.001x}$$

The company will realize a maximum revenue of $\$25{,}000$ when the price of a marker is $\$5$.

Matched Problem 3   An office supply company sells x heavy-duty paper shredders per year at $\$p$ per shredder. The price–demand equation for these shredders is

$$p = 300 - \frac{x}{30}$$

What price should the company charge for the shredders to maximize revenue? What is the maximum revenue?

EXAMPLE 4   **Maximizing Profit** The total annual cost of manufacturing x permanent markers for the office supply company in Example 3 is

$$C(x) = 5,000 + 2x$$

What is the company's maximum profit? What should the company charge for each marker, and how many markers should be produced?

SOLUTION   Using the revenue model in Example 3, we have

$$\text{Profit} = \text{Revenue} - \text{Cost}$$

$$\begin{aligned} P(x) &= R(x) - C(x) \\ &= 10x - 0.001x^2 - 5,000 - 2x \\ &= 8x - 0.001x^2 - 5,000 \end{aligned}$$

The mathematical model for profit is

$$\text{Maximize} \quad P(x) = 8x - 0.001x^2 - 5,000 \qquad 0 \le x \le 10,000$$

The restrictions on x come from the revenue model in Example 3.

$$P'(x) = 8 - 0.002x = 0$$

$$8 = 0.002x$$

$$x = \frac{8}{0.002} = 4,000 \quad \textit{Critical value}$$

$$P''(x) = -0.002 < 0 \quad \text{for all } x$$

Since $x = 4,000$ is the only critical value and $P''(x) < 0$,

$$\text{Max } P(x) = P(4,000) = \$11,000$$

Using the price–demand equation from Example 3 with $x = 4,000$, we find that

$$p = 10 - 0.001(4,000) = \$6 \quad \textit{p = 10 − 0.001x}$$

A maximum profit of \$11,000 is realized when 4,000 markers are manufactured annually and sold for \$6 each.

The results in Examples 3 and 4 are illustrated in Figure 2.

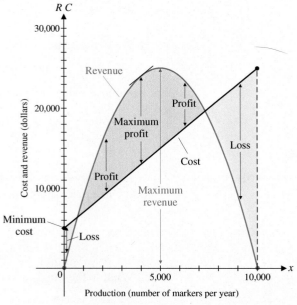

Figure 2

CONCEPTUAL INSIGHT

In Figure 2, notice that the maximum revenue and the maximum profit occur at different production levels. The maximum profit occurs when

$$P'(x) = R'(x) - C'(x) = 0$$

that is, when the marginal revenue is equal to the marginal cost. Notice that the slopes of the revenue function and the cost function are the same at this production level.

Matched Problem 4   The annual cost of manufacturing x paper shredders for the office supply company in Matched Problem 3 is $C(x) = 90,000 + 30x$. What is the company's maximum profit? What should it charge for each shredder, and how many shredders should it produce?

EXAMPLE 5   **Maximizing Profit** The government decides to tax the company in Example 4 $2 for each marker produced. Taking into account this additional cost, how many markers should the company manufacture each week to maximize its weekly profit? What is the maximum weekly profit? How much should the company charge for the markers to realize the maximum weekly profit?

SOLUTION   The tax of $2 per unit changes the company's cost equation:

$$C(x) = \text{original cost} + \text{tax}$$

$$= 5,000 + 2x + 2x$$

$$= 5,000 + 4x$$

The new profit function is

$$P(x) = R(x) - C(x)$$

$$= 10x - 0.001x^2 - 5,000 - 4x$$

$$= 6x - 0.001x^2 - 5,000$$

So, we must solve the following equation:

Maximize $P(x) = 6x - 0.001x^2 - 5,000$ $0 \le x \le 10,000$

$$P'(x) = 6 - 0.002x$$

$$6 - 0.002x = 0$$

$$x = 3,000 \qquad \text{Critical value}$$

$$P''(x) = -0.002 < 0 \quad \text{for all } x$$

$$\text{Max } P(x) = P(3,000) = \$4,000$$

Using the price–demand equation (Example 3) with $x = 3,000$, we find that

$$p = 10 - 0.001(3,000) = \$7 \quad p = 10 - 0.001x$$

The company's maximum profit is $4,000 when 3,000 markers are produced and sold weekly at a price of $7.

Even though the tax caused the company's cost to increase by $2 per marker, the price that the company should charge to maximize its profit increases by only $1. The company must absorb the other $1, with a resulting decrease of $7,000 in maximum profit.

Matched Problem 5   The government decides to tax the office supply company in Matched Problem 4 $20 for each shredder produced. Taking into account this additional cost, how many shredders should the company manufacture each week to maximize its weekly profit? What is the maximum weekly profit? How much should the company charge for the shredders to realize the maximum weekly profit?

EXAMPLE 6   **Maximizing Revenue** When a management training company prices its seminar on management techniques at $400 per person, 1,000 people will attend the seminar. The company estimates that for each $5 reduction in price, an additional 20 people will attend the seminar. How much should the company charge for the seminar in order to maximize its revenue? What is the maximum revenue?

SOLUTION   Let x represent the number of $5 price reductions.

$$400 - 5x = \text{price per customer}$$

$$1{,}000 + 20x = \text{number of customers}$$

$$\text{Revenue} = (\text{price per customer})(\text{number of customers})$$

$$R(x) = (400 - 5x) \times (1{,}000 + 20x)$$

Since price cannot be negative, we have

$$400 - 5x \geq 0$$

$$400 \geq 5x$$

$$80 \geq x \quad \text{or} \quad x \leq 80$$

A negative value of x would result in a price increase. Since the problem is stated in terms of price reductions, we must restrict x so that $x \geq 0$. Putting all this together, we have the following model:

$$\text{Maximize} \quad R(x) = (400 - 5x)(1{,}000 + 20x) \quad \text{for } 0 \leq x \leq 80$$

$$R(x) = 400{,}000 + 3{,}000x - 100x^2$$

$$R'(x) = 3{,}000 - 200x = 0$$

$$3{,}000 = 200x$$

$$x = 15 \quad \textit{Critical value}$$

Table 2

x	$R(x)$
0	400,000
15	422,500
80	0

Since $R(x)$ is continuous on the interval $[0, 80]$, we can determine the behavior of the graph by constructing a table. Table 2 shows that $R(15) = \$422{,}500$ is the absolute maximum revenue. The price of attending the seminar at $x = 15$ is $400 - 5(15) = \$325$. The company should charge $325 for the seminar in order to receive a maximum revenue of $422,500.

Matched Problem 6   A walnut grower estimates from past records that if 20 trees are planted per acre, then each tree will average 60 pounds of nuts per year. If, for each additional tree planted per acre, the average yield per tree drops 2 pounds, then how many trees should be planted to maximize the yield per acre? What is the maximum yield?

EXAMPLE 7   **Maximizing Revenue** After additional analysis, the management training company in Example 6 decides that its estimate of attendance was too high. Its new estimate is that only 10 additional people will attend the seminar for each $5 decrease in price. All other information remains the same. How much should the company charge for the seminar now in order to maximize revenue? What is the new maximum revenue?

SOLUTION   Under the new assumption, the model becomes

$$\text{Maximize} \quad R(x) = (400 - 5x)(1{,}000 + 10x) \qquad 0 \le x \le 80$$

$$= 400{,}000 - 1{,}000x - 50x^2$$

$$R'(x) = -1{,}000 - 100x = 0$$

$$-1{,}000 = 100x$$

$$x = -10 \quad \textit{Critical value}$$

Table 3

x	$R(x)$
0	400,000
80	0

Note that $x = -10$ is not in the interval [0, 80]. Since $R(x)$ is continuous on [0, 80], we can use a table to find the absolute maximum revenue. Table 3 shows that the maximum revenue is $R(0) = \$400{,}000$. The company should leave the price at \$400. Any \$5 decreases in price will lower the revenue.

Matched Problem 7   After further analysis, the walnut grower in Matched Problem 6 determines that each additional tree planted will reduce the average yield by 4 pounds. All other information remains the same. How many additional trees per acre should the grower plant now in order to maximize the yield? What is the new maximum yield?

CONCEPTUAL INSIGHT

The solution in Example 7 is called an **endpoint solution** because the optimal value occurs at the endpoint of an interval rather than at a critical value in the interior of the interval. It is always important to verify that the optimal value has been found.

Inventory Control

EXAMPLE 8   **Inventory Control** A multimedia company anticipates that there will be a demand for 20,000 copies of a certain DVD during the next year. It costs the company \$0.50 to store a DVD for one year. Each time it must make additional DVDs, it costs \$200 to set up the equipment. How many DVDs should the company make during each production run to minimize its total storage and setup costs?

SOLUTION   This type of problem is called an **inventory control problem**. One of the basic assumptions made in such problems is that the demand is uniform. For example, if there are 250 working days in a year, then the daily demand would be $20{,}000 \div 250 = 80$ DVDs. The company could decide to produce all 20,000 DVDs at the beginning of the year. This would certainly minimize the setup costs but would result in very large storage costs. At the other extreme, the company could produce 80 DVDs each day. This would minimize the storage costs but would result in very large setup costs. Somewhere between these two extremes is the optimal solution that will minimize the total storage and setup costs. Let

$$x = \text{number of DVDs manufactured during each production run}$$

$$y = \text{number of production runs}$$

It is easy to see that the total setup cost for the year is $200y$, but what is the total storage cost? If the demand is uniform, then the number of DVDs in storage between production runs will decrease from x to 0, and the average number in storage each day is $x/2$. This result is illustrated in Figure 3.

Since it costs \$0.50 to store a DVD for one year, the total storage cost is $0.5(x/2) = 0.25x$ and the total cost is

$$\text{total cost} = \text{setup cost} + \text{storage cost}$$

$$C = 200y + 0.25x$$

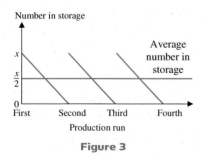

Figure 3

In order to write the total cost C as a function of one variable, we must find a relationship between x and y. If the company produces x DVDs in each of y production runs, then the total number of DVDs produced is xy.

$$xy = 20{,}000$$

$$y = \frac{20{,}000}{x}$$

Certainly, x must be at least 1 and cannot exceed 20,000. We must solve the following equation:

$$\text{Minimize} \quad C(x) = 200\left(\frac{20{,}000}{x}\right) + 0.25x \quad 1 \le x \le 20{,}000$$

$$C(x) = \frac{4{,}000{,}000}{x} + 0.25x$$

$$C'(x) = -\frac{4{,}000{,}000}{x^2} + 0.25$$

$$-\frac{4{,}000{,}000}{x^2} + 0.25 = 0$$

$$x^2 = \frac{4{,}000{,}000}{0.25}$$

$$x^2 = 16{,}000{,}000 \quad -4{,}000 \text{ is not a critical value, since}$$

$$x = 4{,}000 \quad 1 \le x \le 20{,}000.$$

$$C''(x) = \frac{8{,}000{,}000}{x^3} > 0 \quad \text{for } x \in (1, 20{,}000)$$

Therefore,

$$\text{Min } C(x) = C(4{,}000) = 2{,}000$$

$$y = \frac{20{,}000}{4{,}000} = 5$$

The company will minimize its total cost by making 4,000 DVDs five times during the year.

Matched Problem 8   Repeat Example 8 if it costs $250 to set up a production run and $0.40 to store a DVD for one year.

Exercises 5-6

Preliminary word problems:

1. Find two numbers whose sum is 15 and whose product is a maximum.

2. Find two numbers whose sum is 21 and whose product is a maximum.

3. Find two numbers whose difference is 15 and whose product is a minimum.

4. Find two numbers whose difference is 21 and whose product is a minimum.

5. Find two positive numbers whose product is 15 and whose sum is a minimum.

6. Find two positive numbers whose product is 21 and whose sum is a minimum.

7. Find the dimensions of a rectangle with an area of 200 square feet that has the minimum perimeter.

8. Find the dimensions of a rectangle with an area of 108 square feet that has the minimum perimeter.

9. Find the dimensions of a rectangle with a perimeter of 148 feet that has the maximum area.

10. Find the dimensions of a rectangle with a perimeter of 76 feet that has the maximum area.

11. Maximum revenue and profit. A company manufactures and sells x videophones per week. The weekly price–demand and cost equations are, respectively,

$$p = 500 - 0.5x \quad \text{and} \quad C(x) = 20,000 + 135x$$

(A) What price should the company charge for the phones, and how many phones should be produced to maximize the weekly revenue? What is the maximum weekly revenue?

(B) What is the maximum weekly profit? How much should the company charge for the phones, and how many phones should be produced to realize the maximum weekly profit?

12. Maximum revenue and profit. A company manufactures and sells x digital cameras per week. The weekly price–demand and cost equations are, respectively,

$$p = 400 - 0.4x \quad \text{and} \quad C(x) = 2,000 + 160x$$

(A) What price should the company charge for the cameras, and how many cameras should be produced to maximize the weekly revenue? What is the maximum revenue?

(B) What is the maximum weekly profit? How much should the company charge for the cameras, and how many cameras should be produced to realize the maximum weekly profit?

13. Maximum revenue and profit. A company manufactures and sells x television sets per month. The monthly cost and price–demand equations are

$$C(x) = 72,000 + 60x$$

$$p = 200 - \frac{x}{30} \quad 0 \le x \le 6,000$$

(A) Find the maximum revenue.

(B) Find the maximum profit, the production level that will realize the maximum profit, and the price the company should charge for each television set.

(C) If the government decides to tax the company $5 for each set it produces, how many sets should the company manufacture each month to maximize its profit? What is the maximum profit? What should the company charge for each set?

14. Maximum revenue and profit. Repeat Problem 13 for

$$C(x) = 60,000 + 60x$$

$$p = 200 - \frac{x}{50} \quad 0 \le x \le 10,000$$

15. Maximum profit. The following table contains price–demand and total cost data for the production of extreme-cold sleeping bags, where p is the wholesale price (in dollars) of a sleeping bag for an annual demand of x sleeping bags and C is the total cost (in dollars) of producing x sleeping bags:

(A) Find a quadratic regression equation for the price–demand data, using x as the independent variable.

x	p	C
950	240	130,000
1,200	210	150,000
1,800	160	180,000
2,050	120	190,000

(B) Find a linear regression equation for the cost data, using x as the independent variable.

(C) What is the maximum profit? What is the wholesale price per extreme-cold sleeping bag that should be charged to realize the maximum profit? Round answers to the nearest dollar.

16. Maximum profit. The following table contains price–demand and total cost data for the production of regular sleeping bags, where p is the wholesale price (in dollars) of a sleeping bag for an annual demand of x sleeping bags and C is the total cost (in dollars) of producing x sleeping bags:

x	p	C
2,300	98	145,000
3,300	84	170,000
4,500	67	190,000
5,200	51	210,000

(A) Find a quadratic regression equation for the price–demand data, using x as the independent variable.

(B) Find a linear regression equation for the cost data, using x as the independent variable.

(C) What is the maximum profit? What is the wholesale price per regular sleeping bag that should be charged to realize the maximum profit? Round answers to the nearest dollar.

17. Maximum revenue. A deli sells 640 sandwiches per day at a price of $8 each.

(A) A market survey shows that for every $0.10 reduction in price, 40 more sandwiches will be sold. How much should the deli charge for a sandwich in order to maximize revenue?

(B) A different market survey shows that for every $0.20 reduction in the original $8 price, 15 more sandwiches will be sold. Now how much should the deli charge for a sandwich in order to maximize revenue?

18. Maximum revenue. A university student center sells 1,600 cups of coffee per day at a price of $2.40.

(A) A market survey shows that for every $0.05 reduction in price, 50 more cups of coffee will be sold. How much should the student center charge for a cup of coffee in order to maximize revenue?

(B) A different market survey shows that for every $0.10 reduction in the original $2.40 price, 60 more cups of coffee will be sold. Now how much should the student center charge for a cup of coffee in order to maximize revenue?

19. Car rental. A car rental agency rents 200 cars per day at a rate of $30 per day. For each $1 increase in rate, 5 fewer cars are rented. At what rate should the cars be rented to produce the maximum income? What is the maximum income?

20. Rental income. A 300-room hotel in Las Vegas is filled to capacity every night at $80 a room. For each $1 increase in rent, 3 fewer rooms are rented. If each rented room costs $10 to service per day, how much should the management charge for each room to maximize gross profit? What is the maximum gross profit?

21. Agriculture. A commercial cherry grower estimates from past records that if 30 trees are planted per acre, then each tree will yield an average of 50 pounds of cherries per season. If, for each additional tree planted per acre (up to 20), the average yield per tree is reduced by 1 pound, how many trees should be planted per acre to obtain the maximum yield per acre? What is the maximum yield?

22. Agriculture. A commercial pear grower must decide on the optimum time to have fruit picked and sold. If the pears are picked now, they will bring 30¢ per pound, with each tree yielding an average of 60 pounds of salable pears. If the average yield per tree increases 6 pounds per tree per week for the next 4 weeks, but the price drops 2¢ per pound per week, when should the pears be picked to realize the maximum return per tree? What is the maximum return?

23. Manufacturing. A candy box is to be made out of a piece of cardboard that measures 8 by 12 inches. Squares of equal size will be cut out of each corner, and then the ends and sides will be folded up to form a rectangular box. What size square should be cut from each corner to obtain a maximum volume?

24. Packaging. A parcel delivery service will deliver a package only if the length plus girth (distance around) does not exceed 108 inches.

(A) Find the dimensions of a rectangular box with square ends that satisfies the delivery service's restriction and has maximum volume. What is the maximum volume?

(B) Find the dimensions (radius and height) of a cylindrical container that meets the delivery service's requirement and has maximum volume. What is the maximum volume?

Length

Girth

Figure for 24

25. Construction costs. A fence is to be built to enclose a rectangular area of 800 square feet. The fence along three sides is to be made of material that costs $6 per foot. The material for the fourth side costs $18 per foot. Find the dimensions of the rectangle that will allow for the most economical fence to be built.

26. Construction costs. The owner of a retail lumber store wants to construct a fence to enclose an outdoor storage area adjacent to the store, using all of the store as part of one side of the area (see the figure). Find the dimensions that will enclose the largest area if

(A) 240 feet of fencing material are used.

(B) 400 feet of fencing material are used.

100 ft

Figure for 26

27. Inventory control. A paint manufacturer has a uniform annual demand for 16,000 cans of automobile primer. It costs $4 to store one can of paint for one year and $500 to set up the plant for production of the primer. How many times a year should the company produce this primer in order to minimize the total storage and setup costs?

28. Inventory control. A pharmacy has a uniform annual demand for 200 bottles of a certain antibiotic. It costs $10 to store one bottle for one year and $40 to place an order. How many times during the year should the pharmacy order the antibiotic in order to minimize the total storage and reorder costs?

29. Inventory control. A publishing company sells 50,000 copies of a certain book each year. It costs the company $1 to store a book for one year. Each time that it prints additional copies, it costs the company $1,000 to set up the presses. How many books should the company produce during each printing in order to minimize its total storage and setup costs?

30. Operational costs. The cost per hour for fuel to run a train is $v^2/4$ dollars, where v is the speed of the train in miles per hour. (Note that the cost goes up as the square of the speed.) Other costs, including labor, are $300 per hour. How fast should the train travel on a 360-mile trip to minimize the total cost for the trip?

31. Construction costs. A freshwater pipeline is to be run from a source on the edge of a lake to a small resort community on an island 5 miles offshore, as indicated in the figure.

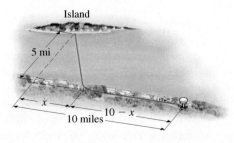

Island

5 mi

x $10 - x$

10 miles

Figure for 31

(A) If it costs 1.4 times as much to lay the pipe in the lake as it does on land, what should x be (in miles) to minimize the total cost of the project?

(B) If it costs only 1.1 times as much to lay the pipe in the lake as it does on land, what should x be to minimize the total cost of the project? [*Note:* Compare with Problem 34.]

32. Drug concentration. The concentration $C(t)$, in milligrams per cubic centimeter, of a particular drug in a patient's bloodstream is given by

$$C(t) = \frac{0.16t}{t^2 + 4t + 4}$$

where t is the number of hours after the drug is taken. How many hours after the drug is taken will the concentration be maximum? What is the maximum concentration?

33. Bacteria control. A lake used for recreational swimming is treated periodically to control harmful bacteria growth. Suppose that t days after a treatment, the concentration of bacteria per cubic centimeter is given by

$$C(t) = 30t^2 - 240t + 500 \qquad 0 \le t \le 8$$

How many days after a treatment will the concentration be minimal? What is the minimum concentration?

34. Bird flights. Some birds tend to avoid flights over large bodies of water during daylight hours. Suppose that an adult bird with this tendency is taken from its nesting area on the edge of a large lake to an island 5 miles offshore and is then released (see the figure).

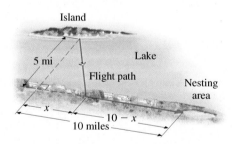

Figure for 34

(A) If it takes 1.4 times as much energy to fly over water as land, how far up the shore (x, in miles) should the bird head to minimize the total energy expended in returning to the nesting area?

(B) If it takes only 1.1 times as much energy to fly over water as land, how far up the shore should the bird head to minimize the total energy expended in returning to the nesting area? [*Note:* Compare with Problem 31.]

35. Botany. If it is known from past experiments that the height (in feet) of a certain plant after t months is given approximately by

$$H(t) = 4t^{1/2} - 2t \qquad 0 \le t \le 2$$

then how long, on average, will it take a plant to reach its maximum height? What is the maximum height?

36. Pollution. Two heavily industrial areas are located 10 miles apart, as shown in the figure. If the concentration of partic-

ulate matter (in parts per million) decreases as the reciprocal of the square of the distance from the source, and if area A_1 emits eight times the particulate matter as A_2, then the concentration of particulate matter at any point between the two areas is given by

$$C(x) = \frac{8k}{x^2} + \frac{k}{(10 - x)^2} \qquad 0.5 \le x \le 9.5, \quad k > 0$$

How far from A_1 will the concentration of particulate matter between the two areas be at a minimum?

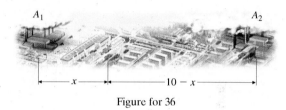

Figure for 36

37. Politics. In a newly incorporated city, it is estimated that the voting population (in thousands) will increase according to

$$N(t) = 30 + 12t^2 - t^3 \qquad 0 \le t \le 8$$

where t is time in years. When will the rate of increase be most rapid?

38. Learning. A large grocery chain found that, on average, a checker can recall $P\%$ of a given price list x hours after starting work, as given approximately by

$$P(x) = 96x - 24x^2 \qquad 0 \le x \le 3$$

At what time x does the checker recall a maximum percentage? What is the maximum?

Answers to Matched Problems

1. The dimensions of the garden with the maximum area of 640 square feet are 16 feet by 40 feet, with one 16-foot side with wood fencing.

2. The minimal cost for enclosing a 1,800-square-foot garden is $480, and the dimensions are 30 feet by 60 feet, with one 30-foot side with wood fencing.

3. The company will realize a maximum revenue of $675,000 when the price of a shredder is $150.

4. A maximum profit of $456,750 is realized when 4,050 shredders are manufactured annually and sold for $165 each.

5. A maximum profit of $378,750 is realized when 3,075 shredders are manufactured annually and sold for $175 each.

6. The maximum yield is 1,250 pounds per acre when 5 additional trees are planted on each acre.

7. The maximum yield is 1,200 pounds when no additional trees are planted.

8. The company should produce 5,000 DVDs four times a year.

Chapter 5 Review

Important Terms, Symbols, and Concepts

5-1 First Derivative and Graphs

- **Increasing and decreasing properties** of a function can be determined by examining a sign chart for the derivative.
- A number c is a **partition number** for $f'(x)$ if $f'(c) = 0$ or $f'(x)$ is discontinuous at c. If c is also in the domain of $f(x)$, then c is a **critical value.**

- Increasing and decreasing properties and **local extrema** for $f(x)$ can be determined by examining the graph of $f'(x)$.

- The **first-derivative test** is used to locate extrema of a function.

5-2 Second Derivative and Graphs

- The **second derivative** of a function f can be used to determine the concavity of the graph of f.
- **Inflection points** on a graph are points where the concavity changes.

- The concavity of the graph of $f(x)$ can also be determined by an examination of the graph of $f'(x)$.
- A **graphing strategy** is used to organize the information obtained from the first and second derivatives.

5-3 L'Hôpital's Rule

- Limits at infinity and infinite limits involving powers of $x - c$, e^x, and $\ln x$ are reviewed.

- The first version of **L'Hôpital's rule** applies to limits involving the indeterminate form $0/0$ as $x \to c$.

- You must always check that L'Hôpital's rule applies.
- L'Hôpital's rule can be applied more than once.
- L'Hôpital's rule applies to one-sided limits and limits at infinity.

- L'Hôpital's rule applies to limits involving the indeterminate form ∞/∞.

5-4 Curve-Sketching Techniques

- The graphing strategy first used in Section 5-2 is expanded to include horizontal and vertical asymptotes.

- If $f(x) = n(x)/d(x)$ is a rational function with the degree of $n(x)$ 1 more than the degree of $d(x)$, then the graph of $f(x)$ has an **oblique asymptote** of the form $y = mx + b$.

5-5 Absolute Maxima and Minima

- The steps involved in finding the **absolute maximum and absolute minimum** values of a continuous function on a closed interval are listed in a procedure.

- The **second-derivative test for local extrema** can be used to test critical values, but it does not work in all cases.
- If a function is continuous on an interval I and has only one critical value in I, then the **second-derivative test for absolute extrema** can be used to find the absolute extrema, but it not does work in all cases.

5-6 Optimization

- The methods used to solve **optimization problems** are summarized and illustrated by examples.

Review Exercises

Work through all the problems in this chapter review, and check your answers in the back of the book. Answers to all review problems are there, along with section numbers in italics to indicate where each type of problem is discussed. Where weaknesses show up, review appropriate sections in the text.

A

Problems 1–8 refer to the following graph of $y = f(x)$. Identify the points or intervals on the x axis that produce the indicated behavior.

1. $f(x)$ is increasing.   **2.** $f'(x) < 0$

3. The graph of f is concave downward.

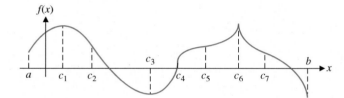

Figure for 1–8

4. Local minima   **5.** Absolute maxima

6. $f'(x)$ appears to be 0.   **7.** $f'(x)$ does not exist.

8. Inflection points

In Problems 9 and 10, use the given information to sketch the graph of f. Assume that f is continuous on its domain and that all intercepts are included in the information given.

9. Domain: All real x

x	-3	-2	-1	0	2	3
$f(x)$	0	3	2	0	-3	0

$f'(x)$ $+ + + \ 0 \ - - - - - - - - - - \ 0 \ - - - \ ND + + +$

$\qquad\qquad\qquad -2 \qquad\qquad\qquad 0 \qquad\quad 2 \qquad\qquad\qquad x$

$f''(x)$ $- - - - - - - - - - \ 0 \ + + + \ 0 \ - - - \ ND - - -$

$\qquad\qquad\qquad\qquad -1 \qquad\quad 0 \qquad\quad 2 \qquad\qquad\qquad x$

10. Domain: All real x

$f(-2) = 1, f(0) = 0, f(2) = 1;$

$f'(0) = 0; f'(x) < 0$ on $(-\infty, 0);$

$f'(x) > 0$ on $(0, \infty);$

$f''(-2) = 0, f''(2) = 0;$

$f''(x) < 0$ on $(-\infty, -2)$ and $(2, \infty);$

$f''(x) > 0$ on $(-2, 2);$

$\lim_{x \to -\infty} f(x) = 2; \lim_{x \to \infty} f(x) = 2$

11. Find $f''(x)$ for $f(x) = x^4 + 5x^3$.

12. Find y'' for $y = 3x + \dfrac{4}{x}$.

In Problems 13 and 14, find the domain and intercepts.

13. $f(x) = \dfrac{5 + x}{4 - x}$ **14.** $f(x) = \ln(x + 2)$

In Problems 15 and 16, find the horizontal and vertical asymptotes.

15. $f(x) = \dfrac{x + 3}{x^2 - 4}$ **16.** $f(x) = \dfrac{2x - 7}{3x + 10}$

In Problems 17 and 18, find the x and y coordinates of all inflection points.

17. $f(x) = x^4 - 12x^2$ **18.** $f(x) = (2x + 1)^{1/3} - 6$

In Problems 19 and 20, find (A) $f'(x)$, (B) the critical values of f, and (C) the partition numbers for f'.

19. $f(x) = x^{1/5}$ **20.** $f(x) = x^{-1/5}$

In Problems 21–30, summarize all the pertinent information obtained by applying the final version of the graphing strategy (Section 5–4) to f, and sketch the graph of f.

21. $f(x) = x^3 - 18x^2 + 81x$ **22.** $f(x) = (x + 4)(x - 2)^2$

23. $f(x) = 8x^3 - 2x^4$ **24.** $f(x) = (x - 1)^3(x + 3)$

25. $f(x) = \dfrac{3x}{x + 2}$ **26.** $f(x) = \dfrac{x^2}{x^2 + 27}$

27. $f(x) = \dfrac{x}{(x + 2)^2}$ **28.** $f(x) = \dfrac{x^3}{x^2 + 3}$

29. $f(x) = 5 - 5e^{-x}$ **30.** $f(x) = x^3 \ln x$

Find each limit in Problems 31–40.

31. $\lim_{x \to 0} \dfrac{e^{3x} - 1}{x}$ **32.** $\lim_{x \to 2} \dfrac{x^2 - 5x + 6}{x^2 + x - 6}$

33. $\lim_{x \to 0^-} \dfrac{\ln(1 + x)}{x^2}$ **34.** $\lim_{x \to 0} \dfrac{\ln(1 + x)}{1 + x}$

35. $\lim_{x \to \infty} \dfrac{e^{4x}}{x^2}$ **36.** $\lim_{x \to 0} \dfrac{e^x + e^{-x} - 2}{x^2}$

37. $\lim_{x \to 0^+} \dfrac{\sqrt{1 + x} - 1}{\sqrt{x}}$ **38.** $\lim_{x \to \infty} \dfrac{\ln x}{x^5}$

39. $\lim_{x \to \infty} \dfrac{\ln(1 + 6x)}{\ln(1 + 3x)}$ **40.** $\lim_{x \to 0} \dfrac{\ln(1 + 6x)}{\ln(1 + 3x)}$

41. Use the graph of $y = f'(x)$ shown here to discuss the graph of $y = f(x)$. Organize your conclusions in a table (see Example 4, Section 5-2). Sketch a possible graph of $y = f(x)$.

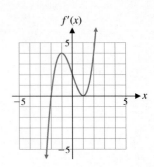

Figure for 41 and 42

42. Refer to the above graph of $y = f'(x)$. Which of the following could be the graph of $y = f''(x)$?

(A)

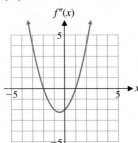

(B)

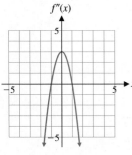

(C)

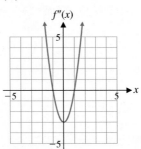

43. Use the second-derivative test to find any local extrema for

$$f(x) = x^3 - 6x^2 - 15x + 12$$

44. Find the absolute maximum and absolute minimum, if either exists, for

$$y = f(x) = x^3 - 12x + 12 \qquad -3 \le x \le 5$$

45. Find the absolute minimum, if it exists, for

$$y = f(x) = x^2 + \frac{16}{x^2} \qquad x > 0$$

46. Find the absolute maximum value, if it exists, for

$$f(x) = 11x - 2x \ln x \qquad x > 0$$

47. Find the absolute maximum value, if it exists, for

$$f(x) = 10xe^{-2x} \qquad x > 0$$

48. Let $y = f(x)$ be a polynomial function with local minima at $x = a$ and $x = b$, $a < b$. Must f have at least one local maximum between a and b? Justify your answer.

49. The derivative of $f(x) = x^{-1}$ is $f'(x) = -x^{-2}$. Since $f'(x) < 0$ for $x \ne 0$, is it correct to say that $f(x)$ is decreasing for all x except $x = 0$? Explain.

50. Discuss the difference between a partition number for $f'(x)$ and a critical value of $f(x)$, and illustrate with examples.

C

51. Find the absolute maximum for $f'(x)$ if

$$f(x) = 6x^2 - x^3 + 8$$

Graph f and f' on the same coordinate system for $0 \le x \le 4$.

52. Find two positive numbers whose product is 400 and whose sum is a minimum. What is the minimum sum?

In Problems 53 and 54, apply the graphing strategy and summarize the pertinent information. Round any approximate values to two decimal places.

53. $f(x) = x^4 + x^3 - 4x^2 - 3x + 4$

54. $f(x) = 0.25x^4 - 5x^3 + 31x^2 - 70x$

55. Find the absolute maximum value, if it exists, for

$$f(x) = 3x - x^2 + e^{-x} \, x > 0$$

56. Find the absolute maximum value, if it exists, for

$$f(x) = \frac{\ln x}{e^x} \, x > 0$$

Applications

57. **Price analysis.** The graph in the figure approximates the rate of change of the price of tomatoes over a 60-month period, where $p(t)$ is the price of a pound of tomatoes and t is time (in months).

(A) Write a brief description of the graph of $y = p(t)$, including a discussion of local extrema and inflection points.

(B) Sketch a possible graph of $y = p(t)$.

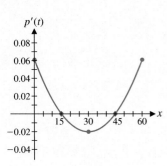

Figure for 57

58. **Maximum revenue and profit.** A company manufactures and sells x e-book readers per month. The monthly cost and price–demand equations are, respectively,

$$C(x) = 350x + 50{,}000$$

$$p = 500 - 0.025x \qquad 0 \le x \le 20{,}000$$

(A) Find the maximum revenue.

(B) How many readers should the company manufacture each month to maximize its profit? What is the maximum monthly profit? How much should the company charge for each reader?

(C) If the government decides to tax the company $20 for each reader it produces, how many readers should the company manufacture each month to maximize its profit? What is the maximum monthly profit? How much should the company charge for each reader?

59. Construction. A fence is to be built to enclose a rectangular area. The fence along three sides is to be made of material that costs $5 per foot. The material for the fourth side costs $15 per foot.

(A) If the area is 5,000 square feet, find the dimensions of the rectangle that will allow for the most economical fence.

(B) If $3,000 is available for the fencing, find the dimensions of the rectangle that will enclose the most area.

60. Rental income. A 200-room hotel in Reno is filled to capacity every night at a rate of $40 per room. For each $1 increase in the nightly rate, 4 fewer rooms are rented. If each rented room costs $8 a day to service, how much should the management charge per room in order to maximize gross profit? What is the maximum gross profit?

61. Inventory control. A computer store sells 7,200 boxes of storage disks annually. It costs the store $0.20 to store a box of disks for one year. Each time it reorders disks, the store must pay a $5.00 service charge for processing the order. How many times during the year should the store order disks to minimize the total storage and reorder costs?

62. Average cost. The total cost of producing x dorm refrigerators per day is given by

$$C(x) = 4{,}000 + 10x + 0.1x^2$$

Find the minimum average cost. Graph the average cost and the marginal cost functions on the same coordinate system. Include any oblique asymptotes.

63. Average cost. The cost of producing x wheeled picnic coolers is given by

$$C(x) = 200 + 50x - 50 \ln x \qquad x \geq 1$$

Find the minimum average cost.

64. Marginal analysis. The price–demand equation for a GPS device is

$$p(x) = 1{,}000e^{-0.02x}$$

where x is the monthly demand and p is the price in dollars. Find the production level and price per unit that produce the maximum revenue. What is the maximum revenue?

65. Maximum revenue. Graph the revenue function from Problem 64 for $0 \leq x \leq 100$.

66. Maximum profit. Refer to Problem 64. If the GPS devices cost the store $220 each, find the price (to the nearest cent) that maximizes the profit. What is the maximum profit (to the nearest dollar)?

67. Maximum profit. The data in the table show the daily demand x for cream puffs at a state fair at various price levels p. If it costs $1 to make a cream puff, use logarithmic regression $(p = a + b \ln x)$ to find the price (to the nearest cent) that maximizes profit.

Demand x	Price per Cream Puff($) p
3,125	1.99
3,879	1.89
5,263	1.79
5,792	1.69
6,748	1.59
8,120	1.49

68. Construction costs. The ceiling supports in a new discount department store are 12 feet apart. Lights are to be hung from these supports by chains in the shape of a "Y." If the lights are 10 feet below the ceiling, what is the shortest length of chain that can be used to support these lights?

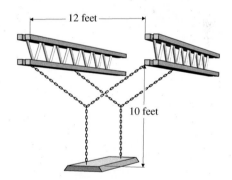

69. Average cost. The table gives the total daily cost y (in dollars) of producing x dozen chocolate chip cookies at various production levels.

Dozens of Cookies x	Total Cost y
50	119
100	187
150	248
200	382
250	505
300	695

(A) Enter the data into a graphing calculator and find a quadratic regression equation for the total cost.

(B) Use the regression equation from part (A) to find the minimum average cost (to the nearest cent) and the corresponding production level (to the nearest integer).

70. Advertising—point of diminishing returns. A company estimates that it will sell $N(x)$ units of a product after spending $\$x$ thousand on advertising, as given by

$$N(x) = -0.25x^4 + 11x^3 - 108x^2 + 3{,}000$$
$$9 \le x \le 24$$

When is the rate of change of sales increasing and when is it decreasing? What is the point of diminishing returns and the maximum rate of change of sales? Graph N and N' on the same coordinate system.

 71. Advertising. A chain of appliance stores uses TV ads to promote its HDTV sales. Analyzing past records produced the data in the following table, where x is the number of ads placed monthly and y is the number of HDTVs sold that month:

Number of Ads	Number of HDTVs
x	y
10	271
20	427
25	526
30	629
45	887
48	917

(A) Enter the data into a graphing calculator, set the calculator to display two decimal places, and find a cubic regression equation for the number of HDTVs sold monthly as a function of the number of ads.

(B) How many ads should be placed each month to maximize the rate of change of sales with respect to the number of ads, and how many HDTVs can be expected to be sold with that number of ads? Round answers to the nearest integer.

72. Bacteria control. If t days after a treatment the bacteria count per cubic centimeter in a body of water is given by

$$C(t) = 20t^2 - 120t + 800 \qquad 0 \le t \le 9$$

then in how many days will the count be a minimum?

73. Politics. In a new suburb, it is estimated that the number of registered voters will grow according to

$$N = 10 + 6t^2 - t^3 \qquad 0 \le t \le 5$$

where t is time in years and N is in thousands. When will the rate of increase be a maximum?

Integration

Introduction

In the preceding three chapters, we studied the *derivative* and its applications. In Chapter 6, we introduce the *integral*, the second key concept of calculus. The integral can be used to calculate areas, volumes, the index of income concentration, and consumers' surplus. At first glance, the integral may appear to be unrelated to the derivative. There is, however, a close connection between these two concepts, which is made precise by the *fundamental theorem of calculus* (Section 6-5). We consider many applications of integrals and differential equations in Chapter 6. See, for example, Problem 67 in Section 6-3, which explores how the age of an archeological site or artifact can be estimated.

6-1   Antiderivatives and Indefinite Integrals

- Antiderivatives
- Indefinite Integrals: Formulas and Properties
- Applications

Many operations in mathematics have reverses—addition and subtraction, multiplication and division, powers and roots. We now know how to find the derivatives of many functions. The reverse operation, *antidifferentiation* (the reconstruction of a function from its derivative), will receive our attention in this and the next two sections.

Antiderivatives

A function F is an **antiderivative** of a function f if $F'(x) = f(x)$.

The function $F(x) = \dfrac{x^3}{3}$ is an antiderivative of the function $f(x) = x^2$ because

$$\frac{d}{dx}\left(\frac{x^3}{3}\right) = x^2$$

However, $F(x)$ is not the only antiderivative of x^2. Note also that

$$\frac{d}{dx}\left(\frac{x^3}{3} + 2\right) = x^2 \qquad \frac{d}{dx}\left(\frac{x^3}{3} - \pi\right) = x^2 \qquad \frac{d}{dx}\left(\frac{x^3}{3} + \sqrt{5}\right) = x^2$$

Therefore,

$$\frac{x^3}{3} + 2 \qquad \frac{x^3}{3} - \pi \qquad \frac{x^3}{3} + \sqrt{5}$$

are also antiderivatives of x^2 because each has x^2 as a derivative. In fact, it appears that

$$\frac{x^3}{3} + C \qquad \text{for any real number } C$$

is an antiderivative of x^2 because

$$\frac{d}{dx}\left(\frac{x^3}{3} + C\right) = x^2$$

Antidifferentiation of a given function does not give a unique function, but an entire family of functions.

Does the expression

$$\frac{x^3}{3} + C \qquad \text{with } C \text{ any real number}$$

include all antiderivatives of x^2? Theorem 1 (stated without proof) indicates that the answer is yes.

THEOREM 1   Antiderivatives

If the derivatives of two functions are equal on an open interval (a, b), then the functions differ by at most a constant. Symbolically, if F and G are differentiable functions on the interval (a, b) and $F'(x) = G'(x)$ for all x in (a, b), then $F(x) = G(x) + k$ for some constant k.

CONCEPTUAL INSIGHT

Suppose that $F(x)$ is an antiderivative of $f(x)$. If $G(x)$ is any other antiderivative of $f(x)$, then by Theorem 1, the graph of $G(x)$ is a vertical translation of the graph of $F(x)$ (see Section 2-2).

EXAMPLE 1   **A Family of Antiderivatives** Note that

$$\frac{d}{dx}\left(\frac{x^2}{2}\right) = x$$

(A) Find all antiderivatives of $f(x) = x$.

(B) Graph the antiderivative of $f(x) = x$ that passes through the point $(0, 0)$; through the point $(0, 1)$; through the point $(0, 2)$.

(C) How are the graphs of the three antiderivatives in part (B) related?

SOLUTION   (A) By Theorem 1, any antiderivative of $f(x)$ has the form

$$F(x) = \frac{x^2}{2} + k$$

where k is a real number.

(B) Because $F(0) = (0^2/2) + k = k$, the functions

$$F_0(x) = \frac{x^2}{2}, \quad F_1(x) = \frac{x^2}{2} + 1, \quad \text{and} \quad F_2(x) = \frac{x^2}{2} + 2$$

pass through the points $(0, 0), (0, 1),$ and $(0, 2)$, respectively (see Fig. 1).

(C) The graphs of the three antiderivatives are vertical translations of each other.

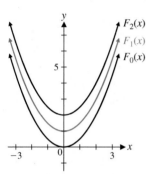

Figure 1

Matched Problem 1   Note that

$$\frac{d}{dx}(x^3) = 3x^2$$

(A) Find all antiderivatives of $f(x) = 3x^2$.

(B) Graph the antiderivative of $f(x) = 3x^2$ that passes through the point $(0, 0)$; through the point $(0, 1)$; through the point $(0, 2)$.

(C) How are the graphs of the three antiderivatives in part (B) related?

Indefinite Integrals: Formulas and Properties

Theorem 1 states that if the derivatives of two functions are equal, then the functions differ by at most a constant. We use the symbol

$$\int f(x)\, dx$$

called the **indefinite integral**, to represent the family of all antiderivatives of $f(x)$, and we write

$$\int f(x)\, dx = F(x) + C \qquad \text{if} \qquad F'(x) = f(x)$$

The symbol $\int$ is called an **integral sign**, and the function $f(x)$ is called the **integrand**. The symbol dx indicates that the antidifferentiation is performed with respect to the variable x. (We will have more to say about the symbols $\int$ and dx later in the chapter.) The arbitrary constant C is called the **constant of integration**. Referring to the preceding discussion, we can write

$$\int x^2\, dx = \frac{x^3}{3} + C \qquad \text{since} \qquad \frac{d}{dx}\left(\frac{x^3}{3} + C\right) = x^2$$

Of course, variables other than x can be used in indefinite integrals. For example,

$$\int t^2 \, dt = \frac{t^3}{3} + C \qquad \text{since} \qquad \frac{d}{dt}\left(\frac{t^3}{3} + C\right) = t^2$$

or

$$\int u^2 \, du = \frac{u^3}{3} + C \qquad \text{since} \qquad \frac{d}{du}\left(\frac{u^3}{3} + C\right) = u^2$$

The fact that indefinite integration and differentiation are reverse operations, except for the addition of the constant of integration, can be expressed symbolically as

$$\frac{d}{dx}\left[\int f(x)\,dx\right] = f(x) \qquad \text{\textit{The derivative of the indefinite integral of f(x) is f(x).}}$$

and

$$\int F'(x)\,dx = F(x) + C \quad \text{\textit{The indefinite integral of the derivative of F(x) is F(x) + C.}}$$

We can develop formulas for the indefinite integrals of certain basic functions from the formulas for derivatives in Chapters 3 and 4.

FORMULAS Indefinite Integrals of Basic Functions

For C a constant,

1. $\displaystyle\int x^n \, dx = \frac{x^{n+1}}{n+1} + C, \qquad n \neq -1$

2. $\displaystyle\int e^x \, dx = e^x + C$

3. $\displaystyle\int \frac{1}{x} \, dx = \ln|x| + C, \qquad x \neq 0$

To justify each formula, show that the derivative of the right-hand side is the integrand of the left-hand side (see Problems 77–80 in Exercise 6-1). Note that formula 1 does not give the antiderivative of x^{-1} (because $x^{n+1}/(n+1)$ is undefined when $n = -1$), but formula 3 does.

EXPLORE & DISCUSS 1

Formulas 1, 2, and 3 do *not* provide a formula for the indefinite integral of the function $\ln x$. Show that if $x > 0$, then

$$\int \ln x \, dx = x \ln x - x + C$$

by differentiating the right-hand side.

We can obtain properties of the indefinite integral from derivative properties that were established in Chapter 3.

PROPERTIES Indefinite Integrals

For k a constant,

4. $\displaystyle\int kf(x)\,dx = k\int f(x)\,dx$

5. $\displaystyle\int [f(x) \pm g(x)]\,dx = \int f(x)\,dx \pm \int g(x)\,dx$

Property 4 states that

> **The indefinite integral of a constant times a function is the constant times the indefinite integral of the function.**

Property 5 states that

> **The indefinite integral of the sum of two functions is the sum of the indefinite integrals, and the indefinite integral of the difference of two functions is the difference of the indefinite integrals.**

To establish property 4, let F be a function such that $F'(x) = f(x)$. Then

$$k\int f(x)\,dx = k\int F'(x)\,dx = k[F(x) + C_1] = kF(x) + kC_1$$

and since $[kF(x)]' = kF'(x) = kf(x)$, we have

$$\int kf(x)\,dx = \int kF'(x)\,dx = kF(x) + C_2$$

But $kF(x) + kC_1$ and $kF(x) + C_2$ describe the same set of functions, because C_1 and C_2 are arbitrary real numbers. Property 4 is established. Property 5 can be established in a similar manner (see Problems 81 and 82 in Exercise 6-1).

⚠ **CAUTION** Property 4 states that **a constant factor can be moved across an integral sign. A variable factor cannot be moved across an integral sign:**

CONSTANT FACTOR

$$\int 5x^{1/2}\,dx = 5\int x^{1/2}\,dx$$

VARIABLE FACTOR

$$\int xx^{1/2}\,dx \neq x\int x^{1/2}\,dx$$

Indefinite integral formulas and properties can be used together to find indefinite integrals for many frequently encountered functions. If $n = 0$, then formula 1 gives

$$\int dx = x + C$$

Therefore, by property 4,

$$\int k\,dx = k(x + C) = kx + kC$$

Because kC is a constant, we replace it with a single symbol that denotes an arbitrary constant (usually C), and write

$$\int k\,dx = kx + C$$

In words,

> **The indefinite integral of a constant function with value k is $kx + C$.**

Similarly, using property 5 and then formulas 2 and 3, we obtain

$$\int\left(e^x + \frac{1}{x}\right)dx = \int e^x\,dx + \int\frac{1}{x}\,dx$$

$$= e^x + C_1 + \ln|x| + C_2$$

Because $C_1 + C_2$ is a constant, we replace it with the symbol C and write

$$\int\left(e^x + \frac{1}{x}\right)dx = e^x + \ln|x| + C$$

EXAMPLE 2 Using Indefinite Integral Properties and Formulas

(A) $\int 5 \, dx = 5x + C$

(B) $\int 9e^x \, dx = 9 \int e^x \, dx = 9e^x + C$

(C) $\int 5t^7 \, dt = 5 \int t^7 \, dt = 5\dfrac{t^8}{8} + C = \dfrac{5}{8}t^8 + C$

(D) $\int (4x^3 + 2x - 1) \, dx = \int 4x^3 \, dx + \int 2x \, dx - \int dx$

$\qquad\qquad\qquad\qquad = 4 \int x^3 \, dx + 2 \int x \, dx - \int dx$

$\qquad\qquad\qquad\qquad = \dfrac{4x^4}{4} + \dfrac{2x^2}{2} - x + C$

$\qquad\qquad\qquad\qquad = x^4 + x^2 - x + C$

Property 4 can be extended to the sum and difference of an arbitrary number of functions.

(E) $\int \left(2e^x + \dfrac{3}{x} \right) dx = 2 \int e^x \, dx + 3 \int \dfrac{1}{x} \, dx$

$\qquad\qquad\qquad\qquad = 2e^x + 3 \ln|x| + C$

To check any of the results in Example 2, we differentiate the final result to obtain the integrand in the original indefinite integral. When you evaluate an indefinite integral, do not forget to include the arbitrary constant C.

Matched Problem 2 Find each indefinite integral:

(A) $\int 2 \, dx$ 　　　　　　　　　(B) $\int 16e^t \, dt$

(C) $\int 3x^4 \, dx$ 　　　　　　　　(D) $\int (2x^5 - 3x^2 + 1) \, dx$

(E) $\int \left(\dfrac{5}{x} - 4e^x \right) dx$

EXAMPLE 3 Using Indefinite Integral Properties and Formulas

(A) $\int \dfrac{4}{x^3} \, dx = \int 4x^{-3} \, dx = \dfrac{4x^{-3+1}}{-3+1} + C = -2x^{-2} + C$

(B) $\int 5\sqrt[3]{u^2} \, du = 5 \int u^{2/3} \, du = 5\dfrac{u^{(2/3)+1}}{\frac{2}{3}+1} + C$

$\qquad\qquad\qquad\qquad = 5\dfrac{u^{5/3}}{\frac{5}{3}} + C = 3u^{5/3} + C$

(C) $\int \dfrac{x^3 - 3}{x^2} \, dx = \int \left(\dfrac{x^3}{x^2} - \dfrac{3}{x^2} \right) dx$

$\qquad\qquad\qquad = \int (x - 3x^{-2}) \, dx$

$\qquad\qquad\qquad = \int x \, dx - 3 \int x^{-2} \, dx$

$\qquad\qquad\qquad = \dfrac{x^{1+1}}{1+1} - 3\dfrac{x^{-2+1}}{-2+1} + C$

$\qquad\qquad\qquad = \tfrac{1}{2}x^2 + 3x^{-1} + C$

(D) $\int \left(\dfrac{2}{\sqrt[3]{x}} - 6\sqrt{x} \right) dx = \int (2x^{-1/3} - 6x^{1/2}) \, dx$

$$= 2 \int x^{-1/3} \, dx - 6 \int x^{1/2} \, dx$$

$$= 2\dfrac{x^{(-1/3)+1}}{-\frac{1}{3}+1} - 6\dfrac{x^{(1/2)+1}}{\frac{1}{2}+1} + C$$

$$= 2\dfrac{x^{2/3}}{\frac{2}{3}} - 6\dfrac{x^{3/2}}{\frac{3}{2}} + C$$

$$= 3x^{2/3} - 4x^{3/2} + C$$

(E) $\int x(x^2 + 2) \, dx = \int (x^3 + 2x) \, dx = \dfrac{x^4}{4} + x^2 + C$

Matched Problem 3 Find each indefinite integral:

(A) $\int \left(2x^{2/3} - \dfrac{3}{x^4} \right) dx$

(B) $\int 4\sqrt[5]{w^3} \, dw$

(C) $\int \dfrac{x^4 - 8x^3}{x^2} \, dx$

(D) $\int \left(8\sqrt[3]{x} - \dfrac{6}{\sqrt{x}} \right) dx$

(E) $\int (x^2 - 2)(x + 3) \, dx$

⚠ **CAUTION**

1. Note from Example 3(E) that

$$\int x(x^2 + 2) \, dx \neq \dfrac{x^2}{2}\left(\dfrac{x^3}{3} + 2x \right) + C$$

In general, the **indefinite integral of a product is not the product of the indefinite integrals.** (This is expected because the derivative of a product is not the product of the derivatives.)

2. $$\int e^x \, dx \neq \dfrac{e^{x+1}}{x+1} + C$$

The power rule applies only to power functions of the form x^n, where the exponent n is a real constant not equal to -1 and the base x is the variable. The function e^x is an exponential function with variable exponent x and constant base e. The correct form is

$$\int e^x \, dx = e^x + C$$

3. Not all elementary functions have elementary antiderivatives. It is impossible, for example, to give a formula for the antiderivative of $f(x) = e^{x^2}$ in terms of elementary functions. Nevertheless, finding such a formula, when it exists, can markedly simplify the solution of certain problems.

Applications

Let's consider some applications of the indefinite integral.

EXAMPLE 4　**Curves** Find the equation of the curve that passes through $(2, 5)$ if the slope of the curve is given by $dy/dx = 2x$ at any point x.

SOLUTION　We want to find a function $y = f(x)$ such that

$$\frac{dy}{dx} = 2x \qquad (1)$$

and

$$y = 5 \quad \text{when} \quad x = 2 \qquad (2)$$

If $dy/dx = 2x$, then

$$y = \int 2x \, dx \qquad (3)$$

$$= x^2 + C$$

Since $y = 5$ when $x = 2$, we determine the *particular value of C* so that

$$5 = 2^2 + C$$

So $C = 1$, and

$$y = x^2 + 1$$

is the *particular antiderivative* out of all those possible from equation (3) that satisfies both equations (1) and (2) (see Fig. 2).

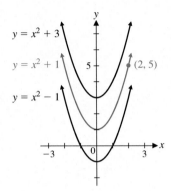

$y = x^2 + 3$

$y = x^2 + 1$

$y = x^2 - 1$

$(2, 5)$

Figure 2 $y = x^2 + C$

Matched Problem 4　Find the equation of the curve that passes through $(2, 6)$ if the slope of the curve is given by $dy/dx = 3x^2$ at any point x.

In certain situations, it is easier to determine the rate at which something happens than to determine how much of it has happened in a given length of time (for example, population growth rates, business growth rates, the rate of healing of a wound, rates of learning or forgetting). If a rate function (derivative) is given and we know the value of the dependent variable for a given value of the independent variable, then we can often find the original function by integration.

EXAMPLE 5　**Cost Function** If the marginal cost of producing x units of a commodity is given by

$$C'(x) = 0.3x^2 + 2x$$

and the fixed cost is \$2,000, find the cost function $C(x)$ and the cost of producing 20 units.

SOLUTION　Recall that marginal cost is the derivative of the cost function and that fixed cost is cost at a zero production level. So we want to find $C(x)$, given

$$C'(x) = 0.3x^2 + 2x \qquad C(0) = 2,000$$

We find the indefinite integral of $0.3x^2 + 2x$ and determine the arbitrary integration constant using $C(0) = 2,000$:

$$C'(x) = 0.3x^2 + 2x$$

$$C(x) = \int (0.3x^2 + 2x) \, dx$$

$$= 0.1x^3 + x^2 + K \qquad \text{Since C represents the cost, we use K for the constant of integration.}$$

But

$$C(0) = (0.1)0^3 + 0^2 + K = 2,000$$

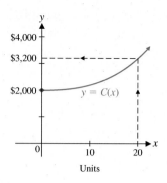

Figure 3

So $K = 2,000$, and the cost function is

$$C(x) = 0.1x^3 + x^2 + 2,000$$

We now find $C(20)$, the cost of producing 20 units:

$$C(20) = (0.1)20^3 + 20^2 + 2,000$$

$$= \$3,200$$

See Figure 3 for a geometric representation.

Matched Problem 5 Find the revenue function $R(x)$ when the marginal revenue is

$$R'(x) = 400 - 0.4x$$

and no revenue results at a zero production level. What is the revenue at a production level of 1,000 units?

EXAMPLE 6 **Advertising** A satellite radio station is launching an aggressive advertising campaign in order to increase the number of daily listeners. The station currently has 27,000 daily listeners, and management expects the number of daily listeners, $S(t)$, to grow at the rate of

$$S'(t) = 60t^{1/2}$$

listeners per day, where t is the number of days since the campaign began. How long should the campaign last if the station wants the number of daily listeners to grow to 41,000?

SOLUTION We must solve the equation $S(t) = 41,000$ for t, given that

$$S'(t) = 60t^{1/2} \qquad \text{and} \qquad S(0) = 27,000$$

First, we use integration to find $S(t)$:

$$\int S(t) = 60t^{1/2} \, dt$$

$$= 60 \frac{t^{3/2}}{\frac{3}{2}} + C$$

$$= 40t^{3/2} + C$$

Since

$$S(0) = 40(0)^{3/2} + C = 27,000$$

we have $C = 27,000$ and

$$S(t) = 40t^{3/2} + 27,000$$

Now we solve the equation $S(t) = 41,000$ for t:

$$40t^{3/2} + 27,000 = 41,000$$

$$40t^{3/2} = 14,000$$

$$t^{3/2} = 350$$

$$t = 350^{2/3} \qquad \text{Use a calculator.}$$

$$= 49.664\ 419\ldots$$

The advertising campaign should last approximately 50 days.

Matched Problem 6   There are 64,000 subscribers to an online fashion magazine. Due to competition from a new magazine, the number $C(t)$ of subscribers is expected to decrease at the rate of

$$C'(t) = -600t^{1/3}$$

subscribers per month, where t is the time in months since the new magazine began publication. How long will it take until the number of subscribers to the online fashion magazine drops to 46,000?

Exercises 6-1

A

In Problems 1–16, find each indefinite integral. Check by differentiating.

1. $\int 7\,dx$ **2.** $\int 10\,dx$

3. $\int 8x\,dx$ **4.** $\int 14x\,dx$

5. $\int 9x^2\,dx$ **6.** $\int 15x^2\,dx$

7. $\int x^5\,dx$ **8.** $\int x^8\,dx$

9. $\int x^{-3}\,dx$ **10.** $\int x^{-4}\,dx$

11. $\int 10x^{3/2}\,dx$ **12.** $\int 8x^{1/3}\,dx$

13. $\int \frac{3}{z}\,dz$ **14.** $\int \frac{7}{z}\,dz$

15. $\int 16e^u\,du$ **16.** $\int 5e^u\,du$

In Problems 17–24, find all the antiderivatives for each derivative.

17. $\frac{dy}{dx} = 200x^4$ **18.** $\frac{dx}{dt} = 42t^5$

19. $\frac{dP}{dx} = 24 - 6x$ **20.** $\frac{dy}{dx} = 3x^2 - 4x^3$

21. $\frac{dy}{dx} = e^x + 3$ **22.** $\frac{dy}{dx} = x - e^x$

23. $\frac{dx}{dt} = 5t^{-1} + 1$ **24.** $\frac{du}{dv} = \frac{4}{v} + \frac{v}{4}$

B

In Problems 25–30, discuss the validity of each statement. If the statement is always true, explain why. If not, give a counterexample.

25. The constant function $f(x) = \pi$ is an antiderivative of the constant function $k(x) = 0$.

26. The constant function $k(x) = 0$ is an antiderivative of the constant function $f(x) = \pi$.

27. If n is an integer, then $x^{n+1}/(n+1)$ is an antiderivative of x^n.

28. The constant function $k(x) = 0$ is an antiderivative of itself.

29. The function $h(x) = 5e^x$ is an antiderivative of itself.

30. The constant function $g(x) = 5e^\pi$ is an antiderivative of itself.

In Problems 31–34, could the three graphs in each figure be antiderivatives of the same function? Explain.

31.   **32.**

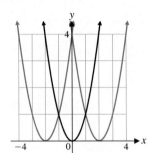

33.   **34.**

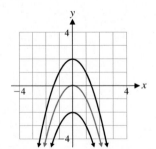

In Problems 35–50, find each indefinite integral. (Check by differentiation.)

35. $\int 5x(1-x)\,dx$ **36.** $\int x^2(1+x^3)\,dx$

37. $\int \frac{du}{\sqrt{u}}$ **38.** $\int \frac{dt}{\sqrt[3]{t}}$

39. $\int \frac{dx}{4x^3}$ **40.** $\int \frac{6\,dm}{m^2}$

41. $\displaystyle\int \frac{4+u}{u}\, du$

42. $\displaystyle\int \frac{1-y^2}{3y}\, dy$

43. $\displaystyle\int (5e^z + 4)\, dz$

44. $\displaystyle\int \frac{e^t - t}{2}\, dt$

45. $\displaystyle\int \left(3x^2 - \frac{2}{x^2}\right) dx$

46. $\displaystyle\int \left(4x^3 + \frac{2}{x^3}\right) dx$

47. $\displaystyle\int \left(3\sqrt{x} + \frac{2}{\sqrt{x}}\right) dx$

48. $\displaystyle\int \left(\frac{2}{\sqrt[3]{x}} - \sqrt[3]{x^2}\right) dx$

49. $\displaystyle\int \frac{e^x - 3x}{4}\, dx$

50. $\displaystyle\int \frac{e^x - 3x^2}{2}\, dx$

In Problems 51–58, find the particular antiderivative of each derivative that satisfies the given condition.

51. $C'(x) = 6x^2 - 4x; C(0) = 3{,}000$

52. $R'(x) = 600 - 0.6x; R(0) = 0$

53. $\dfrac{dx}{dt} = \dfrac{20}{\sqrt{t}}; x(1) = 40$

54. $\dfrac{dR}{dt} = \dfrac{100}{t^2}; R(1) = 400$

55. $\dfrac{dy}{dx} = 2x^{-2} + 3x^{-1} - 1; y(1) = 0$

56. $\dfrac{dy}{dx} = 3x^{-1} + x^{-2}; y(1) = 1$

57. $\dfrac{dx}{dt} = 4e^t - 2; x(0) = 1$

58. $\dfrac{dy}{dt} = 5e^t - 4; y(0) = -1$

59. Find the equation of the curve that passes through (2, 3) if its slope is given by

$$\frac{dy}{dx} = 4x - 3$$

for each x.

60. Find the equation of the curve that passes through (1, 3) if its slope is given by

$$\frac{dy}{dx} = 12x^2 - 12x$$

for each x.

C

In Problems 61–66, find each indefinite integral.

61. $\displaystyle\int \frac{2x^4 - x}{x^3}\, dx$

62. $\displaystyle\int \frac{x^{-1} - x^4}{x^2}\, dx$

63. $\displaystyle\int \frac{x^5 - 2x}{x^4}\, dx$

64. $\displaystyle\int \frac{1 - 3x^4}{x^2}\, dx$

65. $\displaystyle\int \frac{x^2 e^x - 2x}{x^2}\, dx$

66. $\displaystyle\int \frac{1 - xe^x}{x}\, dx$

In Problems 67–72, find the particular antiderivative of each derivative that satisfies the given condition.

67. $\dfrac{dM}{dt} = \dfrac{t^2 - 1}{t^2}; M(4) = 5$

68. $\dfrac{dR}{dx} = \dfrac{1 - x^4}{x^3}; R(1) = 4$

69. $\dfrac{dy}{dx} = \dfrac{5x + 2}{\sqrt[3]{x}}; y(1) = 0$

70. $\dfrac{dx}{dt} = \dfrac{\sqrt{t^3} - t}{\sqrt{t^3}}; x(9) = 4$

71. $p'(x) = -\dfrac{10}{x^2}; p(1) = 20$

72. $p'(x) = \dfrac{10}{x^3}; p(1) = 15$

In Problems 73–76, find the derivative or indefinite integral as indicated.

73. $\dfrac{d}{dx}\left(\displaystyle\int x^3\, dx\right)$

74. $\dfrac{d}{dt}\left(\displaystyle\int \frac{\ln t}{t}\, dt\right)$

75. $\displaystyle\int \frac{d}{dx}(x^4 + 3x^2 + 1)\, dx$

76. $\displaystyle\int \frac{d}{du}(e^{u^2})\, du$

77. Use differentiation to justify the formula

$$\int x^n\, dx = \frac{x^{n+1}}{n+1} + C$$

provided that $n \neq -1$.

78. Use differentiation to justify the formula

$$\int e^x\, dx = e^x + C$$

79. Assuming that $x > 0$, use differentiation to justify the formula

$$\int \frac{1}{x}\, dx = \ln|x| + C$$

80. Assuming that $x < 0$, use differentiation to justify the formula

$$\int \frac{1}{x}\, dx = \ln|x| + C$$

81. Show that the indefinite integral of the sum of two functions is the sum of the indefinite integrals.

[Hint: Assume that $\int f(x)\, dx = F(x) + C_1$ and $\int g(x)\, dx = G(x) + C_2$. Using differentiation, show that $F(x) + C_1 + G(x) + C_2$ is the indefinite integral of the function $s(x) = f(x) + g(x)$.]

82. Show that the indefinite integral of the difference of two functions is the difference of the indefinite integrals.

Applications

83. Cost function. The marginal average cost of producing x sports watches is given by

$$\overline{C}'(x) = -\frac{1,000}{x^2} \qquad \overline{C}(100) = 25$$

where $\overline{C}(x)$ is the average cost in dollars. Find the average cost function and the cost function. What are the fixed costs?

84. Renewable energy. In 2007, U.S. consumption of renewable energy was 6.8 quadrillion Btu (or 6.8×10^{15} Btu). Since the 1960s, consumption has been growing at a rate (in quadrillion Btu's per year) given by

$$f'(t) = 0.004t + 0.062$$

where t is years after 1960. Find $f(t)$ and estimate U.S. consumption of renewable energy in 2020.

85. Production costs. The graph of the marginal cost function from the production of x thousand bottles of sunscreen per month [where cost $C(x)$ is in thousands of dollars per month] is given in the figure.

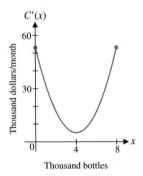

Figure for 85

(A) Using the graph shown, describe the shape of the graph of the cost function $C(x)$ as x increases from 0 to 8,000 bottles per month.

(B) Given the equation of the marginal cost function,

$$C'(x) = 3x^2 - 24x + 53$$

find the cost function if monthly fixed costs at 0 output are $30,000. What is the cost of manufacturing 4,000 bottles per month? 8,000 bottles per month?

(C) Graph the cost function for $0 \le x \le 8$. [Check the shape of the graph relative to the analysis in part (A).]

(D) Why do you think that the graph of the cost function is steeper at both ends than in the middle?

86. Revenue. The graph of the marginal revenue function from the sale of x sports watches is given in the figure.

(A) Using the graph shown, describe the shape of the graph of the revenue function $R(x)$ as x increases from 0 to 1,000.

(B) Find the equation of the marginal revenue function (the linear function shown in the figure).

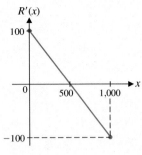

Figure for 86

(C) Find the equation of the revenue function that satisfies $R(0) = 0$. Graph the revenue function over the interval $[0, 1,000]$. [Check the shape of the graph relative to the analysis in part (A).]

(D) Find the price–demand equation and determine the price when the demand is 700 units.

87. Sales analysis. Monthly sales of an SUV model are expected to decline at the rate of

$$S'(t) = -24t^{1/3}$$

SUVs per month, where t is time in months and $S(t)$ is the number of SUVs sold each month. The company plans to stop manufacturing this model when monthly sales reach 300 SUVs. If monthly sales now ($t = 0$) are 1,200 SUVs, find $S(t)$. How long will the company continue to manufacture this model?

88. Sales analysis. The rate of change of the monthly sales of a newly released football game is given by

$$S'(t) = 500t^{1/4} \qquad S(0) = 0$$

where t is the number of months since the game was released and $S(t)$ is the number of games sold each month. Find $S(t)$. When will monthly sales reach 20,000 games?

 89. Sales analysis. Repeat Problem 87 if $S'(t) = -24t^{1/3} - 70$ and all other information remains the same. Use a graphing calculator to approximate the solution of the equation $S(t) = 800$ to two decimal places.

 90. Sales analysis. Repeat Problem 88 if $S'(t) = 500t^{1/4} + 300$ and all other information remains the same. Use a graphing calculator to approximate the solution of the equation $S(t) = 20,000$ to two decimal places.

91. Labor costs. A defense contractor is starting production on a new missile control system. On the basis of data collected during the assembly of the first 16 control systems, the production manager obtained the following function describing the rate of labor use:

$$g(x) = 2,400x^{-1/2}$$

$g(x)$ is the number of labor-hours required to assemble the xth unit of the control system. For example, after assembly of 16 units, the rate of assembly is 600 labor-hours per unit, and after assembly of 25 units, the rate of assembly is 480 labor-hours per unit. The more units assembled, the more efficient the process. If 19,200 labor-hours are required to assemble of the first 16 units, how many labor-hours $L(x)$ will be required to assemble the first x units? The first 25 units?

92. Labor costs. If the rate of labor use in Problem 91 is

$$g(x) = 2{,}000x^{-1/3}$$

and if the first 8 control units require 12,000 labor-hours, how many labor-hours, $L(x)$, will be required for the first x control units? The first 27 control units?

93. Weight–height. For an average person, the rate of change of weight W (in pounds) with respect to height h (in inches) is given approximately by

$$\frac{dW}{dh} = 0.0015h^2$$

Find $W(h)$ if $W(60) = 108$ pounds. Find the weight of an average person who is 5 feet, 10 inches, tall.

94. Wound healing. The area A of a healing wound changes at a rate given approximately by

$$\frac{dA}{dt} = -4t^{-3} \qquad 1 \le t \le 10$$

where t is time in days and $A(1) = 2$ square centimeters. What will the area of the wound be in 10 days?

95. Urban growth. The rate of growth of the population $N(t)$ of a new city t years after its incorporation is estimated to be

$$\frac{dN}{dt} = 400 + 600\sqrt{t} \qquad 0 \le t \le 9$$

If the population was 5,000 at the time of incorporation, find the population 9 years later.

96. Learning. A college language class was chosen for an experiment in learning. Using a list of 50 words, the experiment involved measuring the rate of vocabulary memorization at different times during a continuous 5-hour study session. It was found that the average rate of learning for the entire class was inversely proportional to the time spent studying and was given approximately by

$$V'(t) = \frac{15}{t} \qquad 1 \le t \le 5$$

If the average number of words memorized after 1 hour of study was 15 words, what was the average number of

words memorized after t hours of study for $1 \le t \le 5$? After 4 hours of study? Round answer to the nearest whole number.

Answers to Matched Problems

1. (A) $x^3 + C$
   (B)

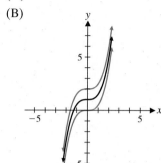

   (C) The graphs are vertical translations of each other.
2. (A) $2x + C$
   (B) $16e^t + C$
   (C) $\frac{3}{5}x^5 + C$
   (D) $\frac{1}{3}x^6 - x^3 + x + C$
   (E) $5\ln|x| - 4e^x + C$
3. (A) $\frac{6}{5}x^{5/3} + x^{-3} + C$
   (B) $\frac{5}{2}w^{8/5} + C$
   (C) $\frac{1}{3}x^3 - 4x^2 + C$
   (D) $6x^{4/3} - 12x^{1/2} + C$
   (E) $\frac{1}{4}x^4 + x^3 - x^2 - 6x + C$
4. $y = x^3 - 2$
5. $R(x) = 400x - 0.2x^2;\ R(1{,}000) = \$200{,}000$
6. $t = (40)^{3/4} \approx 16$ mo

6-2 Integration by Substitution

- Reversing the Chain Rule
- Integration by Substitution
- Additional Substitution Techniques
- Application

Many of the indefinite integral formulas introduced in the preceding section are based on corresponding derivative formulas studied earlier. We now consider indefinite integral formulas and procedures based on the chain rule for differentiation.

Reversing the Chain Rule

Recall the chain rule:

$$\frac{d}{dx}f[g(x)] = f'[g(x)]g'(x)$$

The expression on the right is formed from the expression on the left by taking the derivative of the outside function f and multiplying it by the derivative of the inside function *g.* If we recognize an integrand as a chain-rule form $f'[g(x)]g'(x)$, we can easily find an antiderivative and its indefinite integral:

$$\int f'[g(x)]g'(x)\, dx = f[g(x)] + C \tag{1}$$

We are interested in finding the indefinite integral

$$\int 3x^2 e^{x^3-1}\, dx \tag{2}$$

The integrand appears to be the chain-rule form $e^{g(x)}g'(x)$, which is the derivative of $e^{g(x)}$. Since

$$\frac{d}{dx}e^{x^3-1} = 3x^2 e^{x^3-1}$$

it follows that

$$\int 3x^2 e^{x^3-1}\, dx = e^{x^3-1} + C \tag{3}$$

How does the following indefinite integral differ from integral (2)?

$$\int x^2 e^{x^3-1}\, dx \tag{4}$$

It is missing the constant factor 3. That is, $x^2 e^{x^3-1}$ is within a constant factor of being the derivative of e^{x^3-1}. But because a constant factor can be moved across the integral sign, this causes us little trouble in finding the indefinite integral of $x^2 e^{x^3-1}$. We introduce the constant factor 3 and at the same time multiply by $\frac{1}{3}$ and move the $\frac{1}{3}$ factor outside the integral sign. This is equivalent to multiplying the integrand in integral (4) by 1:

$$\int x^2 e^{x^3-1}\, dx = \int \frac{3}{3} x^2 e^{x^3-1}\, dx \tag{5}$$

$$= \frac{1}{3}\int 3x^2 e^{x^3-1}\, dx = \frac{1}{3}e^{x^3-1} + C$$

The derivative of the rightmost side of equation (5) is the integrand of the indefinite integral (4). Check this.

How does the following indefinite integral differ from integral (2)?

$$\int 3x e^{x^3-1}\, dx \tag{6}$$

It is missing a variable factor *x.* This is more serious. As tempting as it might be, we *cannot* adjust integral (6) by introducing the variable factor *x* and moving $1/x$ outside the integral sign, as we did with the constant 3 in equation (5).

⚠ **CAUTION** A constant factor can be moved across an integral sign, but a variable factor cannot.

There is nothing wrong with educated guessing when you are looking for an antiderivative of a given function. You have only to check the result by differentiation. If you are right, you go on your way; if you are wrong, you simply try another approach.

In Section 4-4, we saw that the chain rule extends the derivative formulas for x^n, e^x, and $\ln x$ to derivative formulas for $[f(x)]^n$, $e^{f(x)}$, and $\ln [f(x)]$. The chain rule can also be used to extend the indefinite integral formulas discussed in Section 6-1. Some general formulas are summarized in the following box:

FORMULAS **General Indefinite Integral Formulas**

1. $\int [f(x)]^n f'(x)\,dx = \dfrac{[f(x)]^{n+1}}{n+1} + C, n \neq -1$

2. $\int e^{f(x)} f'(x)\,dx = e^{f(x)} + C$

3. $\int \dfrac{1}{f(x)} f'(x)\,dx = \ln|f(x)| + C$

We can verify each formula by using the chain rule to show that the derivative of the function on the right is the integrand on the left. For example,

$$\frac{d}{dx}[e^{f(x)} + C] = e^{f(x)} f'(x)$$

verifies formula 2.

EXAMPLE 1 **Reversing the Chain Rule**

(A) $\int (3x+4)^{10}(3)\,dx = \dfrac{(3x+4)^{11}}{11} + C$ Formula 1 with $f(x) = 3x+4$ and $f'(x) = 3$

Check:

$$\frac{d}{dx}\frac{(3x+4)^{11}}{11} = 11\frac{(3x+4)^{10}}{11}\frac{d}{dx}(3x+4) = (3x+4)^{10}(3)$$

(B) $\int e^{x^2}(2x)\,dx = e^{x^2} + C$ Formula 2 with $f(x) = x^2$ and $f'(x) = 2x$

Check:

$$\frac{d}{dx}e^{x^2} = e^{x^2}\frac{d}{dx}x^2 = e^{x^2}(2x)$$

(C) $\int \dfrac{1}{1+x^3}3x^2\,dx = \ln|1+x^3| + C$ Formula 3 with $f(x) = 1+x^3$ and $f'(x) = 3x^2$

Check:

$$\frac{d}{dx}\ln|1+x^3| = \frac{1}{1+x^3}\frac{d}{dx}(1+x^3) = \frac{1}{1+x^3}3x^2$$

Matched Problem 1 Find each indefinite integral.

(A) $\int (2x^3-3)^{20}(6x^2)\,dx$ (B) $\int e^{5x}(5)\,dx$

(C) $\int \dfrac{1}{4+x^2}2x\,dx$

Integration by Substitution

The key step in using formulas 1, 2, and 3 is recognizing the form of the integrand. Some people find it difficult to identify $f(x)$ and $f'(x)$ in these formulas and prefer to use a *substitution* to simplify the integrand. The *method of substitution,* which we now discuss, becomes increasingly useful as one progresses in studies of integration.

We start by introducing the idea of the *differential*. We represented the derivative by the symbol dy/dx taken as a whole. We now define dy and dx as two separate quantities with the property that their ratio is still equal to $f'(x)$:

> **DEFINITION Differentials**
>
> If $y = f(x)$ defines a differentiable function, then
>
> 1. The **differential dx** of the independent variable x is an arbitrary real number.
> 2. The **differential dy** of the dependent variable y is defined as the product of $f'(x)$ and dx:
> $$dy = f'(x)\,dx$$

Differentials involve mathematical subtleties that are treated carefully in advanced mathematics courses. Here, we are interested in them mainly as a bookkeeping device to aid in the process of finding indefinite integrals. We can always check an indefinite integral by differentiating.

EXAMPLE 2   **Differentials**

(A) If $y = f(x) = x^2$, then
$$dy \;\boxed{= f'(x)\,dx} = 2x\,dx$$

(B) If $u = g(x) = e^{3x}$, then
$$du \;\boxed{= g'(x)\,dx} = 3e^{3x}\,dx$$

(C) If $w = h(t) = \ln(4 + 5t)$, then
$$dw \;\boxed{= h'(t)\,dt} = \frac{5}{4 + 5t}\,dt$$

Matched Problem 2   (A) Find dy for $y = f(x) = x^3$.

(B) Find du for $u = h(x) = \ln(2 + x^2)$.

(C) Find dv for $v = g(t) = e^{-5t}$.

The **method of substitution** is developed through Examples 3–6.

EXAMPLE 3   **Using Substitution**   Find $\int (x^2 + 2x + 5)^5 (2x + 2)\,dx$.

SOLUTION   If
$$u = x^2 + 2x + 5$$

then the differential of u is
$$du = (2x + 2)\,dx$$

Notice that du is one of the factors in the integrand. Substitute u for $x^2 + 2x + 5$ and du for $(2x + 2)\,dx$ to obtain

$$\int (x^2 + 2x + 5)^5 (2x + 2)\,dx = \int u^5\,du$$

$$= \frac{u^6}{6} + C$$

$$= \frac{1}{6}(x^2 + 2x + 5)^6 + C \quad \text{Since } u = x^2 + 2x + 5$$

Check:

$$\frac{d}{dx}\frac{1}{6}(x^2 + 2x + 5)^6 = \frac{1}{6}(6)(x^2 + 2x + 5)^5\frac{d}{dx}(x^2 + 2x + 5)$$

$$= (x^2 + 2x + 5)^5(2x + 2)$$

Matched Problem 3   Find $\int (x^2 - 3x + 7)^4(2x - 3)\, dx$ by substitution.

The substitution method is also called the **change-of-variable method** since u replaces the variable x in the process. Substituting $u = f(x)$ and $du = f'(x)\, dx$ in formulas 1, 2, and 3 produces the general indefinite integral formulas 4, 5, and 6:

FORMULAS   General Indefinite Integral Formulas

4. $\displaystyle\int u^n\, du = \frac{u^{n+1}}{n + 1} + C, \qquad n \neq -1$

5. $\displaystyle\int e^u\, du = e^u + C$

6. $\displaystyle\int \frac{1}{u}\, du = \ln|u| + C$

These formulas are valid if u is an independent variable, or if u is a function of another variable and du is the differential of u with respect to that variable.

The substitution method for evaluating certain indefinite integrals is outlined as follows:

PROCEDURE   Integration by Substitution

Step 1   Select a substitution that appears to simplify the integrand. In particular, try to select u so that du is a factor in the integrand.

Step 2   Express the integrand entirely in terms of u and du, completely eliminating the original variable and its differential.

Step 3   Evaluate the new integral if possible.

Step 4   Express the antiderivative found in step 3 in terms of the original variable.

EXAMPLE 4   **Using Substitution**   Use a substitution to find each indefinite integral.

(A) $\displaystyle\int (3x + 4)^6(3)\, dx$

(B) $\displaystyle\int e^{t^2}(2t)\, dt$

SOLUTION   (A) If we let $u = 3x + 4$, then $du = 3\,dx$, and

$$\int (3x + 4)^6(3)\,dx = \int u^6\,du \qquad \text{Use formula 4.}$$

$$= \frac{u^7}{7} + C$$

$$= \frac{(3x + 4)^7}{7} + C \qquad \text{Since } u = 3x + 4$$

Check:

$$\frac{d}{dx}\frac{(3x + 4)^7}{7} = \frac{7(3x + 4)^6}{7}\frac{d}{dx}(3x + 4) = (3x + 4)^6(3)$$

(B) If we let $u = t^2$, then $du = 2t\,dt$, and

$$\int e^{t^2}(2t)\,dt = \int e^u\,du \qquad \text{Use formula 5.}$$

$$= e^u + C$$

$$= e^{t^2} + C \qquad \text{Since } u = t^2$$

Check:

$$\frac{d}{dt}e^{t^2} = e^{t^2}\frac{d}{dt}t^2 = e^{t^2}(2t)$$

Matched Problem 4   Use a substitution to find each indefinite integral.

(A) $\displaystyle\int (2x^3 - 3)^4(6x^2)\,dx$ 　　　　(B) $\displaystyle\int e^{5w}(5)\,dw$

Additional Substitution Techniques

In order to use the substitution method, **the integrand must be expressed entirely in terms of u and du.** In some cases, the integrand must be modified before making a substitution and using one of the integration formulas. Example 5 illustrates this process.

EXAMPLE 5   **Substitution Techniques** Integrate.

(A) $\displaystyle\int \frac{1}{4x + 7}\,dx$ 　　　　(B) $\displaystyle\int te^{-t^2}\,dt$

(C) $\displaystyle\int 4x^2\sqrt{x^3 + 5}\,dx$

SOLUTION   (A) If $u = 4x + 7$, then $du = 4\,dx$. We are missing a factor of 4 in the integrand to match formula 6 exactly. Recalling that a constant factor can be moved across an integral sign, we proceed as follows:

$$\int \frac{1}{4x + 7}\,dx = \int \frac{1}{4x + 7}\frac{4}{4}\,dx$$

$$= \frac{1}{4}\int \frac{1}{4x + 7}4\,dx \quad \text{Substitute } u = 4x + 7 \text{ and } du = 4\,dx.$$

$$= \frac{1}{4}\int \frac{1}{u}\,du \qquad \text{Use formula 6.}$$

$$= \tfrac{1}{4}\ln|u| + C$$

$$= \tfrac{1}{4}\ln|4x + 7| + C \quad \text{Since } u = 4x + 7$$

Check:

$$\frac{d}{dx}\frac{1}{4}\ln|4x+7| = \frac{1}{4}\frac{1}{4x+7}\frac{d}{dx}(4x+7) = \frac{1}{4}\frac{1}{4x+7}4 = \frac{1}{4x+7}$$

(B) If $u = -t^2$, then $du = -2t\,dt$. Proceed as in part (A):

$$\int te^{-t^2}\,dt = \int e^{-t^2}\frac{-2}{-2}t\,dt$$

$$= -\frac{1}{2}\int e^{-t^2}(-2t)\,dt \quad \text{Substitute } u = -t^2 \text{ and } du = -2t\,dt.$$

$$= -\frac{1}{2}\int e^{u}\,du \qquad\qquad \text{Use formula 5.}$$

$$= -\frac{1}{2}e^{u} + C$$

$$= -\frac{1}{2}e^{-t^2} + C \qquad\qquad \text{Since } u = -t^2$$

Check:

$$\frac{d}{dt}\left(-\frac{1}{2}e^{-t^2}\right) = -\frac{1}{2}e^{-t^2}\frac{d}{dt}(-t^2) = -\frac{1}{2}e^{-t^2}(-2t) = te^{-t^2}$$

(C) $\displaystyle\int 4x^2\sqrt{x^3+5}\,dx = 4\int \sqrt{x^3+5}(x^2)\,dx$ 　　Move the 4 across the integral sign and proceed as before.

$$= 4\int \sqrt{x^3+5}\frac{3}{3}(x^2)\,dx$$

$$= \frac{4}{3}\int \sqrt{x^3+5}(3x^2)\,dx \quad \text{Substitute } u = x^3+5 \text{ and } du = 3x^2\,dx.$$

$$= \frac{4}{3}\int \sqrt{u}\,du$$

$$= \frac{4}{3}\int u^{1/2}\,du \qquad\qquad \text{Use formula 4.}$$

$$= \frac{4}{3}\frac{u^{3/2}}{\frac{3}{2}} + C$$

$$= \frac{8}{9}u^{3/2} + C$$

$$= \frac{8}{9}(x^3+5)^{3/2} + C \qquad \text{Since } u = x^3+5$$

Check:

$$\frac{d}{dx}\left[\frac{8}{9}(x^3+5)^{3/2}\right] = \frac{4}{3}(x^3+5)^{1/2}\frac{d}{dx}(x^3+5)$$

$$= \frac{4}{3}(x^3+5)^{1/2}(3x^2) = 4x^2\sqrt{x^3+5}$$

Matched Problem 5　Integrate.

(A) $\displaystyle\int e^{-3x}\,dx$ 　　　　　　　　(B) $\displaystyle\int \frac{x}{x^2-9}\,dx$

(C) $\displaystyle\int 5t^2(t^3+4)^{-2}\,dt$

Even if it is not possible to find a substitution that makes an integrand match one of the integration formulas exactly, a substitution may simplify the integrand sufficiently so that other techniques can be used.

EXAMPLE 6 **Substitution Techniques** Find $\int \dfrac{x}{\sqrt{x+2}}\,dx.$

SOLUTION Proceeding as before, if we let $u = x + 2$, then $du = dx$ and

$$\int \frac{x}{\sqrt{x+2}}\,dx = \int \frac{x}{\sqrt{u}}\,du$$

Notice that this substitution is not complete because we have not expressed the integrand entirely in terms of u and du. As we noted earlier, only a constant factor can be moved across an integral sign, so we cannot move x outside the integral sign. Instead, we must return to the original substitution, solve for x in terms of u, and use the resulting equation to complete the substitution:

$$u = x + 2 \qquad \textit{Solve for x in terms of u.}$$

$$u - 2 = x \qquad \textit{Substitute this expression for x.}$$

Thus,

$$\int \frac{x}{\sqrt{x+2}}\,dx = \int \frac{u-2}{\sqrt{u}}\,du \qquad\qquad \textit{Simplify the integrand.}$$

$$= \int \frac{u-2}{u^{1/2}}\,du$$

$$= \int (u^{1/2} - 2u^{-1/2})\,du$$

$$\boxed{= \int u^{1/2}\,du - 2\int u^{-1/2}\,du}$$

$$= \frac{u^{3/2}}{\frac{3}{2}} - 2\frac{u^{1/2}}{\frac{1}{2}} + C$$

$$= \tfrac{2}{3}(x+2)^{3/2} - 4(x+2)^{1/2} + C \quad \textit{Since u = x + 2}$$

Check:

$$\frac{d}{dx}\left[\tfrac{2}{3}(x+2)^{3/2} - 4(x+2)^{1/2}\right] = (x+2)^{1/2} - 2(x+2)^{-1/2}$$

$$= \frac{x+2}{(x+2)^{1/2}} - \frac{2}{(x+2)^{1/2}}$$

$$= \frac{x}{(x+2)^{1/2}}$$

Matched Problem 6 Find $\int x\sqrt{x+1}\,dx.$

We can find the indefinite integral of some functions in more than one way. For example, we can use substitution to find

$$\int x(1+x^2)^2\,dx$$

by letting $u = 1 + x^2$. As a second approach, we can expand the integrand, obtaining

$$\int (x + 2x^3 + x^5)\,dx$$

for which we can easily calculate an antiderivative. In such a case, choose the approach that you prefer.

There are also some functions for which substitution is not an effective approach to finding the indefinite integral. For example, substitution is not helpful in finding

$$\int e^{x^2} \, dx \qquad \text{or} \qquad \int \ln x \, dx$$

Application

EXAMPLE 7

Price–Demand The market research department of a supermarket chain has determined that, for one store, the marginal price $p'(x)$ at x tubes per week for a certain brand of toothpaste is given by

$$p'(x) = -0.015e^{-0.01x}$$

Find the price–demand equation if the weekly demand is 50 tubes when the price of a tube is \$4.35. Find the weekly demand when the price of a tube is \$3.89.

SOLUTION

$$p(x) = \int -0.015e^{-0.01x} \, dx$$

$$= -0.015 \int e^{-0.01x} \, dx$$

$$= -0.015 \int e^{-0.01x} \frac{-0.01}{-0.01} \, dx$$

$$= \frac{-0.015}{-0.01} \int e^{-0.01x}(-0.01) \, dx \qquad \text{Substitute } u = -0.01x \\ \text{and } du = -0.01 \, dx.$$

$$= 1.5 \int e^u \, du$$

$$= 1.5e^u + C$$

$$= 1.5e^{-0.01x} + C \qquad \text{Since } u = -0.01x$$

We find C by noting that

$$p(50) = 1.5e^{-0.01(50)} + C = \$4.35$$

$$C = \$4.35 - 1.5e^{-0.5} \qquad \text{Use a calculator.}$$

$$= \$4.35 - 0.91$$

$$= \$3.44$$

So,

$$p(x) = 1.5e^{-0.01x} + 3.44$$

To find the demand when the price is \$3.89, we solve $p(x) = \$3.89$ for x:

$$1.5e^{-0.01x} + 3.44 = 3.89$$

$$1.5e^{-0.01x} = 0.45$$

$$e^{-0.01x} = 0.3$$

$$-0.01x = \ln 0.3$$

$$x = -100 \ln 0.3 \approx 120 \text{ tubes}$$

Matched Problem 7   The marginal price $p'(x)$ at a supply level of x tubes per week for a certain brand of toothpaste is given by

$$p'(x) = 0.001e^{0.01x}$$

Find the price–supply equation if the supplier is willing to supply 100 tubes per week at a price of $3.65 each. How many tubes would the supplier be willing to supply at a price of $3.98 each?

We conclude with two final cautions. The first was stated earlier, but it is worth repeating.

⚠ **CAUTION**

1. A variable cannot be moved across an integral sign.

2. An integral must be expressed entirely in terms of u and du before applying integration formulas 4, 5, and 6.

Exercises 6-2

A

In Problems 1–36, find each indefinite integral and check the result by differentiating.

1. $\int (3x + 5)^2 (3)\, dx$

2. $\int (6x - 1)^3 (6)\, dx$

3. $\int (x^2 - 1)^5 (2x)\, dx$

4. $\int (x^6 + 1)^4 (6x^5)\, dx$

5. $\int (5x^3 + 1)^{-3}(15x^2)\, dx$

6. $\int (4x^2 - 3)^{-6}(8x)\, dx$

7. $\int e^{5x}(5)\, dx$

8. $\int e^{x^3}(3x^2)\, dx$

9. $\int \frac{1}{1 + x^2}(2x)\, dx$

10. $\int \frac{1}{5x - 7}(5)\, dx$

11. $\int \sqrt{1 + x^4}\,(4x^3)\, dx$

12. $\int (x^2 + 9)^{-1/2}(2x)\, dx$

B

13. $\int (x + 3)^{10}\, dx$

14. $\int (x - 3)^{-4}\, dx$

15. $\int (6t - 7)^{-2}\, dt$

16. $\int (5t + 1)^3\, dt$

17. $\int (t^2 + 1)^5\, t\, dt$

18. $\int (t^3 + 4)^{-2}\, t^2\, dt$

19. $\int xe^{x^2}\, dx$

20. $\int e^{-0.01x}\, dx$

21. $\int \frac{1}{5x + 4}\, dx$

22. $\int \frac{x}{1 + x^2}\, dx$

23. $\int e^{1-t}\, dt$

24. $\int \frac{3}{2 - t}\, dt$

25. $\int \frac{t}{(3t^2 + 1)^4}\, dt$

26. $\int \frac{t^2}{(t^3 - 2)^5}\, dt$

27. $\int x\sqrt{x + 4}\, dx$

28. $\int x\sqrt{x - 9}\, dx$

29. $\int \frac{x}{\sqrt{x - 3}}\, dx$

30. $\int \frac{x}{\sqrt{x + 5}}\, dx$

31. $\int x(x - 4)^9\, dx$

32. $\int x(x + 6)^8\, dx$

33. $\int e^{2x}(1 + e^{2x})^3\, dx$

34. $\int e^{-x}(1 - e^{-x})^4\, dx$

35. $\int \frac{1 + x}{4 + 2x + x^2}\, dx$

36. $\int \frac{x^2 - 1}{x^3 - 3x + 7}\, dx$

In Problems 37–42, the indefinite integral can be found in more than one way. First use the substitution method to find the indefinite integral. Then find it without using substitution. Check that your answers are equivalent.

37. $\int 5(5x + 3)\, dx$

38. $\int -7(4 - 7x)\, dx$

39. $\int 2x(x^2 - 1)\, dx$

40. $\int 3x^2(x^3 + 1)\, dx$

41. $\int 5x^4(x^5)^4\, dx$

42. $\int 8x^7(x^8)^3\, dx$

 In Problems 43–48, suppose that the indicated "solutions" were given to you by a student whom you are tutoring.

(A) How would you have the student check each solution?

(B) Is the solution right or wrong? If the solution is wrong, explain what is wrong and how it can be corrected.

(C) Show a correct solution for each incorrect solution, and check the result by differentiation.

43. $\int \frac{1}{2x - 3}\, dx = \ln|2x - 3| + C$

44. $\int \frac{x}{x^2 + 5}\, dx = \ln|x^2 + 5| + C$

45. $\int x^3 e^{x^4} \, dx = e^{x^4} + C$

46. $\int e^{4x-5} \, dx = e^{4x-5} + C$

47. $\int 2(x^2 - 2)^2 \, dx = \dfrac{(x^2 - 2)^2}{3x} + C$

48. $\int (-10x)(x^2 - 3)^{-4} \, dx = (x^2 - 3)^{-5} + C$

C

In Problems 49–60, find each indefinite integral and check the result by differentiating.

49. $\int x\sqrt{3x^2 + 7} \, dx$ **50.** $\int x^2\sqrt{2x^3 + 1} \, dx$

51. $\int x(x^3 + 2)^2 \, dx$ **52.** $\int x(x^2 + 2)^2 \, dx$

53. $\int x^2(x^3 + 2)^2 \, dx$ **54.** $\int (x^2 + 2)^2 \, dx$

55. $\int \dfrac{x^3}{\sqrt{2x^4 + 3}} \, dx$ **56.** $\int \dfrac{x^2}{\sqrt{4x^3 - 1}} \, dx$

57. $\int \dfrac{(\ln x)^3}{x} \, dx$ **58.** $\int \dfrac{e^x}{1 + e^x} \, dx$

59. $\int \dfrac{1}{x^2} e^{-1/x} \, dx$ **60.** $\int \dfrac{1}{x \ln x} \, dx$

In Problems 61–66, find the antiderivative of each derivative.

61. $\dfrac{dx}{dt} = 7t^2(t^3 + 5)^6$ **62.** $\dfrac{dm}{dn} = 10n(n^2 - 8)^7$

63. $\dfrac{dy}{dt} = \dfrac{3t}{\sqrt{t^2 - 4}}$ **64.** $\dfrac{dy}{dx} = \dfrac{5x^2}{(x^3 - 7)^4}$

65. $\dfrac{dp}{dx} = \dfrac{e^x + e^{-x}}{(e^x - e^{-x})^2}$ **66.** $\dfrac{dm}{dt} = \dfrac{\ln(t - 5)}{t - 5}$

Applications

67. Price–demand equation. The marginal price for a weekly demand of x bottles of shampoo in a drugstore is given by

$$p'(x) = \dfrac{-6,000}{(3x + 50)^2}$$

Find the price–demand equation if the weekly demand is 150 when the price of a bottle of shampoo is $8. What is the weekly demand when the price is $6.50?

68. Price–supply equation. The marginal price at a supply level of x bottles of shampoo per week is given by

$$p'(x) = \dfrac{300}{(3x + 25)^2}$$

Find the price–supply equation if the distributor of the shampoo is willing to supply 75 bottles a week at a price of $5.00 per bottle. How many bottles would the supplier be willing to supply at a price of $5.15 per bottle?

69. Cost function. The weekly marginal cost of producing x pairs of tennis shoes is given by

$$C'(x) = 12 + \dfrac{500}{x + 1}$$

where $C(x)$ is cost in dollars. If the fixed costs are $2,000 per week, find the cost function. What is the average cost per pair of shoes if 1,000 pairs of shoes are produced each week?

70. Revenue function. The weekly marginal revenue from the sale of x pairs of tennis shoes is given by

$$R'(x) = 40 - 0.02x + \dfrac{200}{x + 1} \qquad R(0) = 0$$

where $R(x)$ is revenue in dollars. Find the revenue function. Find the revenue from the sale of 1,000 pairs of shoes.

71. Marketing. An automobile company is ready to introduce a new line of hybrid cars through a national sales campaign. After test marketing the line in a carefully selected city, the marketing research department estimates that sales (in millions of dollars) will increase at the monthly rate of

$$S'(t) = 10 - 10e^{-0.1t} \qquad 0 \le t \le 24$$

t months after the campaign has started.

(A) What will be the total sales $S(t)$ t months after the beginning of the national campaign if we assume no sales at the beginning of the campaign?

(B) What are the estimated total sales for the first 12 months of the campaign?

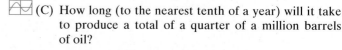 (C) When will the estimated total sales reach $100 million? Use a graphing calculator to approximate the answer to two decimal places.

72. Marketing. Repeat Problem 71 if the monthly rate of increase in sales is found to be approximated by

$$S'(t) = 20 - 20e^{-0.05t} \qquad 0 \le t \le 24$$

73. Oil production. Using production and geological data, the management of an oil company estimates that oil will be pumped from a field producing at a rate given by

$$R(t) = \dfrac{100}{t + 1} + 5 \qquad 0 \le t \le 20$$

where $R(t)$ is the rate of production (in thousands of barrels per year) t years after pumping begins. How many barrels of oil $Q(t)$ will the field produce in the first t years if $Q(0) = 0$? How many barrels will be produced in the first 9 years?

74. Oil production. Assume that the rate in Problem 73 is found to be

$$R(t) = \dfrac{120t}{t^2 + 1} + 3 \qquad 0 \le t \le 20$$

(A) When is the rate of production greatest?

(B) How many barrels of oil $Q(t)$ will the field produce in the first t years if $Q(0) = 0$? How many barrels will be produced in the first 5 years?

(C) How long (to the nearest tenth of a year) will it take to produce a total of a quarter of a million barrels of oil?

75. Biology. A yeast culture is growing at the rate of $w'(t) = 0.2e^{0.1t}$ grams per hour. If the starting culture weighs 2 grams, what will be the weight of the culture $W(t)$ after t hours? After 8 hours?

76. Medicine. The rate of healing for a skin wound (in square centimeters per day) is approximated by $A'(t) = -0.9e^{-0.1t}$. If the initial wound has an area of 9 square centimeters, what will its area $A(t)$ be after t days? After 5 days?

 77. Pollution. A contaminated lake is treated with a bactericide. The rate of increase in harmful bacteria t days after the treatment is given by

$$\frac{dN}{dt} = -\frac{2,000t}{1 + t^2} \qquad 0 \le t \le 10$$

where $N(t)$ is the number of bacteria per milliliter of water. Since dN/dt is negative, the count of harmful bacteria is decreasing.

(A) Find the minimum value of dN/dt.

(B) If the initial count was 5,000 bacteria per milliliter, find $N(t)$ and then find the bacteria count after 10 days.

(C) When (to two decimal places) is the bacteria count 1,000 bacteria per milliliter?

78. Pollution. An oil tanker aground on a reef is losing oil and producing an oil slick that is radiating outward at a rate given approximately by

$$\frac{dR}{dt} = \frac{60}{\sqrt{t + 9}} \qquad t \ge 0$$

where R is the radius (in feet) of the circular slick after t minutes. Find the radius of the slick after 16 minutes if the radius is 0 when $t = 0$.

79. Learning. An average student enrolled in an advanced typing class progressed at a rate of $N'(t) = 6e^{-0.1t}$ words per minute per week t weeks after enrolling in a 15-week course. If, at the beginning of the course, a student could type 40 words per minute, how many words per minute $N(t)$ would the student be expected to type t weeks into the course? After completing the course?

80. Learning. An average student enrolled in a stenotyping class progressed at a rate of $N'(t) = 12e^{-0.06t}$ words per minute per week t weeks after enrolling in a 15-week course. If, at the beginning of the course, a student could stenotype at zero words per minute, how many words per minute $N(t)$ would the student be expected to handle t weeks into the course? After completing the course?

81. College enrollment. The projected rate of increase in enrollment at a new college is estimated by

$$\frac{dE}{dt} = 5,000(t + 1)^{-3/2} \qquad t \ge 0$$

where $E(t)$ is the projected enrollment in t years. If enrollment is 2,000 now ($t = 0$), find the projected enrollment 15 years from now.

Answers to Matched Problems

1. (A) $\frac{1}{21}(2x^3 - 3)^{21} + C$
   (B) $e^{5x} + C$
   (C) $\ln|4 + x^2| + C$ or $\ln(4 + x^2) + C$, since $4 + x^2 > 0$

2. (A) $dy = 3x^2\,dx$
   (B) $du = \frac{2x}{2 + x^2}dx$
   (C) $dv = -5e^{-5t}\,dt$

3. $\frac{1}{5}(x^2 - 3x + 7)^5 + C$

4. (A) $\frac{1}{5}(2x^3 - 3)^5 + C$
   (B) $e^{5w} + C$

5. (A) $-\frac{1}{3}e^{-3x} + C$
   (B) $\frac{1}{2}\ln|x^2 - 9| + C$
   (C) $-\frac{5}{3}(t^3 + 4)^{-1} + C$

6. $\frac{2}{5}(x + 1)^{5/2} - \frac{2}{3}(x + 1)^{3/2} + C$

7. $p(x) = 0.1e^{0.01x} + 3.38$; 179 tubes

6-3 Differential Equations; Growth and Decay

- Differential Equations and Slope Fields
- Continuous Compound Interest Revisited
- Exponential Growth Law
- Population Growth, Radioactive Decay, and Learning
- Comparison of Exponential Growth Phenomena

In the preceding section, we considered equations of the form

$$\frac{dy}{dx} = 6x^2 - 4x \qquad p'(x) = -400e^{-0.04x}$$

These are examples of *differential equations*. In general, an equation is a **differential equation** if it involves an unknown function and one or more of its derivatives. Other examples of differential equations are

$$\frac{dy}{dx} = ky \qquad y'' - xy' + x^2 = 5 \qquad \frac{dy}{dx} = 2xy$$

The first and third equations are called **first-order** equations because each involves a first derivative but no higher derivative. The second equation is called a **second-**

order equation because it involves a second derivative and no higher derivatives. Finding solutions of different types of differential equations (functions that satisfy the equation) is the subject matter of entire books and courses on this topic. Here, we consider only a few special first-order equations that have immediate and significant applications.

We start by looking at some first-order equations geometrically, in terms of *slope fields*. We then consider continuous compound interest as modeled by a first-order differential equation. From this treatment, we can generalize our approach to a wide variety of other types of growth phenomena.

Differential Equations and Slope Fields

We introduce the concept of *slope field* through an example. Consider the first-order differential equation

$$\frac{dy}{dx} = 0.2y \tag{1}$$

A function f is a solution of equation (1) if $y = f(x)$ satisfies equation (1) for all values of x in the domain of f. Geometrically interpreted, equation (1) gives us the slope of a solution curve that passes through the point (x, y). For example, if $y = f(x)$ is a solution of equation (1) that passes through the point $(0, 2)$, then the slope of f at $(0, 2)$ is given by

$$\frac{dy}{dx} = 0.2(2) = 0.4$$

We indicate this relationship by drawing a short segment of the tangent line at the point $(0, 2)$, as shown in Figure 1A. The procedure is repeated for points $(-3, 1)$ and $(2, 3)$. Assuming that the graph of f passes through all three points, we sketch an approximate graph of f in Figure 1B.

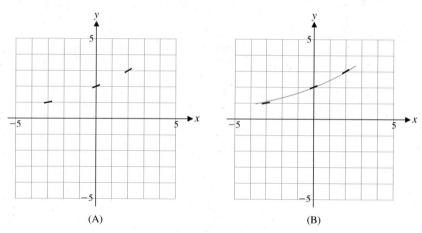

| (A) | (B) |

Figure 1

If we continue the process of drawing tangent line segments at each point grid in Figure 1—a task easily handled by computers, but not by hand—we obtain a *slope field*. A slope field for differential equation (1), drawn by a computer, is shown in Figure 2. In general, a **slope field** for a first-order differential equation is obtained by drawing tangent line segments determined by the equation at each point in a grid.

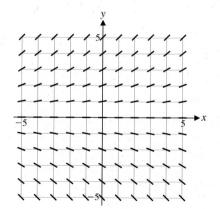

Figure 2

(A) In Figure 1A (or a copy), draw tangent line segments for a solution curve of differential equation (1) that passes through $(-3, -1)$, $(0, -2)$, and $(2, -3)$.

(B) In Figure 1B (or a copy), sketch an approximate graph of the solution curve that passes through the three points given in part (A). Repeat the tangent line segments first.

(C) What type of function, of all the elementary functions discussed in the first two chapters, appears to be a solution of differential equation (1)?

In Explore & Discuss 1, if you guessed that all solutions of equation (1) are exponential functions, you are to be congratulated. We now show that

$$y = Ce^{0.2x} \tag{2}$$

is a solution of equation (1) for any real number C. We substitute $y = Ce^{0.2x}$ into equation (1) to see if the left side is equal to the right side for all real x:

$$\frac{dy}{dx} = 0.2y$$

$$\text{Left side:} \quad \frac{dy}{dx} = \frac{d}{dx}(Ce^{0.2x}) = 0.2Ce^{0.2x}$$

$$\text{Right side:} \quad 0.2y = 0.2Ce^{0.2x}$$

So equation (2) is a solution of equation (1) for C any real number. Which values of C will produce solution curves that pass through $(0, 2)$ and $(0, -2)$, respectively? Substituting the coordinates of each point into equation (2) and solving for C, we obtain

$$y = 2e^{0.2x} \quad \text{and} \quad y = -2e^{0.2x} \tag{3}$$

The graphs of equations (3) are shown in Figure 3, and they confirm the results shown in Figure 1B.

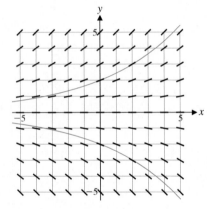

Figure 3

> **CONCEPTUAL INSIGHT**
>
> For a complicated first-order differential equation, say,
>
> $$\frac{dy}{dx} = \frac{3 + \sqrt{xy}}{x^2 - 5y^4}$$
>
> it may be impossible to find a formula analogous to (2) for its solutions. Nevertheless, it is routine to evaluate the right-hand side at each point in a grid. The resulting slope field provides a graphical representation of the solutions of the differential equation.

Drawing slope fields by hand is not a task for human beings: A 20-by-20 grid would require drawing 400 tangent line segments! Repetitive tasks of this type are what computers are for. A few problems in Exercise 6-3 involve interpreting slope fields, not drawing them.

Continuous Compound Interest Revisited

Let P be the initial amount of money deposited in an account, and let A be the amount in the account at any time t. Instead of assuming that the money in the account earns a particular rate of interest, suppose we say that the rate of growth of the amount of money in the account at any time t is proportional to the amount present at that time. Since dA/dt is the rate of growth of A with respect to t, we have

$$\frac{dA}{dt} = rA \qquad A(0) = P \qquad A, P > 0 \tag{4}$$

where r is an appropriate constant. We would like to find a function $A = A(t)$ that satisfies these conditions. Multiplying both sides of equation (4) by $1/A$, we obtain

$$\frac{1}{A}\frac{dA}{dt} = r$$

Now we integrate each side with respect to t:

$$\int \frac{1}{A}\frac{dA}{dt}\,dt = \int r\,dt \qquad \frac{dA}{dt}dt = A'(t)dt = dA$$

$$\int \frac{1}{A}dA = \int r\,dt$$

$$\ln|A| = rt + C \qquad |A| = A, \text{ since } A > 0$$

$$\ln A = rt + C$$

We convert this last equation into the equivalent exponential form

$$A = e^{rt+C} \qquad \text{Definition of logarithmic function:}$$
$$y = \ln x \text{ if and only if } x = e^y$$

$$= e^C e^{rt} \qquad \text{Property of exponents: } b^m b^n = b^{m+n}$$

Since $A(0) = P$, we evaluate $A(t) = e^C e^{rt}$ at $t = 0$ and set the result equal to P:

$$A(0) = e^C e^0 = e^C = P$$

Hence, $e^C = P$, and we can rewrite $A = e^C e^{rt}$ in the form

$$A = Pe^{rt}$$

This is the same continuous compound interest formula obtained in Section 5-1, where the principal P is invested at an annual nominal rate r compounded continuously for t years.

Exponential Growth Law

In general, if the rate of change of a quantity Q with respect to time is proportional to the amount of Q present and $Q(0) = Q_0$, then, proceeding in exactly the same way as we just did, we obtain the following theorem:

THEOREM 1   Exponential Growth Law

If $\dfrac{dQ}{dt} = rQ$ and $Q(0) = Q_0$, then $Q = Q_0 e^{rt}$,

where

$Q_0 =$ amount of Q at $t = 0$
$r =$ relative growth rate (expressed as a decimal)
$t =$ time
$Q =$ quantity at time t

The constant r in the exponential growth law is called the **relative growth rate**. If the relative growth rate is $r = 0.02$, then the quantity Q is growing at a rate $dQ/dt = 0.02Q$ (that is, 2% of the quantity Q per unit of time t). Note the distinction between the relative growth rate r and the rate of growth dQ/dt of the quantity Q. If $r < 0$, then $dQ/dt < 0$ and Q is decreasing. This type of growth is called **exponential decay**.

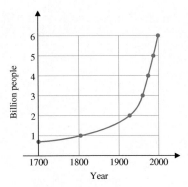

Figure 4 World population growth

Once we know that the rate of growth is proportional to the amount present, we recognize exponential growth and can use Theorem 1 without solving the differential equation each time. The exponential growth law applies not only to money invested at interest compounded continuously, but also to many other types of problems—population growth, radioactive decay, the depletion of a natural resource, and so on.

Population Growth, Radioactive Decay, and Learning

The world population passed 1 billion in 1804, 2 billion in 1927, 3 billion in 1960, 4 billion in 1974, 5 billion in 1987, and 6 billion in 1999, as illustrated in Figure 4. **Population growth** over certain periods often can be approximated by the exponential growth law of Theorem 1.

EXAMPLE 1 **Population Growth** India had a population of about 1.2 billion in 2010 ($t = 0$). Let P represent the population (in billions) t years after 2010, and assume a growth rate of 1.5% compounded continuously.

(A) Find an equation that represents India's population growth after 2010, assuming that the 1.5% growth rate continues.

(B) What is the estimated population (to the nearest tenth of a billion) of India in the year 2030?

(C) Graph the equation found in part (A) from 2000 to 2030.

SOLUTION (A) The exponential growth law applies, and we have

$$\frac{dP}{dt} = 0.015P \qquad P(0) = 1.2$$

Therefore,

$$P = 1.2e^{0.015t} \qquad\qquad (5)$$

(B) Using equation (5), we can estimate the population in India in 2030 ($t = 20$):

$$P = 1.2e^{0.015(20)} = 1.6 \text{ billion people}$$

(C) The graph is shown in Figure 5.

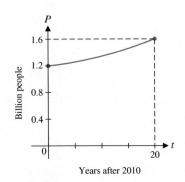

Figure 5 Population of India

Matched Problem 1 Assuming the same continuous compound growth rate as in Example 1, what will India's population be (to the nearest tenth of a billion) in the year 2020?

EXAMPLE 2 **Population Growth** If the exponential growth law applies to Canada's population growth, at what continuous compound growth rate will the population double over the next 100 years?

SOLUTION We must find r, given that $P = 2P_0$ and $t = 100$:

$$P = P_0e^{rt}$$
$$2P_0 = P_0e^{100r}$$
$$2 = e^{100r}$$

Take the natural logarithm of both sides and reverse the equation.

$$100r = \ln 2$$
$$r = \frac{\ln 2}{100}$$
$$\approx 0.0069 \quad \text{or} \quad 0.69\%$$

Matched Problem 2   If the exponential growth law applies to population growth in Nigeria, find the doubling time (to the nearest year) of the population if it grows at 2.1% per year compounded continuously.

We now turn to another type of exponential growth: **radioactive decay**. In 1946, Willard Libby (who later received a Nobel Prize in chemistry) found that as long as a plant or animal is alive, radioactive carbon-14 is maintained at a constant level in its tissues. Once the plant or animal is dead, however, the radioactive carbon-14 diminishes by radioactive decay at a rate proportional to the amount present.

$$\frac{dQ}{dt} = rQ \qquad Q(0) = Q_0$$

This is another example of the exponential growth law. The continuous compound rate of decay for radioactive carbon-14 is 0.000 123 8, so $r = -0.000\ 123\ 8$, since decay implies a negative continuous compound growth rate.

EXAMPLE 3   **Archaeology**   A human bone fragment was found at an archaeological site in Africa. If 10% of the original amount of radioactive carbon-14 was present, estimate the age of the bone (to the nearest 100 years).

SOLUTION   By the exponential growth law for

$$\frac{dQ}{dt} = -0.000\ 123\ 8Q \qquad Q(0) = Q_0$$

we have

$$Q = Q_0 e^{-0.0001238t}$$

We must find t so that $Q = 0.1Q_0$ (since the amount of carbon-14 present now is 10% of the amount Q_0 present at the death of the person).

$$0.1Q_0 = Q_0 e^{-0.0001238t}$$

$$0.1 = e^{-0.0001238t}$$

$$\ln 0.1 = \ln e^{-0.0001238t}$$

$$t = \frac{\ln 0.1}{-0.000\ 123\ 8} \approx 18,600 \text{ years}$$

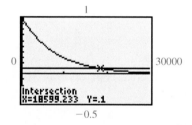

Figure 6 $y_1 = e^{-0.0001238x}$; $y_2 = 0.1$

See Figure 6 for a graphical solution to Example 3.

Matched Problem 3   Estimate the age of the bone in Example 3 (to the nearest 100 years) if 50% of the original amount of carbon-14 is present.

In learning certain skills, such as typing and swimming, one often assumes that there is a maximum skill attainable—say, M—and the rate of improvement is proportional to the difference between what has been achieved y and the maximum attainable M. Mathematically,

$$\frac{dy}{dt} = k(M - y) \qquad y(0) = 0$$

We solve this type of problem with the same technique used to obtain the exponential growth law. First, multiply both sides of the first equation by $1/(M - y)$ to get

$$\frac{1}{M - y}\frac{dy}{dt} = k$$

and then integrate each side with respect to t:

$$\int \frac{1}{M-y} \frac{dy}{dt} dt = \int k\, dt$$

$$-\int \frac{1}{M-y} \left(-\frac{dy}{dt}\right) dt = \int k\, dt \qquad \text{Substitute } u = M - y \text{ and}$$

$$-\int \frac{1}{u} du = \int k\, dt \qquad du = -dy = -\frac{dy}{dt} dt.$$

$$-\ln|u| = kt + C \qquad \text{Substitute } M - y, \text{ which is } > 0, \text{ for } u.$$

$$-\ln(M-y) = kt + C \qquad \text{Multiply both sides by } -1.$$

$$\ln(M-y) = -kt - C$$

Change this last equation to an equivalent exponential form:

$$M - y = e^{-kt-C}$$

$$M - y = e^{-C}e^{-kt}$$

$$y = M - e^{-C}e^{-kt}$$

Now, $y(0) = 0$; hence,

$$y(0) = M - e^{-C}e^0 = 0$$

Solving for e^{-C}, we obtain

$$e^{-C} = M$$

and our final solution is

$$y = M - Me^{-kt} = M(1 - e^{-kt})$$

EXAMPLE 4   **Learning** For a particular person learning to swim, the distance y (in feet) that the person is able to swim in 1 minute after t hours of practice is given approximately by

$$y = 50(1 - e^{-0.04t})$$

What is the rate of improvement (to two decimal places) after 10 hours of practice?

SOLUTION

$$y = 50 - 50e^{-0.04t}$$

$$y'(t) = 2e^{-0.04t}$$

$$y'(10) = 2e^{-0.04(10)} \approx 1.34 \text{ feet per hour of practice}$$

Matched Problem 4   In Example 4, what is the rate of improvement (to two decimal places) after 50 hours of practice?

Comparison of Exponential Growth Phenomena

The graphs and equations given in Table 1 compare several widely used growth models. These models are divided into two groups: unlimited growth and limited growth. Following each equation and graph is a short (and necessarily incomplete) list of areas in which the models are used.

Table 1 Exponential Growth

Description	Model	Solution	Graph	Uses
Unlimited growth: Rate of growth is proportional to the amount present	$\dfrac{dy}{dt} = ky$ $k, t > 0$ $y(0) = c$	$y = ce^{kt}$		• Short-term population growth (people, bacteria, etc.) • Growth of money at continuous compound interest • Price–supply curves
Exponential decay: Rate of growth is proportional to the amount present	$\dfrac{dy}{dt} = -ky$ $k, t > 0$ $y(0) = c$	$y = ce^{-kt}$		• Depletion of natural resources • Radioactive decay • Absorption of light in water • Price–demand curves • Atmospheric pressure (t is altitude)
Limited growth: Rate of growth is proportional to the difference between the amount present and a fixed limit	$\dfrac{dy}{dt} = k(M - y)$ $k, t > 0$ $y(0) = 0$	$y = M(1 - e^{-kt})$		• Sales fads (for example, skateboards) • Depreciation of equipment • Company growth • Learning
Logistic growth: Rate of growth is proportional to the amount present and to the difference between the amount present and a fixed limit	$\dfrac{dy}{dt} = ky(M - y)$ $k, t > 0$ $y(0) = \dfrac{M}{1 + c}$	$y = \dfrac{M}{1 + ce^{-kMt}}$		• Long-term population growth • Epidemics • Sales of new products • Spread of a rumor • Company growth

Exercises 6-3

A

In Problems 1–12, find the general or particular solution, as indicated, for each differential equation.

1. $\dfrac{dy}{dx} = 6x$ **2.** $\dfrac{dy}{dx} = 3x^{-2}$

3. $\dfrac{dy}{dx} = \dfrac{7}{x}$ **4.** $\dfrac{dy}{dx} = e^{0.1x}$

5. $\dfrac{dy}{dx} = e^{0.02x}$ **6.** $\dfrac{dy}{dx} = 8x^{-1}$

7. $\dfrac{dy}{dx} = x^2 - x;\ y(0) = 0$ **8.** $\dfrac{dy}{dx} = \sqrt{x};\ y(0) = 0$

9. $\dfrac{dy}{dx} = -2xe^{-x^2};\ y(0) = 3$ **10.** $\dfrac{dy}{dx} = e^{x-3};\ y(3) = -5$

11. $\dfrac{dy}{dx} = \dfrac{2}{1 + x};\ y(0) = 5$ **12.** $\dfrac{dy}{dx} = \dfrac{1}{4(3 - x)};\ y(0) = 1$

B

Problems 13–18 refer to the following slope fields:

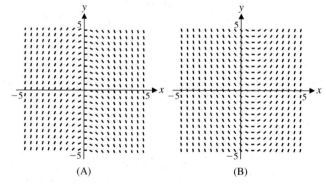

(A) (B)

Figure for 13–18

13. Which slope field is associated with the differential equation $dy/dx = x - 1$? Briefly justify your answer.

14. Which slope field is associated with the differential equation $dy/dx = -x$? Briefly justify your answer.

15. Solve the differential equation $dy/dx = x - 1$ and find the particular solution that passes through $(0, -2)$.

16. Solve the differential equation $dy/dx = -x$ and find the particular solution that passes through $(0, 3)$.

17. Graph the particular solution found in Problem 15 in the appropriate figure A or B (or a copy).

18. Graph the particular solution found in Problem 16 in the appropriate figure A or B (or a copy).

In Problems 19–26, find the general or particular solution, as indicated, for each differential equation.

19. $\dfrac{dy}{dt} = 2y$ **20.** $\dfrac{dy}{dt} = -3y$

21. $\dfrac{dy}{dx} = -0.5y;\ y(0) = 100$

22. $\dfrac{dy}{dx} = 0.1y;\ y(0) = -2.5$

23. $\dfrac{dx}{dt} = -5x$ **24.** $\dfrac{dx}{dt} = 4t$

25. $\dfrac{dx}{dt} = -5t$ **26.** $\dfrac{dx}{dt} = 4x$

C

Problems 27–34 refer to the following slope fields:

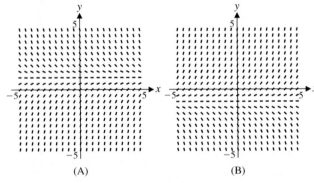

(A)   (B)

Figure for 27–34

27. Which slope field is associated with the differential equation $dy/dx = 1 - y$? Briefly justify your answer.

28. Which slope field is associated with the differential equation $dy/dx = y + 1$? Briefly justify your answer.

29. Show that $y = 1 - Ce^{-x}$ is a solution of the differential equation $dy/dx = 1 - y$ for any real number C. Find the particular solution that passes through $(0, 0)$.

30. Show that $y = Ce^x - 1$ is a solution of the differential equation $dy/dx = y + 1$ for any real number C. Find the particular solution that passes through $(0, 0)$.

31. Graph the particular solution found in Problem 29 in the appropriate figure, Figure A or Figure B (or a copy).

32. Graph the particular solution found in Problem 30 in the appropriate figure A or B (or a copy).

33. Use a graphing calculator to graph $y = 1 - Ce^{-x}$ for $C = -2, -1, 1$, and 2, for $-5 \le x \le 5, -5 \le y \le 5$, all in the same viewing window. Observe how the solution curves go with the flow of the tangent line segments in the corresponding slope field shown in figure A or figure B.

34. Use a graphing calculator to graph $y = Ce^x - 1$ for $C = -2, -1, 1$, and 2, for $-5 \le x \le 5, -5 \le y \le 5$, all in the same viewing window. Observe how the solution curves go with the flow of the tangent line segments in the corresponding slope field shown in figure A or figure B.

35. Show that $y = \sqrt{C - x^2}$ is a solution of the differential equation $dy/dx = -x/y$ for any positive real number C. Find the particular solution that passes through $(3, 4)$.

36. Show that $y = \sqrt{x^2 + C}$ is a solution of the differential equation $dy/dx = x/y$ for any real number C. Find the particular solution that passes through $(-6, 7)$.

37. Show that $y = Cx$ is a solution of the differential equation $dy/dx = y/x$ for any real number C. Find the particular solution that passes through $(-8, 24)$.

38. Show that $y = C/x$ is a solution of the differential equation $dy/dx = -y/x$ for any real number C. Find the particular solution that passes through $(2, 5)$.

39. Show that $y = 1/(1 + ce^{-t})$ is a solution of the differential equation $dy/dt = y(1 - y)$ for any real number c. Find the particular solution that passes through $(0, -1)$.

40. Show that $y = 2/(1 + ce^{-6t})$ is a solution of the differential equation $dy/dt = 3y(2 - y)$ for any real number c. Find the particular solution that passes through $(0, 1)$.

In Problems 41–48, use a graphing calculator to graph the given examples of the various cases in Table 1 on page 379.

41. Unlimited growth:

$y = 1,000e^{0.08t}$
$0 \le t \le 15$
$0 \le y \le 3,500$

42. Unlimited growth:

$y = 5,250e^{0.12t}$
$0 \le t \le 10$
$0 \le y \le 20,000$

43. Exponential decay:

$p = 100e^{-0.05x}$
$0 \le x \le 30$
$0 \le p \le 100$

44. Exponential decay:

$p = 1,000e^{-0.08x}$
$0 \le x \le 40$
$0 \le p \le 1,000$

45. Limited growth:

$N = 100(1 - e^{-0.05t})$
$0 \le t \le 100$
$0 \le N \le 100$

46. Limited growth:

$$N = 1,000(1 - e^{-0.07t})$$
$$0 \le t \le 70$$
$$0 \le N \le 1,000$$

47. Logistic growth:

$$N = \frac{1,000}{1 + 999e^{-0.4t}}$$
$$0 \le t \le 40$$
$$0 \le N \le 1,000$$

48. Logistic growth:

$$N = \frac{400}{1 + 99e^{-0.4t}}$$
$$0 \le t \le 30$$
$$0 \le N \le 400$$

49. Show that the rate of logistic growth, $dy/dt = ky(M - y)$, has its maximum value when $y = M/2$.

50. Find the value of t for which the logistic function

$$y = \frac{M}{1 + ce^{-kMt}}$$

is equal to $M/2$.

51. Let $Q(t)$ denote the population of the world at time t. In 1999, the world population was 6.0 billion and increasing at 1.3% per year; in 2009, it was 6.8 billion and increasing at 1.2% per year. In which year, 1999 or 2009, was dQ/dt (the rate of growth of Q with respect to t) greater? Explain.

52. Refer to Problem 51. Explain why the world population function $Q(t)$ does not satisfy an exponential growth law.

Applications

53. Continuous compound interest. Find the amount A in an account after t years if

$$\frac{dA}{dt} = 0.03A \quad \text{and} \quad A(0) = 1,000$$

54. Continuous compound interest. Find the amount A in an account after t years if

$$\frac{dA}{dt} = 0.02A \quad \text{and} \quad A(0) = 5,250$$

55. Continuous compound interest. Find the amount A in an account after t years if

$$\frac{dA}{dt} = rA \quad A(0) = 8,000 \quad A(2) = 8,260.14$$

56. Continuous compound interest. Find the amount A in an account after t years if

$$\frac{dA}{dt} = rA \quad A(0) = 5,000 \quad A(5) = 5,581.39$$

57. Price–demand. The marginal price dp/dx at x units of demand per week is proportional to the price p. There is no weekly demand at a price of $100 per unit [$p(0) = 100$], and there is a weekly demand of 5 units at a price of $77.88 per unit [$p(5) = 77.88$].

(A) Find the price–demand equation.

(B) At a demand of 10 units per week, what is the price?

(C) Graph the price–demand equation for $0 \le x \le 25$.

58. Price–supply. The marginal price dp/dx at x units of supply per day is proportional to the price p. There is no supply at a price of $10 per unit [$p(0) = 10$], and there is a daily supply of 50 units at a price of $12.84 per unit [$p(50) = 12.84$].

(A) Find the price–supply equation.

(B) At a supply of 100 units per day, what is the price?

(C) Graph the price–supply equation for $0 \le x \le 250$.

59. Advertising. A company is trying to expose a new product to as many people as possible through TV ads. Suppose that the rate of exposure to new people is proportional to the number of those who have not seen the product out of L possible viewers. No one is aware of the product at the start of the campaign, and after 10 days, 40% of L are aware of the product. Mathematically,

$$\frac{dN}{dt} = k(L - N) \quad N(0) = 0 \quad N(10) = 0.4L$$

(A) Solve the differential equation.

(B) What percent of L will have been exposed after 5 days of the campaign?

(C) How many days will it take to expose 80% of L?

(D) Graph the solution found in part (A) for $0 \le t \le 90$.

60. Advertising. Suppose that the differential equation for Problem 59 is

$$\frac{dN}{dt} = k(L - N) \quad N(0) = 0 \quad N(10) = 0.1L$$

(A) Explain what the equation $N(10) = 0.1L$ means.

(B) Solve the differential equation.

(C) How many days will it take to expose 50% of L?

(D) Graph the solution found in part (B) for $0 \le t \le 300$.

61. Biology. For relatively clear bodies of water, the intensity of light is reduced according to

$$\frac{dI}{dx} = -kI \quad I(0) = I_0$$

where I is the intensity of light at x feet below the surface. For the Sargasso Sea off the West Indies, $k = 0.00942$. Find I in terms of x, and find the depth at which the light is reduced to half of that at the surface.

62. Blood pressure. Under certain assumptions, the blood pressure P in the largest artery in the human body (the aorta) changes between beats with respect to time t according to

$$\frac{dP}{dt} = -aP \quad P(0) = P_0$$

where a is a constant. Find $P = P(t)$ that satisfies both conditions.

63. Drug concentration. A single injection of a drug is administered to a patient. The amount Q in the body then decreases at a rate proportional to the amount present. For a particular drug, the rate is 4% per hour. Thus,

$$\frac{dQ}{dt} = -0.04Q \quad Q(0) = Q_0$$

where t is time in hours.

(A) If the initial injection is 3 milliliters [$Q(0) = 3$], find $Q = Q(t)$ satisfying both conditions.

(B) How many milliliters (to two decimal places) are in the body after 10 hours?

(C) How many hours (to two decimal places) will it take for only 1 milliliter of the drug to be left in the body?

(D) Graph the solution found in part (A).

64. Simple epidemic. A community of 1,000 people is homogeneously mixed. One person who has just returned from another community has influenza. Assume that the home community has not had influenza shots and all are susceptible. One mathematical model assumes that influenza tends to spread at a rate in direct proportion to the number N who have the disease and to the number $1,000 - N$ who have not yet contracted the disease. Mathematically,

$$\frac{dN}{dt} = kN(1,000 - N) \qquad N(0) = 1$$

where N is the number of people who have contracted influenza after t days. For $k = 0.0004$, $N(t)$ is given by

$$N(t) = \frac{1,000}{1 + 999e^{-0.4t}}$$

(A) How many people have contracted influenza after 10 days? After 20 days?

(B) How many days will it take until half the community has contracted influenza?

(C) Find $\lim_{t \to \infty} N(t)$.

(D) Graph $N = N(t)$ for $0 \le t \le 30$.

65. Nuclear accident. One of the dangerous radioactive isotopes detected after the Chernobyl nuclear disaster in 1986 was cesium-137. If 93.3% of the cesium-137 emitted during the disaster was still present 3 years later, find the continuous compound rate of decay of this isotope.

66. Insecticides. Many countries have banned the use of the insecticide DDT because of its long-term adverse effects. Five years after a particular country stopped using DDT, the amount of DDT in the ecosystem had declined to 75% of the amount present at the time of the ban. Find the continuous compound rate of decay of DDT.

67. Archaeology. A skull found in an ancient tomb has 5% of the original amount of radioactive carbon-14 present. Estimate the age of the skull. (See Example 3.)

68. Learning. For a person learning to type, the number N of words per minute that the person could type after t hours of practice was given by

$$N = 100(1 - e^{-0.02t})$$

What is the rate of improvement after 10 hours of practice? After 40 hours of practice?

69. Small-group analysis. In a study on small-group dynamics, sociologists found that when 10 members of a discussion group were ranked according to the number of times each participated, the number $N(k)$ of times that the kth-ranked person participated was given by

$$N(k) = N_1 e^{-0.11(k-1)} \qquad 1 \le k \le 10$$

where N_1 is the number of times that the first-ranked person participated in the discussion. If $N_1 = 180$, in a discussion group of 10 people, estimate how many times the sixth-ranked person participated. How about the 10th-ranked person?

70. Perception. The Weber–Fechner law concerns a person's sensed perception of various strengths of stimulation involving weights, sound, light, shock, taste, and so on. One form of the law states that the rate of change of sensed sensation S with respect to stimulus R is inversely proportional to the strength of the stimulus R. So

$$\frac{dS}{dR} = \frac{k}{R}$$

where k is a constant. If we let R_0 be the threshold level at which the stimulus R can be detected (the least amount of sound, light, weight, and so on, that can be detected), then

$$S(R_0) = 0$$

Find a function S in terms of R that satisfies these conditions.

71. Rumor propagation. Sociologists have found that a rumor tends to spread at a rate in direct proportion to the number x who have heard it and to the number $P - x$ who have not, where P is the total population. If a resident of a 400-student dormitory hears a rumor that there is a case of TB on campus, then $P = 400$ and

$$\frac{dx}{dt} = 0.001x(400 - x) \qquad x(0) = 1$$

where t is time (in minutes). From these conditions, it can be shown that

$$x(t) = \frac{400}{1 + 399e^{-0.4t}}$$

(A) How many people have heard the rumor after 5 minutes? after 20 minutes?

(B) Find $\lim_{t \to \infty} x(t)$.

(C) Graph $x = x(t)$ for $0 \le t \le 30$.

72. Rumor propagation. In Problem 71, how long (to the nearest minute) will it take for half of the group of 400 to have heard the rumor?

Answers to Matched Problems

1. 1.4 billion people   **2.** 33 yr

3. 5,600 yr   **4.** 0.27 ft/hr

6-4   The Definite Integral

- Approximating Areas by Left and Right Sums
- The Definite Integral as a Limit of Sums
- Properties of the Definite Integral

The first three sections of this chapter focused on the *indefinite integral*. In this section, we introduce the *definite integral*. The definite integral is used to compute areas, probabilities, average values of functions, future values of continuous income streams, and many other quantities. Initially, the concept of the definite integral may seem unrelated to the notion of the indefinite integral. There is, however, a close connection between the two integrals. The fundamental theorem of calculus, discussed in Section 6-5, makes that connection precise.

Approximating Areas by Left and Right Sums

How do we find the shaded area in Figure 1? That is, how do we find the area bounded by the graph of $f(x) = 0.25x^2 + 1$, the x axis, and the vertical lines $x = 1$ and $x = 5$? [This cumbersome description is usually shortened to "the area under the graph of $f(x) = 0.25x^2 + 1$ from $x = 1$ to $x = 5$."] Our standard geometric area formulas do not apply directly, but the formula for the area of a rectangle can be used indirectly. To see how, we look at a method of approximating the area under the graph by using rectangles. This method will give us any accuracy desired, which is quite different from finding the area exactly. Our first area approximation is made by dividing the interval $[1, 5]$ on the x axis into four equal parts, each of length

$$\Delta x = \frac{5-1}{4} = 1^*$$

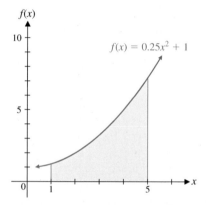

Figure 1 What is the shaded area?

We then place a **left rectangle** on each subinterval, that is, a rectangle whose base is the subinterval and whose height is the value of the function at the left endpoint of the subinterval (see Fig. 2).

Summing the areas of the left rectangles in Figure 2 results in a **left sum** of four rectangles, denoted by L_4, as follows:

$$L_4 = f(1)\cdot 1 + f(2)\cdot 1 + f(3)\cdot 1 + f(4)\cdot 1$$
$$= 1.25 + 2.00 + 3.25 + 5 = 11.5$$

From Figure 3, since $f(x)$ is increasing, we see that the left sum L_4 underestimates the area, and we can write

$$11.5 = L_4 < \text{Area}$$

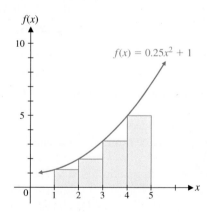

Figure 2 Left rectangles

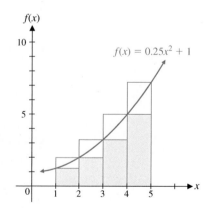

Figure 3 Left and right rectangles

*It is customary to denote the length of the subintervals by Δx, which is read "delta x," since Δ is the Greek capital letter delta.

> **EXPLORE & DISCUSS 1**

If $f(x)$ were decreasing over the interval $[1, 5]$, would the left sum L_4 over- or under-estimate the actual area under the curve? Explain.

Similarly, we use the right endpoint of each subinterval to find the height of the **right rectangle** placed on top of it. Superimposing right rectangles on top of Figure 2, we get Figure 3.

Summing the areas of the right rectangles in Figure 3 results in a **right sum** of four rectangles, denoted by R_4, as follows (compare R_4 with L_4 and note that R_4 can be obtained from L_4 by deleting one rectangular area and adding one more):

$$R_4 = f(2) \cdot 1 + f(3) \cdot 1 + f(4) \cdot 1 + f(5) \cdot 1$$
$$= 2.00 + 3.25 + 5.00 + 7.25 = 17.5$$

From Figure 3, since $f(x)$ is increasing, we see that the right sum R_4 overestimates the area, and we conclude that the actual area is between 11.5 and 17.5. That is,

$$11.5 = L_4 < \text{Area} < R_4 = 17.5$$

> **EXPLORE & DISCUSS 2**

If $f(x)$ in Figure 3 were decreasing over the interval $[1, 5]$, would the right sum R_4 overestimate or underestimate the actual area under the curve? Explain.

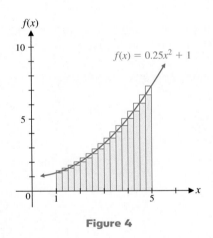

Figure 4

The first approximation of the area under the curve in Figure 1 is fairly coarse, but the method outlined can be continued with increasingly accurate results by dividing the interval $[1, 5]$ into more and more subintervals of equal horizontal length. Of course, this is not a job for hand calculation, but a job that computers are designed to do.* Figure 4 shows left- and right-rectangle approximations for 16 equal subdivisions.

For this case,

$$\Delta x = \frac{5 - 1}{16} = 0.25$$

$$L_{16} = f(1) \cdot \Delta x + f(1.25) \cdot \Delta x + \cdots + f(4.75) \cdot \Delta x$$
$$= 13.59$$

$$R_{16} = f(1.25) \cdot \Delta x + f(1.50) \cdot \Delta x + \cdots + f(5) \cdot \Delta x$$
$$= 15.09$$

Thus, we now know that the area under the curve is between 13.59 and 15.09. That is,

$$13.59 = L_{16} < \text{Area} < R_{16} = 15.09$$

For 100 equal subdivisions, computer calculations give us

$$14.214 = L_{100} < \text{Area} < R_{100} = 14.454$$

The **error in an approximation** is the absolute value of the difference between the approximation and the actual value. In general, neither the actual value nor the error in an approximation is known. However, it is often possible to calculate an **error bound**—a positive number such that the error is guaranteed to be less than or equal to that number.

The error in the approximation of the area under the graph of f from $x = 1$ to $x = 5$ by the left sum L_{16} (or the right sum R_{16}) is less than the sum of the areas of the small rectangles in Figure 4. By stacking those rectangles (see Fig. 5), we see that

$$\text{Error} = |\text{Area} - L_{16}| < |f(5) - f(1)| \cdot \Delta x = 1.5$$

Therefore, 1.5 is an error bound for the approximation of the area under f by L_{16}. We can apply the same stacking argument to any positive function that is increasing on $[a, b]$ or decreasing on $[a, b]$, to obtain the error bound in Theorem 1.

---

*The computer software that accompanies this book will perform these calculations (see the preface).

$f(x)$

10

$f(x) = 0.25x^2 + 1$

5

$f(5) - f(1)$

Δx

0   1   5 x

Figure 5

> **THEOREM 1   Error Bounds for Approximations of Area by Left or Right Sums**
> If $f(x) > 0$ and is either increasing on $[a, b]$ or decreasing on $[a, b]$, then
>
> $$|f(b) - f(a)| \cdot \frac{b - a}{n}$$
>
> is an error bound for the approximation of the area between the graph of f and the x axis, from $x = a$ to $x = b$, by L_n or R_n.

Because the error bound of Theorem 1 approaches 0 as $n \to \infty$, it can be shown that left and right sums, for certain functions, approach the same limit as $n \to \infty$.

> **THEOREM 2   Limits of Left and Right Sums**
> If $f(x) > 0$ and is either increasing on $[a, b]$ or decreasing on $[a, b]$, then its left and right sums approach the same real number as $n \to \infty$.

The number approached as $n \to \infty$ by the left and right sums in Theorem 2 is the area between the graph of f and the x axis from $x = a$ to $x = b$.

EXAMPLE 1   **Approximating Areas**   Given the function $f(x) = 9 - 0.25x^2$, we want to approximate the area under $y = f(x)$ from $x = 2$ to $x = 5$.

(A) Graph the function over the interval $[0, 6]$. Then draw left and right rectangles for the interval $[2, 5]$ with $n = 6$.

(B) Calculate L_6, R_6, and error bounds for each.

(C) How large should n be in order for the approximation of the area by L_n or R_n to be within 0.05 of the true value?

SOLUTION   (A) $\Delta x = 0.5$:

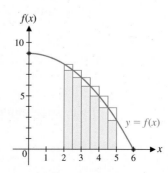

(B) $L_6 = f(2) \cdot \Delta x + f(2.5) \cdot \Delta x + f(3) \cdot \Delta x + f(3.5) \cdot \Delta x + f(4) \cdot \Delta x$

$\qquad + f(4.5) \cdot \Delta x = 18.53$

$R_6 = f(2.5) \cdot \Delta x + f(3) \cdot \Delta x + f(3.5) \cdot \Delta x + f(4) \cdot \Delta x$

$\qquad + f(4.5) \cdot \Delta x + f(5) \cdot \Delta x = 15.91$

The error bound for L_6 and R_6 is

$$\text{error} \leq |f(5) - f(2)|\frac{5 - 2}{6} = |2.75 - 8|(0.5) = 2.625$$

(C) For L_n and R_n, find n such that error ≤ 0.05:

$$|f(b) - f(a)|\frac{b - a}{n} \leq 0.05$$

$$|2.75 - 8|\frac{3}{n} \leq 0.05$$

$$|-5.25|\frac{3}{n} \leq 0.05$$

$$15.75 \leq 0.05n$$

$$n \geq \frac{15.75}{0.05} = 315$$

Matched Problem 1   Given the function $f(x) = 8 - 0.5x^2$, we want to approximate the area under $y = f(x)$ from $x = 1$ to $x = 3$.

(A) Graph the function over the interval $[0, 4]$. Then draw left and right rectangles for the interval $[1, 3]$ with $n = 4$.

(B) Calculate L_4, R_4, and error bounds for each.

(C) How large should n be in order for the approximation of the area by L_n or R_n to be within 0.5 of the true value?

CONCEPTUAL INSIGHT

Note from Example 1(C) that a relatively large value of n ($n = 315$) is required to approximate the area by L_n or R_n to within 0.05. In other words, 315 rectangles must be used, and 315 terms must be summed, to guarantee that the error does not exceed 0.05. We can obtain a more efficient approximation of the area (fewer terms are summed to achieve a given accuracy) by replacing rectangles with trapezoids. The resulting **trapezoidal rule**, and other methods for approximating areas, are discussed in Group Activity 1 in this book's Web site.

The Definite Integral as a Limit of Sums

Left and right sums are special cases of more general sums, called *Riemann sums* [named after the German mathematician Georg Riemann (1826–1866)], that are used to approximate areas by means of rectangles.

Let f be a function defined on the interval $[a, b]$. We partition $[a, b]$ into n subintervals of equal length $\Delta x = (b - a)/n$ with endpoints

$$a = x_0 < x_1 < x_2 < \cdots < x_n = b$$

Then, using **summation notation** (see Appendix B-1), we have

Left sum: $L_n = f(x_0)\Delta x + f(x_1)\Delta x + \cdots + f(x_{n-1})\Delta x = \displaystyle\sum_{k=1}^{n} f(x_{k-1})\Delta x$

Right sum: $R_n = f(x_1)\Delta x + f(x_2)\Delta x + \cdots + f(x_n)\Delta x = \sum\limits_{k=1}^{n} f(x_k)\Delta x$

Riemann sum: $S_n = f(c_1)\Delta x + f(c_2)\Delta x + \cdots + f(c_n)\Delta x = \sum\limits_{k=1}^{n} f(c_k)\Delta x$

In a **Riemann sum,*** each c_k is required to belong to the subinterval $[x_{k-1}, x_k]$. Left and right sums are the special cases of Riemann sums in which c_k is the left endpoint or right endpoint, respectively, of the subinterval. If $f(x) > 0$, then each term of a Riemann sum S_n represents the area of a rectangle having height $f(c_k)$ and width Δx (see Fig. 6). If $f(x)$ has both positive and negative values, then some terms of S_n represent areas of rectangles, and others represent the negatives of areas of rectangles, depending on the sign of $f(c_k)$ (see Fig. 7).

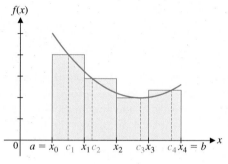

Figure 6

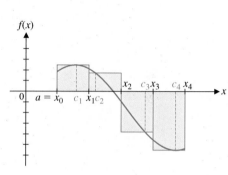

Figure 7

EXAMPLE 2   **Riemann Sums** Consider the function $f(x) = 15 - x^2$ on $[1, 5]$. Partition the interval $[1, 5]$ into four subintervals of equal length. For each subinterval $[x_{k-1}, x_k]$, let c_k be the midpoint. Calculate the corresponding Riemann sum S_4. (Riemann sums for which the c_k are the midpoints of the subintervals are called **midpoint sums**.)

SOLUTION

$$\Delta x = \frac{5 - 1}{4} = 1$$
$$S_4 = f(c_1) \cdot \Delta x + f(c_2) \cdot \Delta x + f(c_3) \cdot \Delta x + f(c_4) \cdot \Delta x$$
$$= f(1.5) \cdot 1 + f(2.5) \cdot 1 + f(3.5) \cdot 1 + f(4.5) \cdot 1$$
$$= 12.75 + 8.75 + 2.75 - 5.25 = 19$$

Matched Problem 2   Consider the function $f(x) = x^2 - 2x - 10$ on $[2, 8]$. Partition the interval $[2, 8]$ into three subintervals of equal length. For each subinterval $[x_{k-1}, x_k]$, let c_k be the midpoint. Calculate the corresponding Riemann sum S_3.

By analyzing properties of a continuous function on a closed interval, it can be shown that the conclusion of Theorem 2 is valid if f is continuous. In that case, not just left and right sums, but Riemann sums, have the same limit as $n \to \infty$.

THEOREM 3   Limit of Riemann Sums

If f is a continuous function on $[a, b]$, then the Riemann sums for f on $[a, b]$ approach a real number limit I as $n \to \infty$.†

---

*The term *Riemann sum* is often applied to more general sums in which the subintervals $[x_{k-1}, x_k]$ are not required to have the same length. Such sums are not considered in this book.

†The precise meaning of this limit statement is as follows: For each $e > 0$, there exists some $d > 0$ such that $|S_n - I| < e$ whenever S_n is a Riemann sum for f on $[a, b]$ for which $\Delta x < d$.

> **DEFINITION Definite Integral**
>
> Let f be a continuous function on $[a, b]$. The limit I of Riemann sums for f on $[a, b]$, guaranteed to exist by Theorem 2, is called the **definite integral** of f from a to b and is denoted as
>
> $$\int_a^b f(x)\, dx$$
>
> The **integrand** is $f(x)$, the **lower limit of integration** is a, and the **upper limit of integration** is b.

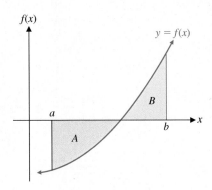

Figure 8 $\displaystyle\int_a^b f(x)\, dx = -A + B$

Because area is a positive quantity, the definite integral has the following geometric interpretation:

$$\int_a^b f(x)\, dx$$

represents the cumulative sum of the signed areas between the graph of f and the x axis from $x = a$ to $x = b$, where the areas above the x axis are counted positively and the areas below the x axis are counted negatively (see Fig. 8, where A and B are the actual areas of the indicated regions).

EXAMPLE 3   Definite Integrals   Calculate the definite integrals by referring to Figure 9.

(A) $\displaystyle\int_a^b f(x)\, dx$

(B) $\displaystyle\int_a^c f(x)\, dx$

(C) $\displaystyle\int_b^c f(x)\, dx$

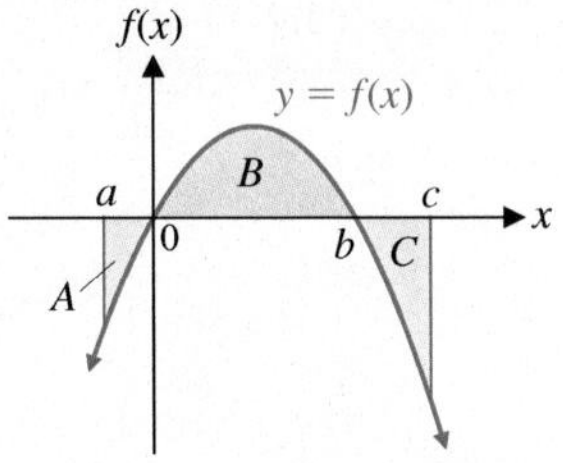

Area A = 2.33
Area B = 10.67
Area C = 5.63

Figure 9

SOLUTION   (A) $\displaystyle\int_a^b f(x)\, dx = -2.33 + 10.67 = 8.34$

(B) $\displaystyle\int_a^c f(x)\, dx = -2.33 + 10.67 - 5.63 = 2.71$

(C) $\displaystyle\int_b^c f(x)\, dx = -5.63$

Matched Problem 3   Referring to the figure for Example 3, calculate the definite integrals.

(A) $\displaystyle\int_a^0 f(x)\, dx$ (B) $\displaystyle\int_0^c f(x)\, dx$ (C) $\displaystyle\int_0^b f(x)\, dx$

Properties of the Definite Integral

Because the definite integral is defined as the limit of Riemann sums, many properties of sums are also properties of the definite integral. Note that Properties 3 and 4 are similar to the indefinite integral properties given in Section 6-1.

PROPERTIES Properties of Definite Integrals

1. $\displaystyle\int_a^a f(x)\, dx = 0$

2. $\displaystyle\int_a^b f(x)\, dx = -\int_b^a f(x)\, dx$

3. $\displaystyle\int_a^b kf(x)\, dx = k\int_a^b f(x)\, dx,\ k$ a constant

4. $\displaystyle\int_a^b [f(x) \pm g(x)]\, dx = \int_a^b f(x)\, dx \pm \int_a^b g(x)\, dx$

5. $\displaystyle\int_a^b f(x)\, dx = \int_a^c f(x)\, dx + \int_c^b f(x)\, dx$

EXAMPLE 4   **Using Properties of the Definite Integral**   If

$$\int_0^2 x\, dx = 2 \qquad \int_0^2 x^2\, dx = \frac{8}{3} \qquad \int_2^3 x^2\, dx = \frac{19}{3}$$

then

(A) $\displaystyle\int_0^2 12x^2\, dx = 12\int_0^2 x^2\, dx = 12\left(\frac{8}{3}\right) = 32$

(B) $\displaystyle\int_0^2 (2x - 6x^2)\, dx = 2\int_0^2 x\, dx - 6\int_0^2 x^2\, dx = 2(2) - 6\left(\frac{8}{3}\right) = -12$

(C) $\displaystyle\int_3^2 x^2\, dx = -\int_2^3 x^2\, dx = -\frac{19}{3}$

(D) $\displaystyle\int_5^5 3x^2\, dx = 0$

(E) $\displaystyle\int_0^3 3x^2\, dx = 3\int_0^2 x^2\, dx + 3\int_2^3 x^2\, dx = 3\left(\frac{8}{3}\right) + 3\left(\frac{19}{3}\right) = 27$

Matched Problem 4   Using the same integral values given in Example 4, find

(A) $\displaystyle\int_2^3 6x^2\, dx$ (B) $\displaystyle\int_0^2 (9x^2 - 4x)\, dx$ (C) $\displaystyle\int_2^0 3x\, dx$

(D) $\displaystyle\int_{-2}^{-2} 3x\, dx$ (E) $\displaystyle\int_0^3 12x^2\, dx$

Exercises 6-4

A

Problems 1–4 refer to the rectangles A, B, C, D, and E in the following figure.

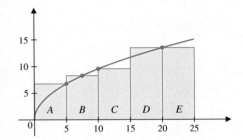

1. Which rectangles are left rectangles?

2. Which rectangles are right rectangles?

3. Which rectangles are neither left nor right rectangles?

4. Which rectangles are both left and right rectangles?

Problems 5–8 refer to the rectangles F, G, H, I, and J in the following figure.

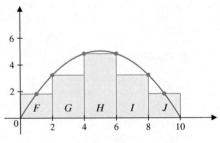

Figure for 5–8

5. Which rectangles are right rectangles?

6. Which rectangles are left rectangles?

7. Which rectangles are both left and right rectangles?

8. Which rectangles are neither left nor right rectangles?

Problems 9–16 involve estimating the area under the curves in Figures A–D from $x = 1$ to $x = 4$. For each figure, divide the interval $[1, 4]$ into three equal subintervals.

9. Draw in left and right rectangles for Figures A and B.

10. Draw in left and right rectangles for Figures C and D.

11. Using the results of Problem 9, compute L_3 and R_3 for Figure A and for Figure B.

12. Using the results of Problem 10, compute L_3 and R_3 for Figure C and for Figure D.

13. Replace the question marks with L_3 and R_3 as appropriate. Explain your choice.

$$? \leq \int_1^4 f(x)\, dx \leq ? \qquad ? \leq \int_1^4 g(x)\, dx \leq ?$$

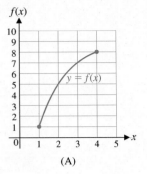

(A)

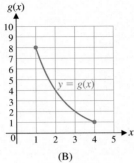

(B)

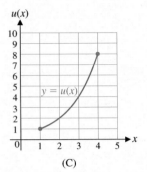

(C)

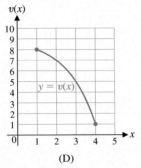

(D)

Figure for 9–16

14. Replace the question marks with L_3 and R_3 as appropriate. Explain your choice.

$$? \leq \int_1^4 u(x)\, dx \leq ? \qquad ? \leq \int_1^4 v(x)\, dx \leq ?$$

15. Compute error bounds for L_3 and R_3 found in Problem 11 for both figures.

16. Compute error bounds for L_3 and R_3 found in Problem 12 for both figures.

In Problems 17–20, calculate the indicated Riemann sum S_n for the function $f(x) = 25 - 3x^2$.

17. Partition $[-2, 8]$ into five subintervals of equal length, and for each subinterval $[x_{k-1}, x_k]$, let $c_k = (x_{k-1} + x_k)/2$.

18. Partition $[0, 12]$ into four subintervals of equal length, and for each subinterval $[x_{k-1}, x_k]$, let $c_k = (x_{k-1} + 2x_k)/3$.

19. Partition $[0, 12]$ into four subintervals of equal length, and for each subinterval $[x_{k-1}, x_k]$, let $c_k = (2x_{k-1} + x_k)/3$.

20. Partition $[-5, 5]$ into five subintervals of equal length, and for each subinterval $[x_{k-1}, x_k]$, let $c_k = (x_{k-1} + x_k)/2$.

In Problems 21–24, calculate the indicated Riemann sum S_n for the function $f(x) = x^2 - 5x - 6$.

21. Partition $[0, 3]$ into three subintervals of equal length, and let $c_1 = 0.7$, $c_2 = 1.8$, and $c_3 = 2.4$.

22. Partition $[0, 3]$ into three subintervals of equal length, and let $c_1 = 0.2$, $c_2 = 1.5$, and $c_3 = 2.8$.

23. Partition $[1, 7]$ into six subintervals of equal length, and let $c_1 = 1, c_2 = 3, c_3 = 3, c_4 = 5, c_5 = 5,$ and $c_6 = 7$.

24. Partition $[1, 7]$ into six subintervals of equal length, and let $c_1 = 2, c_2 = 2, c_3 = 4, c_4 = 4, c_5 = 6,$ and $c_6 = 6$.

In Problems 25–36, calculate the definite integral by referring to the figure with the indicated areas.

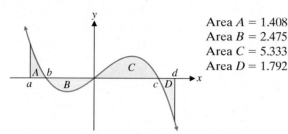

Area $A = 1.408$
Area $B = 2.475$
Area $C = 5.333$
Area $D = 1.792$

Figure for 25–36

25. $\int_b^0 f(x)\,dx$

26. $\int_0^c f(x)\,dx$

27. $\int_a^c f(x)\,dx$

28. $\int_b^d f(x)\,dx$

29. $\int_a^d f(x)\,dx$

30. $\int_0^d f(x)\,dx$

31. $\int_c^0 f(x)\,dx$

32. $\int_d^a f(x)\,dx$

33. $\int_0^a f(x)\,dx$

34. $\int_c^a f(x)\,dx$

35. $\int_d^b f(x)\,dx$

36. $\int_c^b f(x)\,dx$

In Problems 37–48, calculate the definite integral, given that

$$\int_1^4 x\,dx = 7.5 \qquad \int_1^4 x^2\,dx = 21 \qquad \int_4^5 x^2\,dx = \frac{61}{3}$$

37. $\int_1^4 2x\,dx$

38. $\int_1^4 3x^2\,dx$

39. $\int_1^4 (5x + x^2)\,dx$

40. $\int_1^4 (7x - 2x^2)\,dx$

41. $\int_1^4 (x^2 - 10x)\,dx$

42. $\int_1^4 (4x^2 - 9x)\,dx$

43. $\int_1^5 6x^2\,dx$

44. $\int_1^5 -4x^2\,dx$

45. $\int_4^4 (7x - 2)^2\,dx$

46. $\int_5^5 (10 - 7x + x^2)\,dx$

47. $\int_5^4 9x^2\,dx$

48. $\int_4^1 x(1 - x)\,dx$

B

In Problems 49–54, discuss the validity of each statement. If the statement is always true, explain why. If it is not always true, give a counterexample.

49. If $\int_a^b f(x)\,dx = 0$, then $f(x) = 0$ for all x in $[a, b]$.

50. If $f(x) = 0$ for all x in $[a, b]$, then $\int_a^b f(x)\,dx = 0$.

51. If $f(x) = 2x$ on $[0, 10]$, then there is a positive integer n for which the left sum L_n equals the exact area under the graph of f from $x = 0$ to $x = 10$.

52. If $f(x) = 2x$ on $[0, 10]$ and n is a positive integer, then there is some Riemann sum S_n that equals the exact area under the graph of f from $x = 0$ to $x = 10$.

53. If the area under the graph of f on $[a, b]$ is equal to both the left sum L_n and the right sum R_n for some positive integer n, then f is constant on $[a, b]$.

54. If f is a decreasing function on $[a, b]$, then the area under the graph of f is greater than the left sum L_n and less than the right sum R_n, for any positive integer n.

Problems 55 and 56 refer to the following figure showing two parcels of land along a river:

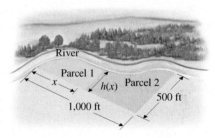

Figure for 55 and 56

55. You want to purchase both parcels of land shown in the figure and make a quick check on their combined area. There is no equation for the river frontage, so you use the average of the left and right sums of rectangles covering the area. The 1,000-foot baseline is divided into 10 equal parts. At the end of each subinterval, a measurement is made from the baseline to the river, and the results are tabulated. Let x be the distance from the left end of the baseline and let $h(x)$ be the distance from the baseline to the river at x. Use L_{10} to estimate the combined area of both parcels, and calculate an error bound for this estimate. How many subdivisions of the baseline would be required so that the error incurred in using L_n would not exceed 2,500 square feet?

x	0	100	200	300	400	500
$h(x)$	0	183	235	245	260	286

x	600	700	800	900	1,000
$h(x)$	322	388	453	489	500

56. Refer to Problem 55. Use R_{10} to estimate the combined area of both parcels, and calculate an error bound for this estimate. How many subdivisions of the baseline would be required so that the error incurred in using R_n would not exceed 1,000 square feet?

C

Problems 57 and 58 refer to the following figure:

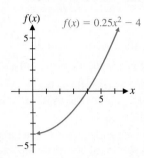

$f(x)$

$f(x) = 0.25x^2 - 4$

Figure for 57 and 58

🖉 **57.** Use L_6 and R_6 to approximate $\int_2^5 (0.25x^2 - 4)\,dx$. Compute error bounds for each. (Round answers to two decimal places.) Describe in geometric terms what the definite integral over the interval $[2, 5]$ represents.

🖉 **58.** Use L_5 and R_5 to approximate $\int_1^6 (0.25x^2 - 4)\,dx$. Compute error bounds for each. (Round answers to two decimal places.) Describe in geometric terms what the definite integral over the interval $[1, 6]$ represents.

For Problems 59–62, use a graphing calculator to determine the intervals on which each function is increasing or decreasing.

59. $f(x) = e^{-x^2}$

60. $f(x) = \dfrac{3}{1 + 2e^{-x}}$

61. $f(x) = x^4 - 2x^2 + 3$

62. $f(x) = e^{x^2}$

In Problems 63–66, the left sum L_n or the right sum R_n is used to approximate the definite integral to the indicated accuracy. How large must n be chosen in each case? (Each function is increasing over the indicated interval.)

63. $\displaystyle\int_1^3 \ln x\,dx = R_n \pm 0.1$

64. $\displaystyle\int_0^{10} \ln(x^2 + 1)\,dx = L_n \pm 0.5$

65. $\displaystyle\int_1^3 x^x\,dx = L_n \pm 0.5$ **66.** $\displaystyle\int_1^4 x^x\,dx = R_n \pm 0.5$

Applications

67. Employee training. A company producing electric motors has established that, on the average, a new employee can assemble $N(t)$ components per day after t days of on-the-job training, as shown in the following table (a new employee's productivity increases continuously with time on the job):

t	0	20	40	60	80	100	120
$N(t)$	10	51	68	76	81	84	86

Use left and right sums to estimate the area under the graph of $N(t)$ from $t = 0$ to $t = 60$. Use three subintervals of equal length for each. Calculate an error bound for each estimate.

68. Employee training. For a new employee in Problem 67, use left and right sums to estimate the area under the graph of $N(t)$ from $t = 20$ to $t = 100$. Use four equal subintervals for each. Replace the question marks with the values of L_4 or R_4 as appropriate:

$$? \le \int_{20}^{100} N(t)\,dt \le ?$$

69. Medicine. The rate of healing, $A'(t)$ (in square centimeters per day), for a certain type of skin wound is given approximately by the following table:

t	0	1	2	3	4	5
$A'(t)$	0.90	0.81	0.74	0.67	0.60	0.55

t	6	7	8	9	10
$A'(t)$	0.49	0.45	0.40	0.36	0.33

(A) Use left and right sums over five equal subintervals to approximate the area under the graph of $A'(t)$ from $t = 0$ to $t = 5$.

(B) Replace the question marks with values of L_5 and R_5 as appropriate:

$$? \le \int_0^5 A'(t)\,dt \le ?$$

70. Medicine. Refer to Problem 69. Use left and right sums over five equal subintervals to approximate the area under the graph of $A'(t)$ from $t = 5$ to $t = 10$. Calculate an error bound for this estimate.

71. Learning. A psychologist found that, on average, the rate of learning a list of special symbols in a code $N'(x)$ after x days of practice was given approximately by the following table values:

x	0	2	4	6	8	10	12
$N'(x)$	29	26	23	21	19	17	15

Use left and right sums over three equal subintervals to approximate the area under the graph of $N'(x)$ from $x = 6$ to $x = 12$. Calculate an error bound for this estimate.

72. Learning. For the data in Problem 71, use left and right sums over three equal subintervals to approximate the area under the graph of $N'(x)$ from $x = 0$ to $x = 6$. Replace the question marks with values of L_3 and R_3 as appropriate:

$$? \le \int_0^6 N'(x)\,dx \le ?$$

Answers to Matched Problems

1. (A) $\Delta x = 0.5$:

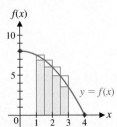

$f(x)$

$y = f(x)$

(B) $L_4 = 12.625$, $R_4 = 10.625$; error for L_4 and $R_4 = 2$

(C) $n > 16$ for L_n and R_n

2. $S_3 = 46$

3. (A) −2.33   (B) 5.04   (C) 10.67

4. (A) 38   (B) 16   (C) −6

(D) 0   (E) 108

6-5   The Fundamental Theorem of Calculus

- Introduction to the Fundamental Theorem
- Evaluating Definite Integrals
- Recognizing a Definite Integral: Average Value

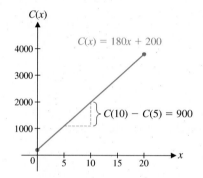

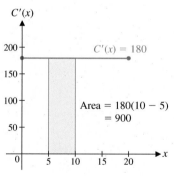

Figure 1

The definite integral of a function f on an interval $[a, b]$ is a number, the area (if $f(x) > 0$) between the graph of f and the x axis from $x = a$ to $x = b$. The indefinite integral of a function is a family of antiderivatives. In this section, we explain the connection between these two integrals, a connection made precise by the fundamental theorem of calculus.

Introduction to the Fundamental Theorem

Suppose that the daily cost function for a small manufacturing firm is given (in dollars) by

$$C(x) = 180x + 200 \qquad 0 \le x \le 20$$

Then the marginal cost function is given (in dollars per unit) by

$$C'(x) = 180$$

What is the change in cost as production is increased from $x = 5$ units to $x = 10$ units? That change is equal to

$$C(10) - C(5) = (180 \cdot 10 + 200) - (180 \cdot 5 + 200)$$

$$= 180(10 - 5)$$

$$= \$900$$

Notice that $180(10 - 5)$ is equal to the area between the graph of $C'(x)$ and the x axis from $x = 5$ to $x = 10$. Therefore,

$$C(10) - C(5) = \int_5^{10} 180 \, dx$$

In other words, the change in cost from $x = 5$ to $x = 10$ is equal to the area between the marginal cost function and the x axis from $x = 5$ to $x = 10$ (see Fig. 1).

> **CONCEPTUAL INSIGHT**
>
> Consider the formula for the slope of a line:
>
> $$m = \frac{y_2 - y_1}{x_2 - x_1}$$
>
> Multiplying both sides of this equation by $x_2 - x_1$ gives
>
> $$y_2 - y_1 = m(x_2 - x_1)$$
>
> The right-hand side, $m(x_2 - x_1)$, is equal to the area of a rectangle of height m and width $x_2 - x_1$. So the change in y coordinates is equal to the area under the constant function with value m from $x = x_1$ to $x = x_2$.

EXAMPLE 1 **Change in Cost vs Area under Marginal Cost** The daily cost function for a company (in dollars) is given by

$$C(x) = -5x^2 + 210x + 400 \qquad 0 \le x \le 20$$

(A) Graph $C(x)$ for $0 \le x \le 20$, calculate the change in cost from $x = 5$ to $x = 10$, and indicate that change in cost on the graph.

(B) Graph the marginal cost function $C'(x)$ for $0 \le x \le 20$, and use geometric formulas (see Appendix C) to calculate the area between $C'(x)$ and the x axis from $x = 5$ to $x = 10$.

(C) Compare the results of the calculations in parts (A) and (B).

SOLUTION (A) $C(10) - C(5) = 2,000 - 1,325 = 675$, and this change in cost is indicated in Figure 2A.

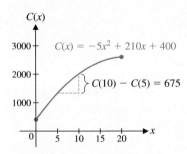

Figure 2(A)

(B) $C'(x) = -10x + 210$, so the area between $C'(x)$ and the x axis from $x = 5$ to $x = 10$ (see Fig. 2B) is the area of a trapezoid (geometric formulas are given in Appendix C):

$$\text{Area} = \frac{C'(5) + C'(10)}{2}(10 - 5) = \frac{160 + 110}{2}(5) = 675$$

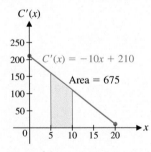

Figure 2(B)

(C) The change in cost from $x = 5$ to $x = 10$ is equal to the area between the marginal cost function and the x axis from $x = 5$ to $x = 10$.

Matched Problem 1 Repeat Example 1 for the daily cost function

$$C(x) = -7.5x^2 + 305x + 625$$

The connection illustrated in Example 1, between the change in a function from $x = a$ to $x = b$ and the area under the derivative of the function, provides the link between antiderivatives (or indefinite integrals) and the definite integral. This link is known as the fundamental theorem of calculus. (See Problems 59 and 60 in Exercise 6-5 for an outline of its proof.)

> **THEOREM 1 Fundamental Theorem of Calculus**
> If f is a continuous function on $[a, b]$, and F is any antiderivative of f, then
> $$\int_a^b f(x)\, dx = F(b) - F(a)$$

CONCEPTUAL INSIGHT

Because a definite integral is the limit of Riemann sums, we expect that it would be difficult to calculate definite integrals exactly. The fundamental theorem, however, gives us an easy method for evaluating definite integrals, *provided that we can find an antiderivative* $F(x)$ of $f(x)$: Simply calculate the difference $F(b) - F(a)$. But what if we are unable to find an antiderivative of $f(x)$? In that case, we must resort to left sums, right sums, or other approximation methods to approximate the definite integral. However, it is often useful to remember that such an approximation is also an estimate of the change $F(b) - F(a)$.

Evaluating Definite Integrals

By the fundamental theorem, we can evaluate $\int_a^b f(x)\, dx$ easily and exactly whenever we can find an antiderivative $F(x)$ of $f(x)$. We simply calculate the difference $F(b) - F(a)$.

Now you know why we studied techniques of indefinite integration before this section—so that we would have methods of finding antiderivatives of large classes of elementary functions for use with the fundamental theorem. It is important to remember that

Any antiderivative of $f(x)$ can be used in the fundamental theorem. One generally chooses the simplest antiderivative by letting $C = 0$, since any other value of C will drop out in computing the difference $F(b) - F(a)$.

In evaluating definite integrals by the fundamental theorem, it is convenient to use the notation $F(x)\big|_a^b$, which represents the change in $F(x)$ from $x = a$ to $x = b$, as an intermediate step in the calculation. This technique is illustrated in the following examples.

EXAMPLE 2 **Evaluating Definite Integrals** Evaluate $\displaystyle\int_1^2 \left(2x + 3e^x - \frac{4}{x}\right) dx$.

SOLUTION
$$\int_1^2 \left(2x + 3e^x - \frac{4}{x}\right) dx = 2\int_1^2 x\, dx + 3\int_1^2 e^x\, dx - 4\int_1^2 \frac{1}{x}\, dx$$
$$= 2\frac{x^2}{2}\bigg|_1^2 + 3e^x\bigg|_1^2 - 4\ln|x|\bigg|_1^2$$
$$= (2^2 - 1^2) + (3e^2 - 3e^1) - (4\ln 2 - 4\ln 1)$$
$$= 3 + 3e^2 - 3e - 4\ln 2 \approx 14.24$$

Matched Problem 2 Evaluate $\displaystyle\int_1^3 \left(4x - 2e^x + \frac{5}{x}\right) dx$.

The evaluation of a definite integral is a two-step process: First, find an antiderivative. Then find the change in that antiderivative. If *substitution techniques* are required to find the antiderivative, there are two different ways to proceed. The next example illustrates both methods.

EXAMPLE 3 **Definite Integrals and Substitution Techniques** Evaluate

$$\int_0^5 \frac{x}{x^2 + 10}\,dx$$

SOLUTION We solve this problem using substitution in two different ways.

Method 1. Use substitution in an indefinite integral to find an antiderivative as a function of x. Then evaluate the definite integral.

$$\int \frac{x}{x^2 + 10}\,dx = \frac{1}{2}\int \frac{1}{x^2 + 10}2x\,dx \quad \text{Substitute } u = x^2 + 10 \text{ and } du = 2x\,dx.$$

$$= \frac{1}{2}\int \frac{1}{u}\,du$$

$$= \tfrac{1}{2}\ln|u| + C$$

$$= \tfrac{1}{2}\ln(x^2 + 10) + C \quad \text{Since } u = x^2 + 10 > 0$$

We choose $C = 0$ and use the antiderivative $\tfrac{1}{2}\ln(x^2 + 10)$ to evaluate the definite integral.

$$\int_0^5 \frac{x}{x^2 + 10}\,dx = \frac{1}{2}\ln(x^2 + 10)\Big|_0^5$$

$$= \tfrac{1}{2}\ln 35 - \tfrac{1}{2}\ln 10 \approx 0.626$$

Method 2. Substitute directly into the definite integral, changing both the variable of integration and the limits of integration. In the definite integral

$$\int_0^5 \frac{x}{x^2 + 10}\,dx$$

the upper limit is $x = 5$ and the lower limit is $x = 0$. When we make the substitution $u = x^2 + 10$ in this definite integral, we must change the limits of integration to the corresponding values of u:

$$x = 5 \quad \text{implies} \quad u = 5^2 + 10 = 35 \quad \text{New upper limit}$$
$$x = 0 \quad \text{implies} \quad u = 0^2 + 10 = 10 \quad \text{New lower limit}$$

We have

$$\int_0^5 \frac{x}{x^2 + 10}\,dx = \frac{1}{2}\int_0^5 \frac{1}{x^2 + 10}2x\,dx$$

$$= \frac{1}{2}\int_{10}^{35} \frac{1}{u}\,du$$

$$= \frac{1}{2}\left(\ln|u|\Big|_{10}^{35}\right)$$

$$= \tfrac{1}{2}(\ln 35 - \ln 10) \approx 0.626$$

Matched Problem 3 Use both methods described in Example 3 to evaluate $\displaystyle\int_0^1 \frac{1}{2x + 4}\,dx$.

EXAMPLE 4 **Definite Integrals and Substitution** Use method 2 described in Example 3 to evaluate

$$\int_{-4}^1 \sqrt{5 - t}\,dt$$

SOLUTION   If $u = 5 - t$, then $du = -dt$, and

$$t = 1 \qquad \text{implies} \qquad u = 5 - 1 = 4 \qquad \text{New upper limit}$$
$$t = -4 \qquad \text{implies} \qquad u = 5 - (-4) = 9 \qquad \text{New lower limit}$$

Notice that the lower limit for u is larger than the upper limit. Be careful not to reverse these two values when substituting into the definite integral:

$$\int_{-4}^{1} \sqrt{5 - t}\, dt = -\int_{-4}^{1} \sqrt{5 - t}\,(-dt)$$

$$= -\int_{9}^{4} \sqrt{u}\, du$$

$$= -\int_{9}^{4} u^{1/2}\, du$$

$$= -\left(\frac{u^{3/2}}{\frac{3}{2}} \bigg|_{9}^{4} \right)$$

$$= -\left[\tfrac{2}{3}(4)^{3/2} - \tfrac{2}{3}(9)^{3/2} \right]$$

$$= -\left[\tfrac{16}{3} - \tfrac{54}{3} \right] = \tfrac{38}{3} \approx 12.667$$

Matched Problem 4   Use method 2 described in Example 3 to evaluate $\displaystyle\int_{2}^{5} \frac{1}{\sqrt{6 - t}}\, dt$.

EXAMPLE 5   **Change in Profit**   A company manufactures x HDTVs per month. The monthly marginal profit (in dollars) is given by

$$P'(x) = 165 - 0.1x \qquad 0 \le x \le 4{,}000$$

The company is currently manufacturing 1,500 HDTVs per month, but is planning to increase production. Find the change in the monthly profit if monthly production is increased to 1,600 HDTVs.

SOLUTION

$$P(1{,}600) - P(1{,}500) = \int_{1{,}500}^{1{,}600} (165 - 0.1x)\, dx$$

$$= (165x - 0.05x^2)\big|_{1{,}500}^{1{,}600}$$

$$= \left[165(1{,}600) - 0.05(1{,}600)^2 \right]$$

$$\qquad - \left[165(1{,}500) - 0.05(1{,}500)^2 \right]$$

$$= 136{,}000 - 135{,}000$$

$$= 1{,}000$$

Increasing monthly production from 1,500 units to 1,600 units will increase the monthly profit by $1,000.

Matched Problem 5   Repeat Example 5 if

$$P'(x) = 300 - 0.2x \qquad 0 \le x \le 3{,}000$$

and monthly production is increased from 1,400 to 1,500 HDTVs.

EXAMPLE 6   **Useful Life**   An amusement company maintains records for each video game installed in an arcade. Suppose that $C(t)$ and $R(t)$ represent the total accumulated costs and revenues (in thousands of dollars), respectively, t years after a particular game has been installed. Suppose also that

$$C'(t) = 2 \qquad R'(t) = 9e^{-0.5t}$$

The value of t for which $C'(t) = R'(t)$ is called the **useful life** of the game.

(A) Find the useful life of the game, to the nearest year.

(B) Find the total profit accumulated during the useful life of the game.

SOLUTION (A)

$$\begin{aligned} R'(t) &= C'(t) \\ 9e^{-0.5t} &= 2 \\ e^{-0.5t} &= \tfrac{2}{9} \qquad \text{Convert to equivalent logarithmic form.} \\ -0.5t &= \ln\tfrac{2}{9} \\ t &= -2\ln\tfrac{2}{9} \approx 3 \text{ years} \end{aligned}$$

y
10
y = R′(t)
y = C′(t)
2
0
3
5
t

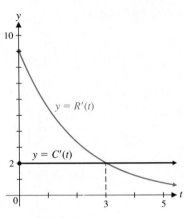

Figure 3 Useful life

Thus, the game has a useful life of 3 years. This is illustrated graphically in Figure 3.

(B) The total profit accumulated during the useful life of the game is

$$\begin{aligned} P(3) - P(0) &= \int_0^3 P'(t)\,dt \\ &= \int_0^3 [R'(t) - C'(t)]\,dt \\ &= \int_0^3 (9e^{-0.5t} - 2)\,dt \\ &= \left(\frac{9}{-0.5}e^{-0.5t} - 2t\right)\Big|_0^3 \qquad \text{Recall: } \int e^{ax}\,dx = \frac{1}{a}e^{ax} + C \\ &= (-18e^{-0.5t} - 2t)\Big|_0^3 \\ &= (-18e^{-1.5} - 6) - (-18e^{0} - 0) \\ &= 12 - 18e^{-1.5} \approx 7.984 \quad \text{or} \quad \$7{,}984 \end{aligned}$$

Matched Problem 6 Repeat Example 6 if $C'(t) = 1$ and $R'(t) = 7.5e^{-0.5t}$.

EXAMPLE 7 **Numerical Integration on a Graphing Calculator** Evaluate $\int_{-1}^{2} e^{-x^2}\,dx$ to three decimal places.

SOLUTION The integrand e^{-x^2} does not have an elementary antiderivative, so we are unable to use the fundamental theorem to evaluate the definite integral. Instead, we use a numerical integration routine that has been preprogrammed into a graphing calculator. (Consult your user's manual for specific details.) Such a routine is an approximation algorithm, more powerful than the left-sum and right-sum methods discussed in Section 6-4. From Figure 4,

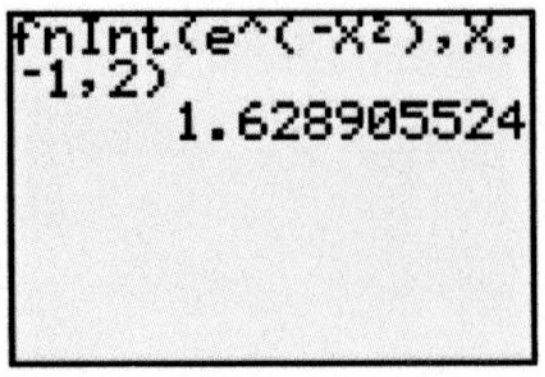

fnInt(e^(-X²),X,
-1,2)
1.628905524

Figure 4

$$\int_{-1}^{2} e^{-x^2}\,dx = 1.629$$

Matched Problem 7 Evaluate $\int_{1.5}^{4.3} \frac{x}{\ln x}\,dx$ to three decimal places.

Recognizing a Definite Integral: Average Value

Recall that the derivative of a function f was defined in Section 3-3 by

$$f'(x) = \lim_{h \to 0} \frac{f(x + h) - f(x)}{h}$$

This form is generally not easy to compute directly but is easy to recognize in certain practical problems (slope, instantaneous velocity, rates of change, and so on). Once we know that we are dealing with a derivative, we proceed to try to compute the derivative with the use of derivative formulas and rules.

Similarly, evaluating a definite integral with the use of the definition

$$\int_a^b f(x)\, dx = \lim_{n \to \infty} [f(c_1)\Delta x_1 + f(c_2)\Delta x_2 + \cdots + f(c_n)\Delta x_n] \qquad (1)$$

is generally not easy, but the form on the right occurs naturally in many practical problems. We can use the fundamental theorem to evaluate the definite integral (once it is recognized) if an antiderivative can be found; otherwise, we will approximate it with a rectangle sum. We will now illustrate these points by finding the *average value* of a continuous function.

Suppose that the temperature F (in degrees Fahrenheit) in the middle of a small shallow lake from 8 AM ($t = 0$) to 6 PM ($t = 10$) during the month of May is given approximately as shown in Figure 5.

How can we compute the average temperature from 8 AM to 6 PM? We know that the average of a finite number of values $a_1, a_2, \ldots, a_n$ is given by

$$\text{average} = \frac{a_1 + a_2 + \cdots + a_n}{n}$$

But how can we handle a continuous function with infinitely many values? It would seem reasonable to divide the time interval $[0, 10]$ into n equal subintervals, compute the temperature at a point in each subinterval, and then use the average of the temperatures as an approximation of the average value of the continuous function $F = F(t)$ over $[0, 10]$. We would expect the approximations to improve as n increases. In fact, we would define the limit of the average of n values as $n \to \infty$ as the *average value of F over* $[0, 10]$ if the limit exists. This is exactly what we will do:

$$\left(\begin{array}{c}\text{average temperature} \\ \text{for } n \text{ values}\end{array}\right) = \frac{1}{n}[F(t_1) + F(t_2) + \cdots + F(t_n)] \qquad (2)$$

Here t_k is a point in the kth subinterval. We will call the limit of equation (2) as $n \to \infty$ the *average temperature over the time interval* $[0, 10]$.

Form (2) resembles form (1), but we are missing the Δt_k. We take care of this by multiplying equation (2) by $(b - a)/(b - a)$, which will change the form of equation (2) without changing its value:

$$\frac{b - a}{b - a} \cdot \frac{1}{n}[F(t_1) + F(t_2) + \cdots + F(t_n)] = \frac{1}{b - a} \cdot \frac{b - a}{n}[F(t_1) + F(t_2) + \cdots + F(t_n)]$$

$$= \frac{1}{b - a}\left[F(t_1)\frac{b - a}{n} + F(t_2)\frac{b - a}{n} + \cdots + F(t_n)\frac{b - a}{n}\right]$$

$$= \frac{1}{b - a}[F(t_1)\Delta t + F(t_2)\Delta t + \cdots + F(t_n)\Delta t]$$

Therefore,

$$\left(\begin{array}{c}\text{average temperature} \\ \text{over } [a, b] = [0, 10]\end{array}\right) = \lim_{n \to \infty}\left\{\frac{1}{b - a}[F(t_1)\Delta t + F(t_2)\Delta t + \cdots + F(t_n)\Delta t]\right\}$$

$$= \frac{1}{b - a}\left\{\lim_{n \to \infty}[F(t_1)\,\Delta t + F(t_2)\,\Delta t + \cdots + F(t_n)\,\Delta t]\right\}$$

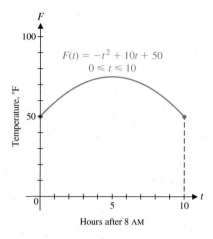

$F(t) = -t^2 + 10t + 50$
$0 \le t \le 10$

Temperature, °F

Hours after 8 AM

Figure 5

The limit inside the braces is of form (1)—that is, a definite integral. So

$$\left(\begin{array}{c} \text{average temperature} \\ \text{over } [a,b] = [0,10] \end{array}\right) = \frac{1}{b-a} \int_a^b F(t) \, dt$$

$$= \frac{1}{10 - 0} \int_0^{10} (-t^2 + 10t + 50) \, dt$$

$$= \frac{1}{10}\left(-\frac{t^3}{3} + 5t^2 + 50t \right)\Big|_0^{10}$$

$$= \frac{200}{3} \approx 67°\text{F}$$

We now use the fundamental theorem to evaluate the definite integral.

Proceeding as before for an arbitrary continuous function f over an interval $[a, b]$, we obtain the following general formula:

DEFINITION   Average Value of a Continuous Function f over $[a, b]$

$$\frac{1}{b-a} \int_a^b f(x) \, dx$$

EXPLORE & DISCUSS 1

In Figure 6, the rectangle shown has the same area as the area under the graph of $y = f(x)$ from $x = a$ to $x = b$. Explain how the average value of $f(x)$ over the interval $[a, b]$ is related to the height of the rectangle.

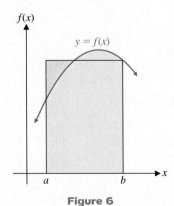

Figure 6

EXAMPLE 8   **Average Value of a Function**   Find the average value of $f(x) = x - 3x^2$ over the interval $[-1, 2]$.

SOLUTION

$$\frac{1}{b-a} \int_a^b f(x) \, dx = \frac{1}{2 - (-1)} \int_{-1}^2 (x - 3x^2) \, dx$$

$$= \frac{1}{3}\left(\frac{x^2}{2} - x^3 \right)\Big|_{-1}^2 = -\frac{5}{2}$$

Matched Problem 8   Find the average value of $g(t) = 6t^2 - 2t$ over the interval $[-2, 3]$.

EXAMPLE 9 **Average Price** Given the demand function

$$p = D(x) = 100e^{-0.05x}$$

find the average price (in dollars) over the demand interval $[40, 60]$.

SOLUTION Average price $= \dfrac{1}{b-a} \displaystyle\int_a^b D(x)\, dx$

$$= \frac{1}{60-40} \int_{40}^{60} 100e^{-0.05x}\, dx$$

$$= \frac{100}{20} \int_{40}^{60} e^{-0.05x}\, dx \qquad \text{Use } \int e^{ax}\, dx = \frac{1}{a}e^{ax}, a \ne 0.$$

$$= -\frac{5}{0.05} e^{-0.05x}\Big|_{40}^{60}$$

$$= 100(e^{-2} - e^{-3}) \approx \$8.55$$

Matched Problem 9 Given the supply equation

$$p = S(x) = 10e^{0.05x}$$

find the average price (in dollars) over the supply interval $[20, 30]$.

Exercises 6-5

A

In Problems 1–4,

(A) *Calculate the change in* $F(x)$ *from* $x = 10$ *to* $x = 15$.

(B) *Graph* $F'(x)$ *and use geometric formulas (see Appendix C) to calculate the area between the graph of* $F'(x)$ *and the* x *axis from* $x = 10$ *to* $x = 15$.

(C) *Verify that your answers to (A) and (B) are equal, as is guaranteed by the fundamental theorem of calculus.*

1. $F(x) = 3x^2 + 160$

2. $F(x) = 9x + 120$

3. $F(x) = -x^2 + 42x + 240$

4. $F(x) = x^2 + 30x + 210$

Evaluate the integrals in Problems 5–24.

5. $\displaystyle\int_0^{10} 4\, dx$

6. $\displaystyle\int_0^8 9x\, dx$

7. $\displaystyle\int_0^6 x^2\, dx$

8. $\displaystyle\int_0^4 x^3\, dx$

9. $\displaystyle\int_1^4 (5x + 3)\, dx$

10. $\displaystyle\int_2^5 (2x - 1)\, dx$

11. $\displaystyle\int_0^1 e^x\, dx$

12. $\displaystyle\int_0^2 4e^x\, dx$

13. $\displaystyle\int_1^2 \frac{1}{x}\, dx$

14. $\displaystyle\int_1^5 \frac{2}{x}\, dx$

15. $\displaystyle\int_{-2}^2 (x^3 + 7x)\, dx$

16. $\displaystyle\int_0^8 (0.25x - 1)\, dx$

17. $\displaystyle\int_2^5 (2x + 9)\, dx$

18. $\displaystyle\int_1^4 (6x - 5)\, dx$

19. $\displaystyle\int_5^2 (2x + 9)\, dx$

20. $\displaystyle\int_4^1 (6x - 5)\, dx$

21. $\displaystyle\int_2^3 (6 - x^3)\, dx$

22. $\displaystyle\int_6^9 (5 - x^2)\, dx$

23. $\displaystyle\int_6^6 (x^2 - 5x + 1)^{10}\, dx$

24. $\displaystyle\int_{-3}^{-3} (x^2 + 4x + 2)^8\, dx$

B

Evaluate the integrals in Problems 25–40.

25. $\displaystyle\int_1^2 (2x^{-2} - 3)\, dx$

26. $\displaystyle\int_1^2 (5 - 16x^{-3})\, dx$

27. $\displaystyle\int_1^4 3\sqrt{x}\, dx$

28. $\displaystyle\int_4^{25} \frac{2}{\sqrt{x}}\, dx$

29. $\displaystyle\int_2^3 12(x^2 - 4)^5 x\, dx$

30. $\displaystyle\int_0^1 32(x^2 + 1)^7 x\, dx$

31. $\displaystyle\int_3^9 \frac{1}{x-1}dx$

32. $\displaystyle\int_2^8 \frac{1}{x+1}dx$

33. $\displaystyle\int_{-5}^{10} e^{-0.05x}\,dx$

34. $\displaystyle\int_{-10}^{25} e^{-0.01x}\,dx$

35. $\displaystyle\int_1^e \frac{\ln t}{t}dt$

36. $\displaystyle\int_e^{e^2} \frac{(\ln t)^2}{t}dt$

37. $\displaystyle\int_0^1 xe^{-x^2}\,dx$

38. $\displaystyle\int_0^1 xe^{x^2}\,dx$

39. $\displaystyle\int_1^1 e^{x^2}\,dx$

40. $\displaystyle\int_{-1}^{-1} e^{-x^2}\,dx$

In Problems 41–48,

(A) Find the average value of each function over the indicated interval.

(B) Use a graphing calculator to graph the function and its average value over the indicated interval in the same viewing window.

41. $f(x) = 500 - 50x;\ [0, 10]$

42. $g(x) = 2x + 7;\ [0, 5]$

43. $f(t) = 3t^2 - 2t;\ [-1, 2]$

44. $g(t) = 4t - 3t^2;\ [-2, 2]$

45. $f(x) = \sqrt{x};\ [1, 8]$

46. $g(x) = \sqrt{x+1};\ [3, 8]$

47. $f(x) = 4e^{-0.2x};\ [0, 10]$

48. $f(x) = 64e^{0.08x};\ [0, 10]$

C

Evaluate the integrals in Problems 49–54.

49. $\displaystyle\int_2^3 x\sqrt{2x^2 - 3}\,dx$

50. $\displaystyle\int_0^1 x\sqrt{3x^2 + 2}\,dx$

51. $\displaystyle\int_0^1 \frac{x-1}{x^2 - 2x + 3}dx$

52. $\displaystyle\int_1^2 \frac{x+1}{2x^2 + 4x + 4}dx$

53. $\displaystyle\int_{-1}^1 \frac{e^{-x} - e^x}{(e^{-x} + e^x)^2}dx$

54. $\displaystyle\int_6^7 \frac{\ln(t-5)}{t-5}dt$

Use a numerical integration routine to evaluate each definite integral in Problems 55–58 (to three decimal places).

55. $\displaystyle\int_{1.7}^{3.5} x\ln x\,dx$

56. $\displaystyle\int_{-1}^1 e^{x^2}\,dx$

57. $\displaystyle\int_{-2}^2 \frac{1}{1+x^2}dx$

58. $\displaystyle\int_0^3 \sqrt{9 - x^2}\,dx$

59. The **mean value theorem** states that if $F(x)$ is a differentiable function on the interval $[a, b]$, then there exists some number c between a and b such that

$$F'(c) = \frac{F(b) - F(a)}{b - a}$$

Explain why the mean value theorem implies that if a car averages 60 miles per hour in some 10-minute interval, then the car's instantaneous velocity is 60 miles per hour at least once in that interval.

60. The fundamental theorem of calculus can be proved by showing that, for every positive integer n, there is a Riemann sum for f on $[a, b]$ that is equal to $F(b) - F(a)$. By the mean value theorem (see Problem 59), within each subinterval $[x_{k-1}, x_k]$ that belongs to a partition of $[a, b]$, there is some c_k such that

$$f(c_k) = F'(c_k) = \frac{F(x_k) - F(x_{k-1})}{x_k - x_{k-1}}$$

Multiplying by the denominator $x_k - x_{k-1}$, we get

$$f(c_k)(x_k - x_{k-1}) = F(x_k) - F(x_{k-1})$$

Show that the Riemann sum

$$S_n = \sum_{k=1}^n f(c_k)(x_k - x_{k-1})$$

is equal to $F(b) - F(a)$.

Applications

61. Cost. A company manufactures mountain bikes. The research department produced the marginal cost function

$$C'(x) = 500 - \frac{x}{3}\qquad 0 \le x \le 900$$

where $C'(x)$ is in dollars and x is the number of bikes produced per month. Compute the increase in cost going from a production level of 300 bikes per month to 900 bikes per month. Set up a definite integral and evaluate it.

62. Cost. Referring to Problem 61, compute the increase in cost going from a production level of 0 bikes per month to 600 bikes per month. Set up a definite integral and evaluate it.

63. Salvage value. A new piece of industrial equipment will depreciate in value, rapidly at first and then less rapidly as time goes on. Suppose that the rate (in dollars per year) at which the book value of a new milling machine changes is given approximately by

$$V'(t) = f(t) = 500(t - 12)\qquad 0 \le t \le 10$$

where $V(t)$ is the value of the machine after t years. What is the total loss in value of the machine in the first 5 years? In the second 5 years? Set up appropriate integrals and solve.

64. Maintenance costs. Maintenance costs for an apartment house generally increase as the building gets older. From past records, the rate of increase in maintenance costs (in dollars per year) for a particular apartment complex is given approximately by

$$M'(x) = f(x) = 90x^2 + 5,000$$

where x is the age of the apartment complex in years and $M(x)$ is the total (accumulated) cost of maintenance for x years. Write a definite integral that will give the total maintenance costs from the end of the second year to the end of the seventh year, and evaluate the integral.

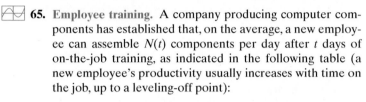

65. Employee training. A company producing computer components has established that, on the average, a new employee can assemble $N(t)$ components per day after t days of on-the-job training, as indicated in the following table (a new employee's productivity usually increases with time on the job, up to a leveling-off point):

t	0	20	40	60	80	100	120
$N(t)$	10	51	68	76	81	84	85

(A) Find a quadratic regression equation for the data, and graph it and the data set in the same viewing window.

(B) Use the regression equation and a numerical integration routine on a graphing calculator to approximate the number of units assembled by a new employee during the first 100 days on the job.

66. Employee training. Refer to Problem 65.

(A) Find a cubic regression equation for the data, and graph it and the data set in the same viewing window.

(B) Use the regression equation and a numerical integration routine on a graphing calculator to approximate the number of units assembled by a new employee during the second 60 days on the job.

67. Useful life. The total accumulated costs $C(t)$ and revenues $R(t)$ (in thousands of dollars), respectively, for a photocopying machine satisfy

$$C'(t) = \tfrac{1}{11}t \quad \text{and} \quad R'(t) = 5te^{-t^2}$$

where t is time in years. Find the useful life of the machine, to the nearest year. What is the total profit accumulated during the useful life of the machine?

68. Useful life. The total accumulated costs $C(t)$ and revenues $R(t)$ (in thousands of dollars), respectively, for a coal mine satisfy

$$C'(t) = 3 \quad \text{and} \quad R'(t) = 15e^{-0.1t}$$

where t is the number of years that the mine has been in operation. Find the useful life of the mine, to the nearest year. What is the total profit accumulated during the useful life of the mine?

69. Average cost. The total cost (in dollars) of manufacturing x auto body frames is $C(x) = 60,000 + 300x$.

(A) Find the average cost per unit if 500 frames are produced. [*Hint*: Recall that $\overline{C}(x)$ is the average cost per unit.]

(B) Find the average value of the cost function over the interval $[0, 500]$.

(C) Discuss the difference between parts (A) and (B).

70. Average cost. The total cost (in dollars) of printing x dictionaries is $C(x) = 20,000 + 10x$.

(A) Find the average cost per unit if 1,000 dictionaries are produced.

(B) Find the average value of the cost function over the interval $[0, 1,000]$.

(C) Discuss the difference between parts (A) and (B).

71. Cost. The marginal cost at various levels of output per month for a company that manufactures sunglasses is shown in the following table, with the output x given in thousands of units per month and the total cost $C(x)$ given in thousands of dollars per month:

x	0	1	2	3	4	5	6	7	8
$C'(x)$	58	30	18	9	5	7	17	33	51

(A) Find a quadratic regression equation for the data, and graph it and the data set in the same viewing window.

(B) Use the regression equation and a numerical integration routine on a graphing calculator to approximate (to the nearest dollar) the increased cost in going from a production level of 2 thousand sunglasses per month to 8 thousand sunglasses per month.

72. Cost. Refer to Problem 71.

(A) Find a cubic regression equation for the data, and graph it and the data set in the same viewing window.

(B) Use the regression equation and a numerical integration routine on a graphing calculator to approximate (to the nearest dollar) the increased cost in going from a production level of 1 thousand sunglasses per month to 7 thousand sunglasses per month.

73. Supply function. Given the supply function

$$p = S(x) = 10(e^{0.02x} - 1)$$

find the average price (in dollars) over the supply interval $[20, 30]$.

74. Demand function. Given the demand function

$$p = D(x) = \frac{1,000}{x}$$

find the average price (in dollars) over the demand interval $[400, 600]$.

75. Labor costs and learning. A defense contractor is starting production on a new missile control system. On the basis of data collected during assembly of the first 16 control systems, the production manager obtained the following function for the rate of labor use:

$$g(x) = 2,400x^{-1/2}$$

$g(x)$ is the number of labor-hours required to assemble the xth unit of a control system. Approximately how many labor-hours will be required to assemble the 17th through the 25th control units? [*Hint*: Let $a = 16$ and $b = 25$.]

76. Labor costs and learning. If the rate of labor use in Problem 75 is

$$g(x) = 2,000x^{-1/3}$$

then approximately how many labor-hours will be required to assemble the 9th through the 27th control units? [*Hint*: Let $a = 8$ and $b = 27$.]

77. Inventory. A store orders 600 units of a product every 3 months. If the product is steadily depleted to 0 by the end of each 3 months, the inventory on hand I at any time t during the year is shown in the following figure:

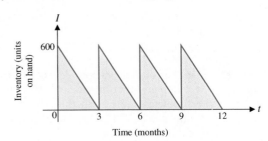

Figure for 77

(A) Write an inventory function (assume that it is continuous) for the first 3 months. [The graph is a straight line joining $(0, 600)$ and $(3, 0)$.]

(B) What is the average number of units on hand for a 3-month period?

78. Repeat Problem 77 with an order of 1,200 units every 4 months.

79. Oil production. Using production and geological data, the management of an oil company estimates that oil will be pumped from a producing field at a rate given by

$$R(t) = \frac{100}{t + 1} + 5 \qquad 0 \le t \le 20$$

where $R(t)$ is the rate of production (in thousands of barrels per year) t years after pumping begins. Approximately how many barrels of oil will the field produce during the first 10 years of production? From the end of the 10th year to the end of the 20th year of production?

80. Oil production. In Problem 79, if the rate is found to be

$$R(t) = \frac{120t}{t^2 + 1} + 3 \qquad 0 \le t \le 20$$

then approximately how many barrels of oil will the field produce during the first 5 years of production? The second 5 years of production?

81. Biology. A yeast culture weighing 2 grams is expected to grow at the rate of $W'(t) = 0.2e^{0.1t}$ grams per hour at a higher controlled temperature. How much will the weight of the culture increase during the first 8 hours of growth? How much will the weight of the culture increase from the end of the 8th hour to the end of the 16th hour of growth?

82. Medicine. The rate of healing of a skin wound (in square centimeters per day) is given approximately by $A'(t) = -0.9e^{-0.1t}$. The initial wound has an area of 9 square centimeters. How much will the area change during the first 5 days? The second 5 days?

83. Temperature. If the temperature $C(t)$ in an aquarium changes according to

$$C(t) = t^3 - 2t + 10 \qquad 0 \le t \le 2$$

(in degrees Celsius) over a 2-hour period, what is the average temperature over this period?

84. Medicine. A drug is injected into the bloodstream of a patient through her right arm. The drug concentration in the bloodstream of the left arm t hours after the injection is given by

$$C(t) = \frac{0.14t}{t^2 + 1}$$

What is the average drug concentration in the bloodstream of the left arm during the first hour after the injection? During the first 2 hours after the injection?

85. Politics. Public awareness of a congressional candidate before and after a successful campaign was approximated by

$$P(t) = \frac{8.4t}{t^2 + 49} + 0.1 \qquad 0 \le t \le 24$$

where t is time in months after the campaign started and $P(t)$ is the fraction of the number of people in the congressional district who could recall the candidate's name. What is the average fraction of the number of people who could recall the candidate's name during the first 7 months of the campaign? During the first 2 years of the campaign?

86. Population composition. The number of children in a large city was found to increase and then decrease rather drastically. If the number of children over a 6-year period was given by

$$N(t) = -\tfrac{1}{4}t^2 + t + 4 \qquad 0 \le t \le 6$$

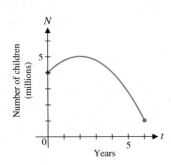

Figure for 86

what was the average number of children in the city over the 6-year period? [Assume that $N = N(t)$ is continuous.]

Answers to Matched Problems

1. (A)

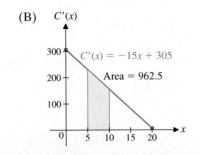

(C) The change in cost from $x = 5$ to $x = 10$ is equal to the area between the marginal cost function and the x axis from $x = 5$ to $x = 10$.

2. $16 + 2e - 2e^3 + 5 \ln 3 \approx -13.241$

3. $\frac{1}{2}(\ln 6 - \ln 4) \approx 0.203$

4. 2   **5.** $\$1,000$

6. (A) $-2 \ln \frac{2}{15} \approx 4$ yr

    (B) $11 - 15e^{-2} \approx 8.970$ or $\$8,970$

7. 8.017   **8.** 13   **9.** $\$35.27$

Chapter 6   Review

6-1 Antiderivatives and Indefinite Integrals

Examples

- A function F is an **antiderivative** of a function f if $F'(x) = f(x)$.

Ex. 1, p. 351

- If F and G are both antiderivatives of f, then F and G differ by a constant; that is, $F(x) = G(x) + k$ for some constant k.

- We use the symbol $\int f(x)\, dx$, called an **indefinite integral,** to represent the family of all antiderivatives of f, and we write

$$\int f(x)\, dx = F(x) + C$$

Ex. 2, p. 354

The symbol $\int$ is called an **integral sign,** $f(x)$ is the **integrand,** and C is the **constant of integration.**

Ex. 3, p. 354

- Indefinite integrals of basic functions are given by the formulas on page 352.

Ex. 4, p. 356

- Properties of indefinite integrals are given on page 352; in particular, a constant factor can be moved across an integral sign. However, a variable factor *cannot* be moved across an integral sign.

Ex. 5, p. 356

Ex. 6, p. 357

6-2 Integration by Substitution

- The **method of substitution** (also called the **change-of-variable method**) is a technique for finding indefinite integrals. It is based on the following formula, which is obtained by reversing the chain rule:

Ex. 1, p. 363

$$\int f'[g(x)]g'(x)\, dx = f[g(x)] + C$$

- This formula implies the general indefinite integral formulas on page 365.

Ex. 2, p. 364

- When using the method of substitution, it is helpful to use differentials as a bookkeeping device:

Ex. 3, p. 364

  1. The **differential dx** of the independent variable x is an arbitrary real number.

Ex. 4, p. 365

  2. The **differential dy** of the dependent variable y is defined by $dy = f'(x)\, dx$.

Ex. 5, p. 366

- Guidelines for using the substitution method are given by the procedure on page 365.

Ex. 6, p. 368

Ex. 7, p. 369

6-3 Differential Equations; Growth and Decay

- An equation is a **differential equation** if it involves an unknown function and one or more of its derivatives.

- The equation

$$\frac{dy}{dx} = 3x(1 + xy^2)$$

is a **first-order** differential equation because it involves the first derivative of the unknown function y but no second or higher order derivative.

- A **slope field** can be constructed for the preceding differential equation by drawing a tangent line segment with slope $3x(1 + xy^2)$ at each point (x, y) of a grid. The slope field gives a graphical representation of the functions that are solutions of the differential equation.

- The differential equation

Ex. 1, p. 376

Ex. 2, p. 376

$$\frac{dQ}{dt} = rQ$$

Ex. 3, p. 377

(in words, the rate at which the unknown function Q increases is proportional to Q) is called the **exponential growth law.** The constant r is called the **relative growth rate.** The solutions of the exponential growth law are the functions

$$Q(t) = Q_0 e^{rt}$$

where Q_0 denotes $Q(0)$, the amount present at time $t = 0$. These functions can be used to solve problems in population growth, continuous compound interest, radioactive decay, blood pressure, and light absorption.

- Table 1 on page 379 gives the solutions of other first-order differential equations that can be used to model the limited or logistic growth of epidemics, sales, and corporations.

Ex. 4, p. 378

6-4   The Definite Integral

- If the function f is positive on $[a, b]$, then the area between the graph of f and the x axis from $x = a$ to $x = b$ can be approximated by partitioning $[a, b]$ into n subintervals $[x_{k-1}, x_k]$ of equal length $\Delta x = (b - a)/n$ and summing the areas of n rectangles. This can be done using **left sums, right sums,** or, more generally, **Riemann sums:**

Ex. 1, p. 385
Ex. 2, p. 387

Left sum: $L_n = \displaystyle\sum_{k=1}^{n} f(x_{k-1}) \Delta x$

Right sum: $R_n = \displaystyle\sum_{k=1}^{n} f(x_k) \Delta x$

Riemann sum: $S_n = \displaystyle\sum_{k=1}^{n} f(c_k) \Delta x$

In a Riemann sum, each c_k is required to belong to the subinterval $[x_{k-1}, x_k]$. Left sums and right sums are the special cases of Riemann sums in which c_k is the left endpoint and right endpoint, respectively, of the subinterval.

- The **error in an approximation** is the absolute value of the difference between the approximation and the actual value. An **error bound** is a positive number such that the error is guaranteed to be less than or equal to that number.

- Theorem 1 on page 385 gives error bounds for the approximation of the area between the graph of a positive function f and the x axis from $x = a$ to $x = b$, by left sums or right sums, if f is either increasing or decreasing.

- If $f(x) > 0$ and is either increasing on $[a, b]$ or decreasing on $[a, b]$, then the left and right sums of $f(x)$ approach the same real number as $n \to \infty$ (Theorem 2, page 385).

- If f is a continuous function on $[a, b]$, then the Riemann sums for f on $[a, b]$ approach a real-number limit I as $n \to \infty$ (Theorem 3, page 387).

- Let f be a continuous function on $[a, b]$. Then the limit I of Riemann sums for f on $[a, b]$, guaranteed to exist by Theorem 3, is called the **definite integral** of f from a to b and is denoted

$$\int_a^b f(x)\, dx$$

The **integrand** is $f(x)$, the **lower limit of integration** is a, and the **upper limit of integration** is b.

- Geometrically, the definite integral

Ex. 3, p. 388

$$\int_a^b f(x)\, dx$$

represents the cumulative sum of the signed areas between the graph of f and the x axis from $x = a$ to $x = b$.

- Properties of the definite integral are given on page 389.

Ex. 4, p. 389

6-5   The Fundamental Theorem of Calculus

- If f is a continuous function on $[a, b]$ and F is any antiderivative of f, then

Ex. 1, p. 394
Ex. 2, p. 395

$$\int_a^b f(x)\, dx = F(b) - F(a)$$

This is the fundamental theorem of calculus (see page 395).

Ex. 3, p. 396
Ex. 4, p. 396
Ex. 5, p. 397
Ex. 6, p. 397
Ex. 7, p. 398

- The fundamental theorem gives an easy and exact method for evaluating definite integrals, provided that we can find an antiderivative $F(x)$ of $f(x)$. In practice, we first find an antiderivative $F(x)$ (when possible), using techniques for computing indefinite integrals. Then we calculate the difference $F(b) - F(a)$. If it is impossible to find an antiderivative, we must resort to left or right sums, or other approximation methods, to evaluate the definite integral. Graphing calculators have a built-in numerical approximation routine, more powerful than left- or right-sum methods, for this purpose.

- If f is a continuous function on $[a, b]$, then the **average value** of f over $[a, b]$ is defined to be

Ex. 8, p. 400

$$\frac{1}{b - a} \int_a^b f(x)\, dx$$

Review Exercises

Work through all the problems in this chapter review and check your answers in the back of the book. Answers to all review problems are there, along with section numbers in italics to indicate where each type of problem is discussed. Where weaknesses show up, review appropriate sections of the text.

A

Find each integral in Problems 1–6.

1. $\displaystyle\int (6x + 3)\, dx$
　　　　2. $\displaystyle\int_{10}^{20} 5\, dx$

3. $\displaystyle\int_{0}^{9} (4 - t^2)\, dt$
　　　　4. $\displaystyle\int (1 - t^2)^3 t\, dt$

5. $\displaystyle\int \frac{1 + u^4}{u}\, du$
　　　　6. $\displaystyle\int_{0}^{1} xe^{-2x^2}\, dx$

In Problems 7 and 8, find the derivative or indefinite integral as indicated.

7. $\displaystyle\frac{d}{dx}\left(\int e^{-x^2}\, dx \right)$
　　　8. $\displaystyle\int \frac{d}{dx}\left(\sqrt{4 + 5x} \right) dx$

9. Find a function $y = f(x)$ that satisfies both conditions:

$$\frac{dy}{dx} = 3x^2 - 2 \qquad f(0) = 4$$

10. Find all antiderivatives of

(A) $\dfrac{dy}{dx} = 8x^3 - 4x - 1$　　(B) $\dfrac{dx}{dt} = e^t - 4t^{-1}$

11. Approximate $\int_1^5 (x^2 + 1)\, dx$, using a right sum with $n = 2$. Calculate an error bound for this approximation.

12. Evaluate the integral in Problem 11, using the fundamental theorem of calculus, and calculate the actual error $|I - R_2|$ produced by using R_2.

13. Use the following table of values and a left sum with $n = 4$ to approximate $\int_1^{17} f(x)\, dx$:

x	1	5	9	13	17
$f(x)$	1.2	3.4	2.6	0.5	0.1

14. Find the average value of $f(x) = 6x^2 + 2x$ over the interval $[-1, 2]$.

15. Describe a rectangle that has the same area as the area under the graph of $f(x) = 6x^2 + 2x$ from $x = -1$ to $x = 2$ (see Problem 14).

In Problems 16 and 17, calculate the indicated Riemann sum S_n for the function $f(x) = 100 - x^2$.

16. Partition $[3, 11]$ into four subintervals of equal length, and for each subinterval $[x_{i-1}, x_i]$, let $c_i = (x_{i-1} + x_i)/2$.

17. Partition $[-5, 5]$ into five subintervals of equal length and let $c_1 = -4$, $c_2 = -1$, $c_3 = 1$, $c_4 = 2$, and $c_5 = 5$.

B

Use the graph and actual areas of the indicated regions in the figure to evaluate the integrals in Problems 18–25:

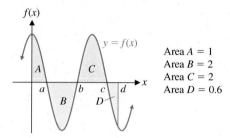

Area $A = 1$
Area $B = 2$
Area $C = 2$
Area $D = 0.6$

Figure for 18–25

18. $\displaystyle\int_a^b 5f(x)\, dx$
　　　19. $\displaystyle\int_b^c \frac{f(x)}{5}\, dx$

20. $\displaystyle\int_b^d f(x)\, dx$
　　　21. $\displaystyle\int_a^c f(x)\, dx$

22. $\displaystyle\int_0^d f(x)\, dx$
　　　23. $\displaystyle\int_b^a f(x)\, dx$

24. $\displaystyle\int_c^b f(x)\, dx$
　　　25. $\displaystyle\int_d^0 f(x)\, dx$

Problems 26–31 refer to the slope field shown in the figure:

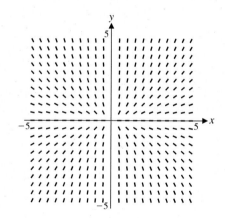

Figure for 26–31

26. (A) For $dy/dx = (2y)/x$, what is the slope of a solution curve at $(2, 1)$? At $(-2, -1)$?

(B) For $dy/dx = (2x)/y$, what is the slope of a solution curve at $(2, 1)$? At $(-2, -1)$?

27. Is the slope field shown in the figure for $dy/dx = (2x)/y$ or for $dy/dx = (2y)/x$? Explain.

28. Show that $y = Cx^2$ is a solution of $dy/dx = (2y)/x$ for any real number C.

29. Referring to Problem 28, find the particular solution of $dy/dx = (2y)/x$ that passes through $(2, 1)$. Through $(-2, -1)$.

30. Graph the two particular solutions found in Problem 29 in the slope field shown (or a copy).

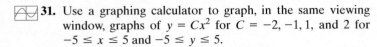

31. Use a graphing calculator to graph, in the same viewing window, graphs of $y = Cx^2$ for $C = -2, -1, 1,$ and 2 for $-5 \leq x \leq 5$ and $-5 \leq y \leq 5$.

Find each integral in Problems 32–42.

32. $\displaystyle\int_{-1}^{1} \sqrt{1 + x}\, dx$

33. $\displaystyle\int_{-1}^{0} x^2(x^3 + 2)^{-2}\, dx$

34. $\displaystyle\int 5e^{-t}\, dt$

35. $\displaystyle\int_{1}^{e} \frac{1 + t^2}{t}\, dt$

36. $\displaystyle\int xe^{3x^2}\, dx$

37. $\displaystyle\int_{-3}^{1} \frac{1}{\sqrt{2 - x}}\, dx$

38. $\displaystyle\int_{0}^{3} \frac{x}{1 + x^2}\, dx$

39. $\displaystyle\int_{0}^{3} \frac{x}{(1 + x^2)^2}\, dx$

40. $\displaystyle\int x^3(2x^4 + 5)^5\, dx$

41. $\displaystyle\int \frac{e^{-x}}{e^{-x} + 3}\, dx$

42. $\displaystyle\int \frac{e^x}{(e^x + 2)^2}\, dx$

43. Find a function $y = f(x)$ that satisfies both conditions:

$$\frac{dy}{dx} = 3x^{-1} - x^{-2} \qquad f(1) = 5$$

44. Find the equation of the curve that passes through $(2, 10)$ if its slope is given by

$$\frac{dy}{dx} = 6x + 1$$

for each x.

45. (A) Find the average value of $f(x) = 3\sqrt{x}$ over the interval $[1, 9]$.

(B) Graph $f(x) = 3\sqrt{x}$ and its average over the interval $[1, 9]$ in the same coordinate system.

C

Find each integral in Problems 46–50.

46. $\displaystyle\int \frac{(\ln x)^2}{x}\, dx$

47. $\displaystyle\int x(x^3 - 1)^2\, dx$

48. $\displaystyle\int \frac{x}{\sqrt{6 - x}}\, dx$

49. $\displaystyle\int_{0}^{7} x\sqrt{16 - x}\, dx$

50. $\displaystyle\int_{1}^{1} (x + 1)^9\, dx$

51. Find a function $y = f(x)$ that satisfies both conditions:

$$\frac{dy}{dx} = 9x^2 e^{x^3} \qquad f(0) = 2$$

52. Solve the differential equation

$$\frac{dN}{dt} = 0.06N \qquad N(0) = 800 \qquad N > 0$$

Graph Problems 53–56 on a graphing calculator, and identify each curve as unlimited growth, exponential decay, limited growth, or logistic growth:

53. $N = 50(1 - e^{-0.07t}); 0 \leq t \leq 80, 0 \leq N \leq 60$

54. $p = 500e^{-0.03x}; 0 \leq x \leq 100, 0 \leq p \leq 500$

55. $A = 200e^{0.08t}; 0 \leq t \leq 20, 0 \leq A \leq 1{,}000$

56. $N = \dfrac{100}{1 + 9e^{-0.3t}}; 0 \leq t \leq 25, 0 \leq N \leq 100$

Use a numerical integration routine to evaluate each definite integral in Problems 57–59 (to three decimal places).

57. $\displaystyle\int_{-0.5}^{0.6} \frac{1}{\sqrt{1 - x^2}}\, dx$

58. $\displaystyle\int_{-2}^{3} x^2 e^x\, dx$

59. $\displaystyle\int_{0.5}^{2.5} \frac{\ln x}{x^2}\, dx$

Applications

60. **Cost.** A company manufactures downhill skis. The research department produced the marginal cost graph shown in the accompanying figure, where $C'(x)$ is in dollars and x is the number of pairs of skis produced per week. Estimate the increase in cost going from a production level of 200 to 600 pairs of skis per week. Use left and right sums over two equal subintervals. Replace the question marks with the values of L_2 and R_2 as appropriate:

$$? \leq \int_{200}^{600} C'(x)\, dx \leq \, ?$$

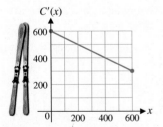

Figure for 60

61. **Cost.** Assuming that the marginal cost function in Problem 60 is linear, find its equation and write a definite integral that represents the increase in costs going from a production level of 200 to 600 pairs of skis per week. Evaluate the definite integral.

62. **Profit and production.** The weekly marginal profit for an output of x units is given approximately by

$$P'(x) = 150 - \frac{x}{10} \qquad 0 \leq x \leq 40$$

What is the total change in profit for a change in production from 10 units per week to 40 units? Set up a definite integral and evaluate it.

63. Profit function. If the marginal profit for producing x units per day is given by

$$P'(x) = 100 - 0.02x \qquad P(0) = 0$$

where $P(x)$ is the profit in dollars, find the profit function P and the profit on 10 units of production per day.

64. Resource depletion. An oil well starts out producing oil at the rate of 60,000 barrels of oil per year, but the production rate is expected to decrease by 4,000 barrels per year. Thus, if $P(t)$ is the total production (in thousands of barrels) in t years, then

$$P'(t) = f(t) = 60 - 4t \qquad 0 \le t \le 15$$

Write a definite integral that will give the total production after 15 years of operation, and evaluate the integral.

65. Inventory. Suppose that the inventory of a certain item t months after the first of the year is given approximately by

$$I(t) = 10 + 36t - 3t^2 \qquad 0 \le t \le 12$$

What is the average inventory for the second quarter of the year?

66. Price–supply. Given the price–supply function

$$p = S(x) = 8(e^{0.05x} - 1)$$

find the average price (in dollars) over the supply interval [40, 50].

67. Useful life. The total accumulated costs C(t) and revenues R(t) (in thousands of dollars), respectively, for a coal mine satisfy

$$C'(t) = 3 \qquad \text{and} \qquad R'(t) = 20e^{-0.1t}$$

where t is the number of years that the mine has been in operation. Find the useful life of the mine, to the nearest year. What is the total profit accumulated during the useful life of the mine?

68. Marketing. The market research department for an automobile company estimates that sales (in millions of dollars) of a new electric car will increase at the monthly rate of

$$S'(t) = 4e^{-0.08t} \qquad 0 \le t \le 24$$

t months after the introduction of the car. What will be the total sales $S(t)$ t months after the car is introduced if we assume that there were 0 sales at the time the car entered the marketplace? What are the estimated total sales during the first 12 months after the introduction of the car? How long will it take for the total sales to reach $40 million?

69. Wound healing. The area of a healing skin wound changes at a rate given approximately by

$$\frac{dA}{dt} = -5t^{-2} \qquad 1 \le t \le 5$$

where t is time in days and $A(1) = 5$ square centimeters. What will be the area of the wound in 5 days?

70. Pollution. An environmental protection agency estimates that the rate of seepage of toxic chemicals from a waste dump (in gallons per year) is given by

$$R(t) = \frac{1,000}{(1 + t)^2}$$

where t is the time in years since the discovery of the seepage. Find the total amount of toxic chemicals that seep from the dump during the first 4 years of its discovery.

71. Population. The population of Mexico was 111 million in 2009 and was growing at a rate of 1.13% per year, compounded continuously.

(A) Assuming that the population continues to grow at this rate, estimate the population of Mexico in the year 2025.

(B) At the growth rate indicated, how long will it take the population of Mexico to double?

72. Archaeology. The continuous compound rate of decay for carbon-14 is $r = -0.000\,123\,8$. A piece of animal bone found at an archaeological site contains 4% of the original amount of carbon-14. Estimate the age of the bone.

73. Learning. An average student enrolled in a typing class progressed at a rate of $N'(t) = 7e^{-0.1t}$ words per minute t weeks after enrolling in a 15-week course. If a student could type 25 words per minute at the beginning of the course, how many words per minute $N(t)$ would the student be expected to type t weeks into the course? After completing the course?

Additional Integration Topics

Introduction

In Chapter 7 we explore additional applications and techniques of integration. We use the integral to find probabilities and to calculate several quantities that are important in business and economics: the total income and future value produced by a continuous income stream, consumers' and producers' surplus, and the Gini index of income concentration. The Gini index is a single number that measures the equality of a country's income distribution (see Problems 87 and 88, for example, in Section 7-1).

7-1 Area Between Curves

- Area Between Two Curves
- Application: Income Distribution

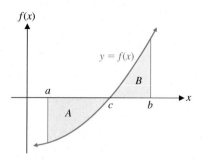

Figure 1 $\int_a^b f(x)\,dx = -A + B$

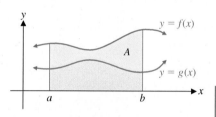

Figure 2

In Chapter 6, we found that the definite integral $\int_a^b f(x)\,dx$ represents the sum of the signed areas between the graph of $y = f(x)$ and the x axis from $x = a$ to $x = b$, where the areas above the x axis are counted positively and the areas below the x axis are counted negatively (see Fig. 1). In this section, we are interested in using the definite integral to find the actual area between a curve and the x axis or the actual area between two curves. These areas are always nonnegative quantities—**area measure is never negative**.

Area Between Two Curves

Consider the area bounded by $y = f(x)$ and $y = g(x)$, where $f(x) \geq g(x) \geq 0$, for $a \leq x \leq b$, as shown in Figure 2.

$$\begin{pmatrix} \text{Area } A \text{ between} \\ f(x) \text{ and } g(x) \end{pmatrix} = \begin{pmatrix} \text{area} \\ \text{under } f(x) \end{pmatrix} - \begin{pmatrix} \text{area} \\ \text{under } g(x) \end{pmatrix}$$
Areas are from x = a to x = b above the x axis.

$$= \int_a^b f(x)\,dx - \int_a^b g(x)\,dx$$
Use definite integral property 4 (Section 6-4).

$$= \int_a^b [f(x) - g(x)]\,dx$$

It can be shown that the preceding result does not require $f(x)$ or $g(x)$ to remain positive over the interval $[a, b]$. A more general result is stated in the following box:

THEOREM 1   Area Between Two Curves

If f and g are continuous and $f(x) \geq g(x)$ over the interval $[a, b]$, then the area bounded by $y = f(x)$ and $y = g(x)$ for $a \leq x \leq b$ is given exactly by

$$A = \int_a^b [f(x) - g(x)]\,dx$$

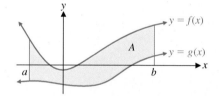

CONCEPTUAL INSIGHT

Theorem 1 requires the graph of f to be *above* (or equal to) the graph of g throughout $[a, b]$, but f and g can be either positive, negative, or 0. In Section 6-4, we considered the special cases of Theorem 1 in which (1) f is positive and g is the zero function on $[a, b]$; and (2) f is the zero function and g is negative on $[a, b]$:

Special case 1. If f is continuous and positive over $[a, b]$, then the area bounded by the graph of f and the x axis for $a \leq x \leq b$ is given exactly by

$$\int_a^b f(x)\,dx$$

Special case 2. If g is continuous and negative over $[a, b]$, then the area bounded by the graph of g and the x axis for $a \leq x \leq b$ is given exactly by

$$\int_a^b -g(x)\,dx$$

EXAMPLE 1 **Area Between a Curve and the x Axis** Find the area bounded by $f(x) = 6x - x^2$ and $y = 0$ for $1 \leq x \leq 4$.

SOLUTION We sketch a graph of the region first (Fig. 3). The solution of every area problem should begin with a sketch. Since $f(x) \geq 0$ on $[1, 4]$,

$$A = \int_1^4 (6x - x^2)\, dx = \left(3x^2 - \frac{x^3}{3}\right)\Bigg|_1^4$$

$$= \left[3(4)^2 - \frac{(4)^3}{3}\right] - \left[3(1)^2 - \frac{(1)^3}{3}\right]$$

$$= 48 - \tfrac{64}{3} - 3 + \tfrac{1}{3}$$

$$= 48 - 21 - 3$$

$$= 24$$

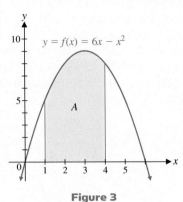

Figure 3

Matched Problem 1 Find the area bounded by $f(x) = x^2 + 1$ and $y = 0$ for $-1 \leq x \leq 3$.

EXAMPLE 2 **Area Between a Curve and the x Axis** Find the area between the graph of $f(x) = x^2 - 2x$ and the x axis over the indicated intervals:

(A) $[1, 2]$ (B) $[-1, 1]$

SOLUTION We begin by sketching the graph of f, as shown in Figure 4.

(A) From the graph, we see that $f(x) \leq 0$ for $1 \leq x \leq 2$, so we integrate $-f(x)$:

$$A_1 = \int_1^2 [-f(x)]\, dx$$

$$= \int_1^2 (2x - x^2)\, dx$$

$$= \left(x^2 - \frac{x^3}{3}\right)\Bigg|_1^2$$

$$= \left[(2)^2 - \frac{(2)^3}{3}\right] - \left[(1)^2 - \frac{(1)^3}{3}\right]$$

$$= 4 - \tfrac{8}{3} - 1 + \tfrac{1}{3} \quad = \tfrac{2}{3} \approx 0.667$$

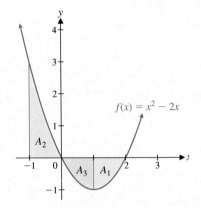

Figure 4

(B) Since the graph shows that $f(x) \geq 0$ on $[-1, 0]$ and $f(x) \leq 0$ on $[0, 1]$, the computation of this area will require two integrals:

$$A = A_2 + A_3$$

$$= \int_{-1}^0 f(x)\, dx + \int_0^1 [-f(x)]\, dx$$

$$= \int_{-1}^0 (x^2 - 2x)\, dx + \int_0^1 (2x - x^2)\, dx$$

$$= \left(\frac{x^3}{3} - x^2\right)\Bigg|_{-1}^0 + \left(x^2 - \frac{x^3}{3}\right)\Bigg|_0^1$$

$$= \tfrac{4}{3} + \tfrac{2}{3} \quad = 2$$

Matched Problem 2   Find the area between the graph of $f(x) = x^2 - 9$ and the x axis over the indicated intervals:

(A) $[0, 2]$ (B) $[2, 4]$

EXAMPLE 3   **Area Between Two Curves** Find the area bounded by the graphs of $f(x) = \frac{1}{2}x + 3$, $g(x) = -x^2 + 1$, $x = -2$, and $x = 1$.

SOLUTION   We first sketch the area (Fig. 5) and then set up and evaluate an appropriate definite integral. We observe from the graph that $f(x) \geq g(x)$ for $-2 \leq x \leq 1$, so

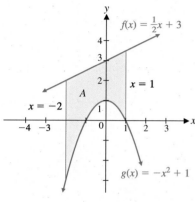

$$A = \int_{-2}^{1} [f(x) - g(x)]\, dx = \int_{-2}^{1} \left[\left(\frac{x}{2} + 3 \right) - (-x^2 + 1) \right] dx$$

$$= \int_{-2}^{1} \left(x^2 + \frac{x}{2} + 2 \right) dx$$

$$= \left(\frac{x^3}{3} + \frac{x^2}{4} + 2x \right) \Big|_{-2}^{1}$$

$$= \left(\frac{1}{3} + \frac{1}{4} + 2 \right) - \left(\frac{-8}{3} + \frac{4}{4} - 4 \right) = \frac{33}{4} = 8.25$$

Figure 5

Matched Problem 3   Find the area bounded by $f(x) = x^2 - 1$, $g(x) = -\frac{1}{2}x - 3$, $x = -1$, and $x = 2$.

EXAMPLE 4   **Area Between Two Curves** Find the area bounded by $f(x) = 5 - x^2$ and $g(x) = 2 - 2x$.

SOLUTION   First, graph f and g on the same coordinate system, as shown in Figure 6. Since the statement of the problem does not include any limits on the values of x, we must determine the appropriate values from the graph. The graph of f is a parabola and the graph of g is a line. The area bounded by these two graphs extends from the intersection point on the left to the intersection point on the right. To find these intersection points, we solve the equation $f(x) = g(x)$ for x:

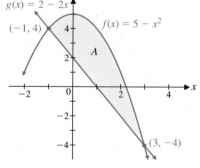

$$f(x) = g(x)$$

$$5 - x^2 = 2 - 2x$$

$$x^2 - 2x - 3 = 0$$

$$x = -1, 3$$

You should check these values in the original equations. (Note that the area between the graphs for $x < -1$ is unbounded on the left, and the area between the graphs for $x > 3$ is unbounded on the right.) Figure 6 shows that $f(x) \geq g(x)$ over the interval $[-1, 3]$, so we have

Figure 6

$$A = \int_{-1}^{3} [f(x) - g(x)]\, dx = \int_{-1}^{3} [5 - x^2 - (2 - 2x)]\, dx$$

$$= \int_{-1}^{3} (3 + 2x - x^2)\, dx$$

$$= \left(3x + x^2 - \frac{x^3}{3} \right) \Big|_{-1}^{3}$$

$$= \left[3(3) + (3)^2 - \frac{(3)^3}{3} \right] - \left[3(-1) + (-1)^2 - \frac{(-1)^3}{3} \right] = \frac{32}{3} \approx 10.667$$

Matched Problem 4   Find the area bounded by $f(x) = 6 - x^2$ and $g(x) = x$.

EXAMPLE 5   **Area Between Two Curves** Find the area bounded by $f(x) = x^2 - x$ and $g(x) = 2x$ for $-2 \le x \le 3$.

SOLUTION   The graphs of f and g are shown in Figure 7. Examining the graph, we see that $f(x) \ge g(x)$ on the interval $[-2, 0]$, but $g(x) \ge f(x)$ on the interval $[0, 3]$. Thus, two integrals are required to compute this area:

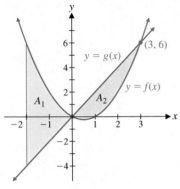

$$A_1 = \int_{-2}^{0} [f(x) - g(x)] \, dx \qquad f(x) \ge g(x) \text{ on } [-2, 0]$$

$$= \int_{-2}^{0} [x^2 - x - 2x] \, dx$$

$$= \int_{-2}^{0} (x^2 - 3x) \, dx$$

$$= \left(\frac{x^3}{3} - \frac{3}{2}x^2 \right) \Big|_{-2}^{0}$$

$$= (0) - \left[\frac{(-2)^3}{3} - \frac{3}{2}(-2)^2 \right] = \frac{26}{3} \approx 8.667$$

$$A_2 = \int_{0}^{3} [g(x) - f(x)] \, dx \qquad g(x) \ge f(x) \text{ on } [0, 3]$$

$$= \int_{0}^{3} [2x - (x^2 - x)] \, dx$$

$$= \int_{0}^{3} (3x - x^2) \, dx$$

$$= \left(\frac{3}{2}x^2 - \frac{x^3}{3} \right) \Big|_{0}^{3}$$

$$= \left[\frac{3}{2}(3)^2 - \frac{(3)^3}{3} \right] - (0) = \frac{9}{2} = 4.5$$

Figure 7

The total area between the two graphs is

$$A = A_1 + A_2 = \tfrac{26}{3} + \tfrac{9}{2} = \tfrac{79}{6} \approx 13.167$$

Matched Problem 5   Find the area bounded by $f(x) = 2x^2$ and $g(x) = 4 - 2x$ for $-2 \le x \le 2$.

EXAMPLE 6   **Computing Areas with a Numerical Integration Routine** Find the area (to three decimal places) bounded by $f(x) = e^{-x^2}$ and $g(x) = x^2 - 1$.

SOLUTION   First, we use a graphing calculator to graph the functions f and g and find their intersection points (see Fig. 8A). We see that the graph of f is bell shaped and the graph of g is a parabola. We note that $f(x) \ge g(x)$ on the interval $[-1.131, 1.131]$ and compute the area A by a numerical integration routine (see Fig. 8B):

$$A = \int_{-1.131}^{1.131} \left[e^{-x^2} - (x^2 - 1) \right] dx = 2.876$$

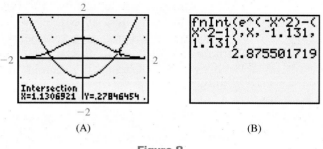

(A)   (B)

Figure 8

Matched Problem 6   Find the area (to three decimal places) bounded by the graphs of $f(x) = x^2 \ln x$ and $g(x) = 3x - 3$.

Application: Income Distribution

The U.S. Census Bureau compiles and analyzes a great deal of data having to do with the distribution of income among families in the United States. For 2006, the Bureau reported that the lowest 20% of families received 3% of all family income and the top 20% received 50%. Table 1 and Figure 9 give a detailed picture of the distribution of family income in 2006.

The graph of $y = f(x)$ in Figure 9 is called a **Lorenz curve** and is generally found by using *regression analysis,* a technique for fitting a function to a data set over a given interval. The variable **x represents the cumulative percentage of families at or below a given income level,** and **y represents the cumulative percentage of total family income received.** For example, data point (0.40, 0.12) in Table 1 indicates that the bottom 40% of families (those with incomes under $38,000) received 12% of the total income for all families in 2006, data point (0.60, 0.27) indicates that the bottom 60% of families received 27% of the total income for all families that year, and so on.

Table 1	Family Income Distribution in the United States, 2006	
Income Level	**x**	**y**
Under $20,000	0.20	0.03
Under $38,000	0.40	0.12
Under $60,000	0.60	0.27
Under $97,000	0.80	0.49

Source: U.S. Census Bureau

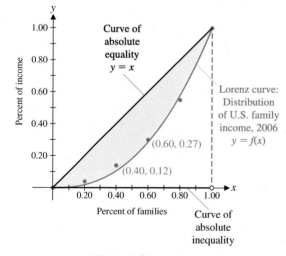

Figure 9 Lorenz curve

Absolute equality of income would occur if the area between the Lorenz curve and $y = x$ were 0. In this case, the Lorenz curve would be $y = x$ and all families would receive equal shares of the total income. That is, 5% of the families would receive 5% of the income, 20% of the families would receive 20% of the income, 65% of the families would receive 65% of the income, and so on. The maximum possible area between a Lorenz curve and $y = x$ is $\frac{1}{2}$, the area of the triangle below $y = x$. In this case, we would have **absolute inequality**: All the income would be in the hands of one family and the rest would have none. In actuality, Lorenz curves lie between these two extremes. But as the shaded area increases, the greater is the inequality of income distribution.

We use a single number, the **Gini index** [named after the Italian sociologist Corrado Gini (1884–1965)], to measure income concentration. The Gini index is the ratio of two areas: the area between $y = x$ and the Lorenz curve, and the area between $y = x$ and the x axis, from $x = 0$ to $x = 1$. The first area equals $\int_0^1 [x - f(x)]\,dx$ and the second (triangular) area equals $\frac{1}{2}$, giving the following definition:

DEFINITION   Gini Index of Income Concentration

If $y = f(x)$ is the equation of a Lorenz curve, then

$$\text{Gini index} = 2 \int_0^1 [x - f(x)]\,dx$$

The Gini index is always a number between 0 and 1:

A Gini index of 0 indicates absolute equality—all people share equally in the income. A Gini index of 1 indicates absolute inequality—one person has all the income and the rest have none.

The closer the index is to 0, the closer the income is to being equally distributed. The closer the index is to 1, the closer the income is to being concentrated in a few hands. The Gini index of income concentration is used to compare income distributions at various points in time, between different groups of people, before and after taxes are paid, between different countries, and so on.

EXAMPLE 7   **Distribution of Income** The Lorenz curve for the distribution of income in a certain country in 2010 is given by $f(x) = x^{2.6}$. Economists predict that the Lorenz curve for the country in the year 2025 will be given by $g(x) = x^{1.8}$. Find the Gini index of income concentration for each curve, and interpret the results.

SOLUTION   The Lorenz curves are shown in Figure 10.

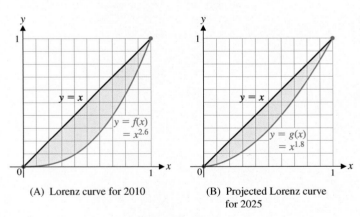

(A) Lorenz curve for 2010

(B) Projected Lorenz curve for 2025

Figure 10

The Gini index in 2010 is (see Fig. 10A)

$$2 \int_0^1 [x - f(x)]\,dx = 2 \int_0^1 [x - x^{2.6}]\,dx = 2\left(\frac{1}{2}x^2 - \frac{1}{3.6}x^{3.6} \right)\Bigg|_0^1$$

$$= 2\left(\frac{1}{2} - \frac{1}{3.6} \right) \approx 0.444$$

The projected Gini index in 2025 is (see Fig. 10B)

$$2\int_0^1 [x - g(x)]\, dx = 2\int_0^1 [x - x^{1.8}]\, dx = 2\left(\frac{1}{2}x^2 - \frac{1}{2.8}x^{2.8}\right)\Big|_0^1$$

$$= 2\left(\frac{1}{2} - \frac{1}{2.8}\right) \approx 0.286$$

If this projection is correct, the Gini index will decrease, and income will be more equally distributed in the year 2025 than in 2010.

Matched Problem 7 Repeat Example 7 if the projected Lorenz curve in the year 2025 is given by $g(x) = x^{3.8}$.

EXPLORE & DISCUSS 1 Do you agree or disagree with each of the following statements (explain your answers by referring to the data in Table 2):

(A) In countries with a low Gini index, there is little incentive for individuals to strive for success, and therefore productivity is low.

(B) In countries with a high Gini index, it is almost impossible to rise out of poverty, and therefore productivity is low.

Table 2

Country	Gini Index	Per Capita Gross Domestic Product
Brazil	0.57	$8,402
China	0.47	6,757
France	0.33	30,386
Germany	0.28	29,461
Japan	0.25	31,267
Jordan	0.39	5,530
Mexico	0.46	10,751
Russia	0.40	10,845
Sweden	0.25	32,525
United States	0.41	41,890

Source: The World Bank

Exercises 7-1

A

Problems 1–6 refer to Figures A–D on page 418. Set up definite integrals in Problems 1–4 that represent the indicated shaded area.

1. Shaded area in Figure B
2. Shaded area in Figure A
3. Shaded area in Figure C
4. Shaded area in Figure D
5. Explain why $\int_a^b h(x)\, dx$ does not represent the area between the graph of $y = h(x)$ and the x axis from $x = a$ to $x = b$ in Figure C.
6. Explain why $\int_a^b [-h(x)]\, dx$ represents the area between the graph of $y = h(x)$ and the x axis from $x = a$ to $x = b$ in Figure C.

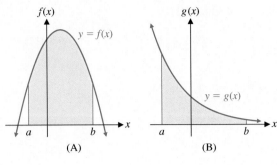

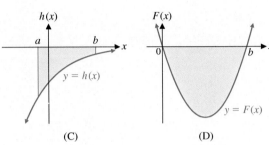

Figures for 1–6

In Problems 7–20, find the area bounded by the graphs of the indicated equations over the given interval. Compute answers to three decimal places.

7. $y = x + 4; y = 0; 0 \le x \le 4$

8. $y = -x + 10; y = 0; -2 \le x \le 2$

9. $y = x^2 - 20; y = 0; -3 \le x \le 0$

10. $y = x^2 + 2; y = 0; 0 \le x \le 3$

11. $y = -x^2 + 10; y = 0; -3 \le x \le 3$

12. $y = -2x^2; y = 0; -6 \le x \le 0$

13. $y = x^3 + 1; y = 0; 0 \le x \le 2$

14. $y = -x^3 + 3; y = 0; -2 \le x \le 1$

15. $y = x(1 - x); y = 0; -1 \le x \le 0$

16. $y = -x(3 - x); y = 0; 1 \le x \le 2$

17. $y = -e^x; y = 0; -1 \le x \le 1$

18. $y = e^x; y = 0; 0 \le x \le 1$

19. $y = \dfrac{1}{x}; y = 0; 1 \le x \le e$

20. $y = -\dfrac{1}{x}; y = 0; -1 \le x \le -\dfrac{1}{e}$

B

In Problems 21–26, use a definite integral to find the area bounded by the graphs of the indicated equations over the given interval. Then check your answer by finding the area without using a definite integral. [Hint: Partition the region into triangles and/or rectangles].

21. $y = x; y = -2; 0 \le x \le 3$

22. $y = -x; y = 8; 0 \le x \le 5$

23. $y = 2x + 3; y = x - 1; 4 \le x \le 6$

24. $y = 3x + 6; y = \dfrac{1}{2}x + 1; 8 \le x \le 10$

25. $y = -4x + 1; y = \dfrac{3}{2}x + 1; 0 \le x \le 4$

26. $y = -2x - 3; y = x - 3; 0 \le x \le 20$

Problems 27–36 refer to Figures A and B. Set up definite integrals in Problems 27–34 that represent the indicated shaded areas over the given intervals.

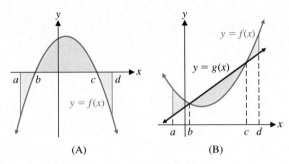

Figures for 27–34

27. Over interval $[a, b]$ in Figure A

28. Over interval $[c, d]$ in Figure A

29. Over interval $[b, d]$ in Figure A

30. Over interval $[a, c]$ in Figure A

31. Over interval $[c, d]$ in Figure B

32. Over interval $[a, b]$ in Figure B

33. Over interval $[a, c]$ in Figure B

34. Over interval $[b, d]$ in Figure B

35. Referring to Figure B, explain how you would use definite integrals and the functions f and g to find the area bounded by the two functions from $x = a$ to $x = d$.

36. Referring to Figure A, explain how you would use definite integrals to find the area between the graph of $y = f(x)$ and the x axis from $x = a$ to $x = d$.

In Problems 37–52, find the area bounded by the graphs of the indicated equations over the given intervals (when stated). Compute answers to three decimal places.

37. $y = -x; y = 0; -2 \le x \le 1$

38. $y = -x + 1; y = 0; -1 \le x \le 2$

39. $y = x^2 - 4; y = 0; 0 \le x \le 3$

40. $y = 4 - x^2; y = 0; 0 \le x \le 4$

41. $y = x^2 - 3x; y = 0; -2 \le x \le 2$

42. $y = -x^2 - 2x; y = 0; -2 \le x \le 1$

43. $y = -2x + 8; y = 12; -1 \le x \le 2$

44. $y = 2x + 6; y = 3; -1 \le x \le 2$

45. $y = 3x^2; y = 12$

46. $y = x^2; y = 9$

47. $y = 4 - x^2; y = -5$

48. $y = x^2 - 1; y = 3$

49. $y = x^2 + 1; y = 2x - 2; -1 \leq x \leq 2$

50. $y = x^2 - 1; y = x - 2; -2 \leq x \leq 1$

51. $y = e^{0.5x}; y = -\dfrac{1}{x}; 1 \leq x \leq 2$

52. $y = \dfrac{1}{x}; y = -e^x; 0.5 \leq x \leq 1$

In Problems 53–58, set up a definite integral that represents the area bounded by the graphs of the indicated equations over the given interval. Find the areas to three decimal places. [Hint: A circle of radius r, with center at the origin, has equation $x^2 + y^2 = r^2$ and area πr^2].

53. $y = \sqrt{9 - x^2}; y = 0; -3 \leq x \leq 3$

54. $y = \sqrt{25 - x^2}; y = 0; -5 \leq x \leq 5$

55. $y = -\sqrt{16 - x^2}; y = 0; 0 \leq x \leq 4$

56. $y = -\sqrt{36 - x^2}; y = 0; -6 \leq x \leq 0$

57. $y = -\sqrt{4 - x^2}; y = \sqrt{4 - x^2}; -2 \leq x \leq 2$

58. $y = -\sqrt{100 - x^2}; y = \sqrt{100 - x^2}; -10 \leq x \leq 10$

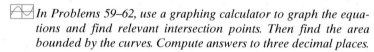 *In Problems 59–62, use a graphing calculator to graph the equations and find relevant intersection points. Then find the area bounded by the curves. Compute answers to three decimal places.*

59. $y = 3 - 5x - 2x^2; y = 2x^2 + 3x - 2$

60. $y = 3 - 2x^2; y = 2x^2 - 4x$

61. $y = -0.5x + 2.25; y = \dfrac{1}{x}$

62. $y = x - 4.25; y = -\dfrac{1}{x}$

C

In Problems 63–68, find the area bounded by the graphs of the indicated equations over the given intervals (when stated). Compute answers to three decimal places.

63. $y = e^x; y = e^{-x}; 0 \leq x \leq 4$

64. $y = e^x; y = -e^{-x}; 1 \leq x \leq 2$

65. $y = x^3; y = 4x$

66. $y = x^3 + 1; y = x + 1$

67. $y = x^3 - 3x^2 - 9x + 12; y = x + 12$

68. $y = x^3 - 6x^2 + 9x; y = x$

In Problems 69–74, use a graphing calculator to graph the equations and find relevant intersection points. Then find the area bounded by the curves. Compute answers to three decimal places.

69. $y = x^3 - x^2 + 2; y = -x^3 + 8x - 2$

70. $y = 2x^3 + 2x^2 - x; y = -2x^3 - 2x^2 + 2x$

71. $y = e^{-x}; y = 3 - 2x$

72. $y = 2 - (x + 1)^2; y = e^{x+1}$

73. $y = e^x; y = 5x - x^3$

74. $y = 2 - e^x; y = x^3 + 3x^2$

In Problems 75–78, use a numerical integration routine on a graphing calculator to find the area bounded by the graphs of the indicated equations over the given interval (when stated). Compute answers to three decimal places.

75. $y = e^{-x}; y = \sqrt{\ln x}; 2 \leq x \leq 5$

76. $y = x^2 + 3x + 1; y = e^{e^x}; -3 \leq x \leq 0$

77. $y = e^{x^2}; y = x + 2$

78. $y = \ln(\ln x); y = 0.01x$

Applications

In the applications that follow, it is helpful to sketch graphs to get a clearer understanding of each problem and to interpret results. A graphing calculator will prove useful if you have one, but it is not necessary.

79. Oil production. Using production and geological data, the management of an oil company estimates that oil will be pumped from a producing field at a rate given by

$$R(t) = \frac{100}{t + 10} + 10 \quad 0 \leq t \leq 15$$

where $R(t)$ is the rate of production (in thousands of barrels per year) t years after pumping begins. Find the area between the graph of R and the t axis over the interval $[5, 10]$ and interpret the results.

80. Oil production. In Problem 79, if the rate is found to be

$$R(t) = \frac{100t}{t^2 + 25} + 4 \quad 0 \leq t \leq 25$$

then find the area between the graph of R and the t axis over the interval $[5, 15]$ and interpret the results.

81. Useful life. An amusement company maintains records for each video game it installs in an arcade. Suppose that $C(t)$ and $R(t)$ represent the total accumulated costs and revenues (in thousands of dollars), respectively, t years after a particular game has been installed. If

$$C'(t) = 2 \quad \text{and} \quad R'(t) = 9e^{-0.3t}$$

then find the area between the graphs of C' and R' over the interval on the t axis from 0 to the useful life of the game and interpret the results.

82. Useful life. Repeat Problem 81 if

$$C'(t) = 2t \quad \text{and} \quad R'(t) = 5te^{-0.1t^2}$$

83. Income distribution. In a study on the effects of World War II on the U.S. economy, an economist used data from the U.S. Census Bureau to produce the following Lorenz curves for the distribution of U.S. income in 1935 and in 1947:

$$f(x) = x^{2.4} \quad \text{Lorenz curve for 1935}$$

$$g(x) = x^{1.6} \quad \text{Lorenz curve for 1947}$$

Find the Gini index of income concentration for each Lorenz curve and interpret the results.

84. Income distribution. Using data from the U.S. Census Bureau, an economist produced the following Lorenz curves for the distribution of U.S. income in 1962 and in 1972:

$$f(x) = \tfrac{3}{10}x + \tfrac{7}{10}x^2 \quad \text{Lorenz curve for 1962}$$

$$g(x) = \tfrac{1}{2}x + \tfrac{1}{2}x^2 \quad \text{Lorenz curve for 1972}$$

Find the Gini index of income concentration for each Lorenz curve and interpret the results.

85. Distribution of wealth. Lorenz curves also can provide a relative measure of the distribution of a country's total assets. Using data in a report by the U.S. Congressional Joint Economic Committee, an economist produced the following Lorenz curves for the distribution of total U.S. assets in 1963 and in 1983:

$$f(x) = x^{10} \quad \text{Lorenz curve for 1963}$$

$$g(x) = x^{12} \quad \text{Lorenz curve for 1983}$$

Find the Gini index of income concentration for each Lorenz curve and interpret the results.

86. Income distribution. The government of a small country is planning sweeping changes in the tax structure in order to provide a more equitable distribution of income. The Lorenz curves for the current income distribution and for the projected income distribution after enactment of the tax changes are as follows:

$$f(x) = x^{2.3} \quad \text{Current Lorenz curve}$$

$$g(x) = 0.4x + 0.6x^2 \quad \text{Projected Lorenz curve after changes in tax laws}$$

Find the Gini index of income concentration for each Lorenz curve. Will the proposed changes provide a more equitable income distribution? Explain.

87. Distribution of wealth. The data in the following table describe the distribution of wealth in a country:

x	0	0.20	0.40	0.60	0.80	1
y	0	0.12	0.31	0.54	0.78	1

(A) Use quadratic regression to find the equation of a Lorenz curve for the data.

(B) Use the regression equation and a numerical integration routine to approximate the Gini index of income concentration.

88. Distribution of wealth. Refer to Problem 87.

(A) Use cubic regression to find the equation of a Lorenz curve for the data.

(B) Use the cubic regression equation you found in Part (A) and a numerical integration routine to approximate the Gini index of income concentration.

89. Biology. A yeast culture is growing at a rate of $W'(t) = 0.3e^{0.1t}$ grams per hour. Find the area between the graph of W' and the t axis over the interval $[0, 10]$ and interpret the results.

90. Natural resource depletion. The instantaneous rate of change in demand for U.S. lumber since 1970 ($t = 0$), in billions of cubic feet per year, is given by

$$Q'(t) = 12 + 0.006t^2 \quad 0 \leq t \leq 50$$

Find the area between the graph of Q' and the t axis over the interval $[15, 20]$, and interpret the results.

91. Learning. A college language class was chosen for a learning experiment. Using a list of 50 words, the experiment measured the rate of vocabulary memorization at different times during a continuous 5-hour study session. The average rate of learning for the entire class was inversely proportional to the time spent studying and was given approximately by

$$V'(t) = \frac{15}{t} \quad 1 \leq t \leq 5$$

Find the area between the graph of V' and the t axis over the interval $[2, 4]$, and interpret the results.

92. Learning. Repeat Problem 91 if $V'(t) = 13/t^{1/2}$ and the interval is changed to $[1, 4]$.

Answers to Matched Problems

1. $A = \int_{-1}^{3} (x^2 + 1)\, dx = \tfrac{40}{3} \approx 13.333$

2. (A) $A = \int_{0}^{2} (9 - x^2)\, dx = \tfrac{46}{3} \approx 15.333$

   (B) $A = \int_{2}^{3} (9 - x^2)\, dx + \int_{3}^{4} (x^2 - 9)\, dx = 6$

3. $A = \int_{-1}^{2} \left[(x^2 - 1) - \left(-\frac{x}{2} - 3 \right) \right] dx = \frac{39}{4} = 9.75$

4. $A = \int_{-3}^{2} [(6 - x^2) - x]\, dx = \tfrac{125}{6} \approx 20.833$

5. $A = \int_{-2}^{1} [(4 - 2x) - 2x^2]\, dx + \int_{1}^{2} [2x^2 - (4 - 2x)]\, dx = \tfrac{38}{3} \approx 12.667$

6. 0.443

7. Gini index of income concentration ≈ 0.583; income will be less equally distributed in 2025.

7-2 Applications in Business and Economics

This section contains important applications of the definite integral to business and economics. Included are three independent topics: probability density functions, continuous income streams, and consumers' and producers' surplus. Any of the three may be covered in any order as time and interests dictate.

Probability Density Functions

We now take a brief, informal look at the use of the definite integral to determine probabilities. A more formal treatment of the subject requires the use of the special "improper" integral form $\int_{-\infty}^{\infty} f(x)\,dx$, which we will not discuss.

Suppose that an experiment is designed in such a way that any real number x on the interval $[c, d]$ is a possible outcome. For example, x may represent an IQ score, the height of a person in inches, or the life of a lightbulb in hours. Technically, we refer to x as a *continuous random variable*.

In certain situations, we can find a function f with x as an independent variable such that the function f can be used to determine the probability that the outcome x of an experiment will be in the interval $[c, d]$. Such a function, called a **probability density function**, must satisfy the following three conditions (see Fig. 1):

1. $f(x) \geq 0$ for all real x.
2. The area under the graph of $f(x)$ over the interval $(-\infty, \infty)$ is exactly 1.
3. If $[c, d]$ is a subinterval of $(-\infty, \infty)$, then

$$\text{Probability } (c \leq x \leq d) = \int_{c}^{d} f(x)\,dx$$

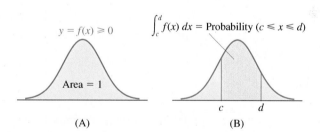

$y = f(x) \geq 0$

$\int_{c}^{d} f(x)\,dx = \text{Probability } (c \leq x \leq d)$

Area = 1

(A)   (B)

Figure 1 Probability density function

EXAMPLE 1 **Duration of Telephone Calls** Suppose that the length of telephone calls (in minutes) is a continuous random variable with the probability density function shown in Figure 2:

$$f(t) = \begin{cases} \frac{1}{4}e^{-t/4} & \text{if } t \geq 0 \\ 0 & \text{otherwise} \end{cases}$$

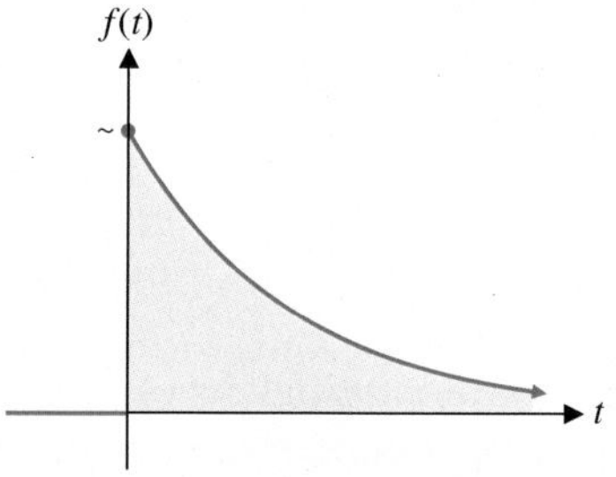

$f(t)$

Figure 2

(A) Determine the probability that a call selected at random will last between 2 and 3 minutes.

(B) Find b (to two decimal places) so that the probability of a call selected at random lasting between 2 and b minutes is .5.

SOLUTION (A) Probability $(2 \leq t \leq 3) = \int_{2}^{3} \frac{1}{4}e^{-t/4}\,dt$

$$= (-e^{-t/4})\big|_{2}^{3}$$

$$= -e^{-3/4} + e^{-1/2} \approx .13$$

(B) We want to find b such that Probability $(2 \le t \le b) = .5$.

$$\int_2^b \tfrac{1}{4}e^{-t/4}\, dt = .5$$

$$-e^{-b/4} + e^{-1/2} = .5 \qquad\qquad \text{Solve for } b.$$

$$e^{-b/4} = e^{-.5} - .5$$

$$-\frac{b}{4} = \ln(e^{-.5} - .5)$$

$$b = 8.96 \text{ minutes}$$

So the probability of a call selected at random lasting from 2 to 8.96 minutes is .5.

Matched Problem 1

(A) In Example 1, find the probability that a call selected at random will last 4 minutes or less.

(B) Find b (to two decimal places) so that the probability of a call selected at random lasting b minutes or less is .9

CONCEPTUAL INSIGHT

The probability that a phone call in Example 1 lasts exactly 2 minutes (not 1.999 minutes, not 1.999 999 minutes) is given by

$$\text{Probability } (2 \le t \le 2) = \int_2^2 \tfrac{1}{4}e^{-t/4}\, dt \quad \text{Use Property 1, Section 6-4}$$

$$= 0$$

In fact, for any *continuous* random variable x with probability density function $f(x)$, the probability that x is exactly equal to a constant c is equal to 0:

$$\text{Probability } (c \le x \le c) = \int_c^c f(x)\, dx \quad \text{Use Property 1, Section 6-4}$$

$$= 0$$

In this respect, a *continuous* random variable differs from a *discrete* random variable. If x, for example, is the discrete random variable that represents the number of dots that appear on the top face when a fair die is rolled, then

$$\text{Probability } (2 \le x \le 2) = \tfrac{1}{6}$$

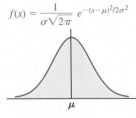

$$f(x) = \frac{1}{\sigma\sqrt{2\pi}}\, e^{-(x-\mu)^2/2\sigma^2}$$

Figure 3 Normal curve

One of the most important probability density functions, the **normal probability density function**, is defined as follows and graphed in Figure 3:

$$f(x) = \frac{1}{\sigma\sqrt{2\pi}}e^{-(x-\mu)^2/2\sigma^2} \qquad \begin{array}{l} \mu \text{ is the mean.} \\ \sigma \text{ is the standard deviation.} \end{array}$$

It can be shown (but not easily) that the area under the normal curve in Figure 3 over the interval $(-\infty, \infty)$ is exactly 1. Since $\int e^{-x^2}\, dx$ is nonintegrable in terms of elementary functions (that is, the antiderivative cannot be expressed as a finite combination of simple functions), probabilities such as

$$\text{Probability } (c \le x \le d) = \frac{1}{\sigma\sqrt{2\pi}} \int_c^d e^{-(x-\mu)^2/2\sigma^2}\, dx$$

can be determined by making an appropriate substitution in the integrand and then using a table of areas under the standard normal curve (that is, the normal curve with $\mu = 0$ and $\sigma = 1$). As an alternative to a table, calculators and computers can be used to compute areas under normal curves.

Continuous Income Stream

We start with a simple example having an obvious solution and generalize the concept to examples having less obvious solutions.

Suppose that an aunt has established a trust that pays you $2,000 a year for 10 years. What is the total amount you will receive from the trust by the end of the 10th year? Since there are 10 payments of $2,000 each, you will receive

$$10 \times \$2,000 = \$20,000$$

We now look at the same problem from a different point of view. Let's assume that the income stream is continuous at a rate of $2,000 per year. In Figure 4, the area under the graph of $f(t) = 2,000$ from 0 to t represents the income accumulated t years after the start. For example, for $t = \frac{1}{4}$ year, the income would be $\frac{1}{4}(2,000) = \$500$; for $t = \frac{1}{2}$ year, the income would be $\frac{1}{2}(2,000) = \$1,000$; for $t = 1$ year, the income would be $1(2,000) = \$2,000$; for $t = 5.3$ years, the income would be $5.3(2,000) = \$10,600$; and for $t = 10$ years, the income would be $10(2,000) = \$20,000$. The total income over a 10-year period—that is, the area under the graph of $f(t) = 2,000$ from 0 to 10—is also given by the definite integral

$$\int_0^{10} 2,000 \, dt = 2,000t\Big|_0^{10} = 2,000(10) - 2,000(0) = \$20,000$$

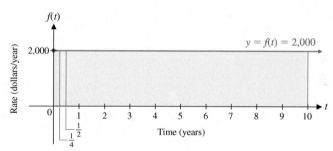

Figure 4 Continuous income stream

EXAMPLE 2 **Continuous Income Stream** The rate of change of the income produced by a vending machine is given by

$$f(t) = 5,000e^{0.04t}$$

where t is time in years since the installation of the machine. Find the total income produced by the machine during the first 5 years of operation.

SOLUTION The area under the graph of the rate-of-change function from 0 to 5 represents the total change in income over the first 5 years (Fig. 5), and is given by a definite integral:

$$\text{Total income} = \int_0^5 5,000e^{0.04t} \, dt$$

$$= 125,000e^{0.04t}\Big|_0^5$$

$$= 125,000e^{0.04(5)} - 125,000e^{0.04(0)}$$

$$= 152,675 - 125,000$$

$$= \$27,675 \qquad \textit{Rounded to the nearest dollar}$$

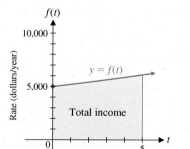

Figure 5 Continuous income stream

The vending machine produces a total income of $27,675 during the first 5 years of operation.

Matched Problem 2 Referring to Example 2, find the total income produced (to the nearest dollar) during the second 5 years of operation.

In reality, income from a vending machine is not usually received as a single payment at the end of each year, even though the rate is given as a yearly rate. Income is usually collected on a daily or weekly basis. In problems of this type, it is convenient to assume that income is actually received in a **continuous stream**; that is, we assume that the rate at which income is received is a continuous function of time. The rate of change is called the **rate of flow** of the continuous income stream. In general, we have the following definition:

DEFINITION Total Income for a Continuous Income Stream

If $f(t)$ is the rate of flow of a continuous income stream, then the **total income** produced during the period from $t = a$ to $t = b$ is

$$\text{Total income} = \int_a^b f(t)\, dt$$

Future Value of a Continuous Income Stream

In Section 4-1, we discussed the continuous compound interest formula

$$A = Pe^{rt}$$

where P is the principal (or present value), A is the amount (or future value), r is the annual rate of continuous compounding (expressed as a decimal), and t is time in years. For example, if money is worth 12% compounded continuously, then the future value of a \$10,000 investment in 5 years is (to the nearest dollar)

$$A = 10,000e^{0.12(5)} = \$18,221$$

We want to apply the future value concept to the income produced by a continuous income stream. Suppose that $f(t)$ is the rate of flow of a continuous income stream, and the income produced by this continuous income stream is invested as soon as it is received at a rate r, compounded continuously. We already know how to find the total income produced after T years, but how can we find the total of the income produced and the interest earned by this income? Since the income is received in a continuous flow, we cannot just use the formula $A = Pe^{rt}$. This formula is valid only for a single deposit P, not for a continuous flow of income. Instead, we use a Riemann sum approach that will allow us to apply the formula $A = Pe^{rt}$ repeatedly. To begin, we divide the time interval $[0, T]$ into n equal subintervals of length Δt and choose an arbitrary point c_k in each subinterval, as shown in Figure 6.

The total income produced during the period from $t = t_{k-1}$ to $t = t_k$ is equal to the area under the graph of $f(t)$ over this subinterval and is approximately equal to $f(c_k)\, \Delta t$, the area of the shaded rectangle in Figure 6. The income received during this period will earn interest for approximately $T - c_k$ years. So, from the future-value formula $A = Pe^{rt}$ with $P = f(c_k)\, \Delta t$ and $t = T - c_k$, the future value of the income produced during the period from $t = t_{k-1}$ to $t = t_k$ is approximately equal to

$$f(c_k)\, \Delta t\, e^{(T-c_k)r}$$

The total of these approximate future values over n subintervals is then

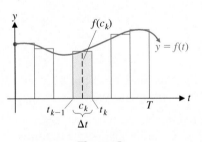

Figure 6

$$f(c_1) \, \Delta t \, e^{(T-c_1)r} + f(c_2) \, \Delta t \, e^{(T-c_2)r} + \cdots + f(c_n) \, \Delta t \, e^{(T-c_n)r} = \sum_{k=1}^{n} f(c_k) e^{r(T-c_k)} \, \Delta t$$

This equation has the form of a Riemann sum, the limit of which is a definite integral. (See the definition of the definite integral in Section 6-4.) Therefore, the *future value FV* of the income produced by the continuous income stream is given by

$$FV = \int_0^T f(t) e^{r(T-t)} \, dt$$

Since r and T are constants, we also can write

$$FV = \int_0^T f(t) e^{rT} e^{-rt} \, dt = e^{rT} \int_0^T f(t) e^{-rt} \, dt \tag{1}$$

This last form is preferable, since the integral is usually easier to evaluate than the first form.

> **DEFINITION** **Future Value of a Continuous Income Stream**
>
> If $f(t)$ is the rate of flow of a continuous income stream, $0 \le t \le T$, and if the income is continuously invested at a rate r, compounded continuously, then the **future value FV** at the end of T years is given by
>
> $$FV = \int_0^T f(t) e^{r(T-t)} \, dt = e^{rT} \int_0^T f(t) e^{-rt} \, dt$$
>
> The future value of a continuous income stream is the total value of all money produced by the continuous income stream (income and interest) at the end of T years.

We return to the trust that your aunt set up for you. Suppose that the $2,000 per year you receive from the trust is invested as soon as it is received at 8%, compounded continuously. We consider the trust income to be a continuous income stream with a flow rate of $2,000 per year. What is its future value (to the nearest dollar) by the end of the 10th year? Using the definite integral for future value from the preceding box, we have

$$FV = e^{rT} \int_0^T f(t) e^{-rt} \, dt$$

$$FV = e^{0.08(10)} \int_0^{10} 2{,}000 e^{-0.08t} \, dt \qquad r = 0.08, \; T = 10, \; f(t) = 2{,}000$$

$$= 2{,}000 e^{0.8} \int_0^{10} e^{-0.08t} \, dt$$

$$= 2{,}000 e^{0.8} \left[\frac{e^{-0.08t}}{-0.08} \right] \Bigg|_0^{10}$$

$$= 2{,}000 e^{0.8} [-12.5 e^{-0.8} + 12.5] = \$30{,}639$$

At the end of 10 years, you will have received $30,639, including interest. How much is interest? Since you received $20,000 in income from the trust, the interest is the difference between the future value and income. So,

$$\$30{,}639 - \$20{,}000 = \$10{,}639$$

is the interest earned by the income received from the trust over the 10-year period.

EXAMPLE 3 **Future Value of a Continuous Income Stream** Using the continuous income rate of flow for the vending machine in Example 2, namely,

$$f(t) = 5{,}000e^{0.04t}$$

find the future value of this income stream at 12%, compounded continuously for 5 years, and find the total interest earned. Compute answers to the nearest dollar.

SOLUTION Using the formula

$$FV = e^{rT} \int_0^T f(t)e^{-rt} \, dt$$

with $r = 0.12$, $T = 5$, and $f(t) = 5{,}000e^{0.04t}$, we have

$$FV = e^{0.12(5)} \int_0^5 5{,}000e^{0.04t} e^{-0.12t} \, dt$$

$$= 5{,}000e^{0.6} \int_0^5 e^{-0.08t} \, dt$$

$$= 5{,}000e^{0.6} \left(\frac{e^{-0.08t}}{-0.08} \right) \Big|_0^5$$

$$= 5{,}000e^{0.6}(-12.5e^{-0.4} + 12.5)$$

$$= \$37{,}545 \quad \textit{Rounded to the nearest dollar}$$

The future value of the income stream at 12% compounded continuously at the end of 5 years is \$37,545.

In Example 2, we saw that the total income produced by this vending machine over a 5-year period was \$27,675. The difference between future value and income is interest. So,

$$\$37{,}545 - \$27{,}675 = \$9{,}870$$

is the interest earned by the income produced by the vending machine during the 5-year period.

Matched Problem 3 Repeat Example 3 if the interest rate is 9%, compounded continuously.

Consumers' and Producers' Surplus

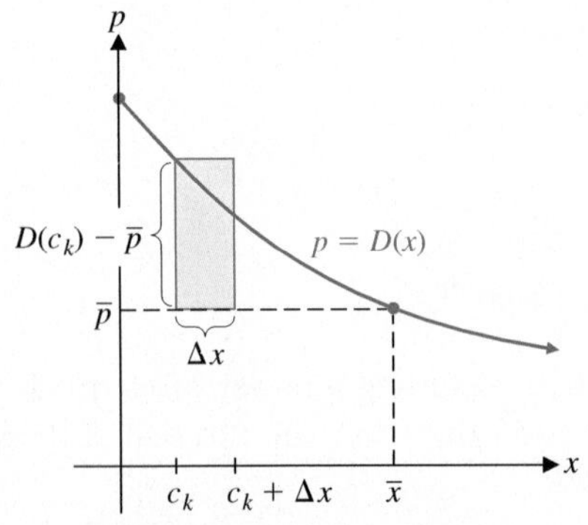

Figure 7

Let $p = D(x)$ be the price–demand equation for a product, where x is the number of units of the product that consumers will purchase at a price of \$p per unit. Suppose that $\bar{p}$, is the current price and $\bar{x}$ is the number of units that can be sold at that price. Then the price–demand curve in Figure 7 shows that if the price is higher than $\bar{p}$, the demand x is less than $\bar{x}$, but some consumers are still willing to pay the higher price. Consumers who are willing to pay more than $\bar{p}$, but who are still able to buy the product at $\bar{p}$, have saved money. We want to determine the total amount saved by all the consumers who are willing to pay a price higher than $\bar{p}$ for the product.

To do this, consider the interval $[c_k, c_k + \Delta x]$, where $c_k + \Delta x < \bar{x}$. If the price remained constant over that interval, the savings on each unit would be the difference between $D(c_k)$, the price consumers are willing to pay, and $\bar{p}$, the price they actually pay. Since Δx represents the number of units purchased by consumers over the interval, the total savings to consumers over this interval is approximately equal to

$$[D(c_k) - \bar{p}] \, \Delta x \quad \text{(savings per unit)} \times \text{(number of units)}$$

which is the area of the shaded rectangle shown in Figure 7. If we divide the interval $[0, \overline{x}]$ into n equal subintervals, then the total savings to consumers is approximately equal to

$$[D(c_1) - \overline{p}]\,\Delta x + [D(c_2) - \overline{p}]\,\Delta x + \cdots + [D(c_n) - \overline{p}]\,\Delta x = \sum_{k=1}^{n}[D(c_k) - \overline{p}]\,\Delta x$$

which we recognize as a Riemann sum for the integral

$$\int_{0}^{\overline{x}}[D(x) - \overline{p}]\,dx$$

We define the *consumers' surplus* to be this integral.

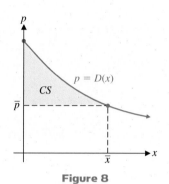

Figure 8

DEFINITION Consumers' Surplus

If $(\overline{x}, \overline{p})$ is a point on the graph of the price–demand equation $p = D(x)$ for a particular product, then the **consumers' surplus CS** at a price level of $\overline{p}$ is

$$CS = \int_{0}^{\overline{x}}[D(x) - \overline{p}]\,dx$$

which is the area between $p = \overline{p}$ and $p = D(x)$ from $x = 0$ to $x = \overline{x}$, as shown in Figure 8.

The consumers' surplus represents the total savings to consumers who are willing to pay more than $\overline{p}$ for the product but are still able to buy the product for $\overline{p}$.

EXAMPLE 4   **Consumers' Surplus** Find the consumers' surplus at a price level of $8 for the price–demand equation

$$p = D(x) = 20 - 0.05x$$

SOLUTION   **Step 1** Find $\overline{x}$, the demand when the price is $\overline{p} = 8$:

$$\overline{p} = 20 - 0.05\overline{x}$$
$$8 = 20 - 0.05\overline{x}$$
$$0.05\overline{x} = 12$$
$$\overline{x} = 240$$

Step 2 Sketch a graph, as shown in Figure 9.

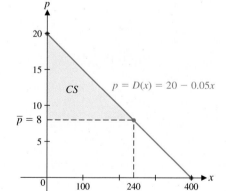

Figure 9

Step 3 Find the consumers' surplus (the shaded area in the graph):

$$CS = \int_{0}^{\overline{x}}[D(x) - \overline{p}]\,dx$$
$$= \int_{0}^{240}(20 - 0.05x - 8)\,dx$$
$$= \int_{0}^{240}(12 - 0.05x)\,dx$$
$$= (12x - 0.025x^2)\Big|_{0}^{240}$$
$$= 2{,}880 - 1{,}440 = \$1{,}440$$

The total savings to consumers who are willing to pay a higher price for the product is $1,440.

Matched Problem 4   Repeat Example 4 for a price level of $4.

If $p = S(x)$ is the price–supply equation for a product, $\overline{p}$ is the current price, and $\overline{x}$ is the current supply, then some suppliers are still willing to supply some units at a lower price than $\overline{p}$. The additional money that these suppliers gain from the higher price is called the *producers' surplus* and can be expressed in terms of a definite integral (proceeding as we did for the consumers' surplus).

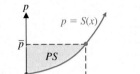

Figure 10

DEFINITION Producers' Surplus

If $(\overline{x}, \overline{p})$ is a point on the graph of the price–supply equation $p = S(x)$, then the **producers' surplus PS** at a price level of $\overline{p}$ is

$$PS = \int_0^{\overline{x}} [\overline{p} - S(x)]\, dx$$

which is the area between $p = \overline{p}$ and $p = S(x)$ from $x = 0$ to $x = \overline{x}$, as shown in Figure 10.

The producers' surplus represents the total gain to producers who are willing to supply units at a lower price than $\overline{p}$ but are still able to supply units at $\overline{p}$.

EXAMPLE 5 **Producers' Surplus** Find the producers' surplus at a price level of $20 for the price–supply equation

$$p = S(x) = 2 + 0.0002x^2$$

SOLUTION **Step 1** Find $\overline{x}$, the supply when the price is $\overline{p} = 20$:

$$\overline{p} = 2 + 0.0002\overline{x}^2$$
$$20 = 2 + 0.0002\overline{x}^2$$
$$0.0002\overline{x}^2 = 18$$
$$\overline{x}^2 = 90{,}000$$
$$\overline{x} = 300 \qquad \text{There is only one solution, since } \overline{x} \geq 0.$$

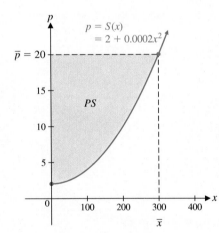

Figure 11

Step 2 Sketch a graph, as shown in Figure 11.

Step 3 Find the producers' surplus (the shaded area in the graph):

$$PS = \int_0^{\overline{x}} [\overline{p} - S(x)]\, dx = \int_0^{300} [20 - (2 + 0.0002x^2)]\, dx$$
$$= \int_0^{300} (18 - 0.0002x^2)\, dx = \left(18x - 0.0002\frac{x^3}{3}\right)\Bigg|_0^{300}$$
$$= 5{,}400 - 1{,}800 = \$3{,}600$$

The total gain to producers who are willing to supply units at a lower price is $3,600.

Matched Problem 5 Repeat Example 5 for a price level of $4.

In a free competitive market, the price of a product is determined by the relationship between supply and demand. If $p = D(x)$ and $p = S(x)$ are the price–demand and price–supply equations, respectively, for a product and if $(\overline{x}, \overline{p})$ is the point of intersection of these equations, then $\overline{p}$ is called the **equilibrium price** and $\overline{x}$ is called the **equilibrium quantity**. If the price stabilizes at the equilibrium price $\overline{p}$, then this is the price level that will determine both the consumers' surplus and the producers' surplus.

EXAMPLE 6   **Equilibrium Price and Consumers' and Producers' Surplus** Find the equilibrium price and then find the consumers' surplus and producers' surplus at the equilibrium price level, if

$$p = D(x) = 20 - 0.05x \qquad \text{and} \qquad p = S(x) = 2 + 0.0002x^2$$

SOLUTION   **Step 1** Find the equilibrium point. Set $D(x)$ equal to $S(x)$ and solve:

$$D(x) = S(x)$$
$$20 - 0.05x = 2 + 0.0002x^2$$
$$0.0002x^2 + 0.05x - 18 = 0$$
$$x^2 + 250x - 90{,}000 = 0$$
$$x = 200, -450$$

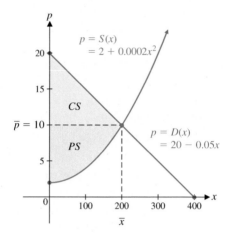

Figure 12

Since x cannot be negative, the only solution is $x = 200$. The equilibrium price can be determined by using $D(x)$ or $S(x)$. We will use both to check our work:

$$\overline{p} = D(200) \qquad\qquad \overline{p} = S(200)$$
$$= 20 - 0.05(200) = 10 \qquad = 2 + 0.0002(200)^2 = 10$$

The equilibrium price is $\overline{p} = 10$, and the equilibrium quantity is $\overline{x} = 200$.

Step 2 Sketch a graph, as shown in Figure 12.

Step 3 Find the consumers' surplus:

$$CS = \int_0^{\overline{x}} [D(x) - \overline{p}]\, dx = \int_0^{200} (20 - 0.05x - 10)\, dx$$
$$= \int_0^{200} (10 - 0.05x)\, dx$$
$$= (10x - 0.025x^2)\big|_0^{200}$$
$$= 2{,}000 - 1{,}000 = \$1{,}000$$

Step 4 Find the producers' surplus:

$$PS = \int_0^{\overline{x}} [\overline{p} - S(x)]\, dx$$
$$= \int_0^{200} [10 - (2 + 0.0002x^2)]\, dx$$
$$= \int_0^{200} (8 - 0.0002x^2)\, dx$$
$$= \left(8x - 0.0002\frac{x^3}{3}\right)\Big|_0^{200}$$
$$= 1{,}600 - \tfrac{1{,}600}{3} \approx \$1{,}067 \qquad \textit{Rounded to the nearest dollar}$$

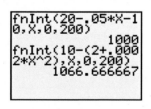

(A)

(B)

Figure 13

A graphing calculator offers an alternative approach to finding the equilibrium point for Example 6 (Fig. 13A). A numerical integration command can then be used to find the consumers' and producers' surplus (Fig. 13B).

Matched Problem 6   Repeat Example 6 for

$$p = D(x) = 25 - 0.001x^2 \qquad \text{and} \qquad p = S(x) = 5 + 0.1x$$

Exercises 7-2

A

In Problems 1–10, evaluate each definite integral to two decimal places.

1. $\int_0^1 e^{-2t}\, dt$

2. $\int_1^3 e^{-t}\, dt$

3. $\int_0^2 e^{4(2-t)}\, dt$

4. $\int_0^1 e^{3(1-t)}\, dt$

5. $\int_0^8 e^{0.06(8-t)}\, dt$

6. $\int_1^{10} e^{0.07(10-t)}\, dt$

7. $\int_0^{20} e^{0.08t}\, e^{0.12(20-t)}\, dt$

8. $\int_0^{15} e^{0.05t}\, e^{0.06(15-t)}\, dt$

9. $\int_0^{30} 500\, e^{0.02t}\, e^{0.09(30-t)}\, dt$

10. $\int_0^{25} 900\, e^{0.03t}\, e^{0.04(25-t)}\, dt$

B

In Problems 11 and 12, explain which of (A), (B), and (C) are equal before evaluating the expressions. Then evaluate each expression to two decimal places.

11. (A) $\int_0^8 e^{0.07(8-t)}\, dt$

(B) $\int_0^8 (e^{0.56} - e^{0.07t})\, dt$

(C) $e^{0.56} \int_0^8 e^{-0.07t}\, dt$

12. (A) $\int_0^{10} 2{,}000 e^{0.05t} e^{0.12(10-t)}\, dt$

(B) $2{,}000 e^{1.2} \int_0^{10} e^{-0.07t}\, dt$

(C) $2{,}000 e^{0.05} \int_0^{10} e^{0.12(10-t)}\, dt$

Applications

Unless stated to the contrary, compute all monetary answers to the nearest dollar.

13. The life expectancy (in years) of a microwave oven is a continuous random variable with probability density function

$$f(x) = \begin{cases} 2/(x+2)^2 & \text{if } x \geq 0 \\ 0 & \text{otherwise} \end{cases}$$

(A) Find the probability that a randomly selected microwave oven lasts at most 6 years.

(B) Find the probability that a randomly selected microwave oven lasts from 6 to 12 years.

(C) Graph $y = f(x)$ for $[0, 12]$ and show the shaded region for part (A).

14. The shelf life (in years) of a laser pointer battery is a continuous random variable with probability density function

$$f(x) = \begin{cases} 1/(x+1)^2 & \text{if } x \geq 0 \\ 0 & \text{otherwise} \end{cases}$$

(A) Find the probability that a randomly selected laser pointer battery has a shelf life of 3 years or less.

(B) Find the probability that a randomly selected laser pointer battery has a shelf life of from 3 to 9 years.

(C) Graph $y = f(x)$ for $[0, 10]$ and show the shaded region for part (A).

15. In Problem 13, find d so that the probability of a randomly selected microwave oven lasting d years or less is .8.

16. In Problem 14, find d so that the probability of a randomly selected laser pointer battery lasting d years or less is .5.

17. A manufacturer guarantees a product for 1 year. The time to failure of the product after it is sold is given by the probability density function

$$f(t) = \begin{cases} .01e^{-.01t} & \text{if } t \geq 0 \\ 0 & \text{otherwise} \end{cases}$$

where t is time in months. What is the probability that a buyer chosen at random will have a product failure

(A) During the warranty period?

(B) During the second year after purchase?

18. In a certain city, the daily use of water (in hundreds of gallons) per household is a continuous random variable with probability density function

$$f(x) = \begin{cases} .15e^{-.15x} & \text{if } x \geq 0 \\ 0 & \text{otherwise} \end{cases}$$

Find the probability that a household chosen at random will use

(A) At most 400 gallons of water per day

(B) Between 300 and 600 gallons of water per day

19. In Problem 17, what is the probability that the product will last at least 1 year? [*Hint:* Recall that the total area under the probability density function curve is 1.]

20. In Problem 18, what is the probability that a household will use more than 400 gallons of water per day? [See the hint in Problem 19.]

21. Find the total income produced by a continuous income stream in the first 5 years if the rate of flow is $f(t) = 2{,}500$.

22. Find the total income produced by a continuous income stream in the first 10 years if the rate of flow is $f(t) = 3{,}000$.

23. Interpret the results of Problem 21 with both a graph and a description of the graph.

24. Interpret the results of Problem 22 with both a graph and a description of the graph.

25. Find the total income produced by a continuous income stream in the first 3 years if the rate of flow is $f(t) = 400e^{0.05t}$.

26. Find the total income produced by a continuous income stream in the first 2 years if the rate of flow is $f(t) = 600e^{0.06t}$.

27. Interpret the results of Problem 25 with both a graph and a description of the graph.

28. Interpret the results of Problem 26 with both a graph and a description of the graph.

29. Starting at age 25, you deposit $2,000 a year into an IRA account. Treat the yearly deposits into the account as a continuous income stream. If money in the account earns 5%, compounded continuously, how much will be in the account 40 years later, when you retire at age 65? How much of the final amount is interest?

30. Suppose in Problem 29 that you start the IRA deposits at age 30, but the account earns 6%, compounded continuously. Treat the yearly deposits into the account as a continuous income stream. How much will be in the account 35 years later when you retire at age 65? How much of the final amount is interest?

31. Find the future value at 3.25% interest, compounded continuously for 4 years, of the continuous income stream with rate of flow $f(t) = 1{,}650e^{-0.02t}$.

32. Find the future value, at 2.95% interest, compounded continuously for 6 years, of the continuous income stream with rate of flow $f(t) = 2{,}000e^{0.06t}$.

33. Compute the interest earned in Problem 31.

34. Compute the interest earned in Problem 32.

35. An investor is presented with a choice of two investments: an established clothing store and a new computer store. Each choice requires the same initial investment and each produces a continuous income stream of 4%, compounded continuously. The rate of flow of income from the clothing store is $f(t) = 12{,}000$, and the rate of flow of income from the computer store is expected to be $g(t) = 10{,}000e^{0.05t}$. Compare the future values of these investments to determine which is the better choice over the next 5 years.

36. Refer to Problem 35. Which investment is the better choice over the next 10 years?

37. An investor has $10,000 to invest in either a bond that matures in 5 years or a business that will produce a continuous stream of income over the next 5 years with rate of flow $f(t) = 2{,}150$. If both the bond and the continuous income stream earn 3.75%, compounded continuously, which is the better investment?

38. Refer to Problem 37. Which is the better investment if the rate of the income from the business is $f(t) = 2{,}250$?

39. A business is planning to purchase a piece of equipment that will produce a continuous stream of income for 8 years with rate of flow $f(t) = 9{,}000$. If the continuous income stream earns 6.95%, compounded continuously, what single deposit into an account earning the same interest rate will produce the same future value as the continuous income stream? (This deposit is called the **present value** of the continuous income stream.)

40. Refer to Problem 39. Find the present value of a continuous income stream at 7.65%, compounded continuously for 12 years, if the rate of flow is $f(t) = 1{,}000e^{0.03t}$.

41. Find the future value at a rate r, compounded continuously for T years, of a continuous income stream with rate of flow $f(t) = k$, where k is a constant.

42. Find the future value at a rate r, compounded continuously for T years, of a continuous income stream with rate of flow $f(t) = ke^{ct}$, where c and k are constants, $c \neq r$.

43. Find the consumers' surplus at a price level of $\overline{p} = \$150$ for the price–demand equation
$$p = D(x) = 400 - 0.05x$$

44. Find the consumers' surplus at a price level of $\overline{p} = \$120$ for the price–demand equation
$$p = D(x) = 200 - 0.02x$$

45. Interpret the results of Problem 43 with both a graph and a description of the graph.

46. Interpret the results of Problem 44 with both a graph and a description of the graph.

47. Find the producers' surplus at a price level of $\overline{p} = \$67$ for the price–supply equation
$$p = S(x) = 10 + 0.1x + 0.0003x^2$$

48. Find the producers' surplus at a price level of $\overline{p} = \$55$ for the price–supply equation
$$p = S(x) = 15 + 0.1x + 0.003x^2$$

49. Interpret the results of Problem 47 with both a graph and a description of the graph.

50. Interpret the results of Problem 48 with both a graph and a description of the graph.

In Problems 51–58, find the consumers' surplus and the producers' surplus at the equilibrium price level for the given price–demand and price–supply equations. Include a graph that identifies the consumers' surplus and the producers' surplus. Round all values to the nearest integer.

51. $p = D(x) = 50 - 0.1x; p = S(x) = 11 + 0.05x$

52. $p = D(x) = 25 - 0.004x^2; p = S(x) = 5 + 0.004x^2$

53. $p = D(x) = 80e^{-0.001x}; p = S(x) = 30e^{0.001x}$

54. $p = D(x) = 185e^{-0.005x}; p = S(x) = 25e^{0.005x}$

55. $p = D(x) = 80 - 0.04x; p = S(x) = 30e^{0.001x}$

56. $p = D(x) = 190 - 0.2x; p = S(x) = 25e^{0.005x}$

57. $p = D(x) = 80e^{-0.001x}; p = S(x) = 15 + 0.0001x^2$

58. $p = D(x) = 185e^{-0.005x}; p = S(x) = 20 + 0.002x^2$

59. The following tables give price–demand and price–supply data for the sale of soybeans at a grain market, where x is the number of bushels of soybeans (in thousands of bushels) and p is the price per bushel (in dollars):

Tables for 59–60

Price–Demand		Price–Supply	
x	$p = D(x)$	x	$p = S(x)$
0	6.70	0	6.43
10	6.59	10	6.45
20	6.52	20	6.48
30	6.47	30	6.53
40	6.45	40	6.62

Use quadratic regression to model the price–demand data and linear regression to model the price–supply data.

(A) Find the equilibrium quantity (to three decimal places) and equilibrium price (to the nearest cent).

(B) Use a numerical integration routine to find the consumers' surplus and producers' surplus at the equilibrium price level.

60. Repeat Problem 59, using quadratic regression to model both sets of data.

Answers to Matched Problems

1. (A) .63   (B) 9.21 min

2. $33,803

3. $FV = \$34,691$; interest $= \$7,016$

4. $2,560

5. $133

6. $\overline{p} = 15$; $CS = \$667$; $PS = \$500$

7-3   Integration by Parts

In Section 6-1, we promised to return later to the indefinite integral

$$\int \ln x \, dx$$

since none of the integration techniques considered up to that time could be used to find an antiderivative for ln x. We now develop a very useful technique, called *integration by parts,* that will enable us to find not only the preceding integral, but also many others, including integrals such as

$$\int x \ln x \, dx \quad \text{and} \quad \int xe^x \, dx$$

The method of integration by parts is based on the product formula for derivatives. If f and g are differentiable functions, then

$$\frac{d}{dx}[f(x)g(x)] = f(x)g'(x) + g(x)f'(x)$$

which can be written in the equivalent form

$$f(x)g'(x) = \frac{d}{dx}[f(x)g(x)] - g(x)f'(x)$$

Integrating both sides, we obtain

$$\int f(x)g'(x) \, dx = \int \frac{d}{dx}[f(x)g(x)] \, dx - \int g(x)f'(x) \, dx$$

The first integral to the right of the equal sign is $f(x)g(x) + C$. Why? We will leave out the constant of integration for now, since we can add it after integrating the second integral to the right of the equal sign. So,

$$\int f(x)g'(x) \, dx = f(x)g(x) - \int g(x)f'(x) \, dx$$

This equation can be transformed into a more convenient form by letting $u = f(x)$ and $v = g(x)$; then $du = f'(x) \, dx$ and $dv = g'(x) \, dx$. Making these substitutions, we obtain the **integration-by-parts formula**:

Integration-by-Parts Formula

$$\int u \, dv = uv - \int v \, du$$

This formula can be very useful when the integral on the left is difficult or impossible to integrate with standard formulas. If u and dv are chosen with care—this is the crucial part of the process—then the integral on the right side may be easier to integrate than the one on the left. The formula provides us with another tool that is helpful in many, but not all, cases. We are able to easily check the results by differentiating to get the original integrand, a good habit to develop.

EXAMPLE 1   **Integration by Parts** Find $\int xe^x \, dx$, using integration by parts, and check the result.

SOLUTION   First, write the integration-by-parts formula:

$$\int u \, dv = uv - \int v \, du \qquad (1)$$

Now try to identify u and dv in $\int xe^x \, dx$ so that $\int v \, du$ on the right side of (1) is easier to integrate than $\int u \, dv = \int xe^x \, dx$ on the left side. There are essentially two reasonable choices in selecting u and dv in $\int xe^x \, dx$:

Choice 1
u dv

$$\int x \, e^x \, dx$$

Choice 2
u dv

$$\int e^x \, x \, dx$$

We pursue choice 1 and leave choice 2 for you to explore (see Explore & Discuss 1 following this example).

From choice 1, $u = x$ and $dv = e^x \, dx$. Looking at formula (1), we need du and v to complete the right side. Let

$$u = x \qquad dv = e^x \, dx$$

Then,

$$du = dx \qquad \int dv = \int e^x \, dx$$

$$v = e^x$$

Any constant may be added to v, but we will always choose 0 for simplicity. The general arbitrary constant of integration will be added at the end of the process.

Substituting these results into formula (1), we obtain

$$\int u \, dv = uv - \int v \, du$$

$$\int xe^x \, dx = xe^x - \int e^x \, dx \qquad \text{The right integral is easy to integrate.}$$

$$= xe^x - e^x + C \qquad \text{Now add the arbitrary constant } C.$$

Check:

$$\frac{d}{dx}(xe^x - e^x + C) = xe^x + e^x - e^x = xe^x$$

EXPLORE & DISCUSS 1	Pursue choice 2 in Example 1, using the integration-by-parts formula, and explain why this choice does not work out.

Matched Problem 1 Find $\int xe^{2x}\, dx$.

EXAMPLE 2 **Integration by Parts** Find $\int x \ln x\, dx$.

SOLUTION As before, we have essentially two choices in choosing u and dv:

$$\text{Choice 1} \qquad\qquad \text{Choice 2}$$

$$\int \overset{u}{\underset{}{x}}\ \overset{dv}{\overline{\ln x\, dx}} \qquad \int \overset{u}{\underset{}{\ln x}}\ \overset{dv}{\overline{x\, dx}}$$

Choice 1 is rejected since we do not yet know how to find an antiderivative of ln x. So we move to choice 2 and choose $u = \ln x$ and $dv = x\, dx$. Then we proceed as in Example 1. Let

$$u = \ln x \qquad dv = x\, dx$$

Then,

$$du = \frac{1}{x}dx \qquad \int dv = \int x\, dx$$

$$v = \frac{x^2}{2}$$

Substitute these results into the integration-by-parts formula:

$$\int u\, dv = uv - \int v\, du$$

$$\int x \ln x\, dx = (\ln x)\left(\frac{x^2}{2}\right) - \int \left(\frac{x^2}{2}\right)\left(\frac{1}{x}\right) dx$$

$$= \frac{x^2}{2}\ln x - \int \frac{x}{2}dx \qquad\qquad \textit{An easy integral to evaluate}$$

$$= \frac{x^2}{2}\ln x - \frac{x^2}{4} + C$$

Check:

$$\frac{d}{dx}\left(\frac{x^2}{2}\ln x - \frac{x^2}{4} + C\right) = x \ln x + \left(\frac{x^2}{2}\cdot\frac{1}{x}\right) - \frac{x}{2} = x \ln x$$

Matched Problem 2 Find $\int x \ln 2x\, dx$.

CONCEPTUAL INSIGHT

As you may have discovered in Explore & Discuss 1, some choices for u and dv will lead to integrals that are more complicated than the original integral. This does not mean that there is an error in either the calculations or the integration-by-parts formula. It simply means that the particular choice of u and dv does not change the problem into one we can solve. When this happens, we must look for a different choice of u and dv. In some problems, it is possible that no choice will work.

Guidelines for selecting u and dv for integration by parts are summarized in the following box:

SUMMARY **Integration by Parts: Selection of u and dv**

For $\int u\,dv = uv - \int v\,du,$

1. The product $u\,dv$ must equal the original integrand.
2. It must be possible to integrate dv (preferably by using standard formulas or simple substitutions).
3. The new integral $\int v\,du$ should not be more complicated than the original integral $\int u\,dv$.
4. For integrals involving $x^p e^{ax}$, try

$$u = x^p \quad \text{and} \quad dv = e^{ax}\,dx$$

5. For integrals involving $x^p(\ln x)^q$, try

$$u = (\ln x)^q \quad \text{and} \quad dv = x^p\,dx$$

In some cases, repeated use of the integration-by-parts formula will lead to the evaluation of the original integral. The next example provides an illustration of such a case.

EXAMPLE 3   **Repeated Use of Integration by Parts** Find $\int x^2 e^{-x}\,dx$.

SOLUTION   Following suggestion 4 in the box, we choose

$$u = x^2 \qquad dv = e^{-x}\,dx$$

Then,

$$du = 2x\,dx \qquad v = -e^{-x}$$

and

$$x^2 e^{-x}\,dx = x^2(-e^{-x}) - (-e^{-x})2x\,dx$$
$$= -x^2 e^{-x} + 2\,xe^{-x}\,dx \qquad\qquad (2)$$

The new integral is not one we can evaluate by standard formulas, but it is simpler than the original integral. Applying the integration-by-parts formula to it will produce an even simpler integral. For the integral $\int xe^{-x}\,dx$, we choose

$$u = x \qquad dv = e^{-x}\,dx$$

Then,

$$du = dx \qquad v = -e^{-x}$$

and

$$\int xe^{-x}\,dx = x(-e^{-x}) - \int(-e^{-x})\,dx$$
$$= -xe^{-x} + \int e^{-x}\,dx$$
$$= -xe^{-x} - e^{-x} \qquad \textit{Choose 0 for the constant.} \qquad (3)$$

Substituting equation (3) into equation (2), we have

$$\int x^2 e^{-x}\,dx = -x^2 e^{-x} + 2(-xe^{-x} - e^{-x}) + C \qquad \textit{Add an arbitrary constant here.}$$
$$= -x^2 e^{-x} - 2xe^{-x} - 2e^{-x} + C$$

Check:

$$\frac{d}{dx}(-x^2 e^{-x} - 2xe^{-x} - 2e^{-x} + C) = x^2 e^{-x} - 2xe^{-x} + 2xe^{-x} - 2e^{-x} + 2e^{-x}$$

$$= x^2 e^{-x}$$

Matched Problem 3 Find $\int x^2 e^{2x}\, dx$.

EXAMPLE 4 **Using Integration by Parts** Find $\int_1^e \ln x\, dx$ and interpret the result geometrically.

SOLUTION First, we find $\int \ln x\, dx$. Then we return to the definite integral. Following suggestion 5 in the box (with $p = 0$), we choose

$$u = \ln x \qquad dv = dx$$

Then,

$$du = \frac{1}{x}dx \qquad v = x$$

$$\int \ln x\, dx = (\ln x)(x) - \int (x)\frac{1}{x}dx$$

$$= x \ln x - x + C$$

This is the important result we mentioned at the beginning of this section. Now we have

$$\int_1^e \ln x\, dx = (x \ln x - x)\big|_1^e$$

$$= (e \ln e - e) - (1 \ln 1 - 1)$$

$$= (e - e) - (0 - 1)$$

$$= 1$$

The integral represents the area under the curve $y = \ln x$ from $x = 1$ to $x = e$, as shown in Figure 1.

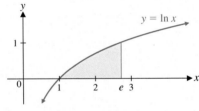

Figure 1

Matched Problem 4 Find $\int_1^2 \ln 3x\, dx$.

EXPLORE & DISCUSS 2 Try using the integration-by-parts formula on $\int e^{x^2}\, dx$, and explain why it does not work.

Exercises 7-3

A

In Problems 1–4, integrate by parts. Assume that $x > 0$ whenever the natural logarithm function is involved.

1. $\int xe^{3x}\, dx$

2. $\int xe^{4x}\, dx$

3. $\int x^2 \ln x\, dx$

4. $\int x^3 \ln x\, dx$

B

5. If you want to use integration by parts to find $\int (x + 1)^5(x + 2)\, dx$, which is the better choice for u: $u = (x + 1)^5$ or $u = x + 2$? Explain your choice and then integrate.

6. If you want to use integration by parts to find $\int (5x - 7)(x - 1)^4\, dx$, which is the better choice for u: $u = 5x - 7$ or $u = (x - 1)^4$? Explain your choice and then integrate.

Problems 7–20 are mixed—some require integration by parts, and others can be solved with techniques considered earlier. Integrate as indicated, assuming $x > 0$ whenever the natural logarithm function is involved.

7. $\int xe^{-x}\,dx$

8. $\int (x-1)e^{-x}\,dx$

9. $\int xe^{x^2}\,dx$

10. $\int xe^{-x^2}\,dx$

11. $\int_0^1 (x-3)e^x\,dx$

12. $\int_0^1 (x+1)e^x\,dx$

13. $\int_1^3 \ln 2x\,dx$

14. $\int_1^2 \ln\left(\dfrac{x}{2}\right)dx$

15. $\int \dfrac{2x}{x^2+1}\,dx$

16. $\int \dfrac{x^2}{x^3+5}\,dx$

17. $\int \dfrac{\ln x}{x}\,dx$

18. $\int \dfrac{e^x}{e^x+1}\,dx$

19. $\int \sqrt{x}\ln x\,dx$

20. $\int \dfrac{\ln x}{\sqrt{x}}\,dx$

In Problems 21–24, the integral can be found in more than one way. First use integration by parts, then use a method that does not involve integration by parts. Which method do you prefer?

21. $\int (x-3)(x+1)^2\,dx$

22. $\int (x+2)(x-1)^2\,dx$

23. $\int (2x+1)(x-2)^2\,dx$

24. $\int (5x-1)(x+2)^2\,dx$

In Problems 25–28, illustrate each integral graphically and describe what the integral represents in terms of areas.

25. Problem 11

26. Problem 12

27. Problem 13

28. Problem 14

C

Problems 29–50 are mixed—some may require use of the integration-by-parts formula along with techniques we have considered earlier; others may require repeated use of the integration-by-parts formula. Assume that $g(x) > 0$ whenever $\ln g(x)$ is involved.

29. $\int x^2 e^x\,dx$

30. $\int x^3 e^x\,dx$

31. $\int xe^{ax}\,dx,\ a \neq 0$

32. $\int \ln(ax)\,dx,\ a > 0$

33. $\int_1^e \dfrac{\ln x}{x^2}\,dx$

34. $\int_1^2 x^3 e^{x^2}\,dx$

35. $\int_0^2 \ln(x+4)\,dx$

36. $\int_0^2 \ln(4-x)\,dx$

37. $\int xe^{x-2}\,dx$

38. $\int xe^{x+1}\,dx$

39. $\int x\ln(1+x^2)\,dx$

40. $\int x\ln(1+x)\,dx$

41. $\int e^x \ln(1+e^x)\,dx$

42. $\int \dfrac{\ln(1+\sqrt{x})}{\sqrt{x}}\,dx$

43. $\int (\ln x)^2\,dx$

44. $\int x(\ln x)^2\,dx$

45. $\int (\ln x)^3\,dx$

46. $\int x(\ln x)^3\,dx$

47. $\int_1^e \ln(x^2)\,dx$

48. $\int_1^e \ln(x^4)\,dx$

49. $\int_0^1 \ln(e^{x^2})\,dx$

50. $\int_1^2 \ln(xe^x)\,dx$

In Problems 51–54, use a graphing calculator to graph each equation over the indicated interval and find the area between the curve and the x axis over that interval. Find answers to two decimal places.

51. $y = x - 2 - \ln x;\ 1 \leq x \leq 4$

52. $y = 6 - x^2 - \ln x;\ 1 \leq x \leq 4$

53. $y = 5 - xe^x;\ 0 \leq x \leq 3$

54. $y = xe^x + x - 6;\ 0 \leq x \leq 3$

Applications

55. Profit. If the marginal profit (in millions of dollars per year) is given by

$$P'(t) = 2t - te^{-t}$$

use an appropriate definite integral to find the total profit (to the nearest million dollars) earned over the first 5 years of operation.

56. Production. An oil field is estimated to produce oil at a rate of $R(t)$ thousand barrels per month t months from now, as given by

$$R(t) = 10te^{-0.1t}$$

Use an appropriate definite integral to find the total production (to the nearest thousand barrels) in the first year of operation.

57. Profit. Interpret the results of Problem 55 with both a graph and a description of the graph.

58. Production. Interpret the results of Problem 56 with both a graph and a description of the graph.

59. Continuous income stream. Find the future value at 3.95%, compounded continuously, for 5 years of a continuous income stream with a rate of flow of

$$f(t) = 1{,}000 - 200t$$

60. Continuous income stream. Find the interest earned at 4.15%, compounded continuously, for 4 years for a continuous income stream with a rate of flow of

$$f(t) = 1{,}000 - 250t$$

61. Income distribution. Find the Gini index of income concentration for the Lorenz curve with equation

$$y = xe^{x-1}$$

62. Income distribution. Find the Gini index of income concentration for the Lorenz curve with equation

$$y = x^2 e^{x-1}$$

63. Income distribution. Interpret the results of Problem 61 with both a graph and a description of the graph.

64. Income distribution. Interpret the results of Problem 62 with both a graph and a description of the graph.

65. Sales analysis. Monthly sales of a particular personal computer are expected to decline at the rate of

$$S'(t) = -4te^{0.1t}$$

computers per month, where t is time in months and $S(t)$ is the number of computers sold each month. The company plans to stop manufacturing this computer when monthly sales reach 800 computers. If monthly sales now ($t = 0$) are 2,000 computers, find $S(t)$. How long, to the nearest month, will the company continue to manufacture the computer?

66. Sales analysis. The rate of change of the monthly sales of a new basketball game is given by

$$S'(t) = 350 \ln(t + 1) \qquad S(0) = 0$$

where t is the number of months since the game was released and $S(t)$ is the number of games sold each month. Find $S(t)$. When, to the nearest month, will monthly sales reach 15,000 games?

67. Consumers' surplus. Find the consumers' surplus (to the nearest dollar) at a price level of $\overline{p} = \$2.089$ for the price–demand equation

$$p = D(x) = 9 - \ln(x + 4)$$

Use $\overline{x}$ computed to the nearest higher unit.

68. Producers' surplus. Find the producers' surplus (to the nearest dollar) at a price level of $\overline{p} = \$26$ for the price–supply equation

$$p = S(x) = 5 \ln(x + 1)$$

Use $\overline{x}$ computed to the nearest higher unit.

69. Consumers' surplus. Interpret the results of Problem 67 with both a graph and a description of the graph.

70. Producers' surplus. Interpret the results of Problem 68 with both a graph and a description of the graph.

71. Pollution. The concentration of particulate matter (in parts per million) t hours after a factory ceases operation for the day is given by

$$C(t) = \frac{20 \ln(t + 1)}{(t + 1)^2}$$

Find the average concentration for the period from $t = 0$ to $t = 5$.

72. Medicine. After a person takes a pill, the drug contained in the pill is assimilated into the bloodstream. The rate of assimilation t minutes after taking the pill is

$$R(t) = te^{-0.2t}$$

Find the total amount of the drug that is assimilated into the bloodstream during the first 10 minutes after the pill is taken.

73. Learning. A student enrolled in an advanced typing class progressed at a rate of

$$N'(t) = (t + 6)e^{-0.25t}$$

words per minute per week t weeks after enrolling in a 15-week course. If a student could type 40 words per minute at the beginning of the course, then how many words per minute $N(t)$ would the student be expected to type t weeks into the course? How long, to the nearest week, should it take the student to achieve the 70-word-per-minute level? How many words per minute should the student be able to type by the end of the course?

74. Learning. A student enrolled in a stenotyping class progressed at a rate of

$$N'(t) = (t + 10)e^{-0.1t}$$

words per minute per week t weeks after enrolling in a 15-week course. If a student had no knowledge of stenotyping (that is, if the student could stenotype at 0 words per minute) at the beginning of the course, then how many words per minute $N(t)$ would the student be expected to handle t weeks into the course? How long, to the nearest week, should it take the student to achieve 90 words per minute? How many words per minute should the student be able to handle by the end of the course?

75. Politics. The number of voters (in thousands) in a certain city is given by

$$N(t) = 20 + 4t - 5te^{-0.1t}$$

where t is time in years. Find the average number of voters during the period from $t = 0$ to $t = 5$.

Answers to Matched Problems

1. $\dfrac{x}{2}e^{2x} - \dfrac{1}{4}e^{2x} + C$

2. $\dfrac{x^2}{2} \ln 2x - \dfrac{x^2}{4} + C$

3. $\dfrac{x^2}{2}e^{2x} - \dfrac{x}{2}e^{2x} + \dfrac{1}{4}e^{2x} + C$

4. $2 \ln 6 - \ln 3 - 1 \approx 1.4849$

7-4   Integration Using Tables

- Using a Table of Integrals
- Substitution and Integral Tables
- Reduction Formulas
- Application

A **table of integrals** is a list of integration formulas used to evaluate integrals. Table II of Appendix C on pages 600–602 contains a list of integral formulas. Some of these formulas can be derived with the integration techniques discussed earlier, while others require techniques we have not considered. However, it is possible to verify each formula by differentiating the right side.

Using a Table of Integrals

The formulas in Table II on pages 600–602 are organized by categories, such as "Integrals Involving $a + bu$," "Integrals Involving $\sqrt{u^2 - a^2}$," and so on. The variable u is the variable of integration. All other symbols represent constants. To use a table to evaluate an integral, you must first find the category that most closely agrees with the form of the integrand and then find a formula in that category that you can make to match the integrand exactly by assigning values to the constants in the formula.

EXAMPLE 1   **Integration Using Tables** Use Table II to find

$$\int \frac{x}{(5 + 2x)(4 - 3x)}\,dx$$

SOLUTION   Since the integrand

$$f(x) = \frac{x}{(5 + 2x)(4 - 3x)}$$

is a rational function involving terms of the form $a + bu$ and $c + du$, we examine formulas 15 to 20 in Table II on page 600 to see if any of the integrands in these formulas can be made to match $f(x)$ exactly. Comparing the integrand in formula 16 with $f(x)$, we see that this integrand will match $f(x)$ if we let $a = 5, b = 2, c = 4,$ and $d = -3$. Letting $u = x$ and substituting for $a, b, c,$ and d in formula 16, we have

$$\int \frac{u}{(a + bu)(c + du)}\,du = \frac{1}{ad - bc}\left(\frac{a}{b}\ln|a + bu| - \frac{c}{d}\ln|c + du|\right) \quad \text{Formula 16}$$

$$\int \frac{x}{\underset{a\quad\; b\quad\; c\quad\; d}{(5 + 2x)(4 - 3x)}}\,dx = \frac{1}{5\cdot(-3) - 2\cdot 4}\left(\frac{5}{2}\ln|5 + 2x| - \frac{4}{-3}\ln|4 - 3x|\right) + C$$
$$\underset{a\cdot d - b\cdot c = 5\cdot(-3) - 2\cdot 4 = -23}{}$$

$$= -\tfrac{5}{46}\ln|5 + 2x| - \tfrac{4}{69}\ln|4 - 3x| + C$$

Notice that the constant of integration, C, is not included in any of the formulas in Table II. However, you must still include C in all antiderivatives.

Matched Problem 1   Use Table II to find $\displaystyle\int \frac{1}{(5 + 3x)^2(1 + x)}\,dx.$

EXAMPLE 2   **Integration Using Tables** Evaluate $\displaystyle\int_3^4 \frac{1}{x\sqrt{25 - x^2}}\,dx.$

SOLUTION   First, we use Table II to find

$$\int \frac{1}{x\sqrt{25 - x^2}}\,dx$$

Since the integrand involves the expression $\sqrt{25 - x^2}$, we examine formulas 29 to 31 in Table II and select formula 29 with $a^2 = 25$ and $a = 5$:

$$\int \frac{1}{u\sqrt{a^2 - u^2}}\,du = -\frac{1}{a}\ln\left|\frac{a + \sqrt{a^2 - u^2}}{u}\right| \qquad \text{Formula 29}$$

$$\int \frac{1}{x\sqrt{25 - x^2}}\,dx = -\frac{1}{5}\ln\left|\frac{5 + \sqrt{25 - x^2}}{x}\right| + C$$

So

$$\int_3^4 \frac{1}{x\sqrt{25 - x^2}}\,dx = -\frac{1}{5}\ln\left|\frac{5 + \sqrt{25 - x^2}}{x}\right|\,\Bigg|_3^4$$

$$= -\frac{1}{5}\ln\left|\frac{5 + 3}{4}\right| + \frac{1}{5}\ln\left|\frac{5 + 4}{3}\right|$$

$$= -\tfrac{1}{5}\ln 2 + \tfrac{1}{5}\ln 3 = \tfrac{1}{5}\ln 1.5 \approx 0.0811$$

Matched Problem 2   Evaluate $\displaystyle\int_6^8 \frac{1}{x^2\sqrt{100 - x^2}}\,dx$.

Substitution and Integral Tables

As Examples 1 and 2 illustrate, if the integral we want to evaluate can be made to match one in the table exactly, then evaluating the indefinite integral consists simply of substituting the correct values of the constants into the formula. But what happens if we cannot match an integral with one of the formulas in the table? In many cases, a substitution will change the given integral into one that corresponds to a table entry.

EXAMPLE 3   **Integration Using Substitution and Tables** Find $\displaystyle\int \frac{x^2}{\sqrt{16x^2 - 25}}\,dx$.

SOLUTION   In order to relate this integral to one of the formulas involving $\sqrt{u^2 - a^2}$ (formulas 40 to 45 in Table II), we observe that if $u = 4x$, then

$$u^2 = 16x^2 \qquad \text{and} \qquad \sqrt{16x^2 - 25} = \sqrt{u^2 - 25}$$

So, we will use the substitution $u = 4x$ to change this integral into one that appears in the table:

$$\int \frac{x^2}{\sqrt{16x^2 - 25}}\,dx = \frac{1}{4}\int \frac{\frac{1}{16}u^2}{\sqrt{u^2 - 25}}\,du \qquad \begin{array}{l}\text{Substitution:}\\ u = 4x,\, du = 4\,dx,\, x = \frac{1}{4}u\end{array}$$

$$= \frac{1}{64}\int \frac{u^2}{\sqrt{u^2 - 25}}\,du$$

This last integral can be evaluated with the aid of formula 44 in Table II with $a = 5$:

$$\int \frac{u^2}{\sqrt{u^2 - a^2}}\,du = \frac{1}{2}\left(u\sqrt{u^2 - a^2} + a^2\ln\left|u + \sqrt{u^2 - a^2}\right|\right) \qquad \text{Formula 44}$$

$$\int \frac{x^2}{\sqrt{16x^2 - 25}}\,dx = \frac{1}{64}\int \frac{u^2}{\sqrt{u^2 - 25}}\,du \qquad \text{Use formula 44 with } a = 5.$$

$$= \tfrac{1}{128}\left(u\sqrt{u^2 - 25} + 25\ln\left|u + \sqrt{u^2 - 25}\right|\right) + C \quad \text{Substitute } u = 4x.$$

$$= \tfrac{1}{128}\left(4x\sqrt{16x^2 - 25} + 25\ln\left|4x + \sqrt{16x^2 - 25}\right|\right) + C$$

Matched Problem 3 Find $\int \sqrt{9x^2 - 16}\, dx$.

EXAMPLE 4 **Integration Using Substitution and Tables** Find $\int \dfrac{x}{\sqrt{x^4 + 1}}\, dx$.

SOLUTION None of the formulas in Table II involve fourth powers; however, if we let $u = x^2$, then

$$\sqrt{x^4 + 1} = \sqrt{u^2 + 1}$$

and this form does appear in formulas 32 to 39. Thus, we substitute $u = x^2$:

$$\int \frac{1}{\sqrt{x^4 + 1}} x\, dx = \frac{1}{2} \int \frac{1}{\sqrt{u^2 + 1}}\, du \qquad \text{Substitution:}$$
$$u = x^2,\, du = 2x\, dx$$

We recognize the last integral as formula 36 with $a = 1$:

$$\int \frac{1}{\sqrt{u^2 + a^2}}\, du = \ln|u + \sqrt{u^2 + a^2}| \qquad \text{Formula 36}$$

$$\int \frac{x}{\sqrt{x^4 + 1}}\, dx = \frac{1}{2} \int \frac{1}{\sqrt{u^2 + 1}}\, du \qquad \text{Use formula 36 with } a = 1.$$

$$= \tfrac{1}{2}\ln|u + \sqrt{u^2 + 1}| + C \qquad \text{Substitute } u = x^2.$$

$$= \tfrac{1}{2}\ln|x^2 + \sqrt{x^4 + 1}| + C$$

Matched Problem 4 Find $\int x\sqrt{x^4 + 1}\, dx$.

Reduction Formulas

EXAMPLE 5 **Using Reduction Formulas** Use Table II to find $\int x^2 e^{3x}\, dx$.

SOLUTION Since the integrand involves the function e^{3x}, we examine formulas 46–48 and conclude that formula 47 can be used for this problem. Letting $u = x$, $n = 2$, and $a = 3$ in formula 47, we have

$$\int u^n e^{au}\, du = \frac{u^n e^{au}}{a} - \frac{n}{a} \int u^{n-1} e^{au}\, du \qquad \text{Formula 47}$$

$$\int x^2 e^{3x}\, dx = \frac{x^2 e^{3x}}{3} - \frac{2}{3} \int x e^{3x}\, dx$$

Notice that the expression on the right still contains an integral, but the exponent of x has been reduced by 1. Formulas of this type are called **reduction formulas** and are designed to be applied repeatedly until an integral that can be evaluated is obtained. Applying formula 47 to $\int x e^{3x}\, dx$ with $n = 1$, we have

$$\int x^2 e^{3x}\, dx = \frac{x^2 e^{3x}}{3} - \frac{2}{3}\left(\frac{x e^{3x}}{3} - \frac{1}{3}\int e^{3x}\, dx\right)$$

$$= \frac{x^2 e^{3x}}{3} - \frac{2x e^{3x}}{9} + \frac{2}{9}\int e^{3x}\, dx$$

This last expression contains an integral that is easy to evaluate:

$$\int e^{3x}\, dx = \tfrac{1}{3}e^{3x}$$

After making a final substitution and adding a constant of integration, we have

$$\int x^2 e^{3x}\, dx = \frac{x^2 e^{3x}}{3} - \frac{2x e^{3x}}{9} + \frac{2}{27}e^{3x} + C$$

Matched Problem 5   Use Table II to find $\int (\ln x)^2 \, dx$.

Application

EXAMPLE 6   **Producers' Surplus** Find the producers' surplus at a price level of \$20 for the price–supply equation

$$p = S(x) = \frac{5x}{500 - x}$$

SOLUTION   **Step 1**   Find $\overline{x}$, the supply when the price is $\overline{p} = 20$:

$$\overline{p} = \frac{5\overline{x}}{500 - \overline{x}}$$

$$20 = \frac{5\overline{x}}{500 - \overline{x}}$$

$$10,000 - 20\overline{x} = 5\overline{x}$$

$$10,000 = 25\overline{x}$$

$$\overline{x} = 400$$

Step 2   Sketch a graph, as shown in Figure 1.

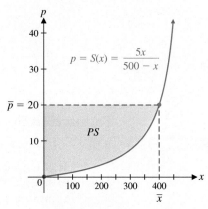

Figure 1

Step 3   Find the producers' surplus (the shaded area of the graph):

$$PS = \int_0^{\overline{x}} [\overline{p} - S(x)] \, dx$$

$$= \int_0^{400} \left(20 - \frac{5x}{500 - x} \right) dx$$

$$= \int_0^{400} \frac{10,000 - 25x}{500 - x} \, dx$$

Use formula 20 with $a = 10,000$, $b = -25$, $c = 500$, and $d = -1$:

$$\int \frac{a + bu}{c + du} \, du = \frac{bu}{d} + \frac{ad - bc}{d^2} \ln|c + du| \qquad \text{Formula 20}$$

$$PS = (25x + 2,500 \ln|500 - x|) \Big|_0^{400}$$

$$= 10,000 + 2,500 \ln|100| - 2,500 \ln|500|$$

$$\approx \$5,976$$

Matched Problem 6   Find the consumers' surplus at a price level of \$10 for the price–demand equation

$$p = D(x) = \frac{20x - 8,000}{x - 500}$$

Exercises 7-4

A

Use Table II on pages 600–602 to find each indefinite integral in Problems 1–14.

1. $\displaystyle\int \frac{1}{x(1 + x)}dx$

2. $\displaystyle\int \frac{1}{x^2(1 + x)}dx$

3. $\displaystyle\int \frac{1}{(3 + x)^2(5 + 2x)}dx$

4. $\displaystyle\int \frac{x}{(5 + 2x)^2(2 + x)}dx$

5. $\displaystyle\int \frac{x}{\sqrt{16 + x}}dx$

6. $\displaystyle\int \frac{1}{x\sqrt{16 + x}}dx$

7. $\displaystyle\int \frac{1}{x\sqrt{1 - x^2}}dx$

8. $\displaystyle\int \frac{\sqrt{9 - x^2}}{x}dx$

9. $\displaystyle\int \frac{1}{x\sqrt{x^2 + 4}}dx$

10. $\displaystyle\int \frac{1}{x^2\sqrt{x^2 - 16}}dx$

11. $\displaystyle\int x^2 \ln x \, dx$

12. $\displaystyle\int x^3 \ln x \, dx$

13. $\displaystyle\int \frac{1}{1 + e^x}dx$

14. $\displaystyle\int \frac{1}{5 + 2e^{3x}}dx$

Evaluate each definite integral in Problems 15–20. Use Table II on pages 600–602 to find the antiderivative.

15. $\displaystyle\int_1^3 \frac{x^2}{3 + x}dx$

16. $\displaystyle\int_2^6 \frac{x}{(6 + x)^2}dx$

17. $\displaystyle\int_0^7 \frac{1}{(3 + x)(1 + x)}dx$

18. $\displaystyle\int_0^7 \frac{x}{(3 + x)(1 + x)}dx$

19. $\displaystyle\int_0^4 \frac{1}{\sqrt{x^2 + 9}}dx$

20. $\displaystyle\int_4^5 \sqrt{x^2 - 16} \, dx$

B

In Problems 21–32, use substitution techniques and Table II to find each indefinite integral.

21. $\displaystyle\int \frac{\sqrt{4x^2 + 1}}{x^2}dx$

22. $\displaystyle\int x^2\sqrt{9x^2 - 1} \, dx$

23. $\displaystyle\int \frac{x}{\sqrt{x^4 - 16}}dx$

24. $\displaystyle\int x\sqrt{x^4 - 16} \, dx$

25. $\displaystyle\int x^2\sqrt{x^6 + 4} \, dx$

26. $\displaystyle\int \frac{x^2}{\sqrt{x^6 + 4}}dx$

27. $\displaystyle\int \frac{1}{x^3\sqrt{4 - x^4}}dx$

28. $\displaystyle\int \frac{\sqrt{x^4 + 4}}{x}dx$

29. $\displaystyle\int \frac{e^x}{(2 + e^x)(3 + 4e^x)}dx$

30. $\displaystyle\int \frac{e^x}{(4 + e^x)^2(2 + e^x)}dx$

31. $\displaystyle\int \frac{\ln x}{x\sqrt{4 + \ln x}}dx$

32. $\displaystyle\int \frac{1}{x \ln x\sqrt{4 + \ln x}}dx$

C

In Problems 33–38, use Table II to find each indefinite integral.

33. $\displaystyle\int x^2 e^{5x} \, dx$

34. $\displaystyle\int x^2 e^{-4x} \, dx$

35. $\displaystyle\int x^3 e^{-x} \, dx$

36. $\displaystyle\int x^3 e^{2x} \, dx$

37. $\displaystyle\int (\ln x)^3 \, dx$

38. $\displaystyle\int (\ln x)^4 \, dx$

Problems 39–46 are mixed—some require the use of Table II, and others can be solved with techniques considered earlier.

39. $\displaystyle\int_3^5 x\sqrt{x^2 - 9} \, dx$

40. $\displaystyle\int_3^5 x^2\sqrt{x^2 - 9} \, dx$

41. $\displaystyle\int_2^4 \frac{1}{x^2 - 1}dx$

42. $\displaystyle\int_2^4 \frac{x}{(x^2 - 1)^2}dx$

43. $\int \dfrac{\ln x}{x^2}\,dx$

44. $\int \dfrac{(\ln x)^2}{x}\,dx$

45. $\int \dfrac{x}{\sqrt{x^2 - 1}}\,dx$

46. $\int \dfrac{x^2}{\sqrt{x^2 - 1}}\,dx$

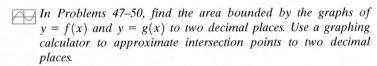 *In Problems 47–50, find the area bounded by the graphs of* $y = f(x)$ *and* $y = g(x)$ *to two decimal places. Use a graphing calculator to approximate intersection points to two decimal places.*

47. $f(x) = \dfrac{10}{\sqrt{x^2 + 1}}$; $g(x) = x^2 + 3x$

48. $f(x) = \sqrt{1 + x^2}$; $g(x) = 5x - x^2$

49. $f(x) = x\sqrt{4 + x}$; $g(x) = 1 + x$

50. $f(x) = \dfrac{x}{\sqrt{x + 4}}$; $g(x) = x - 2$

Applications

Use Table II to evaluate all integrals involved in any solutions of Problems 51–74.

51. **Consumers' surplus.** Find the consumers' surplus at a price level of $\overline{p} = \$15$ for the price–demand equation

$$p = D(x) = \dfrac{7{,}500 - 30x}{300 - x}$$

52. **Producers' surplus.** Find the producers' surplus at a price level of $\overline{p} = \$20$ for the price–supply equation

$$p = S(x) = \dfrac{10x}{300 - x}$$

53. **Consumers' surplus.** Graph the price–demand equation and the price-level equation $\overline{p} = 15$ of Problem 51 in the same coordinate system. What region represents the consumers' surplus?

54. **Producers' surplus.** Graph the price–supply equation and the price-level equation $\overline{p} = 20$ of Problem 52 in the same coordinate system. What region represents the producers' surplus?

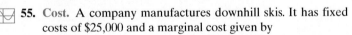 55. **Cost.** A company manufactures downhill skis. It has fixed costs of $25,000 and a marginal cost given by

$$C'(x) = \dfrac{250 + 10x}{1 + 0.05x}$$

where $C(x)$ is the total cost at an output of x pairs of skis. Find the cost function $C(x)$ and determine the production level (to the nearest unit) that produces a cost of $150,000. What is the cost (to the nearest dollar) for a production level of 850 pairs of skis?

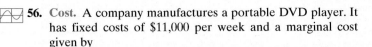 56. **Cost.** A company manufactures a portable DVD player. It has fixed costs of $11,000 per week and a marginal cost given by

$$C'(x) = \dfrac{65 + 20x}{1 + 0.4x}$$

where $C(x)$ is the total cost per week at an output of x players per week. Find the cost function $C(x)$ and determine the production level (to the nearest unit) that produces a cost of $52,000 per week. What is the cost (to the nearest dollar) for a production level of 700 players per week?

57. **Continuous income stream.** Find the future value at 4.4%, compounded continuously, for 10 years for the continuous income stream with rate of flow $f(t) = 50t^2$.

58. **Continuous income stream.** Find the interest earned at 3.7%, compounded continuously, for 5 years for the continuous income stream with rate of flow $f(t) = 200t$.

59. **Income distribution.** Find the Gini index of income concentration for the Lorenz curve with equation

$$y = \tfrac{1}{2}x\sqrt{1 + 3x}$$

60. **Income distribution.** Find the Gini index of income concentration for the Lorenz curve with equation

$$y = \tfrac{1}{2}x^2\sqrt{1 + 3x}$$

61. **Income distribution.** Graph $y = x$ and the Lorenz curve of Problem 59 over the interval $[0, 1]$. Discuss the effect of the area bounded by $y = x$ and the Lorenz curve getting smaller relative to the equitable distribution of income.

62. **Income distribution.** Graph $y = x$ and the Lorenz curve of Problem 60 over the interval $[0, 1]$. Discuss the effect of the area bounded by $y = x$ and the Lorenz curve getting larger relative to the equitable distribution of income.

63. **Marketing.** After test marketing a new high-fiber cereal, the market research department of a major food producer estimates that monthly sales (in millions of dollars) will grow at the monthly rate of

$$S'(t) = \dfrac{t^2}{(1 + t)^2}$$

t months after the cereal is introduced. If we assume 0 sales at the time the cereal is introduced, find $S(t)$, the total sales, t months after the cereal is introduced. Find the total sales during the first 2 years that the cereal is on the market.

64. **Average price.** At a discount department store, the price–demand equation for premium motor oil is given by

$$p = D(x) = \dfrac{50}{\sqrt{100 + 6x}}$$

where x is the number of cans of oil that can be sold at a price of p. Find the average price over the demand interval $[50, 250]$.

65. **Marketing.** For the cereal of Problem 63, show the sales over the first 2 years geometrically, and describe the geometric representation.

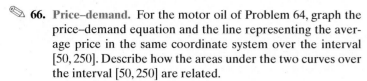

66. Price–demand. For the motor oil of Problem 64, graph the price–demand equation and the line representing the average price in the same coordinate system over the interval [50, 250]. Describe how the areas under the two curves over the interval [50, 250] are related.

67. Profit. The marginal profit for a small car agency that sells x cars per week is given by

$$P'(x) = x\sqrt{2 + 3x}$$

where $P(x)$ is the profit in dollars. The agency's profit on the sale of only 1 car per week is $-\$2,000$. Find the profit function and the number of cars that must be sold (to the nearest unit) to produce a profit of $\$13,000$ per week. How much weekly profit (to the nearest dollar) will the agency have if 80 cars are sold per week?

68. Revenue. The marginal revenue for a company that manufactures and sells x graphing calculators per week is given by

$$R'(x) = \frac{x}{\sqrt{1 + 2x}} \qquad R(0) = 0$$

where $R(x)$ is the revenue in dollars. Find the revenue function and the number of calculators that must be sold (to the nearest unit) to produce $\$10,000$ in revenue per week. How much weekly revenue (to the nearest dollar) will the company have if 1,000 calculators are sold per week?

69. Pollution. An oil tanker is producing an oil slick that is radiating outward at a rate given approximately by

$$\frac{dR}{dt} = \frac{100}{\sqrt{t^2 + 9}} \qquad t \ge 0$$

where R is the radius (in feet) of the circular slick after t minutes. Find the radius of the slick after 4 minutes if the radius is 0 when $t = 0$.

70. Pollution. The concentration of particulate matter (in parts per million) during a 24-hour period is given approximately by

$$C(t) = t\sqrt{24 - t} \qquad 0 \le t \le 24$$

where t is time in hours. Find the average concentration during the period from $t = 0$ to $t = 24$.

71. Learning. A person learns N items at a rate given approximately by

$$N'(t) = \frac{60}{\sqrt{t^2 + 25}} \qquad t \ge 0$$

where t is the number of hours of continuous study. Determine the total number of items learned in the first 12 hours of continuous study.

72. Politics. The number of voters (in thousands) in a metropolitan area is given approximately by

$$f(t) = \frac{500}{2 + 3e^{-t}} \qquad t \ge 0$$

where t is time in years. Find the average number of voters during the period from $t = 0$ to $t = 10$.

73. Learning. Interpret Problem 71 geometrically. Describe the geometric interpretation.

74. Politics. For the voters of Problem 72, graph $y = f(t)$ and the line representing the average number of voters over the interval [0, 10] in the same coordinate system. Describe how the areas under the two curves over the interval [0, 10] are related.

Answers to Matched Problems

1. $\dfrac{1}{2}\left(\dfrac{1}{5 + 3x}\right) + \dfrac{1}{4}\ln\left|\dfrac{1 + x}{5 + 3x}\right| + C$

2. $\frac{7}{1,200} \approx 0.0058$

3. $\frac{1}{6}(3x\sqrt{9x^2 - 16} - 16\ln|3x + \sqrt{9x^2 - 16}|) + C$

4. $\frac{1}{4}(x^2\sqrt{x^4 + 1} + \ln|x^2 + \sqrt{x^4 + 1}|) + C$

5. $x(\ln x)^2 - 2x\ln x + 2x + C$

6. $3,000 + 2,000\ln 200 - 2,000\ln 500 \approx \$1,167$

Chapter 7 Review

Important Terms, Symbols, and Concepts

7-1 Area Between Curves

EXAMPLES

- If f and g are continuous and $f(x) \ge g(x)$ over the interval $[a, b]$, then the area bounded by $y = f(x)$ and $y = g(x)$ for $a \le x \le b$ is given exactly by

$$A = \int_a^b [f(x) - g(x)]\, dx$$

- A graphical representation of the distribution of income among a population can be found by plotting data points (x, y), where **x represents the cumulative percentage of families at or below a given income level** and **y represents the cumulative percentage of total family income received.** Regression analysis can be used to find a particular function $y = f(x)$, called a **Lorenz curve,** that best fits the data.

- A single number, the **Gini index,** measures income concentration:

$$\text{Gini index} = 2\int_0^1 [x - f(x)]\, dx$$

Ex. 1, p. 412
Ex. 2, p. 412
Ex. 3, p. 413
Ex. 4, p. 413
Ex. 5, p. 414
Ex. 6, p. 414

Ex. 7, p. 416

A Gini index of 0 indicates **absolute equality:** All families share equally in the income. A Gini index of 1 indicates **absolute inequality:** One family has all of the income and the rest have none.

7-2 Applications in Business and Economics

- *Probability Density Functions.* If any real number x in an interval is a possible outcome of an experiment, then x is Ex. 1, p. 421 said to be a **continuous random variable.** The probability distribution of a continuous random variable is described by a **probability density function** f that satisfies the following conditions:
  1. $f(x) \geq 0$ for all real x.
  2. The area under the graph of $f(x)$ over the interval $(-\infty, \infty)$ is exactly 1.
  3. If $[c, d]$ is a subinterval of $(-\infty, \infty)$, then

$$\text{Probability} \quad (c \leq x \leq d) = \int_c^d f(x)\, dx$$

- *Continuous Income Stream* If the rate at which income is received—its **rate of flow**—is a continuous function $f(t)$ of Ex. 2, p. 423 time, then the income is said to be a **continuous income stream.** The **total income** produced by a continuous income stream from $t = a$ to $t = b$ is

$$\text{Total income} = \int_a^b f(t)\, dt$$

The **future value** of a continuous income stream that is invested at rate r, compounded continuously, for Ex. 3, p. 426 $0 \leq t \leq T$, is

$$FV = \int_0^T f(t)e^{r(T-t)}\, dt$$

- *Consumers' and Producers' Surplus* If $(\overline{x}, \overline{p})$ is a point on the graph of a price–demand equation $p = D(x)$, then Ex. 4, p. 427 the **consumers' surplus** at a price level of $\overline{p}$ is

$$CS = \int_0^{\overline{x}} [D(x) - \overline{p}]\, dx$$

The consumers' surplus represents the total savings to consumers who are willing to pay more than $\overline{p}$ but are still able to buy the product for $\overline{p}$.

Similarly, for a point $(\overline{x}, \overline{p})$ on the graph of a price–supply equation $p = S(x)$, the **producers' surplus** at a price Ex. 5, p. 428 level of $\overline{p}$ is

$$PS = \int_0^{\overline{x}} [\overline{p} - S(x)]\, dx$$

The producers' surplus represents the total gain to producers who are willing to supply units at a lower price $\overline{p}$, but are still able to supply units at $\overline{p}$.

If $(\overline{x}, \overline{p})$ is the intersection point of a price–demand equation $p = D(x)$ and a price–supply equation $p = S(x)$, Ex. 6, p. 429 then $\overline{p}$ is called the **equilibrium price** and $\overline{x}$ is called the **equilibrium quantity**.

7-3 Integration by Parts

- Some indefinite integrals, but not all, can be found by means of the **integration-by-parts formula** Ex. 1, p. 433
Ex. 2, p. 434

$$\int u\, dv = uv - \int v\, du$$

Ex. 3, p. 435
Ex. 4, p. 436

- Select u and dv with the help of the guidelines in the summary on page 435.

7-4 Integration Using Tables

- A **table of integrals** is a list of integration formulas that can be used to find indefinite or definite integrals of Ex. 1, p. 439 frequently encountered functions. Such a list appears in Table II of Appendix C on pages 600–602.

Ex. 2, p. 439
Ex. 3, p. 440
Ex. 4, p. 441
Ex. 5, p. 441
Ex. 6, p. 442

Review Exercises

Work through all the problems in this chapter review and check your answers in the back of the book. Answers to all review problems are there, along with section numbers in italics to indicate where each type of problem is discussed. Where weaknesses show up, review appropriate sections of the text.

   Compute all numerical answers to three decimal places unless directed otherwise.

A

In Problems 1–3, set up definite integrals that represent the shaded areas in the figure over the indicated intervals.

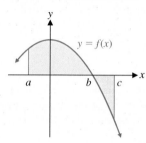

Figure for 1–3

1. Interval $[a, b]$

2. Interval $[b, c]$

3. Interval $[a, c]$

4. Sketch a graph of the area between the graphs of $y = \ln x$ and $y = 0$ over the interval $[0.5, e]$ and find the area.

In Problems 5–10, evaluate each integral.

5. $\displaystyle\int xe^{4x}\,dx$

6. $\displaystyle\int x \ln x\,dx$

7. $\displaystyle\int \frac{\ln x}{x}\,dx$

8. $\displaystyle\int \frac{x}{1 + x^2}\,dx$

9. $\displaystyle\int \frac{1}{x(1 + x)^2}\,dx$

10. $\displaystyle\int \frac{1}{x^2\sqrt{1 + x}}\,dx$

In Problems 11–16, find the area bounded by the graphs of the indicated equations over the given interval.

11. $y = 5 - 2x - 6x^2;\ y = 0, 1 \le x \le 2$

12. $y = 5x + 7;\ y = 12, -3 \le x \le 1$

13. $y = -x + 2;\ y = x^2 + 3, -1 \le x \le 4$

14. $y = \dfrac{1}{x};\ y = -e^{-x}, 1 \le x \le 2$

15. $y = x;\ y = -x^3, -2 \le x \le 2$

16. $y = x^2;\ y = -x^4; -2 \le x \le 2$

B

In Problems 17–20, set up definite integrals that represent the shaded areas in the figure over the indicated intervals.

17. Interval $[a, b]$

18. Interval $[b, c]$

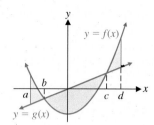

Figure for 17–20

19. Interval $[b, d]$ **20.** Interval $[a, d]$

21. Sketch a graph of the area bounded by the graphs of $y = x^2 - 6x + 9$ and $y = 9 - x$ and find the area.

In Problems 22–27, evaluate each integral.

22. $\displaystyle\int_0^1 xe^x\,dx$

23. $\displaystyle\int_0^3 \frac{x^2}{\sqrt{x^2 + 16}}\,dx$

24. $\displaystyle\int \sqrt{9x^2 - 49}\,dx$

25. $\displaystyle\int te^{-0.5t}\,dt$

26. $\displaystyle\int x^2 \ln x\,dx$

27. $\displaystyle\int \frac{1}{1 + 2e^x}\,dx$

28. Sketch a graph of the area bounded by the indicated graphs, and find the area. In part (B), approximate intersection points and area to two decimal places.

   (A) $y = x^3 - 6x^2 + 9x;\ y = x$

   (B) $y = x^3 - 6x^2 + 9x;\ y = x + 1$

C

In Problems 29–36, evaluate each integral.

29. $\displaystyle\int \frac{(\ln x)^2}{x}\,dx$

30. $\displaystyle\int x(\ln x)^2\,dx$

31. $\displaystyle\int \frac{x}{\sqrt{x^2 - 36}}\,dx$

32. $\displaystyle\int \frac{x}{\sqrt{x^4 - 36}}\,dx$

33. $\displaystyle\int_0^4 x \ln(10 - x)\,dx$

34. $\displaystyle\int (\ln x)^2\,dx$

35. $\displaystyle\int xe^{-2x^2}\,dx$

36. $\displaystyle\int x^2 e^{-2x}\,dx$

37. Use a numerical integration routine on a graphing calculator to find the area in the first quadrant that is below the graph of

$$y = \frac{6}{2 + 5e^{-x}}$$

and above the graph of $y = 0.2x + 1.6$.

Applications

38. Product warranty. A manufacturer warrants a product for parts and labor for 1 year and for parts only for a second year. The time to a failure of the product after it is sold is given by the probability density function

$$f(t) = \begin{cases} 0.21e^{-0.21t} & \text{if } t \ge 0 \\ 0 & \text{otherwise} \end{cases}$$

What is the probability that a buyer chosen at random will have a product failure

(A) During the first year of warranty?

(B) During the second year of warranty?

39. Product warranty. Graph the probability density function for Problem 38 over the interval $[0, 3]$, interpret part (B) of Problem 38 geometrically and describe the geometric representation.

40. Revenue function. The weekly marginal revenue from the sale of x hair dryers is given by

$$R'(x) = 65 - 6\ln(x + 1) \qquad R(0) = 0$$

where $R(x)$ is the revenue in dollars. Find the revenue function and the production level (to the nearest unit) for a revenue of $20,000 per week. What is the weekly revenue (to the nearest dollar) at a production level of 1,000 hair dryers per week?

41. Continuous income stream. The rate of flow (in dollars per year) of a continuous income stream for a 5-year period is given by

$$f(t) = 2,500e^{0.05t} \qquad 0 \le t \le 5$$

(A) Graph $y = f(t)$ over $[0, 5]$ and shade the area that represents the total income received from the end of the first year to the end of the fourth year.

(B) Find the total income received, to the nearest dollar, from the end of the first year to the end of the fourth year.

42. Future value of a continuous income stream. The continuous income stream in Problem 41 is invested at 4%, compounded continuously.

(A) Find the future value (to the nearest dollar) at the end of the 5-year period.

(B) Find the interest earned (to the nearest dollar) during the 5-year period.

43. Income distribution. An economist produced the following Lorenz curves for the current income distribution and the projected income distribution 10 years from now in a certain country:

$$f(x) = 0.1x + 0.9x^2 \qquad \textit{Current Lorenz curve}$$
$$g(x) = x^{1.5} \qquad \textit{Projected Lorenz curve}$$

(A) Graph $y = x$ and the current Lorenz curve on one set of coordinate axes for $[0, 1]$ and graph $y = x$ and the projected Lorenz curve on another set of coordinate axes over the same interval.

(B) Looking at the areas bounded by the Lorenz curves and $y = x$, can you say that the income will be more or less equitably distributed 10 years from now?

(C) Compute the Gini index of income concentration (to one decimal place) for the current and projected curves. What can you say about the distribution of income 10 years from now? Is it more equitable or less?

44. Consumers' and producers' surplus. Find the consumers' surplus and the producers' surplus at the equilibrium price level for each pair of price–demand and price–supply equations. Include a graph that identifies the consumers' surplus and the producers' surplus. Round all values to the nearest integer.

(A) $p = D(x) = 70 - 0.2x$;
$\quad p = S(x) = 13 + 0.0012x^2$

(B) $p = D(x) = 70 - 0.2x; p = S(x) = 13e^{0.006x}$

45. Producers' surplus. The accompanying table gives price–supply data for the sale of hogs at a livestock market, where x is the number of pounds (in thousands) and p is the price per pound (in cents):

Price–Supply	
x	$p = S(x)$
0	43.50
10	46.74
20	50.05
30	54.72
40	59.18

(A) Using quadratic regression to model the data, find the demand at a price of 52.50 cents per pound.

(B) Use a numerical integration routine to find the producers' surplus (to the nearest dollar) at a price level of 52.50 cents per pound.

46. Drug assimilation. The rate at which the body eliminates a certain drug (in milliliters per hour) is given by

$$R(t) = \frac{60t}{(t + 1)^2(t + 2)}$$

where t is the number of hours since the drug was administered. How much of the drug is eliminated during the first hour after it was administered? During the fourth hour?

47. With the aid of a graphing calculator, illustrate Problem 46 geometrically.

48. Medicine. For a particular doctor, the length of time (in hours) spent with a patient per office visit has the probability density function

$$f(t) = \begin{cases} \dfrac{\frac{4}{3}}{(t + 1)^2} & \text{if } 0 \le t \le 3 \\ 0 & \text{otherwise} \end{cases}$$

(A) What is the probability that this doctor will spend less than 1 hour with a randomly selected patient?

(B) What is the probability that this doctor will spend more than 1 hour with a randomly selected patient?

49. Medicine. Illustrate part (B) in Problem 48 geometrically. Describe the geometric interpretation.

50. Politics. The rate of change of the voting population of a city with respect to time t (in years) is estimated to be

$$N'(t) = \frac{100t}{(1 + t^2)^2}$$

where $N(t)$ is in thousands. If $N(0)$ is the current voting population, how much will this population increase during the next 3 years?

51. Psychology. Rats were trained to go through a maze by rewarding them with a food pellet upon successful completion of the run. After the seventh successful run, the probability density function for length of time (in minutes) until success on the eighth trial was given by

$$f(t) = \begin{cases} .5e^{-.5t} & \text{if } t \ge 0 \\ 0 & \text{otherwise} \end{cases}$$

What is the probability that a rat selected at random after seven successful runs will take 2 or more minutes to complete the eighth run successfully? [Recall that the area under a probability density function curve from $-\infty$ to ∞ is 1.]

ANSWERS

Diagnostic Algebra Test

1. (A) $(y + z)x$ (B) $(2 + x) + y$ (C) $2x + 3x$ *(A-1)* **2.** $x^3 - 3x^2 + 4x + 8$ *(A-2)* **3.** $x^3 + 3x^2 - 2x + 12$ *(A-2)*
4. $-3x^5 + 2x^3 - 24x^2 + 16$ *(A-2)* **5.** (A) 1 (B) 1 (C) 2 (D) 3 *(A-2)* **6.** (A) 3 (B) 1 (C) -3 (D) 1 *(A-2)*
7. $14x^2 - 30x$ *(A-2)* **8.** $6x^2 - 5xy - 4y^2$ *(A-2)* **9.** $4a^2 - 12ab + 9b^2$ *(A-2)* **10.** $4xy - 2y^2$ *(A-2)*
11. $9x^6 - 12x^3y + 4y^2$ *(A-2)* **12.** $x^3 - 6x^2y + 12xy^2 - 8y^3$ *(A-2)* **13.** (A) 4.065×10^{12} (B) 7.3×10^{-3} *(A-5)*
14. (A) 255,000,000 (B) 0.000 406 *(A-5)* **15.** (A) T (B) F *(A-1)* **16.** 0 and -3 are two examples of infinitely many. *(A-1)*
17. $6x^5y^{15}$ *(A-5)* **18.** $3u^4/v^2$ *(A-5)* **19.** 6×10^2 *(A-5)* **20.** x^6/y^4 *(A-5)* **21.** $u^{7/3}$ *(A-6)* **22.** $3a^2/b$ *(A-6)* **23.** $\frac{5}{9}$ *(A-5)*
24. $x + 2x^{1/2}y^{1/2} + y$ *(A-6)* **25.** $6x + 7x^{1/2}y^{1/2} - 3y$ *(A-6)* **26.** $(3x - 1)(4x + 3)$ *(A-3)* **27.** $(4x - 3y)(2x - 3y)$ *(A-3)*
28. Not factorable relative to the integers *(A-3)* **29.** $3n(2n - 5)(n + 1)$ *(A-3)* **30.** $(x - y)(7x - y)$ *(A-3)*

31. $3x(2x + 1)(2 - x)$ *(A-3)* **32.** $\dfrac{12a^3b - 40b^2 - 5a}{30a^3b^2}$ *(A-4)* **33.** $\dfrac{7x - 4}{6x(x - 4)}$ *(A-4)* **34.** $\dfrac{-8(x + 2)}{x(x - 4)(x + 4)}$ *(A-4)*

35. $2x + y$ *(A-4)* **36.** $\dfrac{-1}{7(7 + h)}$ *(A-4)* **37.** $\dfrac{xy}{y - x}$ *(A-6)*

38. (A) Subtraction (B) Commutative $(+)$ (C) Distributive (D) Associative $(\cdot)$ (E) Negatives (F) Identity $(+)$ *(A-1)*
39. $6x^{2/5} - 7(x - 1)^{3/4}$ *(A-6)* **40.** $2\sqrt{x} - 3\sqrt[3]{x^2}$ *(A-6)* **41.** $2 - \frac{3}{2}x^{-1/2}$ *(A-6)* **42.** $\sqrt{3x}$ *(A-6)* **43.** $\sqrt{x} + \sqrt{5}$ *(A-6)*

44. $\dfrac{1}{\sqrt{x - 5}}$ *(A-6)* **45.** $\dfrac{1}{\sqrt{u + h} + \sqrt{u}}$ *(A-6)* **46.** $x = 0, 5$ *(A-7)* **47.** $x = \pm\sqrt{7}$ *(A-7)* **48.** $x = -4, 5$ *(A-7)* **49.** $x = 1, \frac{1}{6}$ *(A-7)*

Chapter 3

Exercises 3-1

1. 2 **3.** 1.25 **5.** (A) 2 (B) 2 (C) 2 (D) 2 **7.** (A) 1 (B) 2 (C) Does not exist (D) 2 (E) No **9.** 2 **11.** 0.5
13. (A) 1 (B) 2 (C) Does not exist (D) Does not exist (E) No **15.** (A) 1 (B) 1 (C) 1 (D) 3 (E) Yes
17. (A) -2 (B) -2 (C) -2 (D) 1 (E) Yes **19.** (A) 2 (B) 2 (C) 2 (D) Does not exist (E) Yes

21. 12 **23.** 1 **25.** -4 **27.** -1.5 **29.** 3 **31.** 15 **33.** -6 **35.** $\dfrac{7}{5}$ **37.** 3

39.

41.

43. (A) 1 (B) 1 (C) 1 (D) 1
45. (A) 2 (B) 1 (C) Does not exist (D) Does not exist
47. (A) -6 (B) Does not exist (C) 6
49. (A) 1 (B) -1 (C) Does not exist (D) Does not exist
51. (A) Does not exist (B) $\dfrac{1}{2}$ (C) $\dfrac{1}{4}$ **53.** (A) -5 (B) -3 (C) 0

55. (A) 0 (B) -1 (C) Does not exist **57.** (A) 1 (B) $\dfrac{1}{3}$ (C) $\dfrac{3}{4}$ **59.** False **61.** True **63.** False **65.** 3 **67.** 4

69. (A) $\lim_{x \to 1^-} f(x) = 2$ $\quad$ (B) $\lim_{x \to 1^-} f(x) = 3$ $\quad$ (C) $m = 1.5$ $\quad$ (D) The graph in (A) is broken when it jumps from
$\quad\quad$ $\lim_{x \to 1^+} f(x) = 3$ $\quad\quad$ $\lim_{x \to 1^+} f(x) = 2$ $\quad\quad\quad\quad\quad$ $(1, 2)$ up to $(1, 3)$. The graph in (B) is also

broken when it jumps down from $(1, 3)$ to $(1, 2)$.
The graph in (C) is one continuous piece, with
no breaks or jumps.

71. $2a$ **73.** $1/(2\sqrt{a})$

75. (A) $F(x) = \begin{cases} 0.99 & \text{if } 0 < x \le 20 \\ 0.07x - 0.41 & \text{if } x \ge 20 \end{cases}$

(B)
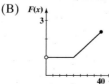

(C) All 3 limits are 0.99.

79. (A) $D(x) = \begin{cases} x & \text{if } 0 \le x < 300 \\ 0.97x & \text{if } 300 \le x < 1,000 \\ 0.95x & \text{if } 1,000 \le x < 3,000 \\ 0.93x & \text{if } 3,000 \le x < 5,000 \\ 0.9x & \text{if } x \ge 5,000 \end{cases}$

(B) $\lim_{x \to 1,000} D(x)$ does not exist because
$\lim_{x \to 1,000^-} D(x) = 970$ and $\lim_{x \to 1,000^+} D(x) = 950$;
$\lim_{x \to 3,000} D(x)$ does not exist because
$\lim_{x \to 3,000^-} D(x) = 2,850$ and $\lim_{x \to 3,000^+} D(x) = 2,790$

81. $F(x) = \begin{cases} 20x & \text{if } 0 < x \le 4{,}000 \\ 80{,}000 & \text{if } x \ge 4{,}000 \end{cases}$

$\lim\limits_{x \to 4{,}000} F(x) = 80{,}000; \quad \lim\limits_{x \to 8{,}000} F(x) = 80{,}000$

83. $\lim\limits_{x \to 5} f(x)$ does not exist; $\quad \lim\limits_{x \to 10} f(x) = 0;$

$\lim\limits_{x \to 5} g(x) = 0; \quad \lim\limits_{x \to 10} g(x) = 1$

Exercises 3-2

1. -2 **3.** $-\infty$ **5.** Does not exist **7.** 0 **9.** (A) $-\infty$ (B) ∞ (C) Does not exist
11. (A) ∞ (B) ∞ (C) ∞ **13.** (A) 3 (B) 3 (C) 3 **15.** (A) $-\infty$ (B) ∞ (C) Does not exist
17. (A) ∞ (B) $-\infty$ **19.** (A) $-\infty$ (B) $-\infty$ **21.** $\lim\limits_{x \to -3^-} f(x) = -\infty; \lim\limits_{x \to -3^+} f(x) = \infty; x = -3$ is a vertical asymptote
23. $\lim\limits_{x \to -2^-} h(x) = \infty; \lim\limits_{x \to -2^+} h(x) = -\infty; \lim\limits_{x \to 2^-} h(x) = -\infty; \lim\limits_{x \to 2^+} h(x) = \infty; x = -2$ and $x = 2$ are vertical asymptotes
25. No zeros of denominator; no vertical asymptotes
27. $\lim\limits_{x \to 1^-} H(x) = -\infty; \lim\limits_{x \to 1^+} H(x) = \infty; \lim\limits_{x \to 3} H(x) = 2; x = 1$ is a vertical asymptote
29. $\lim\limits_{x \to 0} T(x) = -\infty; \lim\limits_{x \to 4} T(x) = \infty; x = 0$ and $x = 4$ are vertical asymptotes

31. (A) $\dfrac{47}{41} \approx 1.146$ (B) $\dfrac{407}{491} \approx 0.829$ (C) $\dfrac{4}{5} = 0.8$ **33.** (A) $\dfrac{2{,}011}{138} \approx 14.572$ (B) $\dfrac{12{,}511}{348} \approx 35.951$ (C) ∞

35. (A) $-\dfrac{8{,}568}{46{,}653} \approx -0.184$ (B) $-\dfrac{143{,}136}{1{,}492{,}989} \approx 0.096$ (C) 0

37. (A) $-\dfrac{7{,}010}{996} \approx -7.038$ (B) $-\dfrac{56{,}010}{7{,}996} \approx -7.005$ (C) -7

39. Horizontal asymptote: $y = 2$; vertical asymptote: $x = -2$
41. Horizontal asymptote: $y = 1$; vertical asymptotes: $x = -1$ and $x = 1$
43. No horizontal asymptotes; no vertical asymptotes **45.** Horizontal asymptote: $y = 0$; no vertical asymptotes
47. No horizontal asymptotes; vertical asymptote: $x = 3$
49. Horizontal asymptote: $y = 2$; vertical asymptotes: $x = -1$ and $x = 2$
51. Horizontal asymptote: $y = 2$; vertical asymptote: $x = -1$
53. False **55.** False **57.** True **59.** If $n \ge 1$ and $a_n > 0$, then the limit is ∞. If $n \ge 1$ and $a_n < 0$, then the limit is $-\infty$.
61. $\lim\limits_{x \to \infty} f(x) = \infty; \lim\limits_{x \to -\infty} f(x) = \infty$ **63.** $\lim\limits_{x \to \infty} f(x) = \infty; \lim\limits_{x \to -\infty} f(x) = -\infty$ **65.** $\lim\limits_{x \to \infty} f(x) = \infty; \lim\limits_{x \to -\infty} f(x) = -\infty$
67. $\lim\limits_{x \to \infty} f(x) = -\infty; \lim\limits_{x \to -\infty} f(x) = -\infty$

69. (A) $C(x) = 180x + 200$

(B) $\overline{C}(x) = \dfrac{180x + 200}{x}$

(C)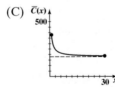

(D) $180 per board

71. (A) $C_e(x) = 950 + 56x; \overline{C}_e(x) = \dfrac{950}{x} + 56$

(B) $C_c(x) = 900 + 66x; \overline{C}_c(x) = \dfrac{900}{x} + 66$

(C) At $x = 5$ years
(D) At $x = 5$ years
(E) $\lim\limits_{x \to \infty} \overline{C}_e(x) = 56; \lim\limits_{x \to \infty} \overline{C}_c(x) = 66$

73. The long-term drug concentration is 5 mg/ml.
75. (A) $18 million
(B) $38 million
(C) $\lim\limits_{x \to 1^-} P(x) = \infty$

77. (C) $V_{\max} = 4, K_M = 20$

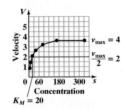

(D) $v(s) = \dfrac{4s}{20 + s}$

(E) $v = \dfrac{12}{7}$ when $s = 15$; $s = 60$ when $v = 3$

79. (A) $C_{\max} = 18, M = 150$

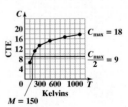

(B) $C(T) = \dfrac{18T}{150 + T}$

(C) $C = 14.4$ when $T = 600$ K; $T = 300$ K when $C = 12$

Exercises 3-3

1. f is continuous at $x = 1$, since $\lim_{x \to 1} f(x) = f(1)$.

3. f is discontinuous at $x = 1$, since $\lim_{x \to 1} f(x) \neq f(1)$.

5. f is discontinuous at $x = 1$, since $\lim_{x \to 1} f(x)$ does not exist.

7. 1.9   **9.** 0.9   **11.** (A) 2   (B) 1   (C) Does not exist   (D) 1   (E) No   **13.** (A) 1   (B) 1   (C) 1   (D) 3   (E) No
15. 0.9   **17.** 2.05   **19.** (A) 1   (B) 1   (C) 1   (D) 3   (E) No   **21.** (A) 2   (B) -1 (C) Does not exist   (D) 2   (E) No

23. All x **25.** All x, except $x = -2$ **27.** All x, except $x = -4$ and $x = 1$ **29.** All x **31.** All x, except $x = \pm\dfrac{3}{2}$

33. (A)

(B) 1   (C) 2   (D) No   (E) All integers

35. $-3 < x < 4$; $(-3, 4)$ **37.** $x < 3$ or $x > 7$; $(-\infty, 3) \cup (7, \infty)$
39. $x < -2$ or $0 < x < 2$; $(-\infty, -2) \cup (0, 2)$ **41.** $-5 < x < 0$ or $x > 3$; $(-5, 0) \cup (3, \infty)$
43. (A) $(-4, -2) \cup (0, 2) \cup (4, \infty)$ (B) $(-\infty, -4) \cup (-2, 0) \cup (2, 4)$
45. (A) $(-\infty, -2.5308) \cup (-0.7198, \infty)$ (B) $(-2.5308, -0.7198)$
47. (A) $(-\infty, -2.1451) \cup (-1, -0.5240) \cup (1, 2.6691)$
(B) $(-2.1451, -1) \cup (-0.5240, 1) \cup (2.6691, \infty)$

49. $[6, \infty)$ **51.** $(-\infty, \infty)$ **53.** $(-\infty, -3] \cup [3, \infty)$ **55.** $(-\infty, \infty)$

57. Since $\lim_{x \to 1^-} f(x) = 2$ and $\lim_{x \to 1^+} f(x) = 4$, $\lim_{x \to 1} f(x)$ does not exist and f is not continuous at $x = 1$.

59. This function is continuous for all x.

61. Since $\lim_{x \to 0} f(x) = 0$ and $f(0) = 1$, $\lim_{x \to 0} f(x) \neq f(0)$ and f is not continuous at $x = 0$.

63. (A) Yes   (B) No   (C) Yes   (D) No   (E) Yes   **65.** True   **67.** False   **69.** True
71. x intercepts: $x = -5, 2$ **73.** x intercepts: $x = -6, -1, 4$ **75.** No, but this does not contradict Theorem 2, since f is discontinuous at $x = 1$.

77. (A)
$$P(x) = \begin{cases} 0.44 & \text{if } 0 < x \leq 1 \\ 0.61 & \text{if } 1 < x \leq 2 \\ 0.78 & \text{if } 2 < x \leq 3 \\ 0.95 & \text{if } 3 < x \leq 3.5 \end{cases}$$

(B)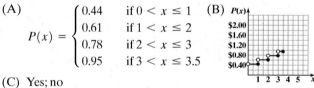

(C) Yes; no

81. (A) $S(x) = \begin{cases} 5 + 0.63x & \text{if } 0 \leq x \leq 50 \\ 14 + 0.45x & \text{if } 50 < x \end{cases}$

(B)

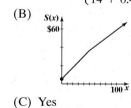

(C) Yes

83. (A)

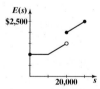

(B) $\lim_{s \to 10,000} E(s) = \$1,000$; $E(10,000) = \$1,000$
(C) $\lim_{s \to 20,000} E(s)$ does not exist; $E(20,000) = \$2,000$
(D) Yes; no

85. (A) t_2, t_3, t_4, t_6, t_7 (B) $\lim_{t \to t_5} N(t) = 7$; $N(t_5) = 7$ (C) $\lim_{t \to t_3} N(t)$ does not exist; $N(t_3) = 4$

Exercises 3-4

1. (A) -3; slope of the secant line through $(1, f(1))$ and $(2, f(2))$
(B) $-2 - h$; slope of the secant line through $(1, f(1))$ and $(1 + h, f(1 + h))$
(C) -2; slope of the tangent line at $(1, f(1))$
3. (A) 15   (B) 15   (C) $6 + 3h$ (D) 6   (E) 6   (F) 6   (G) $y = 6x - 3$
5. $f'(x) = 0$; $f'(1) = 0$, $f'(2) = 0$, $f'(3) = 0$ **7.** $f'(x) = 3$; $f'(1) = 3$, $f'(2) = 3$, $f'(3) = 3$
9. $f'(x) = -6x$; $f'(1) = -6$, $f'(2) = -12$, $f'(3) = -18$ **11.** $f'(x) = 2x + 6$; $f'(1) = 8$, $f'(2) = 10$, $f'(3) = 12$
13. $f'(x) = 4x - 7$; $f'(1) = -3$, $f'(2) = 1$, $f'(3) = 5$ **15.** $f'(x) = -2x + 4$; $f'(1) = 2$, $f'(2) = 0$, $f'(3) = -2$

17. $f'(x) = 6x^2; f'(1) = 6, f'(2) = 24, f'(3) = 54$ **19.** $f'(x) = -\dfrac{4}{x^2}; f'(1) = -4, f'(2) = -1, f'(3) = -\dfrac{4}{9}$

21. $f'(x) = \dfrac{3}{2\sqrt{x}}; f'(1) = \dfrac{3}{2}, f'(2) = \dfrac{3}{2\sqrt{2}}$ or $\dfrac{3\sqrt{2}}{4}, f'(3) = \dfrac{3}{2\sqrt{3}}$ or $\dfrac{\sqrt{3}}{2}$

23. $f'(x) = \dfrac{5}{\sqrt{x+5}}; f'(1) = \dfrac{5}{\sqrt{6}}$ or $\dfrac{5\sqrt{6}}{6}, f'(2) = \dfrac{5}{\sqrt{7}}$ or $\dfrac{5\sqrt{7}}{7}, f'(3) = \dfrac{5}{2\sqrt{2}}$ or $\dfrac{5\sqrt{2}}{4}$

25. $f'(x) = \dfrac{6}{(x+2)^2}; f'(1) = \dfrac{2}{3}, f'(2) = \dfrac{3}{8}, f'(3) = \dfrac{6}{25}$

27. (A) 5 (B) $3 + h$ (C) 3 (D) $y = 3x - 1$ **29.** (A) 5 m/s (B) $3 + h$ m/s (C) 3 m/s

31. Yes **33.** No **35.** Yes **37.** Yes

39. (A) $f'(x) = 2x - 4$ (B) $-4, 0, 4$
(C)

41. $v = f'(x) = 8x - 2$; 6 ft/s, 22 ft/s, 38 ft/s

43. (A) The graphs of g and h are vertical translations of the graph of f. All three functions should have the same derivative.
(B) $2x$

45. True

47. False

49. False

51. f is nondifferentiable at $x = 1$ **53.** f is differentiable for all real numbers **55.** No **57.** No **59.** $f'(0) = 0$ **61.** 6 s; 192 ft/s

63. (A) \$8.75
(B) $R'(x) = 60 - 0.05x$
(C) $R(1,000) = 35,000; R'(1,000) = 10$; At a production level of 1,000 car seats, the revenue is \$35,000 and is increasing at the rate of \$10 per seat.

65. (A) $S'(t) = 1/\sqrt{t + 10}$
(B) $S(15) = 10; S'(15) = 0.2$. After 15 months, the total sales are \$10 million and are increasing at the rate of \$0.2 million, or \$200,000, per month.
(C) The estimated total sales are \$10.2 million after 16 months and \$10.4 million after 17 months.

67. (A) $p'(t) = 328t + 161$
(B) $p(10) = 30,336; p'(10) = 413.4$; In 2015, 30,336 metric tons of tungsten are consumed and this quantity is increasing at the rate of 3,441 metric tons per year.

69. (A)

(B) $R(20) = 1,403.5$ billion kilowatts, $R'(20) = -10.7$ billion kilowatts. In 2020, 1,403.5 billion kilowatts will be sold and the amount sold is decreasing at the rate of 10.7 billion kilowatts per year.

71. (A) $P'(t) = 12 - 2t$
(B) $P(3) = 107; P'(3) = 6$. After 3 hours, the ozone level is 107 ppb and is increasing at the rate of 6 ppb per hour.

Exercises 3-5

1. 0 **3.** $9x^8$ **5.** $3x^2$ **7.** $-4x^{-5}$ **9.** $\dfrac{8}{3}x^{5/3}$ **11.** $-\dfrac{10}{x^{11}}$ **13.** $10x$ **15.** $2.8x^6$ **17.** $\dfrac{x^2}{6}$ **19.** 12 **21.** 2 **23.** 9 **25.** 2 **27.** $4t - 3$

29. $-10x^{-3} - 9x^{-2}$ **31.** $1.5u^{-0.7} - 8.8u^{1.2}$ **33.** $0.5 - 3.3t^2$ **35.** $-\dfrac{8}{5}x^{-5}$ **37.** $3x + \dfrac{14}{5}x^{-3}$ **39.** $-\dfrac{20}{9}w^{-5} + \dfrac{5}{3}w^{-2/3}$

41. $2u^{-1/3} - \dfrac{5}{3}u^{-2/3}$ **43.** $-\dfrac{9}{5}t^{-8/5} + 3t^{-3/2}$ **45.** $-\dfrac{1}{3}x^{-4/3}$ **47.** $-0.6x^{-3/2} + 6.4x^{-3} + 1$

49. (A) $f'(x) = 6 - 2x$ (B) $f'(2) = 2; f'(4) = -2$ (C) $y = 2x + 4; y = -2x + 16$ (D) $x = 3$

51. (A) $f'(x) = 12x^3 - 12x$ (B) $f'(2) = 72; f'(4) = 720$ (C) $y = 72x - 127; y = 720x - 2,215$ (D) $x = -1, 0, 1$

53. (A) $v = f'(x) = 176 - 32x$ (B) $f'(0) = 176$ ft/s; $f'(3) = 80$ ft/s (C) 5.5 s

55. (A) $v = f'(x) = 3x^2 - 18x + 15$ (B) $f'(0) = 15$ ft/s; $f'(3) = -12$ ft/s (C) $x = 1$ s, $x = 5$ s

57. $f'(x) = 2x - 3 - 2x^{-1/2} = 2x - 3 - \dfrac{2}{x^{1/2}}; x = 2.1777$ **59.** $f'(x) = 4\sqrt[3]{x} - 3x - 3; x = -2.9018$

61. $f'(x) = 0.2x^3 + 0.3x^2 - 3x - 1.6; x = -4.4607, -0.5159, 3.4765$

63. $f'(x) = 0.8x^3 - 9.36x^2 + 32.5x - 28.25; x = 1.3050$

69. $8x - 4$ **71.** $-20x^{-2}$ **73.** $-\dfrac{1}{4}x^{-2} + \dfrac{2}{3}x^{-3}$ **75.** True **77.** False **79.** True

81. (A) $S'(t) = 0.09t^2 + t + 2$
(B) $S(5) = 29.25, S'(5) = 9.25$. After 5 months, sales are \$29.25 million and are increasing at the rate of \$9.25 million per month.
(C) $S(10) = 103, S'(10) = 21$. After 10 months, sales are \$103 million and are increasing at the rate of \$21 million per month.

83. (A) $N'(x) = 3{,}780/x^2$
  (B) $N'(10) = 37.8$. At the \$10,000 level of advertising, sales are increasing at the rate of 37.8 boats per \$1,000 spent on advertising.
  $N'(20) = 9.45$. At the \$20,000 level of advertising, sales are increasing at the rate of 9.45 boats per \$1,000 spent on advertising.

85. (A)    (B) In 2016, 55.7% of male high-school graduates enroll in college and the percentage is decreasing at the rate of 1.9% per year.

87. (A) −1.37 beats/min
  (B) −0.58 beat/min

89. (A) 25 items/h
  (B) 8.33 items/h

Exercises 3-6

1. $\Delta x = 3$; $\Delta y = 45$; $\Delta y/\Delta x = 15$ **3.** 12   **5.** 12   **7.** $dy = (24x - 3x^2)\,dx$ **9.** $dy = \left(2x - \dfrac{x^2}{3}\right)dx$ **11.** $dy = -\dfrac{295}{x^{3/2}}\,dx$

13. (A) $12 + 3\Delta x$ (B) 12   **15.** $dy = (8x + 4)\,dx$ **17.** $dy = (1 - 9x^{-2})\,dx$ **19.** $dy = 1.4$; $\Delta y = 1.44$

21. $dy = -3$; $\Delta y = -3\frac{1}{3}$ **23.** 120 in.^{3}

25. (A) $\Delta y = \Delta x + (\Delta x)^2$; $dy = \Delta x$
  (B)   (C)
  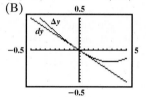

27. (A) $\Delta y = -\Delta x + (\Delta x)^2 + (\Delta x)^3$; $dy = -\Delta x$
  (B)   (C)
  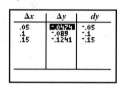

29. True   **31.** False   **33.** $dy = \left(\dfrac{2}{3}x^{-1/3} - \dfrac{10}{3}x^{2/3}\right)dx$ **35.** $dy = 3.9$; $\Delta y = 3.83$ **37.** 40-unit increase; 20-unit increase

39. −\$2.50; \$1.25   **41.** −1.37/min; −0.58/min   **43.** 1.26 mm^2 **45.** 3 wpm
47. (A) 2,100 increase   (B) 4,800 increase   (C) 2,100 increase

Exercises 3-7

1. $C'(x) = 0.8$ **3.** $C'(x) = 4.6 - 0.02x$ **5.** $R'(x) = 4 - 0.02x$ **7.** $R'(x) = 12 - 0.08x$ **9.** $P'(x) = 3.2 - 0.02x$

11. $P'(x) = 7.4 - 0.06x$ **13.** $\overline{C}(x) = 1.1 + \dfrac{145}{x}$ **15.** $\overline{C}'(x) = -\dfrac{145}{x^2}$ **17.** $P(x) = 3.9x - 0.02x^2 - 145$

19. $\overline{P}(x) = 3.9 - 0.02x - \dfrac{145}{x}$ **21.** True   **23.** False   **25.** (A) \$29.50   (B) \$30

27. (A) \$420
  (B) $\overline{C}'(500) = -0.24$. At a production level of 500 frames, average cost is decreasing at the rate of 24¢ per frame.
  (C) Approximately \$419.76

29. (A) \$14.70   (B) \$15

31. (A) $P'(450) = 0.5$. At a production level of 450 cassettes, profit is increasing at the rate of 50¢ per cassette.
  (B) $P'(750) = -2.5$. At a production level of 750 cassettes, profit is decreasing at the rate of \$2.50 per cassette.

33. (A) \$13.50
  (B) $\overline{P}'(50) = \$0.27$. At a production level of 50 mowers, the average profit per mower is increasing at the rate of \$0.27 per mower.
  (C) Approximately \$13.77

35. (A) $p = 100 - 0.025x$, domain: $0 \le x \le 4{,}000$
  (B) $R(x) = 100x - 0.025x^2$, domain: $0 \le x \le 4{,}000$
  (C) $R'(1{,}600) = 20$. At a production level of 1,600 radios, revenue is increasing at the rate of \$20 per radio.
  (D) $R'(2{,}500) = -25$. At a production level of 2,500 radios, revenue is decreasing at the rate of \$25 per radio.

37. (A) $p = 200 - \frac{1}{30}x$, domain: $0 \le x \le 6{,}000$
  (B) $C'(x) = 60$
  (C) $R(x) = 200x - (x^2/30)$, domain: $0 \le x \le 6{,}000$
  (D) $R'(x) = 200 - (x/15)$
  (E) $R'(1{,}500) = 100$. At a production level of 1,500 saws, revenue is increasing at the rate of \$100 per saw.
  $R'(4{,}500) = -100$. At a production level of 4,500 saws, revenue is decreasing at the rate of \$100 per saw.

(F) Break-even points: $(600, 108,000)$ and $(3,600, 288,000)$

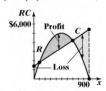

39. (A) $p = 20 - 0.02x$, domain: $0 \le x \le 1,000$
    (B) $R(x) = 20x - 0.02x^2$, domain: $0 \le x \le 1,000$
    (C) $C(x) = 4x + 1,400$

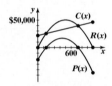

41. (A) $x = 500$
    (B) $P(x) = 176x - 0.2x^2 - 21,900$
    (C) $x = 440$
    (D) Break-even points: $(150, 25,500)$ and $(730, 39,420)$;
        x intercepts for $P(x)$: $x = 150$ and $x = 730$

45. (A)

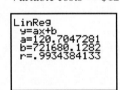

(G) $P(x) = -(x^2/30) + 140x - 72,000$
(H) $P'(x) = -(x/15) + 140$
(I) $P'(1,500) = 40$. At a production level of 1,500 saws, profit is increasing at the rate of $40 per saw.
    $P'(3,000) = -60$. At a production level of 3,000 saws, profit is decreasing at the rate of $60 per saw.

(D) Break-even points: $(100, 1,800)$ and $(700, 4,200)$
(E) $P(x) = 16x - 0.02x^2 - 1,400$
(F) $P'(250) = 6$. At a production level of 250 toasters, profit is increasing at the rate of $6 per toaster. $P'(475) = -3$. At a production level of 475 toasters, profit is decreasing at the rate of $3 per toaster.

43. (A) $R(x) = 20x - x^{3/2}$
    (B) Break-even points: $(44, 588), (258, 1,016)$

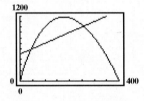

(B) Fixed costs $\approx \$721,680$
    Variable costs $\approx \$121$

(C) $(713, 807,703), (5,423, 1,376,227)$
(D) $\$254 \le p \le \$1,133$

Chapter 3 Review Exercises

1. (A) 16 (B) 8 (C) 8 (D) 4 (E) 4 (F) 4 *(3-2)* 2. $f'(x) = -3$ *(3-2)* 3. (A) 22 (B) 8 (C) 2 (D) -5 *(3-1)*
4. 1.5 *(3-1)* 5. 3.5 *(3-1)* 6. 3.75 *(3-1)* 7. 3.75 *(3-1)* 8. (A) 1 (B) 1 (C) 1 (D) 1 *(3-1)*
9. (A) 2 (B) 3 (C) Does not exist (D) 3 *(3-1)* 10. (A) 4 (B) 4 (C) 4 (D) Does not exist *(3-1)*
11. (A) Does not exist (B) 3 (C) No *(3-3)* 12. (A) 2 (B) Not defined (C) No *(3-3)*
13. (A) 1 (B) 1 (C) Yes *(3-3)* 14. 5 *(3-2)* 15. 5 *(3-2)* 16. ∞ *(3-2)* 17. $-\infty$ *(3-2)* 18. 0 *(3-1)* 19. 0 *(3-1)* 20. 0 *(3-1)*
21. Vertical asymptote: $x = 2$ *(3-3)* 22. Horizontal asymptote: $y = 5$ *(3-2)* 23. $x = 2$ 24. $f'(x) = 10x$ *(3-4)*

25. (A) -3 (B) 6 (C) -2 (D) 3 (E) -11 *(3-5)* 26. $x^2 - 10x$ *(3-5)* 27. $x^{-1/2} - 3 = \dfrac{1}{x^{1/2}} - 3$ *(3-5)* 28. 0 *(3-5)*

29. $-\dfrac{3}{2}x^{-2} + \dfrac{15}{4}x^2 = \dfrac{-3}{2x^2} + \dfrac{15x^2}{4}$ *(3-5)* 30. $-2x^{-5} + x^3 = \dfrac{-2}{x^5} + x^3$ *(3-5)* 31. $f'(x) = 12x^3 + 9x^2 - 2$ *(3-5)*

32. $\Delta x = 2, \Delta y = 10, \Delta y/\Delta x = 5$ *(3-6)* 33. 5 *(3-6)* 34. 6 *(3-6)* 35. $\Delta y = 0.64; dy = 0.6$ *(3-6)*

36. (A) 4 (B) 6 (C) Does not exist (D) 6 (E) No *(3-3)* 37. (A) 3 (B) 3 (C) 3 (D) 3 (E) Yes *(3-3)*
38. (A) $(8, \infty)$ (B) $[0, 8]$ *(3-3)* 39. $(-3, 4)$ *(3-3)* 40. $(-3, 0) \cup (5, \infty)$ *(3-3)* 41. $(-2.3429, -0.4707) \cup (1.8136, \infty)$ *(3-3)*

42. (A) 3 (B) $2 + 0.5h$ (C) 2 *(3-4)* 43. $-x^{-4} + 10x^{-3}$ *(3-4)* 44. $\dfrac{3}{4}x^{-1/2} - \dfrac{5}{6}x^{-3/2} = \dfrac{3}{4\sqrt{x}} - \dfrac{5}{6\sqrt{x^3}}$ *(3-5)*

45. $0.6x^{-2/3} - 0.3x^{-4/3} = \dfrac{0.6}{x^{2/3}} - \dfrac{0.3}{x^{4/3}}$ *(3-4)* 46. $-\dfrac{3}{5}(-3)x^{-4} = \dfrac{9}{5x^4}$ *(3-5)* 47. (A) $m = f'(1) = 2$ (B) $y = 2x + 3$ *(3-4, 3-5)*
48. $x = 5$ *(3-4)* 49. $x = -5, x = 3$ *(3-5)* 50. $x = -1.3401, 0.5771, 2.2630$ *(3-4)* 51. ± 2.4824 *(3-5)*
52. (A) $v = f'(x) = 16x - 4$ (B) 44 ft/sec *(3-5)* 53. (A) $v = f'(x) = -10x + 16$ (B) $x = 1.6$ sec *(3-5)*

54. (A) The graph of g is the graph of f shifted 4 units to the right, and the graph of h is the graph of f shifted 3 units to the left:

(B) The graph of g' is the graph of f' shifted 4 units to the right, and the graph of h' is the graph of f' shifted 3 units to the left:

55. $(-\infty, \infty)$ *(3-3)* **56.** $(-\infty, 2) \cup (2, \infty)$ *(3-3)* **57.** $(-\infty, -4) \cup (-4, 1) \cup (1, \infty)$ *(3-3)* **58.** $(-\infty, \infty)$ *(3-3)*

59. $[-2, 2]$ *(3-3)* **60.** (A) -1 (B) Does not exist (C) $-\dfrac{2}{3}$ *(3-1)* **61.** (A) $\dfrac{1}{2}$ (B) 0 (C) Does not exist *(3-1)*

62. (A) -1 (B) 1 (C) Does not exist *(3-1)* **63.** (A) $-\dfrac{1}{6}$ (B) Does not exist (C) $-\dfrac{1}{3}$ *(3-1)*

64. (A) 0 (B) -1 (C) Does not exist *(3-1)* **65.** (A) $\dfrac{2}{3}$ (B) $\dfrac{2}{3}$ (C) Does not exist *(3-2)*

66. (A) ∞ (B) $-\infty$ (C) ∞ *(3-3)* **67.** (A) 0 (B) 0 (C) Does not exist *(3-2)* **68.** 4 *(3-1)* **69.** $\dfrac{-1}{(x + 2)^2}$ *(3-1)*

70. $2x - 1$ *(3-4)* **71.** $1/(2\sqrt{x})$ *(3-4)* **72.** Yes *(3-4)* **73.** No *(3-4)* **74.** No *(3-4)* **75.** No *(3-4)* **76.** Yes *(3-4)* **77.** Yes *(3-4)*

78. Horizontal asymptote: $y = 5$; vertical asymptote: $x = 7$ *(3-2)*

79. Horizontal asymptote: $y = 0$; vertical asymptote: $x = 4$ *(3-2)*

80. No horizontal asymptotes; vertical asymptote: $x = 3$ *(3-2)*

81. Horizontal asymptotes: $y = 1$; vertical asymptotes: $x = -2, x = 1$ *(3-2)*

82. Horizontal asymptote: $y = 1$; vertical asymptotes: $x = -1, x = 1$ *(3-2)*

83. The domain of $f'(x)$ is all real numbers except $x = 0$. At $x = 0$, the graph of $y = f(x)$ is smooth, but it has a vertical tangent. *(3-4)*

84. (A) $\lim_{x \to 1^-} f(x) = 1$; $\lim_{x \to 1^+} f(x) = -1$ (B) $\lim_{x \to 1^-} f(x) = -1$; $\lim_{x \to 1^+} f(x) = 1$ (C) $m = 1$

(D) The graphs in (A) and (B) have discontinuities at $x = 1$; the graph in (C) does not. *(3-2)*

85. (A) 1 (B) -1 (C) Does not exist (D) No *(3-4)*

86. (A) $S(x) = \begin{cases} 7.47 + 0.4x & \text{if } 0 \le x \le 90 \\ 24.786 + 0.2076x & \text{if } 90 < x \end{cases}$

(B)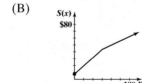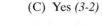

(C) Yes *(3-2)*

87. (A) \$179.90 (B) \$180 *(3-7)*

88. (A) $C(100) = 9{,}500$; $C'(100) = 50$. At a production level of 100 bicycles, the total cost is \$9,500, and cost is increasing at the rate of \$50 per bicycle.

(B) $\overline{C}(100) = 95$; $\overline{C}'(100) = -0.45$. At a production level of 100 bicycles, the average cost is \$95, and average cost is decreasing at a rate of \$0.45 per bicycle. *(3-7)*

89. The approximate cost of producing the 201st printer is greater than that of the 601st printer. Since these marginal costs are decreasing, the manufacturing process is becoming more efficient. *(3-7)*

90. (A) $C'(x) = 2$; $\overline{C}(x) = 2 + \dfrac{9{,}000}{x}$; $\overline{C}'(x) = \dfrac{-9{,}000}{x^2}$

(B) $R(x) = xp = 25x - 0.01x^2$; $R'(x) = 25 - 0.02x$; $\overline{R}(x) = 25 - 0.01x$; $\overline{R}'(x) = -0.01$

(C) $P(x) = R(x) - C(x) = 23x - 0.01x^2 - 9{,}000$; $P'(x) = 23 - 0.02x$;

$\overline{P}(x) = 23 - 0.01x - \dfrac{9{,}000}{x}$; $\overline{P}'(x) = -0.01 + \dfrac{9{,}000}{x^2}$

(D) $(500, 10{,}000)$ and $(1{,}800, 12{,}600)$

(E) $P'(1{,}000) = 3$. Profit is increasing at the rate of \$3 per umbrella.
$P'(1{,}150) = 0$. Profit is flat.
$P'(1{,}400) = -5$. Profit is decreasing at the rate of \$5 per umbrella.

(F)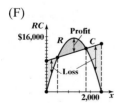

91. (A) 8 (B) 20 *(3-5)*

92. $N(9) = 27$; $N'(t) = 3.5$; After 9 months, 27,000 pools have been sold and the total sales are increasing at the rate of 3,500 pools per month. *(3-5)*

93. (A)

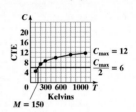

```
CubicReg
y=ax³+bx²+cx+d
a=.001225
b=-.0819285714
c=1.564642857
d=12.08428571
```

(B) $N(50) = 38.6$; $N'(50) = 2.6$. In 2010, natural gas consumption is 38.6 trillion cubic feet and is increasing at the rate of 2.6 trillion cubic feet per year (3-4)

94. (A)

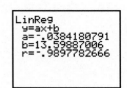

```
LinReg
y=ax+b
a=-.0384180791
b=13.59887006
r=-.9897782666
```

(B) Fixed costs: \$484.21; variable costs per kringle: \$2.11

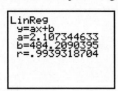

```
LinReg
y=ax+b
a=2.107344633
b=484.2090395
r=.9939318704
```

(C) $(51, 591.15), (248, 1,007.62)$ (D) $\$4.07 < p < \$11.64$ (3-7)

95. $C'(10) = -1$; $C'(100) = -0.001$ (3-5)

96. $F(4) = 98.16$; $F'(4) = -0.32$; After 4 hours the patient's temperature is 98.16°F and is decreasing at the rate of 0.32°F per hour. (3-5)

97. (A) 10 items/h   (B) 5 items/h (3-5)

98. (A)

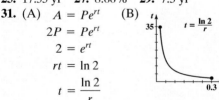

(B) $C(T) = \dfrac{12T}{150 + T}$

(C) $C = 9.6$ at $T = 600$ K, $T = 750$ K when $C = 10$ (3-3)

Chapter 4

Exercises 4-1

1. \$1,221.40; \$1,648.72; \$2,225.54

3.

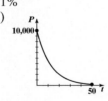

5. 11.55   **7.** 10.99   **9.** 0.14

11.

n	$[1 + (1/n)]^n$
10	2.593 74
100	2.704 81
1,000	2.716 92
10,000	2.718 15
100,000	2.718 27
1,000,000	2.718 28
10,000,000	2.718 28
$\downarrow$	$\downarrow$
∞	$e = 2.718\ 281\ 828\ 459\ldots$

13. $\lim_{n\to\infty}(1 + n)^{1/n} = 1$

15.

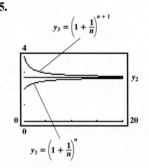

17. (A) \$15,143.71   (B) 14.16 yr

19. \$11,890.41

21. 8.11%

23. (A)

P
10,000

50 t

(B) $\lim_{t\to\infty} 10,000e^{-0.08t} = 0$

25. 17.33 yr   **27.** 8.66%   **29.** 7.3 yr

31. (A) $\quad A = Pe^{rt}$
$\quad 2P = Pe^{rt}$
$\quad 2 = e^{rt}$
$\quad rt = \ln 2$
$\quad t = \dfrac{\ln 2}{r}$

(B)

t
35
$t = \dfrac{\ln 2}{r}$
0.3 r

Although r could be any positive number, the restrictions on r are reasonable in the sense that most investments would be expected to earn a return of between 2% and 30%.

(C) The doubling times (in years) are 13.86, 6.93, 4.62, 3.47, 2.77, and 2.31, respectively.

33. $t = -(\ln 0.5)/0.000\ 433\ 2 \approx 1,600$ yr   **35.** $r = (\ln 0.5)/30 \approx -0.0231$ **37.** 53.3 yr   **39.** 1.39%

Exercises 4-2

1. $5e^x + 3$ **3.** $-\dfrac{2}{x} + 2x$ **5.** $3x^2 - 6e^x$ **7.** $e^x + 1 - \dfrac{1}{x}$ **9.** $\dfrac{3}{x}$ **11.** $5 - \dfrac{5}{x}$ **13.** $\dfrac{2}{x} + 4e^x$ **15.** $f'(x) = \dfrac{1}{x}$; $y = x + 2$

17. $f'(x) = 3e^x$; $y = 3x + 3$ **19.** $f'(x) = \dfrac{3}{x}$; $y = \dfrac{3}{e^x}$ **21.** $f'(x) = e^x$; $y = ex + 2$ **23.** Yes; yes   **25.** No; no

27. $f(x) = 10x + \ln 10 + \ln x$; $f'(x) = 10 + \dfrac{1}{x}$ **29.** $f(x) = \ln 4 - 3\ln x$; $f'(x) = -\dfrac{3}{x}$ **31.** $\dfrac{1}{x\ln 2}$ **33.** $3^x \ln 3$

35. $2 - \dfrac{1}{x\ln 10}$ **37.** $1 + 10^x \ln 10$ **39.** $\dfrac{3}{x} + \dfrac{2}{x\ln 3}$ **41.** $2^x \ln 2$ **43.** $(-0.82, 0.44), (1.43, 4.18), (8.61, 5503.66)$

45. $(0.49, 0.49)$ **47.** $(3.65, 1.30), (332, 105.11, 12.71)$ **51.** $28,447/\text{yr}; \$18,664/\text{yr}; \$11,021/\text{yr}$

53. $A'(t) = 5,000(\ln 4)4^t$; $A'(1) = 27,726$ bacteria/hr (rate of change at the end of the first hour); $A'(5) = 7,097,827$ bacteria/hr
(rate of change at the end of the fifth hour)

55. At the 40-lb weight level, blood pressure would increase at the rate of 0.44 mm of mercury per pound of weight gain. At the 90-lb
weight level, blood pressure would increase at the rate of 0.19 mm of mercury per pound of weight gain.

57. $dR/dS = k/S$

Exercises 4-3

1. $2x^3(2x) + (x^2 - 2)(6x^2) = 10x^4 - 12x^2$ **3.** $(x - 3)(2) + (2x - 1)(1) = 4x - 7$

5. $\dfrac{(x - 3)(1) - x(1)}{(x - 3)^2} = \dfrac{-3}{(x - 3)^2}$ **7.** $\dfrac{(x - 2)(2) - (2x + 3)(1)}{(x - 2)^2} = \dfrac{-7}{(x - 2)^2}$

9. $3xe^x + 3e^x = 3(x + 1)e^x$ **11.** $x^3\left(\dfrac{1}{x}\right) + 3x^2 \ln x = x^2(1 + 3 \ln x)$

13. $(x^2 + 1)(2) + (2x - 3)(2x) = 6x^2 - 6x + 2$ **15.** $(0.4x + 2)(0.5) + (0.5x - 5)(0.4) = 0.4x - 1$

17. $\dfrac{(2x - 3)(2x) - (x^2 + 1)(2)}{(2x - 3)^2} = \dfrac{2x^2 - 6x - 2}{(2x - 3)^2}$ **19.** $(x^2 + 2)2x + (x^2 - 3)2x = 4x^3 - 2x$

21. $\dfrac{(x^2 - 3)2x - (x^2 + 2)2x}{(x^2 - 3)^2} = \dfrac{-10x}{(x^2 - 3)^2}$ **23.** $\dfrac{(x^2 + 1)e^x - e^x(2x)}{(x^2 + 1)^2} = \dfrac{(x - 1)^2 e^x}{(x^2 + 1)^2}$

25. $\dfrac{(1 + x)\left(\dfrac{1}{x}\right) - \ln x}{(1 + x)^2} = \dfrac{1 + x - x \ln x}{x(1 + x)^2}$ **27.** $xf'(x) + f(x)$ **29.** $x^3 f'(x) + 3x^2 f(x)$ **31.** $\dfrac{x^2 f'(x) - 2xf(x)}{x^4}$

33. $\dfrac{f(x) - xf'(x)}{[f(x)]^2}$ **35.** $e^x f'(x) + f(x)e^x = e^x[f'(x) + f(x)]$ **37.** $\dfrac{f(x)\left(\dfrac{1}{x}\right) - (\ln x)f'(x)}{f(x)^2} = \dfrac{f(x) - (x \ln x)f'(x)}{x f(x)^2}$

39. $(2x + 1)(2x - 3) + (x^2 - 3x)(2) = 6x^2 - 10x - 3$ **41.** $(2.5t - t^2)(4) + (4t + 1.4)(2.5 - 2t) = -12t^2 + 17.2t + 3.5$

43. $\dfrac{(x^2 + 2x)(5) - (5x - 3)(2x + 2)}{(x^2 + 2x)^2} = \dfrac{-5x^2 + 6x + 6}{(x^2 + 2x)^2}$ **45.** $\dfrac{(w^2 - 1)(2w - 3) - (w^2 - 3w + 1)(2w)}{(w^2 - 1)^2} = \dfrac{3w^2 - 4w + 3}{(w^2 - 1)^2}$

47. $(1 + x - x^2)e^x + e^x(1 - 2x) = (2 - x - x^2)e^x$ **49.** $f'(x) = (1 + 3x)(-2) + (5 - 2x)(3); y = -11x + 29$

51. $f'(x) = \dfrac{(3x - 4)(1) - (x - 8)(3)}{(3x - 4)^2}; y = 5x - 13$ **53.** $f'(x) = \dfrac{2^x - x(2^x \ln 2)}{2^{2x}}; y = \left(\dfrac{1 - 2\ln 2}{4}\right)x + \ln 2$

55. $f'(x) = (2x - 15)(2x) + (x^2 + 18)(2) = 6(x - 2)(x - 3); x = 2, x = 3$

57. $f'(x) = \dfrac{(x^2 + 1)(1) - x(2x)}{(x^2 + 1)^2} = \dfrac{1 - x^2}{(x^2 + 1)^2}; x = -1, x = 1$ **59.** $7x^6 - 3x^2$ **61.** $-27x^{-4} = -\dfrac{27}{x^4}$

63. $(w + 1)2^w \ln 2 + 2^w = [(w + 1)\ln 2 + 1]2^w$ **65.** $\dfrac{(4x^2 + 5x - 1)(6x - 2) - (3x^2 - 2x + 3)(8x + 5)}{(4x^2 + 5x - 1)^2} = \dfrac{23x^2 - 30x - 13}{(4x^2 + 5x - 1)^2}$

67. $9x^{1/3}(3x^2) + (x^3 + 5)(3x^{-2/3}) = \dfrac{30x^3 + 15}{x^{2/3}}$ **69.** $\dfrac{(1 + x^2)\dfrac{1}{x \ln 2} - 2x \log_2 x}{(1 + x^2)^2} = \dfrac{1 + x^2 - 2x^2 \ln x}{x(1 + x^2)^2 \ln 2}$

71. $\dfrac{(x^2 - 3)(2x^{-2/3}) - 6x^{1/3}(2x)}{(x^2 - 3)^2} = \dfrac{-10x^2 - 6}{(x^2 - 3)^2 x^{2/3}}$ **73.** $g'(t) = \dfrac{(3t^2 - 1)(0.2) - (0.2t)(6t)}{(3t^2 - 1)^2} = \dfrac{-0.6t^2 - 0.2}{(3t^2 - 1)^2}$

75. $(20x)\dfrac{1}{x \ln 10} + 20 \log x = \dfrac{20(1 + \ln x)}{\ln 10}$ **77.** $x^{-2/3}(3x^2 - 4x) + (x^3 - 2x^2)\left(-\tfrac{2}{3}x^{-5/3}\right) = -\tfrac{8}{3}x^{1/3} + \tfrac{7}{3}x^{4/3}$

79. $\dfrac{(x^2 + 1)[(2x^2 - 1)(2x) + (x^2 + 3)(4x)] - (2x^2 - 1)(x^2 + 3)(2x)}{(x^2 + 1)^2} = \dfrac{4x^5 + 8x^3 + 16x}{(x^2 + 1)^2}$

81. $\dfrac{e^t(1 + \ln t) - (t \ln t)e^t}{e^{2t}} = \dfrac{1 + \ln t - t \ln t}{e^t}$

83. (A) $S'(t) = \dfrac{(t^2 + 50)(180t) - 90t^2(2t)}{(t^2 + 50)^2} = \dfrac{9,000t}{(t^2 + 50)^2}$

(B) $S(10) = 60; S'(10) = 4$. After 10 months, the total sales are 60,000 DVDs and sales are increasing at the rate of 4,000 DVDs
per month.

(C) Approximately 64,000 DVDs

85. (A) $\dfrac{dx}{dp} = \dfrac{(0.1p + 1)(0) - 4,000(0.1)}{(0.1p + 1)^2} = \dfrac{-400}{(0.1p + 1)^2}$

   (B) $x = 800$; $dx/dp = -16$. At a price level of \$40, the demand is 800 DVD players per week and demand is decreasing at the rate of 16 players per dollar.

   (C) Approximately 784 DVD players

87. (A) $C'(t) = \dfrac{(t^2 + 1)(0.14) - 0.14t(2t)}{(t^2 + 1)^2} = \dfrac{0.14 - 0.14t^2}{(t^2 + 1)^2}$

   (B) $C'(0.5) = 0.0672$. After 0.5 h, concentration is increasing at the rate of 0.0672 mg/cm³ per hour.
   $C'(3) = -0.0112$. After 3 h, concentration is decreasing at the rate of 0.0112 mg/cm³ per hour.

89. (A) $N'(x) = \dfrac{(x + 32)(100) - (100x + 200)}{(x + 32)^2} = \dfrac{3,000}{(x + 32)^2}$

   (B) $N'(4) = 2.31$; $N'(68) = 0.30$

Exercises 4-4

1. $(3x^2 + 2)^3$ **3.** e^{-x^2} **5.** $y = u^4; u = 3x^2 - x + 5$ **7.** $y = e^u; u = 1 + x + x^2$ **9.** 3   **11.** $(-4x)$
13. $2x$ **15.** $4x^3$ **17.** $2(x + 3)$ **19.** $6(2x + 5)^2$ **21.** $-8(5 - 2x)^3$ **23.** $5(4 + 0.2x)^4(0.2) = (4 + 0.2x)^4$ **25.** $30x(3x^2 + 5)^4$

27. $5e^x$ **29.** $5e^{5x}$ **31.** $-18e^{-6x}$ **33.** $(2x - 5)^{-1/2} = \dfrac{1}{(2x - 5)^{1/2}}$ **35.** $-8x^3(x^4 + 1)^{-3} = \dfrac{-8x^3}{(x^4 + 1)^3}$ **37.** $-\dfrac{2}{x}$ **39.** $\dfrac{6x}{1 + x^2}$

41. $\dfrac{3(1 + \ln x)^2}{x}$ **43.** $f'(x) = 6(2x - 1)^2; y = 6x - 5; x = \frac{1}{2}$ **45.** $f'(x) = 2(4x - 3)^{-1/2} = \dfrac{2}{(4x - 3)^{1/2}}; y = \dfrac{2}{3}x + 1;$ none

47. $f'(x) = 10(x - 2)e^{x^2 - 4x + 1}; y = -20ex + 5e; x = 2$ **49.** $12(x^2 - 2)^3(2x) = 24x(x^2 - 2)^3$

51. $-6(t^2 + 3t)^{-4}(2t + 3) = \dfrac{-6(2t + 3)}{(t^2 + 3t)^4}$ **53.** $\dfrac{1}{2}(w^2 + 8)^{-1/2}(2w) = \dfrac{w}{\sqrt{w^2 + 8}}$ **55.** $12xe^{3x} + 4e^{3x} = 4(3x + 1)e^{3x}$

57. $\dfrac{x^3\left(\dfrac{1}{1 + x}\right) - 3x^2 \ln(1 + x)}{x^6} = \dfrac{x - 3(1 + x)\ln(1 + x)}{x^4(1 + x)}$ **59.** $6te^{3(t^2 + 1)}$ **61.** $\dfrac{3x}{x^2 + 3}$

63. $-5(w^3 + 4)^{-6}(3w^2) = \dfrac{-15w^2}{(w^3 + 4)^6}$ **65.** $f'(x) = (4 - x)^3 - 3x(4 - x)^2 = 4(4 - x)^2(1 - x); y = -16x + 48$

67. $f'(x) = \dfrac{(2x - 5)^3 - 6x(2x - 5)^2}{(2x - 5)^6} = \dfrac{-4x - 5}{(2x - 5)^4}; y = -17x + 54$ **69.** $f'(x) = \dfrac{1}{2x\sqrt{\ln x}}; y = \dfrac{1}{2e^x} + \dfrac{1}{2}$

71. $f'(x) = 2x(x - 5)^3 + 3x^2(x - 5)^2 = 5x(x - 5)^2(x - 2); x = 0, 2, 5$

73. $f'(x) = \dfrac{(2x + 5)^2 - 4x(2x + 5)}{(2x + 5)^4} = \dfrac{5 - 2x}{(2x + 5)^3}; x = \frac{5}{2}$

75. $f'(x) = (x^2 - 8x + 20)^{-1/2}(x - 4) = \dfrac{x - 4}{(x^2 - 8x + 20)^{1/2}}; x = 4$ **77.** No; yes

79. $18x^2(x^2 + 1)^2 + 3(x^2 + 1)^3 = 3(x^2 + 1)^2(7x^2 + 1)$ **81.** $\dfrac{24x^5(x^3 - 7)^3 - (x^3 - 7)^46x^2}{4x^6} = \dfrac{3(x^3 - 7)^3(3x^3 + 7)}{2x^4}$

83. $\dfrac{1}{\ln 2}\left(\dfrac{6x}{3x^2 - 1}\right)$ **85.** $(2x + 1)(10^{x^2 + x})(\ln 10)$ **87.** $\dfrac{12x^2 + 5}{(4x^3 + 5x + 7)\ln 3}$ **89.** $2^{x^3 - x^2 + 4x + 1}(3x^2 - 2x + 4)\ln 2$

91. (A) $C'(x) = (2x + 16)^{-1/2} = \dfrac{1}{(2x + 16)^{1/2}}$

   (B) $C'(24) = \frac{1}{8}$, or \$12.50. At a production level of 24 cell phones, total cost is increasing at the rate of \$12.50 per cell phone and the cost of producing the 25th cell phone is approximately \$12.50.
   $C'(42) = \frac{1}{10}$, or \$10.00. At a production level of 42 cell phones, total cost is increasing at the rate of \$10.00 per cell phone and the cost of producing the 43rd cell phone is approximately \$10.00.

93. (A) $\dfrac{dx}{dp} = 40(p + 25)^{-1/2} = \dfrac{40}{(p + 25)^{1/2}}$ (B) $x = 400$ and $dx/dp = 4$. At a price of \$75, the supply is 400 bicycle helmets per week and supply is increasing at the rate of 4 bicycle helmets per dollar.

95. (A) After 1 hr, the concentration is decreasing at the rate of 1.60 mg/mL per hour; after 4 hr, the concentration is decreasing at the rate of 0.08 mg/mL per hour.

   (B)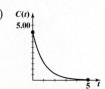

97. 2.27 mm of mercury/yr; 0.81 mm of mercury/yr; 0.41 mm of mercury/yr
99. (A) $f'(n) = n(n - 2)^{-1/2} + 2(n - 2)^{1/2}$

   (B) $f'(11) = \frac{29}{3} \approx 9.67$. When the list contains 11 items, the learning time is increasing at the rate of 9.67 min per item.
   $f'(27) = \frac{77}{5} = 15.4$. When the list contains 27 items, the learning time is increasing at the rate of 15.4 min per item.

Exercises 4-5

1. $y' = -\frac{3}{5}$ **3.** $y' = \frac{3x}{2}$ **5.** $y' = 10x; 10$ **7.** $y' = \frac{2x}{3y^2}; \frac{4}{3}$ **9.** $y' = -\frac{3}{2y + 2}; -\frac{3}{4}$ **11.** $y' = -\frac{y}{x}; -\frac{3}{2}$

13. $y' = -\frac{2y}{2x + 1}; 4$ **15.** $y' = \frac{6 - 2y}{x}; -1$ **17.** $y' = \frac{2x}{e^y - 2y}; 2$ **19.** $y' = \frac{3x^2y}{y + 1}; \frac{3}{2}$ **21.** $y' = \frac{6x^2y - y\ln y}{x + 2y}; 2$

23. $x' = \frac{2tx - 3t^2}{2x - t^2}; 8$ **25.** $y'|_{(1.6, 1.8)} = -\frac{3}{4}; y'|_{(1.6, 0.2)} = \frac{3}{4}$ **27.** $y = -x + 5$ **29.** $y = \frac{2}{5}x - \frac{12}{5}; y = \frac{3}{5}x + \frac{12}{5}$

31. $y' = -\frac{1}{x}$ **33.** $y' = \frac{1}{3(1 + y)^2 + 1}; \frac{1}{13}$ **35.** $y' = \frac{3(x - 2y)^2}{6(x - 2y)^2 + 4y}; \frac{3}{10}$ **37.** $y' = \frac{3x^2(7 + y^2)^{1/2}}{y}; 16$

39. $y' = \frac{y}{2xy^2 - x}; 1$ **41.** $y = 0.63x + 1.04$ **43.** $p' = \frac{1}{2p - 2}$ **45.** $p' = -\frac{\sqrt{10,000 - p^2}}{p}$

47. $\frac{dL}{dV} = \frac{-(L + m)}{V + n}$ **49.** $\frac{dT}{dv} = \frac{2}{k}\sqrt{T}$ **51.** $\frac{dv}{dT} = \frac{k}{2\sqrt{T}}$

Exercises 4-6

1. 30 **3.** $-\frac{16}{3}$ **5.** $-\frac{16}{7}$ **7.** Decreasing at 9 units/sec **9.** Approx. -3.03 ft/sec **11.** $dA/dt \approx 126$ ft^2/sec
13. 3,768 cm^3/min **15.** 6 lb/in.^{2}/hr **17.** $-\frac{9}{4}$ ft/sec **19.** $\frac{20}{3}$ ft/sec **21.** 0.0214 ft/sec; 0.0135 ft/sec; yes, at $t = 0.000\ 19$ sec
23. 3.835 units/sec **25.** (A) $dC/dt = \$15,000$/wk (B) $dR/dt = -\$50,000$/wk (C) $dP/dt = -\$65,000$/wk
27. $ds/dt = \$2,207$/wk **29.** (A) $dx/dt = -12.73$ units/month (B) $dp/dt = \$1.53$/month **31.** Approximately 100 ft^3/min

Exercises 4-7

1. $\frac{35 - 0.8x}{35x - 0.4x^2}$ **3.** $-\frac{4e^{-x}}{7 + 4e^x}$ **5.** $\frac{5}{x(12 + 5\ln x)}$ **7.** 0 **9.** -0.017 **11.** -0.034 **13.** 1.013 **15.** 0.405 **17.** 11.8%

19. 5.4% **21.** -14.7% **23.** -431.6% **25.** $E(p) = \frac{450p}{25,000 - 450p}$ **27.** $E(p) = \frac{8p^2}{4,800 - 4p^2}$ **29.** $E(p) = \frac{0.6pe^p}{98 - 0.6e^p}$

31. (A) Inelastic (B) Unit elasticity (C) Elastic **33.** (A) Inelastic (B) Unit elasticity (C) Elastic

35. (A) $x = 6,000 - 200p$ $0 \le p \le 30$
   (B) $E(p) = \frac{p}{30 - p}$
   (C) $E(10) = 0.5$; 5% decrease
   (D) $E(25) = 5$; 50% decrease
   (E) $E(15) = 1$; 10% decrease

37. (A) $x = 3,000 - 50p$ $0 \le p \le 60$
   (B) $R(p) = 3,000p - 50p^2$
   (C) $E(p) = \frac{p}{60 - p}$
   (D) Elastic on $(30, 60)$; inelastic on $(0, 30)$
   (E) Increasing on $(0, 30)$; decreasing on $(30, 60)$
   (F) Decrease
   (G) Increase

39. Elastic on $(3.5, 7)$; inelastic on $(0, 3.5)$
41. Elastic on $(25/\sqrt{3}, 25)$; inelastic on $(0, 25/\sqrt{3})$
43. Elastic on $(48, 72)$; inelastic on $(0, 48)$
45. Elastic on $(25, 25\sqrt{2})$; inelastic on $(0, 25)$

47. $R(p) = 20p(10 - p)$

49. $R(p) = 40p(p - 15)^2$

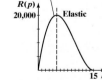

51. $R(p) = 30p - 10p\sqrt{p}$

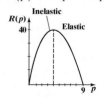

53. $\frac{3}{2}$ **55.** $\frac{1}{2}$

57. Elastic on $(0, 300)$; inelastic on $(300, 600)$
59. Elastic on $(0, 10\sqrt{3})$; inelastic on $(10\sqrt{3}, 30)$
61. k
63. $75 per day

65. Increase **67.** Decrease **69.** \$3.75 **71.** $p(t) = \frac{31}{0.31t + 18.5}$ **73.** -0.08

Chapter 4 Review Exercises

1. \$3,136.62; \$4,919.21; \$12,099.29 *(4-1)* **2.** $\dfrac{2}{x} + 3e^x$ *(4-2)* **3.** $2e^{2x-3}$ *(4-4)* **4.** $\dfrac{2}{2x + 7}$ *(4-4)*

5. (A) $y = \ln(3 + e^x)$ (B) $\dfrac{dy}{dx} = \dfrac{e^x}{3 + e^x}$ *(4-4)* **6.** $y' = \dfrac{9x^2}{4y}; \dfrac{9}{8}$ *(4-5)* **7.** $dy/dt = 216$ *(4-6)*

8. (A) $x = 1{,}000 - 25p$ (B) $\dfrac{p}{40 - p}$ (C) 0.6; demand is inelastic and insensitive to small changes in price.

(D) $1{,}000p - 25p^2$ (E) Revenue increases *(4-7)*

9. -10 *(4-2)* **10.** $\lim\limits_{n \to \infty}\left(1 + \dfrac{2}{n}\right)^n = e^2 \approx 7.389\,06$ *(4-1)* **11.** $\dfrac{7[(\ln z)^6 + 1]}{z}$ *(4-4)* **12.** $x^5(1 + 6\ln x)$ *(4-3)* **13.** $\dfrac{e^x(x - 6)}{x^7}$ *(4-3)*

14. $\dfrac{6x^2 - 3}{2x^3 - 3x}$ *(4-4)* **15.** $(3x^2 - 2x)e^{x^3 - x^2}$ *(4-4)* **16.** $\dfrac{1 - 2x\ln 5x}{xe^{2x}}$ *(4-4)* **17.** $y = -x + 2; y = -ex + 1$ *(4-4)*

18. $y' = \dfrac{3y - 2x}{8y - 3x}; \dfrac{8}{19}$ *(4-5)* **19.** $x' = \dfrac{4tx}{3x^2 - 2t^2}; -4$ *(4-5)* **20.** $y' = \dfrac{1}{e^y + 2y}; 1$ *(4-5)* **21.** $y' = \dfrac{2xy}{1 + 2y^2}; \dfrac{2}{3}$ *(4-5)*

22. $dy/dt = -2$ units/sec *(4-6)* **23.** 0.27 ft/sec *(4-6)* **24.** $dR/dt = 1/\pi \approx 0.318$ in./min *(4-6)*
25. Elastic for $5 < p < 15$; inelastic for $0 < p < 5$ *(4-7)*

26.

27. (A) $y = [\ln(4 - e^x)]^3$ (B) $\dfrac{dy}{dx} = \dfrac{-3e^x[\ln(4 - e^x)]^2}{4 - e^x}$ *(4-4)*

28. $2x(5^{x^2-1})(\ln 5)$ *(4-4)* **29.** $\left(\dfrac{1}{\ln 5}\right)\dfrac{2x - 1}{x^2 - x}$ *(4-4)*

30. $\dfrac{2x + 1}{2(x^2 + x)\sqrt{\ln(x^2 + x)}}$ *(4-4)* **31.** $y' = \dfrac{2x - e^{xy}y}{xe^{xy} - 1}; 0$ *(4-5)*

32. The rate of increase of area is proportional to the radius R, so the rate is smallest when $R = 0$, and has no largest value. *(4-6)*

33. Yes, for $-\sqrt{3}/3 < x < \sqrt{3}/3$ *(4-6)* **34.** (A) 15 yr (B) 13.9 yr *(4-1)*
35. $A'(t) = 10e^{0.1t}; A'(1) = \$11.05/\text{yr}; A'(10) = \$27.18/\text{yr}$ *(4-1)* **36.** $R'(x) = (1{,}000 - 20x)e^{-0.02x}$ *(4-4)*
37. $p' = \dfrac{-(5{,}000 - 2p^3)^{1/2}}{3p^2}$ *(4-5)* **38.** $dR/dt = \$2{,}242/\text{day}$ *(4-6)* **39.** Decrease price *(4-7)* **40.** 0.02125 *(4-7)*
41. -1.111 mg/mL per hour; -0.335 mg/mL per hour *(4-4)* **42.** $dR/dt = -3/(2\pi)$; approx. 0.477 mm/day *(4-6)*
43. (A) Increasing at the rate of 2.68 units/day at the end of 1 day of training; increasing at the rate of 0.54 unit/day after 5 days of training
  (B) 7 days *(4-4)*
44. $dT/dt = -1/27 \approx -0.037$ min/operation hour *(4-6)*

Chapter 5

Exercises 5-1

1. $(a, b); (d, f); (g, h)$ **3.** $(b, c); (c, d); (f, g)$ **5.** c, d, f **7.** b, f
9. Local maximum at $x = a$; local minimum at $x = c$; no local extrema at $x = b$ and $x = d$ **11.** e **13.** d **15.** f
17. c **19.** (A) $f'(x) = 3x^2 - 12$ (B) $-2, 2$ (C) $-2, 2$ **21.** (A) $f'(x) = \dfrac{1}{3}(x + 5)^{-2/3}$ (B) -5 (C) -5
23. (A) $f'(x) = -\dfrac{6}{(x + 2)^2}$ (B) None (C) -2 **25.** (A) $f'(x) = \begin{cases} -1 \text{ if } x < 0 \\ 1 \text{ if } x > 0 \end{cases}$ (B) 0 (C) 0
27. Decreasing on $(-\infty, 1)$; increasing on $(1, \infty)$; $f(1) = -2$ is a local minimum
29. Increasing on $(-\infty, -4)$; decreasing on $(-4, \infty)$; $f(-4) = 7$ is a local maximum
31. Increasing for all x; no local extrema
33. Increasing on $(-\infty, -2)$ and $(3, \infty)$; decreasing on $(-2, 3)$; $f(-2) = 44$ is a local maximum, $f(3) = -81$ is a local minimum
35. Decreasing on $(-\infty, 1)$; increasing on $(1, \infty)$; $f(1) = 4$ is a local minimum
37. Increasing on $(-\infty, 2)$; decreasing on $(2, \infty)$; $f(2) = e^{-2} \approx 0.135$ is a local maximum
39. Increasing on $(-\infty, 8)$; decreasing on $(8, \infty)$; $f(8) = 4$ is a local maximum
41. Critical values: $x = -0.77, 1.08, 2.69$; decreasing on $(-\infty, -0.77)$ and $(1.08, 2.69)$; increasing on $(-0.77, 1.08)$ and $(2.69, \infty)$; local minima at $x = -0.77$ and $x = 2.69$; local maximum at $x = 1.08$
43. Critical values: $x = 1.34, 2.82$; decreasing on $(0, 1.34)$ and $(2.82, \infty)$; increasing on $(1.34, 2.82)$; local minimum at $x = 1.34$; and local maximum at $x = 2.82$
45. Critical values: $0.36, 2.15$; increasing on $(-\infty, 0.36)$ and $(2.15, \infty)$; decreasing on $(0.36, 2.15)$; local maximum at $x = 0.36$; local minimum at $x = 2.15$

47. Increasing on $(-\infty, 4)$
Decreasing on $(4, \infty)$
Horizontal tangent at $x = 4$

49. Increasing on $(-\infty, -1), (1, \infty)$
Decreasing on $(-1, 1)$
Horizontal tangents at $x = -1, 1$

51. Decreasing for all x
Horizontal tangent at $x = 2$

53. Decreasing on $(-\infty, -3)$ and $(0, 3)$;
increasing on $(-3, 0)$ and $(3, \infty)$
Horizontal tangents at $x = -3, 0, 3$

55.

57.

59.

61.

63. g_4
65. g_6
67. g_2

69. Increasing on $(-1, 2)$; decreasing on $(-\infty, -1)$ and $(2, \infty)$; local minimum at $x = -1$; local maximum at $x = 2$

71. Increasing on $(-1, 2)$ and $(2, \infty)$; decreasing on $(-\infty, -1)$; local minimum at $x = -1$

73. Increasing on $(-2, 0)$ and $(3, \infty)$; decreasing on $(-\infty, -2)$ and $(0, 3)$; local minima at $x = -2$ and $x = 3$; local maximum at $x = 0$

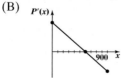

75. $f'(x) > 0$ on $(-\infty, -1)$ and $(3, \infty)$; $f'(x) < 0$ on $(-1, 3)$; $f'(x) = 0$ at $x = -1$ and $x = 3$

77. $f'(x) > 0$ on $(-2, 1)$ and $(3, \infty)$; $f'(x) < 0$ on $(-\infty, -2)$ and $(1, 3)$; $f'(x) = 0$ at $x = -2, x = 1$, and $x = 3$

79. Critical values: $x = -2, x = 2$; increasing on $(-\infty, -2)$ and $(2, \infty)$; decreasing on $(-2, 0)$ and $(0, 2)$; local maximum at $x = -2$; local minimum at $x = 2$

81. Critical value: $x = -2$; increasing on $(-2, 0)$; decreasing on $(-\infty, -2)$ and $(0, \infty)$; local minimum at $x = -2$

83. Critical values: $x = 0, x = 4$; increasing on $(-\infty, 0)$ and $(4, \infty)$; decreasing on $(0, 2)$ and $(2, 4)$; local maximum at $x = 0$; local minimum at $x = 4$

85. Critical values: $x = 0, x = 4, x = 6$; increasing on $(0, 4)$ and $(6, \infty)$; decreasing on $(-\infty, 0)$ and $(4, 6)$; local maximum at $x = 4$; local minima at $x = 0$ and $x = 6$

87. (A) There are no critical values and no local extrema. The function is increasing for all x.
(B) There are two critical values, $x = \pm\sqrt{-k/3}$. The function increases on $(-\infty, -\sqrt{-k/3})$ to a local maximum at $x = -\sqrt{-k/3}$, decreases on $(-\sqrt{-k/3}, \sqrt{-k/3})$ to a local minimum at $x = \sqrt{-k/3}$, and increases on $(\sqrt{-k/3}, \infty)$.
(C) The only critical value is $x = 0$. There are no local extrema. The function is increasing for all x.

89. (A) The marginal profit is positive on $(0, 600)$, 0 at $x = 600$, and negative on $(600, 1{,}000)$.
(B)

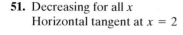

91. (A) The price decreases for the first 15 months to a local minimum, increases for the next 40 months to a local maximum, and then decreases for the remaining 15 months.
(B)

93. (A) $\overline{C}(x) = 0.05x + 20 + \dfrac{320}{x}$

(B) Critical value: $x = 80$; decreasing for $0 < x < 80$; increasing for $80 < x < 150$; local minimum at $x = 80$
95. $P(x)$ is increasing over (a, b) if $P'(x) = R'(x) - C'(x) > 0$ over (a, b); that is, if $R'(x) > C'(x)$ over (a, b).
97. Critical value: $t = 2$; increasing on $(0, 2)$; decreasing on $(2, 24)$; $C(2) = 0.07$ is a local maximum.

Exercises 5-2

1. (A) $(a, c), (c, d), (e, g)$ (B) $(d, e), (g, h)$ (C) $(d, e), (g, h)$ (D) $(a, c), (c, d), (e, g)$ (E) $(a, c), (c, d), (e, g)$ (F) $(d, e), (g, h)$
(G) d, e, g (H) d, e, g **3.** (C) **5.** (D) **7.** $12x - 8$ **9.** $4x^{-3} - 18x^{-4}$

11. $2 + \dfrac{9}{2}x^{-3/2}$ **13.** $8(x^2 + 9)^3 + 48x^2(x^2 + 9)^2 = 8(x^2 + 9)^2(7x^2 + 9)$

15. $-2e^{-x^2} + 4x^2e^{-x^2} = 2e^{-x^2}(2x^2 - 1)$ **17.** $\dfrac{x^3\left(-\dfrac{2}{x}\right) - (1 - 2\ln x)3x^2}{x^6} = \dfrac{6\ln x - 5}{x^4}$ **19.** $(-10, 2{,}000)$ **21.** $(0, 2)$ **23.** None

25. Concave upward for all x; no inflection points
27. Concave downward on $(-\infty, \frac{4}{3})$; concave upward on $(\frac{4}{3}, \infty)$; inflection point at $x = \frac{4}{3}$
29. Concave downward on $(-\infty, 0)$ and $(6, \infty)$; concave upward on $(0, 6)$; inflection points at $x = 0$ and $x = 6$
31. Concave upward on $(-2, 4)$; concave downward on $(-\infty, -2)$ and $(4, \infty)$; inflection points at $x = -2$ and $x = 4$
33. Concave upward on $(-\infty, \ln 2)$; concave downward on $(\ln 2, \infty)$; inflection point at $x = \ln 2$

35.   **37.**   **39.**   **41.**

43. Domain: All real numbers
y intercept: 16; x intercepts: $2 - 2\sqrt{3}, 2, 2 + 2\sqrt{3}$
Increasing on $(-\infty, 0)$ and $(4, \infty)$
Decreasing on $(0, 4)$
Local maximum at $x = 0$, local minimum at $x = 4$
Concave downward on $(-\infty, 2)$
Concave upward on $(2, \infty)$
Inflection point at $x = 2$

45. Domain: All real numbers
y intercept: 2; x intercept: -1
Increasing on $(-\infty, \infty)$
Concave downward on $(-\infty, 0)$
Concave upward on $(0, \infty)$
Inflection point at $x = 0$

47. Domain: All real numbers
y intercept: 0; x intercepts: 0, 4
Increasing on $(-\infty, 3)$
Decreasing on $(3, \infty)$
Local maximum at $x = 3$
Concave upward on $(0, 2)$
Concave downward on $(-\infty, 0)$ and $(2, \infty)$
Inflection points at $x = 0$ and $x = 2$

49. Domain: All real numbers
y intercept: 0; x intercepts: 0, 1
Increasing on $(0.25, \infty)$
Decreasing on $(-\infty, 0.25)$
Local minimum at $x = 0.25$
Concave upward on $(-\infty, 0.5)$ and $(1, \infty)$
Concave downward on $(0.5, 1)$
Inflection points at $x = 0.5$ and $x = 1$

51. Domain: All real numbers
y intercept: 27; x intercepts: $-3, 3$
Increasing on $(-\infty, -\sqrt{3})$ and $(0, \sqrt{3})$
Decreasing on $(-\sqrt{3}, 0)$ and $(\sqrt{3}, \infty)$
Local maxima at $x = -\sqrt{3}$ and $x = \sqrt{3}$
Local minimum at $x = 0$
Concave upward on $(-1, 1)$
Concave downward on $(-\infty, -1)$ and $(1, \infty)$
Inflection points at $x = -1$ and $x = 1$

53. Domain: All real numbers
y intercept: 16; x intercepts: $-2, 2$
Decreasing on $(-\infty, -2)$ and $(0, 2)$
Increasing on $(-2, 0)$ and $(2, \infty)$
Local minima at $x = -2$ and $x = 2$
Local maximum at $x = 0$
Concave upward on $(-\infty, -2\sqrt{3}/3)$ and $(2\sqrt{3}/3, \infty)$
Concave downward on $(-2\sqrt{3}/3, 2\sqrt{3}/3)$
Inflection points at $x = -2\sqrt{3}/3$ and $x = 2\sqrt{3}/3$

55. Domain: All real numbers
y intercept: 0; x intercepts: 0, 1.5
Decreasing on $(-\infty, 0)$ and $(0, 1.25)$
Increasing on $(1.25, \infty)$
Local minimum at $x = 1.25$
Concave upward on $(-\infty, 0)$ and $(1, \infty)$
Concave downward on $(0, 1)$
Inflection points at $x = 0$ and $x = 1$

57. Domain: All real numbers
y intercept: 0; x intercept: 0
Increasing on $(-\infty, \infty)$
Concave downward on $(-\infty, \infty)$

59. Domain: All real numbers
y intercept: 5
Decreasing on $(-\infty, \ln 4)$
Increasing on $(\ln 4, \infty)$
Local minimum at $x = \ln 4$
Concave upward on $(-\infty, \infty)$

61. Domain: $(0, \infty)$
x intercept: e^2
Increasing on $(-\infty, \infty)$
Concave downward on $(-\infty, \infty)$

63. Domain: $(-4, \infty)$
x intercept: $e^2 - 4$
Increasing on $(-4, \infty)$
Concave downward on $(-4, \infty)$

65.

x	$f'(x)$	$f(x)$
$-\infty < x < -1$	Positive and decreasing	Increasing and concave downward
$x = -1$	x intercept	Local maximum
$-1 < x < 0$	Negative and decreasing	Decreasing and concave downward
$x = 0$	Local minimum	Inflection point
$0 < x < 2$	Negative and increasing	Decreasing and concave upward
$x = 2$	Local maximum	Inflection point
$2 < x < \infty$	Negative and decreasing	Decreasing and concave downward

67.

x	$f'(x)$	$f(x)$
$-\infty < x < -2$	Negative and increasing	Decreasing and concave upward
$x = -2$	Local maximum	Inflection point
$-2 < x < 0$	Negative and decreasing	Decreasing and concave downward
$x = 0$	Local minimum	Inflection point
$0 < x < 2$	Negative and increasing	Decreasing and concave upward
$x = 2$	Local maximum	Inflection point
$2 < x < \infty$	Negative and decreasing	Decreasing and concave downward

69. Domain: All real numbers
x intercepts: $-1.18, 0.61, 1.87, 3.71$
y intercept: -5
Decreasing on $(-\infty, -0.53)$ and $(1.24, 3.04)$
Increasing on $(-0.53, 1.24)$ and $(3.04, \infty)$
Local minima at $x = -0.53$ and $x = 3.04$
Local maximum at $x = 1.24$
Concave upward on $(-\infty, 0.22)$ and $(2.28, \infty)$
Concave downward on $(0.22, 2.28)$
Inflection points at $x = 0.22$ and $x = 2.28$

71. Domain: All real numbers
y intercept: 100; x intercepts: 8.01, 13.36
Increasing on $(-0.10, 4.57)$ and $(11.28, \infty)$
Decreasing on $(-\infty, -0.10)$ and $(4.57, 11.28)$
Local maximum at $x = 4.57$
Local minima at $x = -0.10$ and $x = 11.28$
Concave upward on $(-\infty, 1.95)$ and $(8.55, \infty)$
Concave downward on $(1.95, 8.55)$
Inflection points at $x = 1.95$ and $x = 8.55$

73. Domain: All real numbers
x intercepts: $-2.40, 1.16$; y intercept: 3
Increasing on $(-\infty, -1.58)$
Decreasing on $(-1.58, \infty)$
Local maximum at $x = -1.58$
Concave downward on $(-\infty, -0.88)$ and $(0.38, \infty)$
Concave upward on $(-0.88, 0.38)$
Inflection points at $x = -0.88$ and $x = 0.38$

75. Domain: All real numbers
x intercepts: $-6.68, -3.64, -0.72$; y intercept: 30
Decreasing on $(-5.59, -2.27)$ and $(1.65, 3.82)$
Increasing on $(-\infty, -5.59)$, $(-2.27, 1.65)$, and $(3.82, \infty)$
Local minima at $x = -2.27$ and $x = 3.82$
Local maxima at $x = -5.59$ and $x = 1.65$
Concave upward on $(-4.31, -0.40)$ and $(2.91, \infty)$
Concave downward on $(-\infty, -4.31)$ and $(-0.40, 2.91)$
Inflection points at $x = -4.31, x = -0.40$, and $x = 2.91$

77. If $f'(x)$ has a local extremum at $x = c$, then $f'(x)$ must change from increasing to decreasing or from decreasing to increasing at $x = c$. The graph of $y = f(x)$ must change concavity at $x = c$, and there must be an inflection point at $x = c$.

79. If there is an inflection point on the graph of $y = f(x)$ at $x = c$, then $f(x)$ must change concavity at $x = c$. Consequently, $f'(x)$ must change from increasing to decreasing or from decreasing to increasing at $x = c$, and $x = c$ is a local extremum for $f'(x)$.

81. The graph of the CPI is concave upward.

83. The graph of $y = C'(x)$ is positive and decreasing. Since marginal costs are decreasing, the production process is becoming more efficient as production increases.

85. (A) Local maximum at $x = 60$
 (B) Concave downward on the whole interval $(0, 80)$

87. (A) Local maximum at $x = 1$
 (B) Concave downward on $(-\infty, 2)$;
 concave upward on $(2, \infty)$

89. Increasing on $(0, 10)$; decreasing on $(10, 15)$; point of diminishing returns is $x = 10$, max $T'(x) = T'(10) = 500$

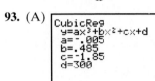

91. Increasing on $(24, 36)$; decreasing on $(36, 45)$; point of diminishing returns is $x = 36$, max $N'(x) = N'(36) = 3{,}888$

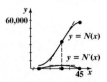
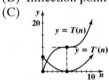

93. (A)

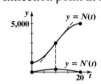

 (B) 32 ads to sell 574 cars per month

95. (A) Increasing on $(0, 10)$;
 decreasing on $(10, 20)$
 (B) Inflection point at $t = 10$
 (C)

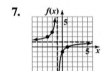

 (D) $N'(10) = 300$

97. (A) Increasing on $(5, \infty)$;
 decreasing on $(0, 5)$
 (B) Inflection point at $n = 5$
 (C)

 (D) $T'(5) = 0$

Exercises 5-3

1. $\frac{8}{3}$ **3.** $\frac{1}{2}$ **5.** 1 **7.** 4 **9.** 0 **11.** ∞ **13.** ∞ **15.** 5 **17.** ∞ **19.** $-\frac{1}{8}$ **21.** 17 **23.** 8 **25.** 0 **27.** ∞ **29.** ∞ **31.** $\frac{1}{3}$
33. -2 **35.** $-\infty$ **37.** 0 **39.** 0 **41.** 0 **43.** $\frac{1}{4}$ **45.** $\frac{1}{3}$ **47.** 0 **49.** 0 **51.** ∞ **53.** 1 **55.** 1

Exercises 5-4

1. (A) $(-\infty, b), (0, e), (e, g)$ (B) $(b, d), (d, 0), (g, \infty)$ (C) $(b, d), (d, 0), (g, \infty)$ (D) $(-\infty, b), (0, e), (e, g)$ (E) $x = 0$
 (F) $x = b, x = g$ (G) $(-\infty, a), (d, e), (h, \infty)$ (H) $(a, d), (e, h)$ (I) $(a, d), (e, h)$ (J) $(-\infty, a), (d, e), (h, \infty)$
 (K) $x = a, x = h$ (L) $y = L$ (M) $x = d, x = e$

3.
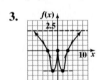

5.

7.

9.

11. Domain: $[-4, \infty)$ y intercept: 2; x intercept: -4 **13.** Domain: All real numbers y intercept: 75; x intercept: 15
15. Domain: All real numbers, except 5 y intercept: -19

17. Domain: All real numbers, except 3
 y intercept: -1; x intercept: -3
 Horizontal asymptote: $y = 1$
 Vertical asymptote: $x = 3$
 Decreasing on $(-\infty, 3)$ and $(3, \infty)$
 Concave upward on $(3, \infty)$
 Concave downward on $(-\infty, 3)$

19. Domain: All real numbers, except 2
 y intercept: 0; x intercept: 0
 Horizontal asymptote: $y = 1$
 Vertical asymptote: $x = 2$
 Decreasing on $(-\infty, 2)$ and $(2, \infty)$
 Concave downward on $(-\infty, 2)$
 Concave upward on $(2, \infty)$

21. Domain: $(-\infty, \infty)$
 y intercept: 10
 Horizontal asymptote: $y = 5$
 Decreasing on $(-\infty, \infty)$
 Concave upward on $(-\infty, \infty)$

23. Domain: $(-\infty, \infty)$
 y intercept: 0; x intercept: 0
 Horizontal asymptote: $y = 0$
 Increasing on $(-\infty, 5)$
 Decreasing on $(5, \infty)$
 Local maximum at $x = 5$
 Concave upward on $(10, \infty)$
 Concave downward on $(-\infty, 10)$
 Inflection point at $x = 10$

25. Domain: $(-\infty, 1)$
 y intercept: 0; x intercept: 0
 Vertical asymptote: $x = 1$
 Decreasing on $(-\infty, 1)$
 Concave downward on $(-\infty, 1)$

27. Domain: $(0, \infty)$
 Vertical asymptote: $x = 0$
 Increasing on $(1, \infty)$
 Decreasing on $(0, 1)$
 Local minimum at $x = 1$
 Concave upward on $(0, \infty)$

29. Domain: All real numbers, except ± 2
y intercept: 0; x intercept: 0
Horizontal asymptote: $y = 0$
Vertical asymptotes: $x = -2$, $x = 2$
Decreasing on $(-\infty, -2)$, $(-2, 2)$,
and $(2, \infty)$
Concave upward on $(-2, 0)$ and $(2, \infty)$
Concave downward on $(-\infty, -2)$ and $(0, 2)$
Inflection point at $x = 0$

31. Domain: All real numbers
y intercept: 1
Horizontal asymptote: $y = 0$
Increasing on $(-\infty, 0)$
Decreasing on $(0, \infty)$
Local maximum at $x = 0$
Concave upward on $(-\infty, -\sqrt{3}/3)$ and $(\sqrt{3}/3, \infty)$
Concave downward on $\quad (-\sqrt{3}/3, \sqrt{3}/3)$
Inflection points at $\quad x = -\sqrt{3}/3$ and $x = \sqrt{3}/3$

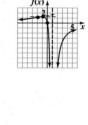

33. Domain: All real numbers except -1 and 1
y intercept: 0; x intercept: 0
Horizontal asymptote: $y = 0$
Vertical asymptote: $x = -1$ and $x = 1$
Increasing on $(-\infty, -1)$, $(-1, 1)$, and $(1, \infty)$
Concave upward on $(-\infty, -1)$ and $(0, 1)$
Concave downward on $(-1, 0)$ and $(1, \infty)$
Inflection point at $x = 0$

35. Domain: All real numbers except 1
y intercept: 0; x intercept: 0
Horizontal asymptote: $y = 0$
Vertical asymptote: $x = 1$
Increasing on $(-\infty, -1)$ and $(1, \infty)$
Decreasing on $(-1, 1)$
Local maximum at $x = -1$
Concave upward on $(-\infty, -2)$
Concave downward on $(-2, 1)$ and $(1, \infty)$
Inflection point at $x = -2$

37. Domain: All real numbers except 0
Horizontal asymptote: $y = 1$
Vertical asymptote: $x = 0$
Increasing on $(0, 4)$
Decreasing on $(-\infty, 0)$ and $(4, \infty)$
Local maximum at $x = 4$
Concave upward on $(6, \infty)$
Concave downward on $(-\infty, 0)$ and $(0, 6)$
Inflection point at $x = 6$

39. Domain: All real numbers except 1
y intercept: 0; x intercept: 0
Vertical asymptote: $x = 1$
Increasing on $(-\infty, 0)$ and $(2, \infty)$
Decreasing on $(0, 1)$ and $(1, 2)$
Local maximum at $x = 0$
Local minimum at $x = 2$
Concave upward on $(1, \infty)$
Concave downward on $(-\infty, 1)$

41. Domain: All real numbers except -3, 3
y intercept: $-\frac{2}{9}$
Horizontal asymptote: $y = 3$
Vertical asymptotes: $x = -3$, $x = 3$
Increasing on $(-\infty, -3)$ and $(-3, 0)$
Decreasing on $(0, 3)$ and $(3, \infty)$
Local maximum at $x = 0$
Concave upward on $(-\infty, -3)$ and $(3, \infty)$
Concave downward on $(-3, 3)$

43. Domain: All real numbers except 2
y intercept: 0; x intercept: 0
Vertical asymptote: $x = 2$
Increasing on $(3, \infty)$
Decreasing on $(-\infty, 2)$ and $(2, 3)$
Local minimum at $x = 3$
Concave upward on $(-\infty, 0)$ and $(2, \infty)$
Concave downward on $(0, 2)$
Inflection point at $x = 0$

45. Domain: All real numbers
y intercept: 3; x intercept: 3
Horizontal asymptote: $y = 0$
Increasing on $(-\infty, 2)$
Decreasing on $(2, \infty)$
Local maximum at $x = 2$
Concave upward on $(-\infty, 1)$
Concave downward on $(1, \infty)$
Inflection point at $x = 1$

47. Domain: $(-\infty, \infty)$
y intercept: 1
Horizontal asymptote: $y = 0$
Increasing on $(-\infty, 0)$
Decreasing on $(0, \infty)$
Local maximum at $x = 0$
Concave upward on $(-\infty, -1)$ and $(1, \infty)$
Concave downward on $(-1, 1)$
Inflection points at $x = -1$ and $x = 1$

49. Domain: $(0, \infty)$
x intercept: 1
Increasing on $(e^{-1/2}, \infty)$
Decreasing on $(0, e^{-1/2})$
Local minimum at $x = e^{-1/2}$
Concave upward on $(e^{-3/2}, \infty)$
Concave downward on $(0, e^{-3/2})$
Inflection point at $x = e^{-3/2}$

51. Domain: $(0, \infty)$
x intercept: 1
Vertical asymptote: $x = 0$
Increasing on $(1, \infty)$
Decreasing on $(0, 1)$
Local minimum at $x = 1$
Concave upward on $(0, e)$
Concave downward on (e, ∞)
Inflection point at $x = e$

53. Domain: All real numbers except $-4, 2$
y intercept: $-1/8$
Horizontal asymptote: $y = 0$
Vertical asymptote: $x = -4, x = 2$
Increasing on $(-\infty, -4)$ and $(-4, -1)$
Decreasing on $(-1, 2)$ and $(2, \infty)$
Local maximum at $x = -1$
Concave upward on $(-\infty, -4)$ and $(2, \infty)$
Concave downward on $(-4, 2)$

55. Domain: All real numbers except $-\sqrt{3}, \sqrt{3}$
y intercept: 0; x intercept: 0
Vertical asymptote: $x = -\sqrt{3}, x = \sqrt{3}$
Increasing on $(-3, -\sqrt{3}), (-\sqrt{3}, \sqrt{3})$, and $(\sqrt{3}, 3)$
Decreasing on $(-\infty, -3)$ and $(3, \infty)$
Local maximum at $x = 3$
Local minimum at $x = -3$
Concave upward on $(-\infty, -\sqrt{3})$ and $(0, \sqrt{3})$
Concave downward on $(-\sqrt{3}, 0)$ and $(\sqrt{3}, \infty)$
Inflection point at $x = 0$

57. Domain: All real numbers except 0
Vertical asymptote: $x = 0$
Oblique asymptote: $y = x$
Increasing on $(-\infty, -2)$ and $(2, \infty)$
Decreasing on $(-2, 0)$ and $(0, 2)$
Local maximum at $x = -2$
Local minimum at $x = 2$
Concave upward on $(0, \infty)$
Concave downward on $(-\infty, 0)$

59. Domain: All real numbers except 0
x intercept: $\sqrt[3]{4}$
Vertical asymptote: $x = 0$
Oblique asymptote: $y = x$
Increasing on $(-\infty, -2)$ and $(0, \infty)$
Local maximum at $x = -2$
Decreasing on $(-2, 0)$
Concave downward on $(-\infty, 0)$ and $(0, \infty)$

61. Domain: All real numbers except 0
x intercepts: $-\sqrt{3}, \sqrt{3}$
Vertical asymptote: $x = 0$
Oblique asymptote: $y = x$
Increasing on $(-\infty, 0)$ and $(0, \infty)$
Concave upward on $(-\infty, 0)$
Concave downward on $(0, \infty)$

63. Domain: All real numbers except 0
Vertical asymptote: $x = 0$
Oblique asymptote: $y = x$
Increasing on $(-\infty, -2)$ and $(2, \infty)$
Decreasing on $(-2, 0)$ and $(0, 2)$
Local maximum at $x = -2$
Local minimum at $x = 2$
Concave upward on $(0, \infty)$
Concave downward on $(-\infty, 0)$

65. Domain: All real numbers except $2, 4$
y intercept: $-3/4$; x intercept: -3
Vertical asymptote: $x = 4$
Horizontal asymptote: $y = 1$
Decreasing on $(-\infty, 2), (2, 4)$, and $(4, \infty)$
Concave upward on $(4, \infty)$
Concave downward on $(-\infty, 2)$ and $(2, 4)$

67. Domain: All real numbers except $-3, 3$
y intercept: $5/3$; x intercept: 2.5
Vertical asymptote: $x = 3$
Horizontal asymptote: $y = 2$
Decreasing on $(-\infty, -3), (-3, 3)$, and $(3, \infty)$
Concave upward on $(3, \infty)$
Concave downward on $(-\infty, -3)$ and $(-3, 3)$

69. Domain: All real numbers except $-1, 2$
y intercept: 0; x intercepts: $0, 3$
Vertical asymptote: $x = -1$
Increasing on $(-\infty, -3), (1, 2)$, and $(2, \infty)$
Decreasing on $(-3, -1)$ and $(-1, 1)$
Local maximum at $x = -3$
Local minimum at $x = 1$
Concave upward on $(-1, 2)$ and $(2, \infty)$
Concave downward on $(-\infty, -1)$

71. Domain: All real numbers except 1
y intercept: -2; x intercept: -2
Vertical asymptote: $x = 1$
Horizontal asymptote: $y = 1$
Decreasing on $(-\infty, 1)$ and $(1, \infty)$
Concave upward on $(1, \infty)$
Concave downward on $(-\infty, 1)$

73.

75. (A) Increasing on $(0, 1)$
(B) Concave upward on $(0, 1)$
(C) $x = 1$ is a vertical asymptote
(D) The origin is both an x and a y intercept
(E)

77. (A) $\overline{C}(n) = \dfrac{3,200}{n} + 250 + 50n$

(B)

(C) 8 yr

79. (A)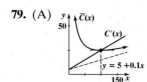

(B) 25 at $x = 100$

81. (A)

(B) Minimum average cost is $4.35 when 177 pizzas are produced daily.

83.

85.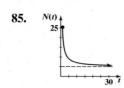

Exercises 5-5

1. Min $f(x) = f(0) = 0$; Max $f(x) = f(10) = 14$ **3.** Min $f(x) = f(0) = 0$; Max $f(x) = f(3) = 9$
5. Min $f(x) = f(1) = f(7) = 5$; Max $f(x) = f(10) = 14$ **7.** Min $f(x) = f(1) = f(7) = 5$; Max $f(x) = f(3) = f(9) = 9$
9. Min $f(x) = f(5) = 7$; Max $f(x) = f(3) = 9$ **11.** Max $f(x) = f(3) = 21$; Min $f(x) = f(2) = 17$
13. Max $f(x) = f(-1) = e \approx 2.718$; Min $f(x) = e^{-1} \approx 0.368$ **15.** Max $f(x) = f(0) = 9$; Min $f(x) = f(\pm 4) = -7$
17. Min $f(x) = f(1) = 2$; no maximum **19.** Max $f(x) = f(-3) = 18$; no minimum **21.** No absolute extrema
23. Max $f(x) = f(3) = 54$; no minimum **25.** No absolute extrema **27.** Min $f(x) = f(0) = 0$; no maximum
29. Max $f(x) = f(1) = 1$; Min $f(x) = f(-1) = -1$ **31.** Min $f(x) = f(0) = -1$, no maximum **33.** Min $f(x) = f(2) = -2$
35. Max $f(x) = f(2) = 4$ **37.** Min $f(x) = f(2) = 0$ **39.** No maximum **41.** Max $f(x) = f(2) = 8$

43. Min $f(x) = f(4) = 22$ **45.** Min $f(x) = f(\sqrt{10}) = 14/\sqrt{10}$ **47.** Min $f(x) = f(2) = \dfrac{e^2}{4} \approx 1.847$

49. Min $f(x) = f(3) = \dfrac{27}{e^3} \approx 1.344$ **51.** Max $f(x) = f(e^{1.5}) = 2e^{1.5} \approx 8.963$

53. Min $f(x) = f(e^{2.5}) = \dfrac{e^5}{2} \approx 74.207$ **55.** Max $f(x) = f(1) = -1$

57. (A) Max $f(x) = f(5) = 14$; Min $f(x) = f(-1) = -22$ (B) Max $f(x) = f(1) = -2$; Min $f(x) = f(-1) = -22$
 (C) Max $f(x) = f(5) = 14$; Min $f(x) = f(3) = -6$
59. (A) Max $f(x) = f(0) = 126$; Min $f(x) = f(2) = -26$ (B) Max $f(x) = f(7) = 49$; Min $f(x) = f(2) = -26$
 (C) Max $f(x) = f(6) = 6$; Min $f(x) = f(3) = -15$
61. (A) Max $f(x) = f(-1) = 10$; Min $f(x) = f(2) = -11$ (B) Max $f(x) = f(0) = f(4) = 5$; Min $f(x) = f(3) = -22$
 (C) Max $f(x) = f(-1) = 10$; Min $f(x) = f(1) = 2$
63. Local minimum **65.** Unable to determine **67.** Neither **69.** Local maximum

Exercises 5-6

1. 7.5 and 7.5 **3.** 7.5 and -7.5 **5.** $\sqrt{15}$ and $\sqrt{15}$ **7.** $10\sqrt{2}$ ft by $10\sqrt{2}$ ft **9.** 37 ft by 37 ft
11. (A) Maximum revenue is $125,000 when 500 phones are produced and sold for $250 each.
 (B) Maximum profit is $46,612.50 when 365 phones are produced and sold for $317.50 each.
13. (A) Max $R(x) = R(3,000) = \$300,000$
 (B) Maximum profit is $75,000 when 2,100 sets are manufactured and sold for $130 each.
 (C) Maximum profit is $64,687.50 when 2,025 sets are manufactured and sold for $132.50 each.
15. (A) 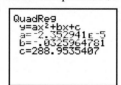 (B)  (C) The maximum profit is $118,996 when the price per sleeping bag is $195.

17. (A) $4.80 (B) $8 **19.** $35; $6,125 **21.** 40 trees; 1,600 lb **23.** $(10 - 2\sqrt{7})/3 = 1.57$ in. squares
25. 20 ft by 40 ft (with the expensive side being one of the short sides) **27.** 8 production runs per year
29. 10,000 books in 5 printings **31.** (A) $x = 5.1$ mi (B) $x = 10$ mi **33.** 4 days; 20 bacteria/cm^3
35. 1 month; 2 ft **37.** 4 yr from now

Chapter 5 Review Exercises

1. (a, c_1), (c_3, c_6) (5-1, 5-2) **2.** (c_1, c_3), (c_6, b) (5-1, 5-2) **3.** (a, c_2), (c_4, c_5), (c_7, b) (5-1, 5-2) **4.** c_3 (5-1)
5. c_1, c_6 (5-1) **6.** c_1, c_3, c_5 (5-1) **7.** c_4, c_6 (5-1) **8.** c_2, c_4, c_5, c_7 (5-2) **11.** $f''(x) = 12x^2 + 30x$ (5-2)
9. (5-2)   **10.** (5-2)   **12.** $y'' = 8/x^3$ (5-2)
13. Domain: All real numbers, except 4
 y intercept: $\frac{5}{4}$; x intercept: -5 (5-2)
14. Domain: $(-2, \infty)$
 y intercept: $\ln 2$; x intercept: -1 (5-2)

15. Horizontal asymptote: $y = 0$;
     Vertical asymptotes: $x = -2$, $x = 2$ *(5-4)*

16. Horizontal asymptote: $y = \frac{2}{3}$;
     Vertical asymptote: $x = -\frac{10}{3}$ *(5-4)*

17. $(-\sqrt{2}, -20)$, $(\sqrt{2}, -20)$ *(5-2)*   **18.** $(-\frac{1}{2}, -6)$ *(5-2)*   **19.** (A) $f'(x) = \frac{1}{5}x^{-1/5}$ (B) 0   (C) 0 *(5-1)*

20. (A) $f'(x) = -\frac{1}{5}x^{-6/5}$ (B) None   (C) 0 *(5-1)*

21. Domain: All real numbers
     y intercept: 0; x intercepts: 0, 9
     Increasing on $(-\infty, 3)$ and $(9, \infty)$
     Decreasing on $(3, 9)$
     Local maximum at $x = 3$
     Local minimum at $x = 9$
     Concave upward on $(6, \infty)$
     Concave downward on $(-\infty, 6)$
     Inflection point at $x = 6$ *(5-4)*

22. Domain: All real numbers
     y intercept: 16; x intercepts: -4, 2
     Increasing on $(-\infty, -2)$ and $(2, \infty)$
     Decreasing on $(-2, 2)$
     Local maximum at $x = -2$
     Local minimum at $x = 2$
     Concave upward on $(0, \infty)$
     Concave downward on $(-\infty, 0)$
     Inflection point at $x = 0$ *(5-4)*

23. Domain: All real numbers
     y intercept: 0; x intercepts: 0, 4
     Increasing on $(-\infty, 3)$
     Decreasing on $(3, \infty)$
     Local maximum at $x = 3$
     Concave upward on $(0, 2)$
     Concave downward on $(-\infty, 0)$ and $(2, \infty)$
     Inflection points at $x = 0$ and $x = 2$ *(5-4)*

24. Domain: all real numbers
     y intercept: -3; x intercepts: -3, 1
     No vertical or horizontal asymptotes
     Increasing on $(-2, \infty)$
     Decreasing on $(-\infty, -2)$
     Local minimum at $x = -2$
     Concave upward on $(-\infty, -1)$ and $(1, \infty)$
     Concave downward on $(-1, 1)$
     Inflection points at $x = -1$ and $x = 1$ *(5-4)*

25. Domain: All real numbers, except -2
     y intercept: 0; x intercept: 0
     Horizontal asymptote: $y = 3$
     Vertical asymptote: $x = -2$
     Increasing on $(-\infty, -2)$ and $(-2, \infty)$
     Concave upward on $(-\infty, -2)$
     Concave downward on $(-2, \infty)$ *(5-4)*

26. Domain: All real numbers
     y intercept: 0; x intercept: 0
     Horizontal asymptote: $y = 1$
     Increasing on $(0, \infty)$
     Decreasing on $(-\infty, 0)$
     Local minimum at $x = 0$
     Concave upward on $(-3, 3)$
     Concave downward on $(-\infty, -3)$ and $(3, \infty)$
     Inflection points at $x = -3$, 3 *(5-4)*

27. Domain: All real numbers except $x = -2$
     y intercept: 0; x intercept: 0
     Horizontal asymptote: $y = 0$
     Vertical asymptote: $x = -2$
     Increasing on $(-2, 2)$
     Decreasing on $(-\infty, -2)$ and $(2, \infty)$
     Local maximum at $x = 2$
     Concave upward on $(4, \infty)$
     Concave downward on $(-\infty, -2)$ and $(-2, 4)$
     Inflection point at $x = 4$ *(5-4)*

28. Domain: All real numbers
     y intercept: 0; x intercept: 0
     Increasing on $(-\infty, \infty)$
     Concave upward on $(-\infty, -3)$ and $(0, 3)$
     Concave downward on $(-3, 0)$ and $(3, \infty)$
     Inflection points at $x = -3, 0, 3$ *(5-4)*

29. Domain: All real numbers
     y intercept: 0; x intercept: 0
     Horizontal asymptote: $y = 5$
     Increasing on $(-\infty, \infty)$
     Concave downward on $(-\infty, \infty)$

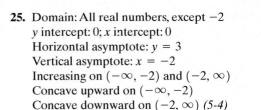

30. Domain: $(0, \infty)$
     x intercept: 1
     Increasing on $(e^{-1/3}, \infty)$
     Decreasing on $(0, e^{-1/3})$
     Local minimum at $x = e^{-1/3}$
     Concave upward on $(e^{-5/6}, \infty)$
     Concave downward on $(0, e^{-5/6})$
     Inflection point at $x = e^{-5/6}$

31. 3 *(5-3)*   **32.** $-\frac{1}{5}$ *(5-3)*   **33.** $-\infty$ *(5-3)*   **34.** 0 *(5-3)*   **35.** 0 *(5-3)*
36. 1 *(5-3)*   **37.** 0 *(5-3)*   **38.** 0 *(5-3)*   **39.** 1 *(5-3)*   **40.** 2 *(5-3)*

41.

x	f'(x)	f(x)
$-\infty < x < -2$	Negative and increasing	Decreasing and concave upward
$x = -2$	x intercept	Local minimum
$-2 < x < -1$	Positive and increasing	Increasing and concave upward
$x = -1$	Local maximum	Inflection point
$-1 < x < 1$	Positive and decreasing	Increasing and concave downward
$x = 1$	Local minimum	Inflection point
$1 < x < \infty$	Positive and increasing	Increasing and concave upward

42. (C) *(5-2)*   **43.** Local maximum at $x = -1$; local minimum at $x = 5$ *(5-5)*
44. Min $f(x) = f(2) = -4$; Max $f(x) = f(5) = 77$ *(5-5)*   **45.** Min $f(x) = f(2) = 8$ *(5-5)*
46. Max $f(x) = f(e^{4.5}) = 2e^{4.5} \approx 180.03$ *(5-5)*   **47.** Max $f(x) = f(0.5) = 5e^{-1} \approx 1.84$ *(5-5)*
48. Yes. Since f is continuous on $[a, b]$, f has an absolute maximum on $[a, b]$. But each endpoint is a local minimum; hence, the absolute maximum must occur between a and b. *(5-5)*
49. No, increasing/decreasing properties apply to intervals in the domain of f. It is correct to say that $f(x)$ is decreasing on $(-\infty, 0)$ and $(0, \infty)$. *(5-1)*
50. A critical value for $f(x)$ is a partition number for $f'(x)$ that is also in the domain of f. For example, if $f(x) = x^{-1}$, then 0 is a partition number for $f'(x) = -x^{-2}$, but 0 is not a critical value for $f(x)$ since 0 is not in the domain of f. *(5-1)*
51. Max $f'(x) = f'(2) = 12$ *(5-2, 5-5)*

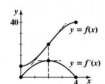

52. Each number is 20; minimum sum is 40 *(5-6)*
53. Domain: All real numbers
x intercepts: 0.79, 1.64; y intercept: 4
Increasing on $(-1.68, -0.35)$ and $(1.28, \infty)$
Decreasing on $(-\infty, -1.68)$ and $(-0.35, 1.28)$
Local minima at $x = -1.68$ and $x = 1.28$
Local maximum at $x = -0.35$
Concave downward on $(-1.10, 0.60)$
Concave upward on $(-\infty, -1.10)$ and $(0.60, \infty)$
Inflection points at $x = -1.10$ and $x = 0.60$ *(5-4)*

54. Domain: All real numbers
x intercepts: 0, 11.10; y intercept: 0
Increasing on $(1.87, 4.19)$ and $(8.94, \infty)$
Decreasing on $(-\infty, 1.87)$ and $(4.19, 8.94)$
Local maximum at $x = 4.19$
Local minima at $x = 1.87$ and $x = 8.94$
Concave upward on $(-\infty, 2.92)$ and $(7.08, \infty)$
Concave downward on $(2.92, 7.08)$
Inflection points at $x = 2.92$ and $x = 7.08$ *(5-4)*

55. Max $f(x) = f(1.373) = 2.487$ *(5-5)*
56. Max $f(x) = f(1.763) = 0.097$ *(5-5)*

57. (A) For the first 15 months, the graph of the price is increasing and concave downward, with a local maximum at $t = 15$. For the next 15 months, the graph of the price is decreasing and concave downward, with an inflection point at $t = 30$. For the next 15 months, the graph of the price is decreasing and concave upward, with a local minimum at $t = 45$. For the remaining 15 months, the graph of the price is increasing and concave upward.

(B) 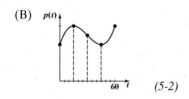   *(5-2)*

58. (A) Max $R(x) = R(10,000) = \$2,500,000$
(B) Maximum profit is $175,000 when 3,000 readers are manufactured and sold for $425 each.
(C) Maximum profit is $119,000 when 2,600 readers are manufactured and sold for $435 each. *(5-6)*
59. (A) The expensive side is 50 ft; the other side is 100 ft.
(B) The expensive side is 75 ft; the other side is 150 ft. *(5-6)*
60. $49; $6,724 *(5-6)*   **61.** 12 orders/yr *(5-6)*   **62.** Min $\overline{C}(x) = \overline{C}(200) = 50$
63. Min $\overline{C}(x) = \overline{C}(e^5) \approx \$49.66$ *(5-4)*   **64.** A maximum revenue of $18,394 is realized at a production level of 50 units at $367.88 each. *(5-6)*

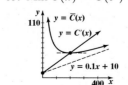

65.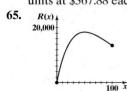

66. $549.15; $9,864 *(5-6)*
67. $1.52 *(5-6)*
68. 20.39 feet *(5-6)*
69. (A)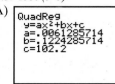

```
QuadReg
 y=ax²+bx+c
 a=.0061285714
 b=.1224285714
 c=102.2
```

(B) Min $\overline{C}(x) = \overline{C}(129) = \$1.71$ *(5-4)*

70. Increasing on $(0, 18)$; decreasing on $(18, 24)$; point of diminishing returns is $x = 18$, max $N'(x) = N'(18) = 972$ *(5-2)*

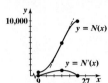

71. (A)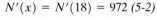

```
CubicReg
 y=ax³+bx²+cx+d
 a=-.01
 b=.83
 c=-2.3
 d=221
```

(B) 28 ads to sell 588 refrigerators per month *(5-2)*

72. 3 days *(5-1)*

73. 2 yr from now *(5-1)*

Chapter 6

Exercises 6-1

1. $7x + C$ **3.** $4x^2 + C$ **5.** $3x^3 + C$ **7.** $(x^6/6) + C$ **9.** $(-x^{-2}/2) + C$ **11.** $4x^{5/2} + C$ **13.** $3 \ln|z| + C$ **15.** $16e^u + C$
17. $y = 40x^5 + C$ **19.** $P = 24x - 3x^2 + C$ **21.** $y = e^x + 3x + C$ **23.** $x = 5 \ln|t| + t + C$ **25.** True **27.** False **29.** True
31. No, since one graph cannot be obtained from another by a vertical translation.
33. Yes, since one graph can be obtained from another by a vertical translation.
35. $(5x^2/2) - (5x^3/3) + C$ **37.** $2\sqrt{u} + C$ **39.** $-(x^{-2}/8) + C$ **41.** $4 \ln|u| + u + C$ **43.** $5e^z + 4z + C$
45. $x^3 + 2x^{-1} + C$ **47.** $2x^{3/2} + 4x^{1/2} + C$ **49.** $(e^x/4) - (3x^2/8) + C$ **51.** $C(x) = 2x^3 - 2x^2 + 3,000$
53. $x = 40\sqrt{t}$ **55.** $y = -2x^{-1} + 3 \ln|x| - x + 3$ **57.** $x = 4e^t - 2t - 3$ **59.** $y = 2x^2 - 3x + 1$ **61.** $x^2 + x^{-1} + C$
63. $\frac{1}{2}x^2 + x^{-2} + C$ **65.** $e^x - 2 \ln|x| + C$ **67.** $M = t + t^{-1} + \frac{3}{4}$ **69.** $y = 3x^{5/3} + 3x^{2/3} - 6$
71. $p(x) = 10x^{-1} + 10$ **73.** x^3 **75.** $x^4 + 3x^2 + C$ **83.** $\overline{C}(x) = 15 + \dfrac{1,000}{x}; C(x) = 15x + 1,000; C(0) = \$1,000$

85. (A) The cost function increases from 0 to 8, is concave downward from 0 to 4, and is concave upward from 4 to 8. There is an inflection point at $x = 4$.
(B) $C(x) = x^3 - 12x^2 + 53x + 30; C(4) = \$114,000; C(8) = \$198,000$
(C)

C(x)
200

8 x

(D) Manufacturing plants are often inefficient at low and high levels of production.

87. $S(t) = 1,200 - 18t^{4/3}; 50^{3/4} \approx 19$ mo
89. $S(t) = 1,200 - 18t^{4/3} - 70t; t \approx 4.05$ mo
91. $L(x) = 4,800x^{1/2}; 24,000$ labor-hours
93. $W(h) = 0.0005h^3; 171.5$ lb
95. 19,400

Exercises 6-2

1. $\frac{1}{3}(3x + 5)^3 + C$ **3.** $\frac{1}{6}(x^2 - 1)^6 + C$ **5.** $-\frac{1}{2}(5x^3 + 1)^{-2} + C$ **7.** $e^{5x} + C$ **9.** $\ln|1 + x^2| + C$ **11.** $\frac{2}{3}(1 + x^4)^{3/2} + C$
13. $\frac{1}{11}(x + 3)^{11} + C$ **15.** $-\frac{1}{6}(6t - 7)^{-1} + C$ **17.** $\frac{1}{12}(t^2 + 1)^6 + C$ **19.** $\frac{1}{2}e^{x^2} + C$ **21.** $\frac{1}{5}\ln|5x + 4| + C$
23. $-e^{1-t} + C$ **25.** $-\frac{1}{18}(3t^2 + 1)^{-3} + C$ **27.** $\frac{2}{5}(x + 4)^{5/2} - \frac{8}{3}(x + 4)^{3/2} + C$ **29.** $\frac{2}{3}(x - 3)^{3/2} + 6(x - 3)^{1/2} + C$
31. $\frac{1}{11}(x - 4)^{11} + \frac{2}{5}(x - 4)^{10} + C$ **33.** $\frac{1}{8}(1 + e^{2x})^4 + C$ **35.** $\frac{1}{2}\ln|4 + 2x + x^2| + C$ **37.** $\frac{1}{2}(5x + 3)^2 + C$
39. $\frac{1}{2}(x^2 - 1)^2 + C$ **41.** $\frac{1}{5}(x^5)^5 + C$ **49.** $\frac{1}{9}(3x^2 + 7)^{3/2} + C$ **51.** $\frac{1}{8}x^8 + \frac{4}{5}x^5 + 2x^2 + C$ **53.** $\frac{1}{9}(x^3 + 2)^3 + C$
55. $\frac{1}{4}(2x^4 + 3)^{1/2} + C$ **57.** $\frac{1}{4}(\ln x)^4 + C$ **59.** $e^{-1/x} + C$ **61.** $x = \frac{1}{3}(t^3 + 5)^7 + C$ **63.** $y = 3(t^2 - 4)^{1/2} + C$
65. $p = -(e^x - e^{-x})^{-1} + C$ **67.** $p(x) = \dfrac{2,000}{3x + 50} + 4; 250$ bottles **69.** $C(x) = 12x + 500 \ln(x + 1) + 2,000; \overline{C}(1,000) = \$17.45$
71. (A) $S(t) = 10t + 100e^{-0.1t} - 100, 0 \le t \le 24$ (B) \$50 million (C) 18.41 mo
73. $Q(t) = 100 \ln(t + 1) + 5t, 0 \le t \le 20; 275$ thousand barrels **75.** $W(t) = 2e^{0.1t}; 4.45$ g
77. (A) $-1,000$ bacteria/mL per day (B) $N(t) = 5,000 - 1,000 \ln(1 + t^2); 385$ bacteria/mL (C) 7.32 days
79. $N(t) = 100 - 60e^{-0.1t}, 0 \le t \le 15; 87$ words/min
81. $E(t) = 12,000 - 10,000 (t + 1)^{-1/2}; 9,500$ students

Exercises 6-3

1. $y = 3x^2 + C$ **3.** $y = 7 \ln|x| + C$ **5.** $y = 50e^{0.02x} + C$ **7.** $y = \dfrac{x^3}{3} - \dfrac{x^2}{2}$ **9.** $y = e^{-x^2} + 2$
11. $y = 2 \ln|1 + x| + 5$

13. Figure B. When $x = 1$, the slope $dy/dx = 1 - 1 = 0$ for any y. When $x = 0$, the slope $dy/dx = 0 - 1 = -1$ for any y. Both are consistent with the slope field shown in Figure B.

15. $y = \dfrac{x^2}{2} - x + C; y = \dfrac{x^2}{2} - x - 2$

17.

19. $y = Ce^{2t}$ **21.** $y = 100e^{-0.5x}$ **23.** $x = Ce^{-5t}$ **25.** $x = -(5t^2/2) + C$
27. Figure A. When $y = 1$, the slope $dy/dx = 1 - 1 = 0$ for any x. When $y = 2$, the slope
   $dy/dx = 1 - 2 = -1$ for any x. Both are consistent with the slope field shown in Figure A.
29. $y = 1 - e^{-x}$

31.

33.

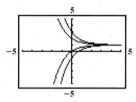

35. $y = \sqrt{25 - x^2}$ **37.** $y = -3x$ **39.** $y = 1/(1 - 2e^{-t})$

41.

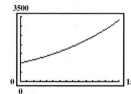

43.

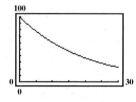

45.

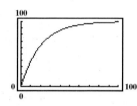

47.

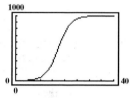

49. Apply the second-derivative test to $f(y) = ky(M - y)$.   **51.** 2009   **53.** $A = 1{,}000e^{0.03t}$ **55.** $A = 8{,}000e^{0.016t}$

57. (A) $p(x) = 100e^{-0.05x}$
   (B) $60.65 per unit
   (C)

59. (A) $N = L(1 - e^{-0.051t})$
   (B) 22.5%
   (C) 32 days
   (D)

61. $I = I_0e^{-0.00942x}$; $x \approx 74$ ft
63. (A) $Q = 3e^{-0.04t}$ (B) $Q(10) = 2.01$ mL
   (C) 27.47 hr
   (D)
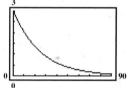

65. 0.023 117   **67.** Approx. 24,200 yr   **69.** 104 times; 67 times
71. (A) 7 people; 353 people   (B) 400
   (C)
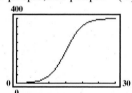

Exercises 6-4

1. C, E   **3.** B   **5.** H, I   **7.** H
9.
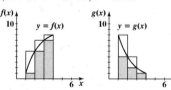

11. Figure A: $L_3 = 13$, $R_3 = 20$; Figure B: $L_3 = 14$, $R_3 = 7$
13. $L_3 \le \int_1^4 f(x)\,dx \le R_3$; $R_3 \le \int_1^4 g(x)\,dx \le L_3$; since $f(x)$ is increasing, L_3
   underestimates the area and R_3 overestimates the area; since $g(x)$ is decreasing, the
   reverse is true.
15. In both figures, the error bound for L_3 and R_3 is 7.
17. $S_5 = -260$ **19.** $S_4 = -1{,}194$ **21.** $S_3 = -33.01$ **23.** $S_6 = -38$ **25.** -2.475
27. 4.266   **29.** 2.474   **31.** -5.333 **33.** 1.067   **35.** -1.066 **37.** 15   **39.** 58.5

41. -54 **43.** 248   **45.** 0   **47.** -183 **49.** False   **51.** False   **53.** False
55. $L_{10} = 286{,}100$ ft^2; error bound is 50,000 ft^2; $n \ge 200$
57. $L_6 = -3.53$, $R_6 = -0.91$; error bound for L_6 and R_6 is 2.63. Geometrically, the definite integral over the interval $[2, 5]$ is the sum
   of the areas between the curve and the x axis from $x = 2$ to $x = 5$, with the areas below the x axis counted negatively and those
   above the x axis counted positively.
59. Increasing on $(-\infty, 0]$; decreasing on $[0, \infty)$
61. Increasing on $[-1, 0]$ and $[1, \infty)$; decreasing on $(-\infty, -1]$ and $[0, 1]$ **63.** $n \ge 22$ **65.** $n \ge 104$
67. $L_3 = 2{,}580$, $R_3 = 3{,}900$; error bound for L_3 and R_3 is 1,320
69. (A) $L_5 = 3.72$; $R_5 = 3.37$ (B) $R_5 = 3.37 \le \int_0^5 A'(t)\,dt \le 3.72 = L_5$
71. $L_3 = 114$, $R_3 = 102$; error bound for L_3 and R_3 is 12

Exercises 6-5

1. (A) $F(15) - F(10) = 375$
   (B)
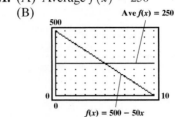

3. (A) $F(15) - F(10) = 85$
   (B)
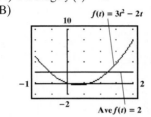

5. 40 **7.** 72 **9.** 46.5 **11.** $e - 1 \approx 1.718$
13. $\ln 2 \approx 0.693$ **15.** 0 **17.** 48 **19.** -48
21. -10.25 **23.** 0 **25.** -2 **27.** 14
29. $5^6 = 15,625$ **31.** $\ln 4 \approx 1.386$
33. $20(e^{0.25} - e^{-0.5}) \approx 13.550$ **35.** $\frac{1}{2}$
37. $\frac{1}{2}(1 - e^{-1}) \approx 0.316$ **39.** 0

41. (A) Average $f(x) = 250$
   (B)
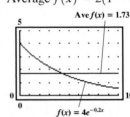
$f(x) = 500 - 50x$

43. (A) Average $f(t) = 2$
   (B)
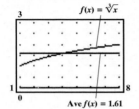

45. (A) Average $f(x) = \frac{45}{28} \approx 1.61$
   (B)
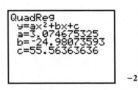

47. (A) Average $f(x) = 2(1 - e^{-2}) \approx 1.73$
   (B)
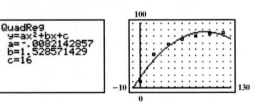
$f(x) = 4e^{-0.2x}$

49. $\frac{1}{6}(15^{3/2} - 5^{3/2}) \approx 7.819$ **51.** $\frac{1}{2}(\ln 2 - \ln 3) \approx -0.203$ **53.** 0

55. 4.566 **57.** 2.214 **61.** $\int_{300}^{900}\left(500 - \frac{x}{3}\right)dx = \$180,000$

63. $\int_0^5 500(t - 12)\,dt = -\$23,750$; $\int_5^{10} 500(t - 12)\,dt = -\$11,250$

65. (A)

```
QuadReg
y=ax²+bx+c
a=-.0082142857
b=1.528571429
c=16
```

(B) 6,505

67. Useful life $= \sqrt{\ln 55} \approx 2$ yr; total
profit $= \frac{51}{22} - \frac{5}{2}e^{-4} \approx 2.272$ or \$2,272
69. (A) \$420 (B) \$135,000

71. (A)

```
QuadReg
y=ax²+bx+c
a=3.074675325
b=-24.98073593
c=55.56363636
```

(B) \$100,505

73. $50e^{0.6} - 50e^{0.4} - 10 \approx \$6.51$
75. 4,800 labor-hours
77. (A) $I = -200t + 600$
   (B) $\frac{1}{3}\int_0^3 (-200t + 600)\,dt = 300$
79. $100\ln 11 + 50 \approx 290$ thousand barrels;
$100\ln 21 - 100\ln 11 + 50 \approx 115$ thousand barrels

81. $2e^{0.8} - 2 \approx 2.45$ g; $2e^{1.6} - 2e^{0.8} \approx 5.45$ g **83.** $10°C$
85. $0.6\ln 2 + 0.1 \approx 0.516$; $(4.2\ln 625 + 2.4 - 4.2\ln 49)/24 \approx 0.546$

Chapter 6 Review Exercises

1. $3x^2 + 3x + C$ (6-1) **2.** 50 (6-5) **3.** -207 (6-5) **4.** $-\frac{1}{8}(1 - t^2)^4 + C$ (6-2) **5.** $\ln|u| + \frac{1}{4}u^4 + C$ (6-1)
6. 0.216 (6-5) **7.** e^{-x^2} (6-1) **8.** $\sqrt{4 + 5x} + C$ (6-1) **9.** $y = f(x) = x^3 - 2x + 4$ (6-3)
10. (A) $2x^4 - 2x^2 - x + C$ (B) $e^t - 4\ln|t| + C$ (6-1) **11.** $R_2 = 72$; error bound for R_2 is 48 (6-4)
12. $\int_1^5(x^2 + 1)\,dx = \dfrac{136}{3} \approx 45.33$; actual error is $\dfrac{80}{3} \approx 26.67$ (6-5) **13.** $L_4 = 30.8$ (6-4)
14. 7 (6-5) **15.** Width $= 2 - (-1) = 3$; height $=$ average $f(x) = 7$ (6-5) **16.** $S_4 = 368$ (6-4) **17.** $S_5 = 906$ (6-4)
18. -10 (6-4) **19.** 0.4 (6-4) **20.** 1.4 (6-4) **21.** 0 (6-4) **22.** 0.4 (6-4) **23.** 2 (6-4) **24.** -2 (6-4)
25. -0.4 (6-4) **26.** (A) 1;1 (B) 4;4 (6-3)
27. $dy/dx = (2y)/x$; the slopes computed in Problem 26A are compatible with the slope field shown. (6-3)
29. $y = \frac{1}{4}x^2$; $y = -\frac{1}{4}x^2$ (6-3)

30. *(6-3)*

31. *(6-3)*

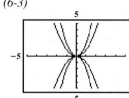

32. $\frac{2}{3}(2)^{3/2} \approx 1.886$ *(6-5)*   **33.** $\frac{1}{6} \approx 0.167$ *(6-5)*
34. $-5e^{-t} + C$ *(6-1)*   **35.** $\frac{1}{2}(1 + e^2)$ *(6-1)*
36. $\frac{1}{6}e^{3x^2} + C$ *(6-2)*   **37.** $2(\sqrt{5} - 1) \approx 2.472$ *(6-5)*
38. $\frac{1}{2}\ln 10 \approx 1.151$ *(6-5)*   **39.** 0.45 *(6-5)*
40. $\frac{1}{48}(2x^4 + 5)^6 + C$ *(6-2)*   **41.** $-\ln(e^{-x} + 3) + C$ *(6-2)*
42. $-(e^x + 2)^{-1} + C$ *(6-2)*

43. $y = f(x) = 3\ln|x| + x^{-1} + 4$ *(6-2, 6-3)*   **44.** $y = 3x^2 + x - 4$ *(6-3)*

45. (A) Average $f(x) = 6.5$
(B)

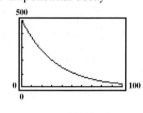

(6-5)

46. $\frac{1}{3}(\ln x)^3 + C$ *(6-2)*
47. $\frac{1}{8}x^8 - \frac{2}{5}x^5 + \frac{1}{2}x^2 + C$ *(6-2)*
48. $\frac{2}{3}(6 - x)^{3/2} - 12(6 - x)^{1/2} + C$ *(6-2)*
49. $\frac{1,234}{15} \approx 82.267$ *(6-5)*
50. 0 *(6-5)*
51. $y = 3e^{x^3} - 1$ *(6-3)*
52. $N = 800e^{0.06t}$ *(6-3)*

53. Limited growth

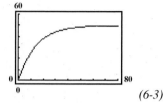

(6-3)

54. Exponential decay

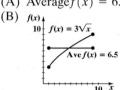

(6-3)

55. Unlimited growth

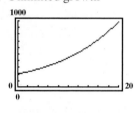

(6-3)

56. Logistic growth

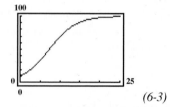

(6-3)

57. 1.167 *(6-5)*   **58.** 99.074 *(6-5)*   **59.** -0.153 *(6-5)*   **60.** $L_2 = \$180,000; R_2 = \$140,000; \$140,000 \le \int_{200}^{600} C'(x)\, dx \le \$180,000$ *(6-4)*

61. $\int_{200}^{600} \left(600 - \frac{x}{2}\right) dx = \$160,000$ *(6-5)*   **62.** $\int_{10}^{40} \left(150 - \frac{x}{10}\right) dx = \$4,425$ *(6-5)*   **63.** $P(x) = 100x - 0.01x^2; P(10) = \$999$ *(6-3)*

64. $\int_{0}^{15}(60 - 4t)\, dt = 450$ thousand barrels *(6-5)*   **65.** 109 items *(6-5)*   **66.** $16e^{2.5} - 16e^2 - 8 \approx \$68.70$ *(6-5)*

67. Useful life $= 10\ln\frac{20}{3} \approx 19$ yr; total profit $= 143 - 200e^{-1.9} \approx 113.086$ or $\$113,086$ *(6-5)*

68. $S(t) = 50 - 50e^{-0.08t}; 50 - 50e^{-0.96} \approx \$31$ million; $-(\ln 0.2)/0.08 \approx 20$ mo *(6-3)*   **69.** 1 cm^2 *(6-3)*   **70.** 800 gal *(6-5)*

71. (A) 133 million   (B) About 61 years *(6-3)*   **72.** $\dfrac{-\ln 0.04}{0.000\ 123\ 8} \approx 26,000$ yr *(6-3)*

73. $N(t) = 95 - 70e^{-0.1t}; N(15) \approx 79$ words/min *(6-3)*

Chapter 7

Exercises 7-1

1. $\int_a^b g(x)\, dx$ **3.** $\int_a^b [-h(x)]\, dx$

5. Since the shaded region in Figure C is below the x axis, $h(x) \le 0$; so, $\int_a^b h(x)\, dx$ represents the negative of the area.
7. 24 **9.** 51 **11.** 42 **13.** 6 **15.** 0.833 **17.** 2.350 **19.** 1 **21.** 10.5 **23.** 18 **25.** 44
27. $\int_a^b [-f(x)]\, dx$ **29.** $\int_b^c f(x)\, dx + \int_c^d [-f(x)]\, dx$ **31.** $\int_c^d [f(x) - g(x)]\, dx$
33. $\int_a^b [f(x) - g(x)]\, dx + \int_b^c [g(x) - f(x)]\, dx$
35. Find the intersection points by solving $f(x) = g(x)$ on the interval $[a, d]$ to determine b and c. Then observe that $f(x) \ge g(x)$
over $[a, b], g(x) \ge f(x)$ over $[b, c]$, and $f(x) \ge g(x)$ over $[c, d]$.
Area $= \int_a^b [f(x) - g(x)]\, dx + \int_b^c [g(x) - f(x)]\, dx + \int_c^d [f(x) - g(x)]\, dx$.
37. 2.5 **39.** 7.667 **41.** 12 **43.** 15 **45.** 32 **47.** 36 **49.** 9 **51.** 2.832
53. $\int_{-3}^{3}\sqrt{9 - x^2}\, dx; 14.137$ **55.** $\int_{0}^{4}\sqrt{16 - x^2}\, dx; 12.566$ **57.** $\int_{-2}^{2} 2\sqrt{9 - x^2}\, dx; 12.566$
59. 18 **61.** 1.858 **63.** 52.616 **65.** 8 **67.** 101.75 **69.** 17.979 **71.** 5.113 **73.** 8.290 **75.** 3.166 **77.** 1.385
79. Total production from the end of the fifth year to the end of the 10th year is $50 + 100\ln 20 - 100\ln 15 \approx 79$ thousand barrels.
81. Total profit over the 5-yr useful life of the game is $20 - 30e^{-1.5} \approx 13.306$, or $\$13,306$.

83. 1935: 0.412; 1947: 0.231; income was more equally distributed in 1947.
85. 1963: 0.818; 1983: 0.846; total assets were less equally distributed in 1983.
87. (A) $f(x) = 0.3125x^2 + 0.7175x - 0.015$ (B) 0.104
89. Total weight gain during the first 10 hr is $3e - 3 \approx 5.15$ g.
91. Average number of words learned from $t = 2$ hr to $t = 4$ hr is $15 \ln 4 - 15 \ln 2 \approx 10$.

Exercises 7-2

1. 0.43   **3.** 744.99   **5.** 10.27   **7.** 151.75   **9.** 93,268.66   **11.** (A) 10.72   (B) 3.28   (C) 10.72
13. (A) .75   (B) .11
   (C) $f(x)$

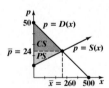

15. 8 yr   **17.** (A) .11   B) .10
19. $P(t \geq 12) = 1 - P(0 \leq t \leq 12) = .89$
21. \$12,500
23. If $f(t)$ is the rate of flow of a continuous income stream, then the total income produced from 0 to 5 yr is the area under the graph of $y = f(t)$ from $t = 0$ to $t = 5$.

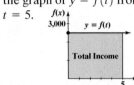

25. $8,000(e^{0.15} - 1) \approx \$1,295$
27. If $f(t)$ is the rate of flow of a continuous income stream, then the total income produced from 0 to 3 yr is the area under the graph of $y = f(t)$ from $t = 0$ to $t = 3$.

29. \$255,562; \$175,562   **31.** \$6,779.52   **33.** \$436.62
35. Clothing store: \$66,420.83; computer store: \$62,622.66; the clothing store is the better investment.
37. Bond: \$12,062.30 business: \$11,823.87; the bond is the better investment.   **39.** \$55,230

41. $\dfrac{k}{r}(e^{rT} - 1)$ **43.** \$625,000

45. The shaded area is the consumers' surplus and represents the total savings to consumers who are willing to pay more than \$150 for a product but are still able to buy the product for \$150.

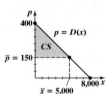

47. \$9,900
49. The area of the region PS is the producers' surplus and represents the total gain to producers who are willing to supply units at a lower price than \$67 but are still able to supply the product at \$67.

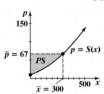

51. $CS = \$3,380; PS = \$1,690$

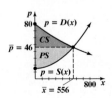

53. $CS = \$6,980; PS = \$5,041$

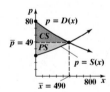

55. $CS = \$7,810; PS = \$8,336$

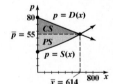

57. $CS = \$8,544; PS = \$11,507$

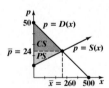

59. (A) $\bar{x} = 21.457; \bar{p} = \$6.51$
   (B) $CS = 1.774$ or \$1,774; $PS = 1.087$or \$1,087

Exercises 7-3

1. $\frac{1}{3}xe^{3x} - \frac{1}{9}e^{3x} + C$ **3.** $\dfrac{x^3}{3}\ln x - \dfrac{x^3}{9} + C$ **5.** $u = x + 2; \dfrac{(x + 2)(x + 1)^6}{6} - \dfrac{(x + 1)^7}{42} + C$ **7.** $-xe^{-x} - e^{-x} + C$
9. $\frac{1}{2}e^{x^2} + C$ **11.** $(xe^x - 4e^x)|_0^1 = -3e + 4 \approx -4.1548$ **13.** $(x \ln 2x - x)|_1^3 = (3 \ln 6 - 3) - (\ln 2 - 1) \approx 2.6821$
15. $\ln(x^2 + 1) + C$ **17.** $(\ln x)^2/2 + C$ **19.** $\frac{2}{3}x^{3/2} \ln x - \frac{4}{9}x^{3/2} + C$
21. $\dfrac{(x - 3)(x + 1)^3}{3} - \dfrac{(x + 1)^4}{12} + C$ or $\dfrac{x^4}{4} - \dfrac{x^3}{3} - \dfrac{5x^2}{2} - 3x + C$

23. $\dfrac{(2x+1)(x-2)^3}{3} - \dfrac{(x-2)^4}{6} + C$ or $\dfrac{x^4}{2} - \dfrac{7x^3}{3} + 2x^2 + 4x + C$

25. The integral represents the negative of the area between the graph of $y = (x-3)e^x$ and the x axis from $x = 0$ to $x = 1$.

27. The integral represents the area between the graph of $y = \ln 2x$ and the x axis from $x = 1$ to $x = 3$.

29. $(x^2 - 2x + 2)e^x + C$ **31.** $\dfrac{xe^{ax}}{a} - \dfrac{e^{ax}}{a^2} + C$ **33.** $\left(-\dfrac{\ln x}{x} - \dfrac{1}{x}\right)\Big|_1^e = -\dfrac{2}{e} + 1 \approx 0.2642$

35. $6\ln 6 - 4\ln 4 - 2 \approx 3.205$ **37.** $xe^{x-2} - e^{x-2} + C$ **39.** $\frac{1}{2}(1 + x^2)\ln(1 + x^2) - \frac{1}{2}(1 + x^2) + C$

41. $(1 + e^x)\ln(1 + e^x) - (1 + e^x) + C$ **43.** $x(\ln x)^2 - 2x\ln x + 2x + C$ **45.** $x(\ln x)^3 - 3x(\ln x)^2 + 6x\ln x - 6x + C$

47. 2   **49.** $\dfrac{1}{3}$ **51.** 1.56   **53.** 34.98   **55.** $\int_0^5 (2t - te^{-t})\,dt = \$24$ million

57. The total profit for the first 5 yr (in millions of dollars) is the same as the area under the marginal profit function, $P'(t) = 2t - te^{-t}$, from $t = 0$ to $t = 5$.

59. \$2,854.88   **61.** 0.264

63. The area bounded by $y = x$ and the Lorenz curve $y = xe^{x-1}$, divided by the area under the graph of $y = x$ from $x = 0$ to $x = 1$, is the Gini index of income concentration. The closer this index is to 0, the more equally distributed the income; the closer the index is to 1, the more concentrated the income in a few hands.

65. $S(t) = 1,600 + 400e^{0.1t} - 40te^{0.1t}$; 15 mo   **67.** \$977

69. The area bounded by the price–demand equation, $p = 9 - \ln(x + 4)$, and the price equation, $y = \bar{p} = 2.089$, from $x = 0$ to $x = \bar{x} = 1,000$, represents the consumers' surplus. This is the amount consumers who are willing to pay more than \$2,089 save.

71. 2.1388 ppm

73. $N(t) = -4te^{-0.25t} - 40e^{-0.25t} + 80$; 8 wk; 78 words/min

75. 20,980

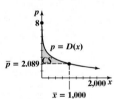

Exercises 7-4

1. $\ln\left|\dfrac{x}{1 + x}\right| + C$ **3.** $\dfrac{1}{3 + x} + 2\ln\left|\dfrac{5 + 2x}{3 + x}\right| + C$ **5.** $\dfrac{2(x - 32)}{3}\sqrt{16 + x} + C$ **7.** $-\ln\left|\dfrac{1 + \sqrt{1 - x^2}}{x}\right| + C$

9. $\dfrac{1}{2}\ln\left|\dfrac{x}{2 + \sqrt{x^2 + 4}}\right| + C$ **11.** $\frac{1}{3}x^3\ln x - \frac{1}{9}x^3 + C$ **13.** $x - \ln|1 + e^x| + C$ **15.** $9\ln\frac{3}{2} - 2 \approx 1.6492$

17. $\frac{1}{2}\ln\frac{12}{5} \approx 0.4377$ **19.** $\ln 3 \approx 1.0986$ **21.** $-\dfrac{\sqrt{4x^2 + 1}}{x} + 2\ln|2x + \sqrt{4x^2 + 1}| + C$ **23.** $\frac{1}{2}\ln|x^2 + \sqrt{x^4 - 16}| + C$

25. $\frac{1}{6}(x^3\sqrt{x^6 + 4} + 4\ln|x^3 + \sqrt{x^6 + 4}|) + C$ **27.** $-\dfrac{\sqrt{4 - x^4}}{8x^2} + C$ **29.** $\frac{1}{5}\ln\left|\dfrac{3 + 4e^x}{2 + e^x}\right| + C$ **31.** $\frac{2}{3}(\ln x - 8)\sqrt{4 + \ln x} + C$

33. $\frac{1}{5}x^2e^{5x} - \frac{2}{25}xe^{5x} + \frac{2}{125}e^{5x} + C$ **35.** $-x^3e^{-x} - 3x^2e^{-x} - 6xe^{-x} - 6e^{-x} + C$ **37.** $x(\ln x)^3 - 3x(\ln x)^2 + 6x\ln x - 6x + C$

39. $\frac{64}{3}$ **41.** $\frac{1}{2}\ln\frac{9}{5} \approx 0.2939$ **43.** $\dfrac{-1 - \ln x}{x} + C$ **45.** $\sqrt{x^2 - 1} + C$ **47.** 31.38   **49.** 5.48   **51.** $3,000 + 1,500\ln\frac{1}{3} \approx \$1,352$

53.

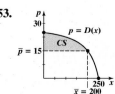

55. $C(x) = 200x + 1,000\ln(1 + 0.05x) + 25,000$; 608; \$198,773

57. \$18,673.95   **59.** 0.1407

61. As the area bounded by the two curves gets smaller, the Lorenz curve approaches $y = x$ and the distribution of income approaches perfect equality—all persons share equally in the income available.

63. $S(t) = 1 + t - \dfrac{1}{1 + t} - 2\ln|1 + t|$; $24.96 - 2\ln 25 \approx \$18.5$ million

65. The total sales (in millions of dollars) over the first 2 yr (24 mo) is the area under the graph of $y = S'(t)$ from $t = 0$ to $t = 24$.

67. $P(x) = \dfrac{2(9x - 4)}{135}(2 + 3x)^{3/2} - 2{,}000.83$; 54; \$37,932

69. $100\ln 3 \approx 110$ ft

71. $60\ln 5 \approx 97$ items

73. The area under the graph of $y = N'(t)$ from $t = 0$ to $t = 12$ represents the total number of items learned in that time interval.

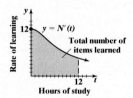

Chapter 7 Review Exercises

1. $\int_a^b f(x)\, dx$ *(7-1)*   **2.** $\int_b^c [-f(x)]\, dx$ *(7-1)*   **3.** $\int_a^b f(x)\, dx + \int_b^c [-f(x)]\, dx$ *(7-1)*

4. Area = 1.153 *(7-1)*   **5.** $\frac{1}{4}xe^{4x} - \frac{1}{16}e^{4x} + C$ *(7-3, 7-4)*   **6.** $\frac{1}{2}x^2\ln x - \frac{1}{4}x^2 + C$ *(7-3, 7-4)*

7. $\dfrac{(\ln x)^2}{2} + C$ *(6-2)*   **8.** $\dfrac{\ln(1 + x^2)}{2} + C$ *(7-2)*   **9.** $\dfrac{1}{1 + x} + \ln\left|\dfrac{x}{1 + x}\right| + C$ *(7-4)*

10. $-\dfrac{\sqrt{1 + x}}{x} - \dfrac{1}{2}\ln\left|\dfrac{\sqrt{1 + x} - 1}{\sqrt{1 + x} + 1}\right| + C$ *(7-4)*   **11.** 12 *(7-1)*   **12.** 40 *(7-1)*   **13.** 34.167 *(7-1)*

14. 0.926 *(7-1)*   **15.** 12 *(7-1)*   **16.** 18.133 *(7-1)*   **17.** $\int_a^b [f(x) - g(x)]\, dx$ *(7-1)*

18. $\int_b^c [g(x) - f(x)]\, dx$ *(7-1)*   **19.** $\int_b^c [g(x) - f(x)]\, dx + \int_c^d [f(x) - g(x)]\, dx$ *(7-1)*

20. $\int_a^b [f(x) - g(x)]\, dx + \int_b^c [g(x) - f(x)]\, dx + \int_c^d [f(x) - g(x)]\, dx$ *(7-1)*

21. Area = 20.833 *(7-1)*

22. 1 *(7-3, 7-4)*   **23.** $\frac{15}{2} - 8\ln 8 + 8\ln 4 \approx 1.955$ *(7-4)*

24. $\frac{1}{6}(3x\sqrt{9x^2 - 49} - 49\ln|3x + \sqrt{9x^2 - 49}|) + C$ *(7-4)*

25. $-2te^{-0.5t} - 4e^{-0.5t} + C$ *(7-3, 7-4)*   **26.** $\frac{1}{3}x^3\ln x - \frac{1}{9}x^3 + C$ *(7-3, 7-4)*

27. $x - \ln|1 + 2e^x| + C$ *(7-4)*

28. (A) Area = 8   (B) Area = 8.38 *(7-1)*

29. $\frac{1}{3}(\ln x)^3 + C$ *(6-2)*

30. $\frac{1}{2}x^2(\ln x)^2 - \frac{1}{2}x^2\ln x + \frac{1}{4}x^2 + C$ *(7-3, 7-4)*

31. $\sqrt{x^2 - 36} + C$ *(6-2)*

32. $\frac{1}{2}\ln|x^2 + \sqrt{x^4 - 36}| + C$ *(7-4)*

33. $50\ln 10 - 42\ln 6 - 24 \approx 15.875$ *(7-3, 7-4)*

34. $x(\ln x)^2 - 2x\ln x + 2x + C$ *(7-3, 7-4)*

35. $-\frac{1}{4}e^{-2x^2} + C$ *(6-2)*

36. $-\frac{1}{2}x^2e^{-2x} - \frac{1}{2}xe^{-2x} - \frac{1}{4}e^{-2x} + C$ *(7-3, 7-4)*

37. 1.703 *(7-1)*   **38.** (A) .189   (B) .154 *(7-2)*

39. The probability that the product will fail during the second year of warranty is the area under the probability density function $y = f(t)$ from $t = 1$ to $t = 2$. *(7-2)*

40. $R(x) = 65x - 6[(x + 1)\ln(x + 1) - x]$; 618/wk; \$29,506 *(7-3)*

41. (A) 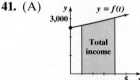   (B) \$8,507 *(7-2)*

42. (A) \$15,655.66   (B) \$1,454.39 *(7-2)*

43. (A)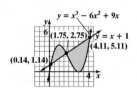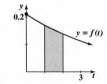

(B) More equitably distributed, since the area bounded by the two curves will have decreased.

(C) Current = 0.3; projected = 0.2; income will be more equitably distributed 10 years from now. *(7-1)*

44. (A) $CS = \$2,250;$ (B) $CS = \$2,890;$
   $PS = \$2,700$ $PS = \$2,278$ *(7-2)*

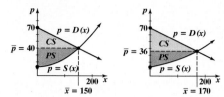

48. $.667; .333$ *(7-2)*

49. The probability that the doctor will spend more than an hour with a randomly selected patient is the area under the probability density function $y = f(t)$ from $t = 1$ to $t = 3$. *(7-2)*

45. (A) 25.403 or $25,403$ lb
   (B) $PS = 121.6$ or $\$1,216$ *(7-2)*

46. 4.522 mL; 1.899 mL *(6-5, 7-4)*

47.

(6-5, 7-1)

50. 45 thousand *(6-5, 7-1)*   **51.** $.368$ *(7-2)*

SUBJECT INDEX

Note: Page numbers followed by fn refer to footnotes.

A

Abscissa, 13, 39
Absolute equality of income, 415–416, 445
Absolute extrema, 324. *See also* Absolute maxima and minima
Absolute inequality of income, 415–416, 445
Absolute maxima and minima, 323–331, 344. *See also* Extrema
  extreme value theorem, 324
  locating absolute extrema, 325–326, 329
  optimization problems (*See* Optimization)
  second derivative and, 326–330
Absolute value, 60
Absolute value function, 59–60, 129
Addition. *See also* Sum
  of fractions, 545
  of polynomials, 549
  of rational expressions, 560–562
Addition properties of real numbers, 542–543
Algebra, compared to calculus, 126
Algebraic expressions, 547
Alternating series, 586
Amount (future value), 101
Analytic geometry, fundamental theorem of, 13
Angles, 520–521, 523, 537
Antiderivatives, 350–351, 394, 395, 405
Antidifferentiation, 350
  partial, 495–498
Approximating areas by left and right sums, 383–386
Approximation, least squares, 485–490
Applications. *See Index of Applications*, I-9–I-10
Approximations using differentials, 190–192
Area(s)
  approximating by left and right sums, 383–386
  formulas for geometric figures, 598–599
  as function of several variables, 452
  in fundamental theorem of calculus, 393–394
  optimization problems, 332–333
  under sine and cosine curves, 533
  between two curves, 411–420, 445
Arithmetic mean, 586
Arithmetic sequence, 588–590
Arithmetic series, 590–591
Associative properties of real numbers, 542–543
Asymptotes. *See* Horizontal asymptotes; Vertical asymptotes
Average cost, 199, 205, 317–318
Average profit, 199
Average rate of change, 28, 166, 204
Average revenue, 199
Average value, 399–401, 406
  of continuous function over [a, b], 399–400
  over rectangular regions, 500–501, 515
Average velocity, 167–168
Axis of parabola, 74–75

B

Base, change-of-base formulas, 112, 221fn, 263
Base 2, logarithmic function with, 107

Base *e* exponential functions, 98–99
Base *e* logarithms, 110, 217
Base of exponential function, 96, 546
Basic elementary functions, 59–60, 118
Best approximation, 486
Best fit, 30, 39
Binomial, 547
Binomial formula, 595–596
Binomial theorem, 596–597
Bioclimatic rule for temperate climates, 494–495
Boiling point, 25
Bounded function, 91
Box surface area, 5
Break-even analysis, 9–10, 51, 118
Break-even points, 78, 118, 197
British thermal unit (Btu), 163fn

C

Calculator. *See* Graphing calculators
Calculus
  compared to algebra, 126
  fundamental theorem of (*See* Fundamental theorem of calculus)
  multivariable (*See* Multivariable calculus)
Canceling, in fractions, 559
Cartesian coordinate system, 13, 39
Cautions, 114, 136, 200, 218, 353, 355, 362, 370, 556, 569
Cephalic index, 458
Chain rule, 233–243, 263
  about, 237–240
  composite functions, 233–234, 237
  general derivative rules, 239–240
  general power rule, 233, 235–237
  partial derivatives using, 460
  reversing, 361–363
Change in *x* or *y*, 188
Change-of-base formulas, 112, 221fn, 263
Change-of-variable method, 365, 405
Circle, 245–246, 598
Closed interval, 6
  continuous function on, 157
  finding absolute extrema on, 325–326
Cobb-Douglas production function, 452–453, 461, 479
Coefficients, 547
  leading, 86
Common difference, in arithmetic sequence, 588
Common factors, 553
Common logarithms, 110, 119, 219
Common ratio, in geometric sequence, 589
Commutative properties of real numbers, 542–543
Competitive products, 466
Complementary products, 466
Completing the square, 73, 118, 577–578
Complex number system, 579
Composite functions, 233–234, 237, 263
Compound fractions, 562–563
Compound interest, 119. *See also* Continuous compound interest
  as exponential function, 101–103

  formula for, 101–103
  as function of several variables, 452
Compound interest formula, 263
Computer, finding area under a curve, 384
Concave downward, 284–287, 293
Concave upward, 284–287, 293
Concavity, 284–287
Conceptual Insight, 6, 17, 50, 60, 70, 71, 74, 90, 97, 108, 132, 135, 144, 148, 156, 168, 170, 179, 188, 191, 196, 211, 213, 220, 223, 227, 234, 237, 246, 251, 258, 259–260, 269, 271, 286, 289–290, 293, 304, 305, 309, 324, 329, 334, 337, 339, 350, 374, 386, 393, 395, 411, 422, 434, 455, 464, 469, 483, 489, 502, 506, 507, 524, 528, 535, 543, 559, 570, 576, 596
Cone, right circular, 599
Constant *e*, 98–99, 211, 217, 263
Constant function rule, 179
Constant functions, 48, 118
  continuity properties, 158
  differentiating, 179
  indefinite integral of, 353
Constant multiple property, 181–182
Constant of integration, 351, 405
Constraint, 476, 478
Constraint equation, 480
Consumers' surplus, 426–427, 429, 446
Continuity, 154–164, 204
  continuous functions, 154–157
  defined, 155
  discontinuous function, 154–155
  properties of, 157–158
  sign properties on an interval (a, b), 159
  solving inequalities using properties of, 159–160
Continuous compound interest, 102–103, 211–214, 263, 374–375. *See also* Compound interest
Continuous compound interest formula, 212, 424
Continuous functions, 154–157, 204, 270, 524
Continuous graph, 86, 118
Continuous income stream, 423–424, 446
  future value of, 424–426
Continuous random variable, 421–422, 446
Conversion, degree-radian measures, 521
Coordinate axes, 13
Coordinate on number line, 542
Coordinates of a point, 13, 39
Coordinate system, 13, 39, 453–455
Correspondence in a function, 45–46
Cosecant functions, 524, 538
Cosine functions, 521–524, 538
  derivative of, 527–528
  integrals of, 533–536
Cosine of *θ*, 521
Cost function, 51, 196. *See also* Marginal average cost
Cost per unit, 199
Costs, 9, 51, 118
Cotangent functions, 524, 538
Coterminal angles, 520, 537
Critical points, 468, 477
  multiple, 470–471

INDEX OF APPLICATIONS

A LIBRARY OF ELEMENTARY FUNCTIONS

BASIC FUNCTIONS

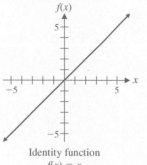

Identity function
$f(x) = x$

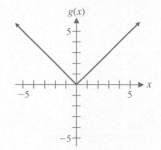

Absolute value function
$g(x) = |x|$

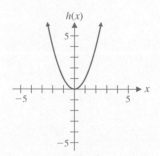

Square function
$h(x) = x^2$

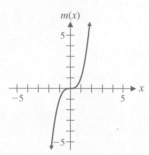

Cube function
$m(x) = x^3$

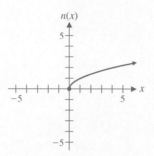

Square root function
$n(x) = \sqrt{x}$

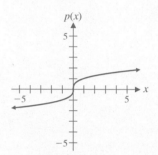

Cube root function
$p(x) = \sqrt[3]{x}$

LINEAR AND CONSTANT FUNCTIONS

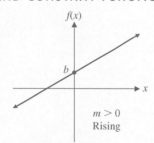

$m > 0$
Rising

Linear function
$f(x) = mx + b$

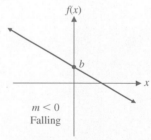

$m < 0$
Falling

Linear function
$f(x) = mx + b$

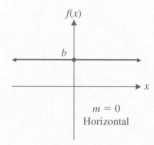

$m = 0$
Horizontal

Constant function
$f(x) = b$

QUADRATIC FUNCTIONS

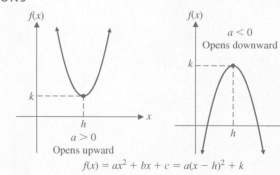

$a > 0$
Opens upward

$a < 0$
Opens downward

$$f(x) = ax^2 + bx + c = a(x - h)^2 + k$$